Stanley Gibbons
Stamp Catalo

C000255667

Poland

1st edition 2015

STANLEY GIBBONS
CATALOGUES
150 YEARS
—1865 - 2015—

Stanley Gibbons Ltd • London and Ringwood

By Appointment to
Her Majesty The Queen
Philatelists
Stanley Gibbons Ltd,
London

1st Edition – 2015

Published by Stanley Gibbons Ltd
Editorial, Publications Sales Offices
and Distribution Centre:
7 Parkside, Christchurch Road, Ringwood,
Hants BH24 3SH

© Stanley Gibbons Ltd 2015

British Library Cataloguing in
Publication Data.
A catalogue record for this book is available
from the British Library.

Errors and omissions excepted. The colour
reproduction of stamps is only as accurate as
the printing process will allow.

ISBN-10 0-85259-969-2
ISBN-13 978-0-85259-969-3

Item No. R1425-15

Printed by
Gomer Press Limited, Wales

Stanley Gibbons Foreign Catalogue Parts 2–22

150 YEARS OF CATALOGUES

It is over 35 years since the present split into 'Parts 2 to 22' was announced, dividing up what had up to then been an alphabetical listing of European and Overseas countries over seven large volumes into handy-sized catalogues, bringing together countries or groups of countries, generally united by geography or political affiliations.

Back in 1979 the new 'Parts' catalogues proved to be very popular with collectors, but over time these volumes have grown in size, with the ever increasing numbers of new issues.

This year Stanley Gibbons celebrates 150 years of catalogue production and it seemed the right time to take a look at the structure and break down of our Foreign catalogue range.

This new catalogue contains Poland and in the future a second volume containing Czech Republic, Czechoslovakia and Slovakia will be published.

Apart from the stamps of the current issuing countries, this catalogue also contains: German Occupation of Poland, Polish Military Post, Polish Occupation – Central Lithuania, Polish Post Offices Abroad (Constantinople, Danzig, Odessa), Allenstein, Danzig, Marienwerder, Upper Silesia.

- There have been many new varieties added to this catalogue; see next page for a detailed list.

- Pricing has been thoroughly revised and brought up to date throughout the catalogue.

The first supplement to this catalogue appeared in *Gibbons Stamp Monthly* for December 2015.

Hugh Jefferies, Editor
Clare de la Feuillade, Deputy Editor
Michelle England, Designer and page layout
Barbara Hawkins, Pricing Assistant
Sue Price, New Issues Listings

STAMPS ADDED

POLAND: 27b
304a, 304b, D311b, 499b, 500b, 501b, 507a, 507b, 531a, 532a, 533a, 549a, 552a, 716b, 864b, 1031a, 1045a, 1045b, 1148a, 1171a, 1399a, 1485a, 1493a, 1819a, 1906a, 2822a, 3576a, 3577a, 3947a, 3951a, 4096b,

STAMPS ALTERED

579/594 – set rewritten
MS594c now **MS**615a
386a/e now 391a/e
MS1399a now **MS**1399b
1684b/1692b now 1684a/1692a

SPECIALIST SOCIETIES

Society for Polish Philately in Great Britain
Hon. Secretary - A. Swidlicki
6 Midmoor Road
Wimbledon
London SW19 4JD

Chairman - Mr. Jan Korzeniowski
E-mail: jkorzeniowski@talktalk.net

Polonus Philatelic Society
P.O.Box 489
Maryville
IL 62062
USA

Website: www.polonus.org

Contents

Stanley Gibbons Holdings Plc

Stanley Gibbons Limited,
Stanley Gibbons Auctions
399 Strand, London WC2R 0LX
Tel: +44 (0)207 836 8444
Fax: +44 (0)207 836 7342
E-mail: help@stanleygibbons.com
Website: www.stanleygibbons.com
for all departments, Auction and
Specialist Stamp Departments.
Open Monday–Friday 9.30 a.m. to 5 p.m.
Shop. Open Monday–Friday 9 a.m. to
5.30 p.m. and Saturday 9.30 a.m.
to 5.30 p.m.

Stanley Gibbons Publications,
Gibbons Stamp Monthly and
Philatelic Exporter
7 Parkside, Christchurch Road,
Ringwood, Hampshire BH24 3SH.
Tel: +44 (0)1425 472363
Fax: +44 (0)1425 470247
E-mail: help@stanleygibbons.com
Publications Mail Order.
FREEPHONE 0800 611622
Monday–Friday 8.30 a.m. to 5 p.m.

Stanley Gibbons (Guernsey) Limited
18–20 Le Bordage, St Peter Port,
Guernsey GY1 1DE.
Tel: +44 (0)1481 708270
Fax: +44 (0)1481 708279
E-mail: investment@stanleygibbons.com

Stanley Gibbons (Jersey) Limited
2nd Floor, Minden House,
Minden Place,St Helier, Jersey, Channel
Islands JE2 5WQ.
Tel: +44 (0)1534 766711
Fax: +44 (0)1534 766177
E-mail: investment@stanleygibbons.com

Stanley Gibbons Investments
Tel: +44 (0)845 026 7170
or +44 1534 766 711
E-mail: investment@stanleygibbons.com
Web: sginvest.co.uk

Stanley Gibbons (Asia) Limited
6/F, 100 Queen's Road Central
Central Hong Kong
Tel: +852 3180 9370
E-mail: elee@stanleygibbons.com

Stanley Gibbons Publications Overseas Representation
Stanley Gibbons Publications are represented overseas by the following

Fraser's
(a division of Stanley Gibbons Group plc)
Bloomsbury House, 24 Maddox Street,
Mayfair, London W1S 1PP
Autographs, photographs, letters and
documents
Tel: +44 (0)207 836 9325
Fax: +44 (0)207 495 9499
E-mail: sales@frasersautographs.com
Website: www.frasersautographs.com
Monday–Friday 9 a.m. to 5.30 p.m.
and Saturday 10 a.m. to 4 p.m.

Australia
Renniks Publications PTY LTD
Unit 3 37-39 Green Street,
Banksmeadow, NSW 2019, Australia
Tel: +612 9695 7055
Website: www.renniks.com

Canada
Unitrade Associates
99 Floral Parkway, Toronto,
Ontario M6L 2C4, Canada
Tel: +1 416 242 5900
Website: www.unitradeassoc.com

Germany
Schaubek Verlag Leipzig
Am Glaeschen 23, D-04420
Markranstaedt, Germany
Tel: +49 34 205 67823
Website: www.schaubek.de

Italy
Ernesto Marini S.R.L.
V. Struppa, 300, Genova, 16165, Italy
Tel: +3901 0247-3530
Website: www.ernestomarini.it

Japan
Japan Philatelic
PO Box 2, Suginami-Minami,
Tokyo 168-8081, Japan
Tel: +81 3330 41641
Website: www.yushu.co.jp

Netherlands (also covers Belgium
Denmark, Finland & France)
Uitgeverij Davo BV
PO Box 411, Ak Deventer, 7400
Netherlands
Tel: +315 7050 2700
Website: www.davo.nl

New Zealand
House of Stamps
PO Box 12, Paraparaumu,
New Zealand
Tel: +61 6364 8270
Website: www.houseofstamps.co.nz

New Zealand
Philatelic Distributors
PO Box 863
15 Mount Edgecumbe Street
New Plymouth 4615, New Zealand
Tel: +6 46 758 65 68
Website: www.stampcollecta.com

Norway
SKANFIL A/S
SPANAV. 52 / BOKS 2030
N-5504 HAUGESUND, Norway
Tel: +47-52703940
E-mail: magne@skanfil.no

Singapore
C S Philatelic Agency
Peninsula Shopping Centre #04-29
3 Coleman Street, 179804, Singapore
Tel: +65 6337-1859
Website: www.cs.com.sg

South Africa
Mr. Thematic
737 Redwood Street,
Randparkridge Ext 14
Gauteng, South Africa
Tel: +1606 553107
E-mail: ianfrith146@gmail.com
chrisb@asapcc.co.za

Sweden
Chr Winther Sorensen AB
Box 43, S-310 20 Knaered, Sweden
Tel: +46 43050743
Website: www.collectia.se

USA
Regency Superior Ltd
229 North Euclid Avenue
Saint Louis, Missouri 63108, USA
PO Box 8277, St Louis,
MO 63156-8277, USA
Toll Free Tel: (800) 782-0066
Tel: (314) 361-5699
Website: www.RegencySuperior.com
Email: info@regencysuperior.com

General Philatelic Information and Guidelines to the Scope of Stanley Gibbons Foreign Catalogues

These notes reflect current practice in compiling the Foreign Catalogue.

The *Stanley Gibbons Stamp Catalogue* has a very long history and the vast quantity of information it contains has been carefully built up by successive generations through the work of countless individuals. Philately itself is never static and the Catalogue has evolved and developed during this long time-span. These notes apply to current policy – some of the older listings were prepared using slightly different criteria – and we hope you find them useful in using the catalogue.

THE CATALOGUE IN GENERAL

Contents. The Catalogue is confined to adhesive postage stamps, including miniature sheets. For particular categories the rules are:
- (a) Revenue (fiscal) stamps or telegraph stamps are listed only where they have been expressly authorised for postal duty.
- (b) Stamps issued only precancelled are included, but normally issued stamps available additionally with precancel have no separate precancel listing unless the face value is changed.
- (c) Stamps prepared for use but not issued, hitherto accorded full listing, are nowadays footnoted with a price (where possible).
- (d) Bisects (trisects, etc.) are only listed where such usage was officially authorised.
- (e) Stamps issued only on first day covers and not available separately are not listed but priced (on the cover) in a footnote.
- (f) New printings, as such, are not listed, though stamps from them may qualify under another category, e.g. when a prominent new shade results.
- (g) Official and unofficial reprints are dealt with by footnote.
- (h) Stamps from imperforate printings of modern issues which also occur perforated are covered by footnotes or general notes, but are listed where widely available for postal use.

Exclusions. The following are excluded:
- (a) non-postal revenue or fiscal stamps;
- (b) postage stamps used fiscally;
- (c) local carriage labels and private local issues;
- (d) telegraph stamps;
- (e) bogus or phantom stamps;
- (f) railway or airline letter fee stamps, bus or road transport company labels;
- (g) cut-outs;
- (h) all types of non-postal labels;
- (i) documentary labels for the postal service, e.g. registration, recorded delivery, airmail etiquettes, etc.;
- (j) privately applied embellishments to official issues and privately commissioned items generally;
- (k) stamps for training postal officers;
- (l) specimen stamps.

Full listing. "Full listing" confers our recognition and implies allotting a catalogue number and (wherever possible) a price quotation.

In judging status for inclusion in the catalogue broad considerations are applied to stamps. They must be issued by a legitimate postal authority, recognised by the government concerned, and must be adhesives valid for proper postal use in the class of service for which they are inscribed. Stamps, with the exception of such categories as postage dues and officials, must be available to the general public, at face value, in reasonable quantities without any artificial restrictions being imposed on their distribution.

We record as abbreviated Appendix entries, without catalogue numbers or prices, stamps from countries which either persist in having far more issues than can be justified by postal need or have failed to maintain control over their distribution so that they have not been available to the public in reasonable quantities at face value. Miniature sheets and imperforate stamps are not mentioned in these entries.

The publishers of this catalogue have observed, with concern, the proliferation of "artificial" stamp-issuing territories. On several occasions this has resulted in separately inscribed issues for various component parts of otherwise united states or territories. Stanley Gibbons Publications have decided that where such circumstances occur, they will not, in the future, list these items in the SG catalogue without first satisfying themselves that the stamps represent a genuine political, historical or postal division within the country concerned. Any such issues which do not fulfil this stipulation will be recorded in the Catalogue Appendix only.

For errors and varieties the criterion is legitimate (albeit inadvertent) sale over a post office counter in the normal course of business. Details of provenance are always important; printers' waste and fraudulently manufactured material is excluded.

Certificates. In assessing unlisted items due weight is given to Certificates from recognised Expert Committees and, where appropriate, we will usually ask to see them.

New issues. New issues are listed regularly in the Catalogue Supplement in *Gibbons Stamp Monthly*, then consolidated into the next available edition of the Catalogue.

Date of issue. Where local issue dates differ from dates of release by agencies, "date of issue" is the local date. Fortuitous stray usage before the officially intended date is disregarded in listing.

Catalogue numbers. Stamps of each country are catalogued chronologically by date of issue. Subsidiary classes (e.g. postage due stamps) are integrated into one list with postage and commemorative stamps and distinguished by a letter prefix to the catalogue number.

The catalogue number appears in the extreme left column. The boldface type numbers in the next column are merely cross-references to illustrations. Catalogue numbers in the *Gibbons Stamp Monthly* Supplement are provisional only and may need to be altered when the lists are consolidated. Miniature sheets only purchasable intact at a post office have a single MS number; sheetlets – individual stamps available – number each stamp separately. The catalogue no longer gives full listing to designs originally issued in normal sheets, which subsequently appear in sheetlets showing changes of colour, perforation, printing process or face value. Such stamps will be covered by footnotes.

Once published in the Catalogue, numbers are changed as little as possible; really serious renumbering is reserved for the occasions when a complete country or an entire issue is being rewritten. The edition first affected includes cross-reference tables of old and new numbers.

Our catalogue numbers are universally recognised in specifying stamps and as a hallmark of status.

Illustrations. Stamps are illustrated at three-quarters linear size. Stamps not illustrated are the same size and format as the value shown unless otherwise indicated. Stamps issued only as miniature sheets have the stamp alone illustrated but sheet size is also quoted. Overprints, surcharges, watermarks and postmarks are normally actual size. Illustrations of varieties are often enlarged to show the detail.

CONTACTING THE CATALOGUE EDITOR

The editor is always interested in hearing from people who have new information which will improve or correct the Catalogue. As a general rule he must see and examine the actual stamps before they can be considered for listing; photographs or photocopies are insufficient evidence. Neither he nor his staff give opinions as to the genuineness of stamps.

Submissions should be made in writing to the Catalogue Editor, Stanley Gibbons Publications, 7 Parkside, Christchurch Road, Ringwood, Hants BH24 3SH. The cost of return postage for items submitted is appreciated, and this should include the registration fee if required.

Where information is solicited purely for the benefit of the enquirer, the editor cannot undertake to reply if the answer is already contained in these published notes or if return postage is omitted. Written communications are greatly preferred to enquiries by telephone or e-mail and the editor regrets that he or his staff cannot see personal callers without a prior appointment being made.

The editor welcomes close contact with study circles and is interested, too, in finding local correspondents who will verify and supplement official information in overseas countries where this is deficient.

We regret we do not give opinions as to the genuineness of stamps, nor do we identify stamps or number them by our Catalogue.

TECHNICAL MATTERS

The meanings of the technical terms used in the Catalogue will be found in *Philatelic Terms Illustrated*, published by Stanley Gibbons (Price £14.95 plus postage).

1. Printing

Printing errors. Errors in printing are of major interest to the Catalogue. Authenticated items meriting consideration would include background, centre or frame inverted or omitted; centre or subject transposed; error of colour; error or omission of value; double prints and impressions; printed both sides; and so on. Designs *tête-bêche*, whether intentionally or by accident, are listable. *Se-tenant* arrangements of stamps are recognised in the listings or footnotes. Gutter pairs (a pair of stamps separated by blank margin) are excluded unless they have some philatelic importance. Colours only partially omitted are not listed, neither are stamps printed on the gummed side.

Printing varieties. Listing is accorded to major changes in the printing base which lead to completely new types. In recess-printing this could be a design re-engraved, in photogravure or photolithography a screen altered in whole or in part. It can also encompass flat-bed and rotary printing if the results are readily distinguishable.

To be considered at all, varieties must be constant.

Early stamps, produced by primitive methods, were prone to numerous imperfections; the lists reflect this, recognising re-entries, retouches, broken frames, misshapen letters, and so on. Printing technology has, however, radically improved over the years, during which time photogravure and lithography have become predominant. Varieties nowadays are more in the nature of flaws and these, being too specialised for a general catalogue, are almost always outside the scope. We therefore do not list such items as dry prints, kiss prints, doctor-blade flaws, blanket set-offs, doubling through blanket stretch, plate cracks and scratches, registration flaws (leading to colour shifts), lithographic ring flaws, and so on. Neither do we recognise fortuitous happenings like paper creases or confetti flaws.

Overprints (and surcharges). Overprints of different types qualify for separate listing. These include overprints in different colours; overprints from different printing processes such as litho and typo; overprints in totally different typefaces, etc.

Overprint errors and varieties. Major errors in machine-printed overprints are important and listable. They include overprint inverted or omitted; overprint double (treble, etc.); overprint diagonal; overprint double, one inverted; pairs with one overprint omitted, e.g. from a radical shift to an adjoining stamp; error of colour; error of type fount; letters inverted or omitted, etc. If the overprint is handstamped, few of these would qualify and a distinction is drawn.

Varieties occurring in overprints will often take the form of broken letters, slight differences in spacing, rising spacers, etc. Only the most important would be considered for footnote mention.

Sheet positions. If space permits we quote sheet positions of listed varieties and authenticated data is solicited for this purpose.

2. Paper

All stamps listed are deemed to be on "ordinary" paper of the wove type and white in colour; only departures from this are mentioned.

Types. Where classification so requires we distinguish such other types of paper as, for example, vertically and horizontally laid; wove and laid bâtonné; card(board); carton; cartridge, enamelled; glazed; GC (Grande Consommation); granite; native; pelure; porous; quadrillé; ribbed; rice; and silk thread.

The "traditional" method of indentifying chalk-surfaced papers has been that, when touched with a silver wire, a black mark is left on the paper, and the listings in this catalogue are based on that test. However, the test itself is now largely discredited, for, although the mark can be removed by a soft rubber, some damage to the stamp will result from its use.

The difference between chalk-surfaced and pre-war ordinary papers is fairly clear: chalk-surfaced papers being smoother to the touch and showing a characteristic sheen when light is reflected off their surface. Under good magnification tiny bubbles or pock marks can be seen on the surface of the stamp and at the tips of the perforations the surfacing appears "broken". Traces of paper fibres are evident on the surface of ordinary paper and the ink shows a degree of absorption into it.

The various makeshifts for normal paper are listed as appropriate. They include printing on: unfinished banknotes, war maps, ruled paper, Post Office forms, and the unprinted side of glossy magazines. The varieties of double paper and joined paper are recognised.

Descriptive terms. The fact that a paper is hand-made (and thus probably of uneven thickness) is mentioned where necessary. Such descriptive terms as "hard" and "soft"; "smooth" and "rough"; "thick", "medium" and "thin" are applied where there is philatelic merit in classifying papers.

Coloured, very white and toned papers. A coloured paper is one that is coloured right through (front and back of the stamp). In the Catalogue the colour of the paper is given in italics, thus

   black/*rose* = black design on rose paper.

Papers have been made specially white in recent years by, for example, a very heavy coating of chalk. We do not classify shades of whiteness of paper as distinct varieties. There does exist, however, a type of paper from early days called toned. This is off-white, often brownish or buffish, but it cannot be assigned a definite colour. A toning effect brought on by climate, incorrect storage or gum staining is disregarded here, as this was not the state of the paper when issued.

Safety devices. The Catalogue takes account of such safety devices as varnish lines, grills, burelage or imprinted patterns on the front or moiré on the back of stamps.

Modern developments. Two modern developments also affect the listings, printing on self-adhesive paper and the tendency, philatelic in origin, for conventional paper to be reinforced or replaced by different materials. Some examples are the use of foils in gold, silver, aluminium, palladium and steel; application of an imitation wood veneer; printing on plastic moulded in relief; and use of a plastic laminate to give a three-dimensional effect. Examples also occur of stamps impregnated with scent; printed on silk; and incorporating miniature gramophone records.

3. Perforation and Rouletting

Perforation gauge. The gauge of a perforation is the number of holes in a length of 2 cm. For correct classification the size of the holes (large or small) may need to be distinguished; in a few cases the actual number of holes on each edge of the stamp needs to be quoted.

Measurement. The Gibbons Instanta gauge is the standard for measuring perforations. The stamp is viewed against a dark background with the transparent gauge put on top of it. Though the gauge measures to decimal accuracy, perforations read from it are generally quoted in the Catalogue to the nearest half. For example:

Just over perf.
12¾ to just under perf. 13¼   = perf. 13
Perf. 13¼ exactly, rounded up   = perf. 13½
Just over perf.
13¼ to just under perf. 13¾   = perf. 13½
Perf. 13¾ exactly, rounded up   = perf. 14

However, where classification depends on it, actual quarter-perforations are quoted.

Notation. Where no perforation is quoted for an issue it is imperforate. Perforations are usually abbreviated (and spoken) as follows, though sometimes they may be spelled out for clarity. This notation for rectangular stamps (the majority) applies to diamond shapes if "top" is read as the edge to the top right.

P 14: perforated alike on all sides (read: "perf. 14").

P 14×15: the first figure refers to top and bottom, the second to left and right sides (read: "perf. 14 by 15"). This is a compound perforation. For an upright triangular stamp the first figure refers to the two sloping sides and the second to the base. In inverted triangulars the base is first and the second figure refers to the sloping sides.

P 14-15: perforation measuring anything between 14 and 15: the holes are irregularly spaced, thus the gauge may vary along a single line or even along a single edge of the stamp (read: "perf. 14 to 15").

P 14 irregular. perforated 14 from a worn perforator, giving badly aligned holes irregular spaced (read "irregular perf. 14").

P *comp(ound)* 14×15: two gauges in use but not necessarily on opposite sides of the stamp. It could be one side in one gauge and three in the other, or two adjacent sides with the same gauge (Read: "perf. compound of 14 and 15"). For three gauges or more, abbreviated as "P 14, 14½, 15 or compound" for example.

P 14, 14½: perforated approximately 14¼ (read: "perf. 14 or 14½"). It does not mean two stamps, one perf. 14 and the other perf. 14½. This obsolescent notation is gradually being replaced in the Catalogue.

Imperf: imperforate (not perforated).

Imperf × P 14: imperforate at top and bottom and perf 14 at sides.

P 14 × *imperf* = perf 14 at top and bottom and imperforate at sides.

Such headings as "P 13 × 14 (vert) and P 14 × 13 (horiz)" indicate which perforations apply to which stamp format – vertical or horizontal.

Some stamps are additionally perforated so that a label or tab is detachable; others have been perforated suitably for use as two halves. Listings are normally for whole stamps, unless stated otherwise.

Other terms. Perforation almost always gives circular holes; where other shapes have been used they are specified, e.g. square holes; lozenge perf. Interrupted perfs are brought about by the omission of pins at regular intervals. Perforations have occasionally been simulated by being printed as part of the design. With few exceptions, privately applied perforations are not listed.

Perforation errors and varieties. Authenticated errors, where a stamp normally perforated is accidentally issued imperforate, are listed provided no traces of perforation (blind holes or indentations) remain. They must be provided as pairs, both stamps wholly imperforate, and are only priced in that form.

Stamps merely imperforate between stamp and margin (fantails) are not listed.

Imperforate-between varieties are recognised, where one row of perfs has been missed. They are listed and priced in pairs:

Imperf between (horiz pair): a horizontal pair of stamps with perfs all around the edges but none between the stamps.

Imperf between (vert pair): a vertical pair of stamps with perfs all around the edges but none between the stamps.

Where several of the rows have escaped perforation the resulting varieties are listable. Thus:

Imperf vert (horiz pair): a horizontal pair of stamps perforated top and bottom; all three vertical directions are imperf – the two outer edges and between the stamps.

Imperf horiz (vert pair): a vertical pair perforated at left and right edges; all three horizontal directions are imperf – the top, bottom and between the stamps.

Straight edges. Large sheets cut up before issue to post offices can cause stamps with straight edges, i.e. imperf on one side or on two sides at right angles. They are not usually listable in this condition and are worth less than corresponding stamps properly perforated all round. This does not, however, apply to certain stamps, mainly from coils and booklets, where straight edges on various sides are the manufacturing norm affecting every stamp. The listings and notes make clear which sides are correctly imperf.

Malfunction. Varieties of double, misplaced or partial perforation caused by error or machine malfunction are not listable, neither are freaks, such as perforations placed diagonally from paper folds. Likewise disregarded are missing holes caused by broken pins, and perforations "fading out" down a sheet, the machinery progressively disengaging to leave blind perfs and indentations to the paper.

Centering. Well-centred stamps have designs surrounded by equal opposite margins. Where this condition affects the price the fact is stated.

Type of perforating. Where necessary for classification, perforation types are distinguished. These include:

Line perforation from one line of pins punching single rows of holes at a time.

Comb perforation from pins disposed across the sheet in comb formation, punching out holes at three sides of the stamp a row at a time.

Harrow perforation applied to a whole pane or sheet at one stroke.

Rotary perforation from the toothed wheels operating across a sheet, then crosswise.

Sewing-machine perforation. The resultant condition, clean-cut or rough, is distinguished where required.

Pin-perforation is the commonly applied term for pin-roulette in which, instead of being punched out, round holes are pricked by sharp-pointed pins and no paper is removed.

Punctured stamps. Perforation holes can be punched into the face of the stamp. Patterns of small holes, often in the shape of initial letters, are privately applied devices against pilferage. These "perfins" are outside the scope. Identification devices, when officially inspired, are listed or noted; they can be shapes, or letters or words formed from holes, sometimes converting one class of stamp into another.

Rouletting. In rouletting the paper is cut, for ease of separation, but none is removed. The gauge is measured, when needed, as for perforations. Traditional French terms descriptive of the type of cut are often used and types include:

Arc roulette (percé en arc). Cuts are minute, spaced arcs, each roughly a semicircle.

Cross roulette (percé en croix). Cuts are tiny diagonal crosses.

Line roulette (parcé en ligne or en ligne droite). Short straight cuts parallel to the frame of the stamp. The commonest basic roulette. Where not further described, "roulette" means this type.

Rouletted in colour or coloured roulette (percé en lignes colorees or en lignes de couleur). Cuts with coloured edges, arising from notched rule inked simultaneously with the printing plate.

Saw-tooth roulette (percé en scie). Cuts applied zigzag fashion to resemble the teeth of a saw.

Serpentine roulette (percé en serpentin). Cuts as sharply wavy lines.

Zigzag roulettes (percé en zigzags). Short straight cuts at angles in alternate directions, producing sharp points on separation. U.S. usage favours "serrate(d) roulette" for this type.

Pin-roulette (originally *percé en points* and now *perforés trous d'epingle)* is commonly called pin-perforation in English.

4. Gum

All stamps listed are assumed to have gum of some kind; if they were issued without gum this is stated. Original gum (o.g.) means that which was present on the stamp as issued to the public. Deleterious climates and the presence of certain chemicals can cause gum to crack and, with early stamps, even make the paper deteriorate. Unscrupulous fakers are adept in removing it and regumming the stamp to meet the unreasoning demand often made for "full o.g." in cases where such a thing is virtually impossible.

Until recent times the gum used for stamps has been gum arabic, but various synthetic adhesives – tinted or invisible-looking – have been in use since the 1960s. Stamps existing with more than one type of gum are not normally listed separately, though the fact is noted where it is of philatelic significance, e.g. in distinguishing reprints or new printings.

The distinct variety of grilled gum is, however, recognised. In this the paper is passed through a gum breaker prior to printing to prevent subsequent curling. As the patterned rollers were sufficient to impress a grill into the paper beneath the gum we can quote prices for both unused and used examples.

Self-adhesive stamps are issued on backing paper from which they are peeled before affixing to mail. Unused examples are priced as for backing paper intact. Used examples are best kept on cover or on piece.

Prices from 1940 onwards are for unmounted mint.

5. Watermarks

Stamps are on unwatermarked paper except where the heading to the set says otherwise.

Detection. Watermarks are detected for Catalogue description by one of four methods:

(1) holding stamps to the light;

(2) laying stamps face down on a dark background;

(3) adding a few drops of petroleum ether 40/60 to the stamp laid face down in a watermark tray; or

(4) by use of the Stanley Gibbons Detectamark, or other equipment, which works by revealing the thinning of the paper at the watermark. (Note that petroleum ether is highly inflammable in use and can damage photogravure stamps.)

Listable types. Stamps occurring on both watermarked and unwatermarked papers are different types and both receive full listing.

Single watermarks (devices occurring once on every stamp) can be modified in size and shape as between different issues; the types are noted but not usually separately listed. Fortuitous absence of watermark from a single stamp or its gross displacement would not be listable.

To overcome registration difficulties the device may be repeated at close intervals (a **multiple watermark**), single stamps thus showing parts of several devices. Similarly a large **sheet watermark** (or all-over watermark) covering numerous stamps can be used. We give informative notes and illustrations for them. The designs may be such that numbers of stamps in the sheet automatically lack watermark; this is not a listable variety. Multiple and all-over watermarks sometimes undergo modifications, but if the various types are difficult to distinguish from single stamps notes are given but not separate listings.

Papermakers' watermarks are noted where known but not listed separately, since most stamps in the sheet will lack them. Sheet watermarks which are nothing more than officially adopted papermakers' watermarks are, however, given normal listing.

Marginal watermarks, falling outside the pane of stamps, are ignored except where misplacement causes the adjoining row to be affected, in which case they may be footnoted.

Watermark errors and varieties. Watermark errors are recognised as of major importance. They comprise stamps intended to be on unwatermarked paper but issued watermarked by mistake, or stamps printed on paper with the wrong watermark. Watermark varieties, on the other hand, such as broken or deformed bits on the dandy roll, are not listable.

Watermark positions. Paper has a side intended for printing and watermarks are usually impressed so that they read normally when looked through from that printed side.

Illustrations in the Catalogue are of watermarks in normal positions (from the front of the stamps) and are actual size where possible.

Differences in watermark position are collectable as distinct varieties. In this Catalogue, however, only normal sideways watermarks are listed (and "sideways inverted" is treated as "sideways"). Inverted and reversed watermarks have always been outside its scope: in the early days of flat-bed printing, sheets of watermarked paper were fed indiscriminately through the press and the resulting watermark positions had no particular philatelic significance. Similarly, the special make-up of sheets for booklets can in some cases give equal quantities of normal and inverted watermarks.

6. Colours

Stamps in two or three colours have these named in order of appearance, from the centre moving outwards.

Four colours or more are usually listed as multicoloured.

In compound colour names the second is the predominant one, thus:

orange-red = a red tending towards orange;

red-orange = an orange containing more red than usual.

Standard colours used. The 200 colours most used for stamp identification are given in the Stanley Gibbons Colour Key. The Catalogue has used the Key as a standard for describing new issues for some years. The names are also introduced as lists are rewritten, though exceptions are made for those early issues where traditional names have become universally established.

Determining colours. When comparing actual stamps with colour samples in the Key, view in a good north daylight (or its best substitute: fluorescent "colour-matching" light). Sunshine is not recommended. Choose a solid portion of the stamp design; if available, marginal markings such as solid bars of colour or colour check dots are helpful. Shading lines in the design can be misleading as they appear lighter than solid colour. Postmarked portions of a stamp appear darker than normal. If more than one colour is present, mask off the extraneous ones as the eye tends to mix them.

Errors of colour. Major colour errors in stamps or overprints which qualify for listing are: wrong colours; one colour inverted in relation to the rest; albinos (colourless impressions), where these have Expert Committee certificates; colours completely omitted, but only on unused stamps (if found on used stamps the information is footnoted).

Colours only partially omitted are not recognised.

Colour shifts, however spectacular, are not listed.

Shades. Shades in philately refer to variations in the intensity of a colour or the presence of differing amounts of other colours. They are particularly significant when they can be linked to specific printings. In general, shades need to be quite marked to fall within the scope of this Catalogue; it does not favour nowadays listing the often numerous shades of a stamp, but chooses a single applicable colour name which will indicate particular groups of outstanding shades. Furthermore, the listings refer to colours as issued: they may deteriorate into something different through the passage of time.

Modern colour printing by lithography is prone to marked differences of shade, even within a single run, and variations can occur within the same sheet. Such shades are not listed.

Aniline colours. An aniline colour meant originally one derived from coal-tar; it now refers more widely to colour of a particular brightness suffused on the surface of a stamp and showing through clearly on the back.

Colours of overprints and surcharges. All overprints and surcharges are in black unless otherwise in the heading or after the description of the stamp.

7. Luminescence

Machines which sort mail electronically have been introduced in recent years. In consequence some countries have issued stamps on fluorescent or phosphorescent papers, while others have marked their stamps with phosphor bands.

The various papers can only be distinguished by ultraviolet lamps emitting particular wavelengths. They are separately listed only when the stamps have some other means of distinguishing them, visible without the use of these lamps. Where this is not so, the papers are recorded in footnotes or headings. (Collectors using the lamps should exercise great care in their use as exposure to their light is extremely dangerous to the eyes.)

Phosphor bands are listable, since they are visible to the naked eye (by holding stamps at an angle to the light and looking along them, the bands appear dark). Stamps existing with and without phosphor bands or with differing numbers of bands are given separate listings. Varieties such as double bands, misplaced or omitted bands, bands printed on the wrong side, are not listed.

8. Coil Stamps

Stamps issued only in coil form are given full listing. If stamps are issued in both sheets and coils the coil stamps are listed separately only where there is some feature (e.g. perforation) by which singles can be distinguished. Coil strips containing different stamps *se-tenant* are also listed.

Coil join pairs are too random and too easily faked to permit of listing; similarly ignored are coil stamps which have accidentally suffered an extra row of perforations from the claw mechanism in a malfunctioning vending machine.

9. Booklet Stamps

Single stamps from booklets are listed if they are distinguishable in some way (such as watermark or perforation) from similar sheet stamps. Booklet panes, provided they are distinguishable from blocks of sheet stamps, are listed for most countries; booklet panes containing more than one value *se-tenant* are listed under the lowest of the values concerned.

Lists of stamp booklets are given for certain countries and it is intended to extend this generally.

10. Forgeries and Fakes

Forgeries. Where space permits, notes are considered if they can give a concise description that will permit unequivocal detection of a forgery. Generalised warnings, lacking detail, are not nowadays inserted since their value to the collector is problematic.

Fakes. Unwitting fakes are numerous, particularly "new shades" which are colour changelings brought about by exposure to sunlight, soaking in water contaminated with dyes from adherent paper, contact with oil and dirt from a pocketbook, and so on. Fraudulent operators, in addition, can offer to arrange: removal of hinge marks; repairs of thins on white or coloured papers; replacement of missing margins or perforations; reperforating in true or false gauges; removal of fiscal cancellations; rejoining of severed pairs, strips and blocks; and (a major hazard) regumming. Collectors can only be urged to purchase from reputable sources and to insist upon Expert Committee certification where there is any doubt.

The Catalogue can consider footnotes about fakes where these are specific enough to assist in detection.

PRICES

Prices quoted in this Catalogue are the selling prices of Stanley Gibbons Ltd at the time when the book went to press. They are for stamps in fine condition for the issue concerned; in issues where condition varies they may ask more for the superb and less for the sub-standard.

All prices are subject to change without prior notice and Stanley Gibbons Ltd may from time to time offer stamps at other than catalogue prices in consequence of special purchases or particular promotions.

No guarantee is given to supply all stamps priced, since it is not possible to keep every catalogued item in stock. Commemorative issues may, at times, only be available in complete sets and not as individual values.

Quotations of prices. The prices in the left-hand column are for unused stamps and those in the right-hand column are for used.

Prices are expressed in pounds and pence sterling. One pound comprises 100 pence (£1 = 100p).

The method of notation is as follows: pence in numerals (e.g. 10 denotes ten pence); pounds and pence up to £100, in numerals (e.g. 425 denotes four pounds and twenty-five pence); prices above £100 expressed in whole pounds with the "£" sign shown.

Unused stamps. Prices for stamps issued up to the end of 1939 are for lightly hinged examples and more may be asked if they are in unmounted mint condition. Prices from 1940 unused stamps are for unmounted mint. Where not available in this condition, lightly hinged stamps are often available at a lower price.

Used stamps. The used prices are normally for stamps postally used but may be for stamps cancelled-to-order where this practice exists.

A pen-cancellation on early issues can sometimes correctly denote postal use. Instances are individually noted in the Catalogue in explanation of the used price given.

Prices quoted for bisects on cover or on large piece are for those dated during the period officially authorised.

Stamps not sold unused to the public but affixed by postal officials before use (e.g. some parcel post stamps) are priced used only.

Minimum price. The minimum catalogue price quoted is 10p. For individual stamps prices between 10p and 95p are provided as a guide for catalogue users. The lowest price charged for individual stamps purchased

from Stanley Gibbons Ltd. is £1.

Set prices. Set prices are generally for one of each value, excluding shades and varieties, but including major coulour changes. Where there are alternative shades, etc, the cheapest is usually included. The number of stamps in the set is always stated for clarity.

Where prices are given for *se-tenant* blocks or strips, any mint set price quoted for such an issue is for the complete *se-tenant* strip plus any other stamps included in the set. Used set prices are always for a set of single stamps.

Repricing. Collectors will be aware that the market factors of supply and demand directly influence the prices quoted in this Catalogue. Whatever the scarcity of a particular stamp, if there is no one in the market who wishes to buy it it cannot be expected to achieve a high price. Conversely, the same item actively sought by numerous potential buyers may cause the price to rise.

All the prices in this Catalogue are examined during the preparation of each new edition by expert staff of Stanley Gibbons and repriced as necessary. They take many factors into account, including supply and demand, and are in close touch with the international stamp market and the auction world.

GUARANTEE

All stamps are guaranteed genuine originals in the following terms:

If not as described, and returned by the purchaser, we undertake to refund the price paid to us in the original transaction. If any stamp is certified as genuine by the Expert Committee of the Royal Philatelic Society, London, or by B.P.A. Expertising Ltd, the purchaser shall not be entitled to make claim against us for any error, omission or mistake in such certificate. Consumers' statutory rights are not affected by this guarantee.

The establishment Expert Committees in this country are those of the Royal Philatelic Society, 41 Devonshire Place, London W1N 1PE, and B.P.A. Expertising Ltd, P.O. Box 137, Leatherhead, Surrey KT22 0RG. They do not undertake valuations under any circumstances and fees are payable for their services.

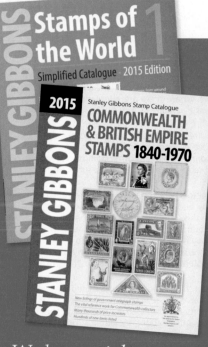

Abbreviations

Printers

A.B.N. Co.	American Bank Note Co, New York.
B.A.B.N.	British American Bank Note Co. Ottawa
B.D.T.	B.D.T. International Security Printing Ltd, Dublin, Ireland
B.W.	Bradbury Wilkinson & Co, Ltd.
Cartor	Cartor S.A., La Loupe, France
C.B.N.	Canadian Bank Note Co, Ottawa.
Continental	Continental Bank Note Co. B.N. Co.
Courvoisier	Imprimerie Courvoisier S.A., La-Chaux-de-Fonds, Switzerland.
D.L.R.	De La Rue & Co, Ltd, London.
Enschedé	Joh. Enschedé en Zonen, Haarlem, Netherlands.
Format	Format International Security Printers Ltd., London
Harrison	Harrison & Sons, Ltd. London
J.W.	John Waddington Security Print Ltd., Leeds
P.B.	Perkins Bacon Ltd, London.
Questa	Questa Colour Security Printers Ltd, London
Walsall	Walsall Security Printers Ltd
Waterlow	Waterlow & Sons, Ltd, London.

General Abbreviations

Alph	Alphabet
Anniv	Anniversary
Comp	Compound (perforation)
Des	Designer; designed
Diag	Diagonal; diagonally
Eng	Engraver; engraved
F.C.	Fiscal Cancellation
H/S	Handstamped
Horiz	Horizontal; horizontally
Imp, Imperf	Imperforate
Inscr	Inscribed
L	Left
Litho	Lithographed
mm	Millimetres
MS	Miniature sheet
N.Y.	New York
Opt(d)	Overprint(ed)
P or P-c	Pen-cancelled
P, Pf or Perf	Perforated
Photo	Photogravure
Pl	Plate
Pr	Pair
Ptd	Printed
Ptg	Printing
R	Right

R.	Row
Recess	Recess-printed
Roto	Rotogravure
Roul	Rouletted
S	Specimen (overprint)
Surch	Surcharge(d)
T.C.	Telegraph Cancellation
T	Type
Typo	Typographed
Un	Unused
Us	Used
Vert	Vertical; vertically
W or wmk	Watermark
Wmk s	Watermark sideways

(†) = Does not exist
(–) (or blank price column) = Exists, or may exist, but no market price is known.
/ between colours means "on" and the colour following is that of the paper on which the stamp is printed.

Colours of Stamps

Bl (blue); blk (black); brn (brown); car, carm (carmine); choc (chocolate); clar (claret); emer (emerald); grn (green); ind (indigo); mag (magenta); mar (maroon); mult (multicoloured); mve (mauve); ol (olive); orge (orange); pk (pink); pur (purple); scar (scarlet); sep (sepia); turq (turquoise); ultram (ultramarine); verm (vermilion); vio (violet); yell (yellow).

Colour of Overprints and Surcharges

(B.) = blue, (Blk.) = black, (Br.) = brown, (C.) = carmine, (G.) = green, (Mag.) = magenta, (Mve.) = mauve, (Ol.) = olive, (O.) = orange, (P.) = purple, (Pk.) = pink, (R.) = red, (Sil.) = silver, (V.) = violet, (Vm.) or (Verm.) = vermilion, (W.) = white, (Y.) = yellow.

Arabic Numerals

As in the case of European figures, the details of the Arabic numerals vary in different stamp designs, but they should be readily recognised with the aid of this illustration.

.	١	٢	٣	٤	٥	٦	٧	٨	٩
0	1	2	3	4	5	6	7	8	9

International Philatelic Glossary

English	French	German	Spanish	Italian
Agate	Agate	Achat	Agata	Agata
Air stamp	Timbre de la poste aérienne	Flugpostmarke	Sello de correo aéreo	Francobollo per posta aerea
Apple Green	Vert-pomme	Apfelgrün	Verde manzana	Verde mela
Barred	Annulé par barres	Balkenentwertung	Anulado con barras	Sbarrato
Bisected	Timbre coupé	Halbiert	Partido en dos	Frazionato
Bistre	Bistre	Bister	Bistre	Bistro
Bistre-brown	Brun-bistre	Bisterbraun	Castaño bistre	Bruno-bistro
Black	Noir	Schwarz	Negro	Nero
Blackish Brown	Brun-noir	Schwärzlichbraun	Castaño negruzco	Bruno nerastro
Blackish Green	Vert foncé	Schwärzlichgrün	Verde negruzco	Verde nerastro
Blackish Olive	Olive foncé	Schwärzlicholiv	Oliva negruzco	Oliva nerastro
Block of four	Bloc de quatre	Viererblock	Bloque de cuatro	Bloco di quattro
Blue	Bleu	Blau	Azul	Azzurro
Blue-green	Vert-bleu	Blaugrün	Verde azul	Verde azzuro
Bluish Violet	Violet bleuâtre	Bläulichviolett	Violeta azulado	Violtto azzurrastro
Booklet	Carnet	Heft	Cuadernillo	Libretto
Bright Blue	Bleu vif	Lebhaftblau	Azul vivo	Azzurro vivo
Bright Green	Vert vif	Lebhaftgrün	Verde vivo	Verde vivo
Bright Purple	Mauve vif	Lebhaftpurpur	Púrpura vivo	Porpora vivo
Bronze Green	Vert-bronze	Bronzegrün	Verde bronce	Verde bronzo
Brown	Brun	Braun	Castaño	Bruno
Brown-lake	Carmin-brun	Braunlack	Laca castaño	Lacca bruno
Brown-purple	Pourpre-brun	Braunpurpur	Púrpura castaño	Porpora bruno
Brown-red	Rouge-brun	Braunrot	Rojo castaño	Rosso bruno
Buff	Chamois	Sämisch	Anteado	Camoscio
Cancellation	Oblitération	Entwertung	Cancelación	Annullamento
Cancelled	Annulé	Gestempelt	Cancelado	Annullato
Carmine	Carmin	Karmin	Carmín	Carminio
Carmine-red	Rouge-carmin	Karminrot	Rojo carmín	Rosso carminio
Centred	Centré	Zentriert	Centrado	Centrato
Cerise	Rouge-cerise	Kirschrot	Color de ceresa	Color Ciliegia
Chalk-surfaced paper	Papier couché	Kreidepapier	Papel estucado	Carta gessata
Chalky Blue	Bleu terne	Kreideblau	Azul turbio	Azzurro smorto
Charity stamp	Timbre de bienfaisance	Wohltätigkeitsmarke	Sello de beneficenza	Francobollo di beneficenza
Chestnut	Marron	Kastanienbraun	Castaño rojo	Marrone
Chocolate	Chocolat	Schokolade	Chocolate	Cioccolato
Cinnamon	Cannelle	Zimtbraun	Canela	Cannella
Claret	Grenat	Weinrot	Rojo vinoso	Vinaccia
Cobalt	Cobalt	Kobalt	Cobalto	Cobalto
Colour	Couleur	Farbe	Color	Colore
Comb-perforation	Dentelure en peigne	Kammzähnung, Reihenzähnung	Dentado de peine	Dentellatura e pettine
Commemorative stamp	Timbre commémoratif	Gedenkmarke	Sello conmemorativo	Francobollo commemorativo
Crimson	Cramoisi	Karmesin	Carmesí	Cremisi
Deep Blue	Blue foncé	Dunkelblau	Azul oscuro	Azzurro scuro
Deep bluish Green	Vert-bleu foncé	Dunkelbläulichgrün	Verde azulado oscuro	Verde azzurro scuro
Design	Dessin	Markenbild	Diseño	Disegno
Die	Matrice	Urstempel. Type,	Cuño	Conio, Matrice

English	French	German	Spanish	Italian
		Platte		
Double	Double	Doppelt	Doble	Doppio
Drab	Olive terne	Trüboliv	Oliva turbio	Oliva smorto
Dull Green	Vert terne	Trübgrün	Verde turbio	Verde smorto
Dull purple	Mauve terne	Trübpurpur	Púrpura turbio	Porpora smorto
Embossing	Impression en relief	Prägedruck	Impresión en relieve	Impressione a relievo
Emerald	Vert-eméraude	Smaragdgrün	Esmeralda	Smeraldo
Engraved	Gravé	Graviert	Grabado	Inciso
Error	Erreur	Fehler, Fehldruck	Error	Errore
Essay	Essai	Probedruck	Ensayo	Saggio
Express letter stamp	Timbre pour lettres par exprès	Eilmarke	Sello de urgencia	Francobollo per espresso
Fiscal stamp	Timbre fiscal	Stempelmarke	Sello fiscal	Francobollo fiscale
Flesh	Chair	Fleischfarben	Carne	Carnicino
Forgery	Faux, Falsification	Fälschung	Falsificación	Falso, Falsificazione
Frame	Cadre	Rahmen	Marco	Cornice
Granite paper	Papier avec fragments de fils de soie	Faserpapier	Papel con filamentos	Carto con fili di seta
Green	Vert	Grün	Verde	Verde
Greenish Blue	Bleu verdâtre	Grünlichblau	Azul verdoso	Azzurro verdastro
Greenish Yellow	Jaune-vert	Grünlichgelb	Amarillo verdoso	Giallo verdastro
Grey	Gris	Grau	Gris	Grigio
Grey-blue	Bleu-gris	Graublau	Azul gris	Azzurro grigio
Grey-green	Vert gris	Graugrün	Verde gris	Verde grigio
Gum	Gomme	Gummi	Goma	Gomma
Gutter	Interpanneau	Zwischensteg	Espacio blanco entre dos grupos	Ponte
Imperforate	Non-dentelé	Geschnitten	Sin dentar	Non dentellato
Indigo	Indigo	Indigo	Azul indigo	Indaco
Inscription	Inscription	Inschrift	Inscripción	Dicitura
Inverted	Renversé	Kopfstehend	Invertido	Capovolto
Issue	Émission	Ausgabe	Emisión	Emissione
Laid	Vergé	Gestreift	Listado	Vergato
Lake	Lie de vin	Lackfarbe	Laca	Lacca
Lake-brown	Brun-carmin	Lackbraun	Castaño laca	Bruno lacca
Lavender	Bleu-lavande	Lavendel	Color de alhucema	Lavanda
Lemon	Jaune-citron	Zitrongelb	Limón	Limone
Light Blue	Bleu clair	Hellblau	Azul claro	Azzurro chiaro
Lilac	Lilas	Lila	Lila	Lilla
Line perforation	Dentelure en lignes	Linienzähnung	Dentado en linea	Dentellatura lineare
Lithography	Lithographie	Steindruck	Litografía	Litografia
Local	Timbre de poste locale	Lokalpostmarke	Emisión local	Emissione locale
Lozenge roulette	Percé en losanges	Rautenförmiger Durchstich	Picadura en rombos	Perforazione a losanghe
Magenta	Magenta	Magentarot	Magenta	Magenta
Margin	Marge	Rand	Borde	Margine
Maroon	Marron pourpré	Dunkelrotpurpur	Púrpura rojo oscuro	Marrone rossastro
Mauve	Mauve	Malvenfarbe	Malva	Malva
Multicoloured	Polychrome	Mehrfarbig	Multicolores	Policromo
Myrtle Green	Vert myrte	Myrtengrün	Verde mirto	Verde mirto
New Blue	Bleu ciel vif	Neublau	Azul nuevo	Azzurro nuovo
Newspaper stamp	Timbre pour journaux	Zeitungsmarke	Sello para periódicos	Francobollo per giornali
Obliteration	Oblitération	Abstempelung	Matasello	Annullamento
Obsolete	Hors (de) cours	Ausser Kurs	Fuera de curso	Fuori corso
Ochre	Ocre	Ocker	Ocre	Ocra

English	French	German	Spanish	Italian
Official stamp	Timbre de service	Dienstmarke	Sello de servicio	Francobollo di
Olive-brown	Brun-olive	Olivbraun	Castaño oliva	Bruno oliva
Olive-green	Vert-olive	Olivgrün	Verde oliva	Verde oliva
Olive-grey	Gris-olive	Olivgrau	Gris oliva	Grigio oliva
Olive-yellow	Jaune-olive	Olivgelb	Amarillo oliva	Giallo oliva
Orange	Orange	Orange	Naranja	Arancio
Orange-brown	Brun-orange	Orangebraun	Castaño naranja	Bruno arancio
Orange-red	Rouge-orange	Orangerot	Rojo naranja	Rosso arancio
Orange-yellow	Jaune-orange	Orangegelb	Amarillo naranja	Giallo arancio
Overprint	Surcharge	Aufdruck	Sobrecarga	Soprastampa
Pair	Paire	Paar	Pareja	Coppia
Pale	Pâle	Blass	Pálido	Pallido
Pane	Panneau	Gruppe	Grupo	Gruppo
Paper	Papier	Papier	Papel	Carta
Parcel post stamp	Timbre pour colis postaux	Paketmarke	Sello para paquete postal	Francobollo per pacchi postali
Pen-cancelled	Oblitéré à plume	Federzugentwertung	Cancelado a pluma	Annullato a penna
Percé en arc	Percé en arc	Bogenförmiger Durchstich	Picadura en forma de arco	Perforazione ad arco
Percé en scie	Percé en scie	Bogenförmiger Durchstich	Picado en sierra	Foratura a sega
Perforated	Dentelé	Gezähnt	Dentado	Dentellato
Perforation	Dentelure	Zähnung	Dentar	Dentellatura
Photogravure	Photogravure, Heliogravure	Rastertiefdruck	Fotograbado	Rotocalco
Pin perforation	Percé en points	In Punkten durchstochen	Horadado con alfileres	Perforato a punti
Plate	Planche	Platte	Plancha	Lastra, Tavola
Plum	Prune	Pflaumenfarbe	Color de ciruela	Prugna
Postage Due stamp	Timbre-taxe	Portomarke	Sello de tasa	Segnatasse
Postage stamp	Timbre-poste	Briefmarke, Freimarke, Postmarke	Sello de correos	Francobollo postale
Postal fiscal stamp	Timbre fiscal-postal	Stempelmarke als Postmarke verwendet	Sello fiscal-postal	Fiscale postale
Postmark	Oblitération postale	Poststempel	Matasello	Bollo
Printing	Impression, Tirage	Druck	Impresión	Stampa, Tiratura
Proof	Épreuve	Druckprobe	Prueba de impresión	Prova
Provisionals	Timbres provisoires	Provisorische Marken. Provisorien	Provisionales	Provvisori
Prussian Blue	Bleu de Prusse	Preussischblau	Azul de Prusia	Azzurro di Prussia
Purple	Pourpre	Purpur	Púrpura	Porpora
Purple-brown	Brun-pourpre	Purpurbraun	Castaño púrpura	Bruno porpora
Recess-printing	Impression en taille douce	Tiefdruck	Grabado	Incisione
Red	Rouge	Rot	Rojo	Rosso
Red-brown	Brun-rouge	Rotbraun	Castaño rojizo	Bruno rosso
Reddish Lilac	Lilas rougeâtre	Rötlichlila	Lila rojizo	Lilla rossastro
Reddish Purple	Poupre-rouge	Rötlichpurpur	Púrpura rojizo	Porpora rossastro
Reddish Violet	Violet rougeâtre	Rötlichviolett	Violeta rojizo	Violetto rossastro
Red-orange	Orange rougeâtre	Rotorange	Naranja rojizo	Arancio rosso
Registration stamp	Timbre pour lettre chargée (recommandée)	Einschreibemarke	Sello de certificado lettere	Francobollo per raccomandate
Reprint	Réimpression	Neudruck	Reimpresión	Ristampa
Reversed	Retourné	Umgekehrt	Invertido	Rovesciato
Rose	Rose	Rosa	Rosa	Rosa
Rose-red	Rouge rosé	Rosarot	Rojo rosado	Rosso rosa
Rosine	Rose vif	Lebhaftrosa	Rosa vivo	Rosa vivo
Roulette	Percage	Durchstich	Picadura	Foratura
Rouletted	Percé	Durchstochen	Picado	Forato
Royal Blue	Bleu-roi	Königblau	Azul real	Azzurro reale

English	French	German	Spanish	Italian
Sage green	Vert-sauge	Salbeigrün	Verde salvia	Verde salvia
Salmon	Saumon	Lachs	Salmón	Salmone
Scarlet	Écarlate	Scharlach	Escarlata	Scarlatto
Sepia	Sépia	Sepia	Sepia	Seppia
Serpentine roulette	Percé en serpentin	Schlangenliniger Durchstich	Picado a serpentina	Perforazione a serpentina
Shade	Nuance	Tönung	Tono	Gradazione de colore
Sheet	Feuille	Bogen	Hoja	Foglio
Slate	Ardoise	Schiefer	Pizarra	Ardesia
Slate-blue	Bleu-ardoise	Schieferblau	Azul pizarra	Azzurro ardesia
Slate-green	Vert-ardoise	Schiefergrün	Verde pizarra	Verde ardesia
Slate-lilac	Lilas-gris	Schierferlila	Lila pizarra	Lilla ardesia
Slate-purple	Mauve-gris	Schieferpurpur	Púrpura pizarra	Porpora ardesia
Slate-violet	Violet-gris	Schieferviolett	Violeta pizarra	Violetto ardesia
Special delivery stamp	Timbre pour exprès	Eilmarke	Sello de urgencia	Francobollo per espressi
Specimen	Spécimen	Muster	Muestra	Saggio
Steel Blue	Bleu acier	Stahlblau	Azul acero	Azzurro acciaio
Strip	Bande	Streifen	Tira	Striscia
Surcharge	Surcharge	Aufdruck	Sobrecarga	Soprastampa
Tête-bêche	Tête-bêche	Kehrdruck	Tête-bêche	Tête-bêche
Tinted paper	Papier teinté	Getöntes Papier	Papel coloreado	Carta tinta
Too-late stamp	Timbre pour lettres en retard	Verspätungsmarke	Sello para cartas retardadas	Francobollo per le lettere in ritardo
Turquoise-blue	Bleu-turquoise	Türkisblau	Azul turquesa	Azzurro turchese
Turquoise-green	Vert-turquoise	Türkisgrün	Verde turquesa	Verde turchese
Typography	Typographie	Buchdruck	Tipografia	Tipografia
Ultramarine	Outremer	Ultramarin	Ultramar	Oltremare
Unused	Neuf	Ungebraucht	Nuevo	Nuovo
Used	Oblitéré, Usé	Gebraucht	Usado	Usato
Venetian Red	Rouge-brun terne	Venezianischrot	Rojo veneciano	Rosso veneziano
Vermilion	Vermillon	Zinnober	Cinabrio	Vermiglione
Violet	Violet	Violett	Violeta	Violetto
Violet-blue	Bleu-violet	Violettblau	Azul violeta	Azzurro violetto
Watermark	Filigrane	Wasserzeichen	Filigrana	Filigrana
Watermark sideways	Filigrane couché	Wasserzeichen liegend	Filigrana acostado	Filigrana coricata
Wove paper	Papier ordinaire, Papier uni	Einfaches Papier	Papel avitelado	Carta unita
Yellow	Jaune	Gelb	Amarillo	Giallo
Yellow-brown	Brun-jaune	Gelbbraun	Castaño amarillo	Bruno giallo
Yellow-green	Vert-jaune	Gelbgrün	Verde amarillo	Verde giallo
Yellow-olive	Olive-jaunâtre	Gelboliv	Oliva amarillo	Oliva giallastro
Yellow-orange	Orange jaunâtre	Gelborange	Naranja amarillo	Arancio giallastro
Zig-zag roulette	Percé en zigzag	Sägezahnartiger Durchstich	Picado en zigzag	Perforazione a zigzag

Guide to Entries

(A) Country of Issue – When a country changes its name, the catalogue listing changes to reflect the name change, for example Namibia was formerly known as South West Africa, the stamps in Southern Africa are all listed under Namibia, but split into South West Africa and then Namibia.

(B) Country Information – Brief geographical and historical details for the issuing country.

(C) Currency – Details of the currency, and dates of earliest use where applicable, on the face value of the stamps.

(D) Illustration – Generally, the first stamp in the set. Stamp illustrations are reduced to 75%, with overprints and surcharges shown actual size.

(E) Illustration or Type Number – These numbers are used to help identify stamps, either in the listing, type column, design line or footnote, usually the first value in a set. These type numbers are in a bold type face – **123**; when bracketed (**123**) an overprint or a surcharge is indicated. Some type numbers include a lower-case letter – **123a**, this indicates they have been added to an existing set.

(F) Date of issue – This is the date that the stamp/set of stamps was issued by the post office and was available for purchase. When a set of definitive stamps has been issued over several years the Year Date given is for the earliest issue. Commemorative sets are listed in chronological order. Stamps of the same design, or issue are usually grouped together, for example some of the New Zealand landscapes definitive series were first issued in 2003 but the set includes stamps issued to May 2007.

(G) Number Prefix – Stamps other than definitives and commemoratives have a prefix letter before the catalogue number.
Their use is explained in the text: some examples are A for airmail, D for postage due and O for official stamps.

(H) Footnote – Further information on background or key facts on issues.

(I) Stanley Gibbons Catalogue number – This is a unique number for each stamp to help the collector identify stamps in the listing. The Stanley Gibbons numbering system is universally recognized as definitive.
Where insufficient numbers have been left to provide for additional stamps to a listing, some stamps will have a suffix letter after the catalogue number (for example 214a). If numbers have been left for additions to a set and not used they will be left vacant.
The separate type numbers (in bold) refer to illustrations (see **E**).

(J) Colour – If a stamp is printed in three or fewer colours then the colours are listed, working from the centre of the stamp outwards (see **R**).

(K) Design line – Further details on design variations

(L) Key Type – Indicates a design type on which the stamp is based. These are the bold figures found below each illustration, for example listed in Cameroon, in the West Africa catalogue, is the Key type A and B showing the ex-Kaiser's yacht *Hohenzollern*. The type numbers are also given in bold in the second column of figures alongside the stamp description to indicate the design of each stamp. Where an issue comprises stamps of similar design, the corresponding type number should be taken as indicating the general design. Where there are blanks in the type number column it means that the type of the corresponding stamp

is that shown by the number in the type column of the same issue. A dash (–) in the type column means that the stamp is not illustrated. Where type numbers refer to stamps of another country, e.g. where stamps of one country are overprinted for use in another, this is always made clear in the text.

(M) Coloured Papers – Stamps printed on coloured paper are shown – e.g. "brown/*yellow*" indicates brown printed on yellow paper.

(N) Surcharges and Overprints – Usually described in the headings. Any actual wordings are shown in bold type. Descriptions clarify words and figures used in the overprint. Stamps with the same overprints in different colours are not listed separately. Numbers in brackets after the descriptions are the catalogue numbers of the non-overprinted stamps. The words "inscribed" or "inscription" refer to the wording incorporated in the design of a stamp and not surcharges or overprints.

(O) Face value – This refers to the value of each stamp and is the price it was sold for at the Post Office when issued. Some modern stamps do not have their values in figures but instead it is shown as a letter, for example Great Britain use 1st or 2nd on their stamps as opposed to the actual value.

(P) Catalogue Value – Mint/Unused. Prices quoted for Queen Victoria to King George V stamps are for lightly hinged examples.

(Q) Catalogue Value – Used. Prices generally refer to fine postally used examples. For certain issues they are for cancelled-to-order.

Prices
Prices are given in pence and pounds. Stamps worth £100 and over are shown in whole pounds:

Shown in Catalogue as	Explanation
10	10 pence
1.75	£1.75
15.00	£15
£150	£150
£2300	£2300

Prices assume stamps are in 'fine condition'; we may ask more for superb and less for those of lower quality. The minimum catalogue price quoted is 10p and is intended as a guide for catalogue users. The lowest price for individual stamps purchased from Stanley Gibbons is £1.

Prices quoted are for the cheapest variety of that particular stamp. Differences of watermark, perforation, or other details, often increase the value. Prices quoted for mint issues are for single examples, unless otherwise stated. Those in *se-tenant* pairs, strips, blocks or sheets may be worth more. Where no prices are listed it is either because the stamps are not known to exist (usually shown by a †) in that particular condition, or, more usually, because there is no reliable information on which to base their value.

All prices are subject to change without prior notice and we cannot guarantee to supply all stamps as priced. Prices quoted in advertisements are also subject to change without prior notice.

(R) Multicoloured – Nearly all modern stamps are multicoloured (more than three colours); this is indicated in the heading, with a description of the stamp given in the listing.

(S) Perforations – Please see page xiii for a detailed explanation of perforations.

(A) Country of issue ————•

Bangladesh

(B) Country Information

In elections during December 1970 the Awami League party won all but two of the seats in the East Pakistan province and, in consequence, held a majority in the National Assembly. On 1 March 1971 the Federal Government postponed the sitting of the Assembly with the result that unrest spread throughout the eastern province. Pakistan army operations against the dissidents forced the leaders of the League to flee to India from where East Pakistan was proclaimed independent as Bangladesh. In early December the Indian army moved against Pakistan troops in Bangladesh and civilian government was re-established on 22 December 1971.

From 20 December 1971 various Pakistan issues were overprinted by local postmasters, mainly using handstamps. Their use was permitted until 30 April 1973. These are of philatelic interest, but are outside the scope of the catalogue.

(C) Currency ————————• **(Currency. 100 paisa = 1 rupee)**

(D) Illustration

5c
N.Z. GOVERNMENT LIFE INSURANCE OFFICE

L **17** •————

(E) Illustration or Type number

(F) Date of issue————•**1978** (8 Mar). No. *L* 57 surch with Type *L* **16**. Chalky paper.

L63	L **14**	25c. on 2½c. ultramarine, green and buff	75	1·75

(Des A. G. Mitchell. Litho Harrison)

1981 (3 June). P 14½.

(G) Number prefix————•

			(P) Mint	**(Q)** Used
L64	L **17**	5c. multicoloured	10	10
L65		10c. multicoloured	10	10
L66		20c. multicoloured	15	15
L67		30c. multicoloured	25	25
L68		40c. multicoloured	30	30
L69		50c. multicoloured	30	45
L64/9 *Set of 6*			1·00	1·25

(H) Footnote ————• Issues for the Government Life Insurance Department were withdrawn on 1 December 1989 when it became the privatised Tower Corporation.

(Des G. R. Bull and G. R. Smith. Photo Harrison)

(I) Stanley Gibbons catalogue number ————• **1959** (2 Mar). Centenary of Marlborough Province. T **198** and similar horiz designs. W **98** (sideways). P 14½×14.

772		2d. green	30	10
773		3d. deep blue	30	10
774		8d. light brown	1·25	2·25
772/4 *Set of 3*			1·60	2·25

(J) Colour

(K) Design line ————• Designs:—3d. Shipping wool, Wairau Bar, 1857; 8d. Salt industry, Grassmere.

1915 (12 July). Stamps of German Kamerun. Types *A* and *B*, surch as T **1** (Nos. B1/9) or **2**. (Nos. B10/13) in black or blue.

(L) Key type column ————•

B1	A	1½d. on 3pf. (No. k7) (B.)	13·00	42·00
		a. Different fount "d"	£150	£350

340	41	2d. purple (1903)	£350	£325
341	28	3d. bistre-brown (1906)	£700	£600
342	37	4d. blue and chestnut/*bluish* (1904)	£300	£350
		a. *Blue and yellow-brown/bluish*	£300	£350

(M) Coloured papers

(N) Surcharges and overprints ————• **1913** (1 Dec). Auckland Industrial Exhibition. Nos. 387aa, 389, 392 and 405 optd with T **59** by Govt Printer, Wellington.

412	51	½d. deep green	20·00	55·00
413	53	1d. carmine	25·00	48·00
		a. "Feather" flaw	£225	
414	52	3d. chestnut	£130	£250
415		6d. carmine	£160	£300
412/15 *Set of 4*			£300	£600

(O) Face value

(P) Catalogue value – Mint

(Q) Catalogue value – Used

These overprinted stamps were only available for letters in New Zealand and to Australia.

(Des Martin Bailey. Litho Southern Colour Print)

(R) Multicoloured stamp ————• **2008** (2 July). Olympic Games, Beijing. T **685** and similar diamond-shaped designs. Multicoloured. Phosphorised paper. P 14½.

(S) Perforations

3056		50c. Type **685**	1·00	85

Stanley Gibbons

399 Strand

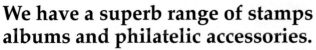

Unsure how to progress your collection?

Visit 399 Strand to get advice from our experienced and knowledgeable staff. They will help you choose the stamps and philatelic accessories that will enhance and develop your collection. They will also offer guidance on techniques for the care and storage of your stamps and covers.

We have a superb range of stamps albums and philatelic accessories.

We strive to cater for every need a collector might have, and if we don't have the exact item you need, we will recommend an equivalent or an alternative.

Come in, browse our range and choose what's best for you.

Before you commit to a particular album, take the time to talk to our staff who will help you weigh up the pros and cons before you make your decision. We are always happy to demonstrate anything we sell from tweezers to Frank Godden luxury albums.

Everything for the philatelic collector.

Just down the road from the Savoy Hotel, two minutes from Charing Cross Tube station

For more information, please contact Stephen Bowyer on:
Tel. +44 (0)207 557 4436 or sbowyer@stanleygibbons.com
399 Strand opening hours   Mon-Fri 9am-5.30pm   Sat 9:30am-5.30pm   Sun Closed

Est 1856

STANLEY GIBBONS

Stanley Gibbons Limite
399 Strand, London, WC2R 0L
+44 (0)20 7557 444
www.stanleygibbons.cor

Poland

1860. 100 Kopeks = 1 Rouble
1918. 100 Pfennig = 1 Mark
1918. 100 Halerzy = 1 Korona (South Poland)
1918. 100 Fenigów = 1 Marka (North Poland and throughout the country in 1919)
1924. 100 Groszy = 1 Zloty

I. RUSSIAN PROVINCE

The ancient Kingdom of Poland was partitioned between Russia, Austria and Prussia in 1772–95. Napoleon I created a Grand Duchy of Warsaw and in 1815 most of this became a new Kingdom of Poland, with the Tsar of Russia as king. Following a revolt in 1830–31, Poland became a Russian province in 1832.

1 Russian Arms

(Eng H. Mejer. Typo Govt Ptg Office, Warsaw)

1860 (1 Jan). Wove paper. P 11½ to 12½.

1	1	10k. deep blue and carmine	£3500	£475
		a. Blue and rose	£2750	£350
		b. Pale blue and pale rose	£2750	£275
		c. Frame of oval ptd twice, in rose and in blue	£7000	£900
		d. Imperf	£33000	£21000

As 1 January 1860 was a Sunday when post offices were closed, No. 1 was not available until 2 January (local Gregorian calendar). Letters to Russia had to have town postmark in Russian; as Russia still used the Julian calendar at this time the corresponding date was 20 December 1859.

Another Polish revolt in 1863–64 led to the incorporation of Poland in the Russian postal system on 13 February 1865 and the replacement of Polish stamps by Russian stamps. No. 1 was demonetized 13 April 1865 (Gregorian calendar).

II. REPUBLIC

From 1915 to 1918, Poland was in German and Austro-Hungarian occupation. Overprinted German stamps were used in the German Zone (see German Occupation issues at the end of this list) and Austro-Hungarian Military Post stamps in the Austro-Hungarian Zone. On 3 November 1918 a Polish Republic was proclaimed; during 1919–21 Poland acquired large areas from surrounding states. Western Galicia, part of the Austrian Empire, was awarded to Poland by the Powers on 8 May 1919. On 20 November 1919 the Powers agreed that Eastern Galicia (which in 1918–19 had been the West Ukrainian Republic) should be under Polish protection for 25 years; on 14 March 1923 this decision was repealed, and the area was integrated with Poland. The German province of Posen (Poznań) and parts of West Prussia and Lower Silesia were awarded to Poland by the Treaty of Versailles, 28 June 1919, and part of Upper Silesia was awarded to her after plebiscite in 1921. After almost continual warfare between Poland and Russia from 1918 to 1920, the Treaty of Riga, 18 March 1921, gave Poland large parts of White Russia and Volhynia. Central Lithuania was acquired on 8 April 1922.

A. REGIONAL ISSUES

2 Sigismund III Vasa Column, Warsaw

3 Arms of Warsaw

4 Polish Eagle

5 Jan III Sobieski Monument, Warsaw

(6a)

(6b)

T **6**: Distance between 2nd and 3rd bars:
6a—3¼ mm (1st ptg, 5.12.18)
6b—4 mm (2nd ptg, 15.1.19)

(Des E. Trojanowski. Litho)

1918 (17 Nov). Warsaw issue. Stamps prepared for use by Warsaw Citizens' Post, surch and optd "Poczta Polska" as in T **2/5**. Background of central design in buff. Wmk Horiz Wavy Lines. P 11½.

2	2	5 FEN. on 2g. brown	1·80	1·30
		a. Surch inverted	£225	£200
		b. Surch double	£600	
3	3	10 FEN. on 6g. green	1·30	1·10
		a. Surch inverted	20·00	16·00
		b. Surch double	£600	
		c. Watermark omitted	£500	£325
4	4	25 FEN. on 10g. carmine	9·75	3·25
		a. Surch inverted	36·00	30·00
		b. Error. "52" instead of "25"	£11000	
5	5	50 FEN. on 20g. blue	9·50	7·50
		a. Surch inverted	£450	£400
		b. Surch double	£1300	

1918 (5 Dec)–**19**. Issue for former area of German Occupation. Nos. 6 etc. of German Occupation of Poland (German stamps optd "Gen, Gouv Warschau").

*A. Surch or overprinted as T **6a***

7A	17	5pf. green	2·30	90
8A	24	5 on 2½pf. grey	1·00	50
9A	17	5 on 3pf. brown	12·00	4·75
10A		10pf. carmine	1·20	40
11A	24	15pf. slate-violet	80	40
12A	17	20pf. deep blue	1·00	55
		c. Violet-blue	1·00	55
13A	24	25 on 7½pf. orange	1·10	40
14A	17	30pf. black and orange/buff	80	40
15A		40pf. black and carmine	2·00	1·90
16A		60pf. magenta	1·30	1·30
7A/16A Set of 10			21·00	11·00

*B. Surch as T **6b** (15.1.19)*

6B	17	3pf. brown	42·00	33·00
7B		5pf. green	3·00	1·30
8B	24	5 on 2½pf. grey	1·30	55
9B	17	5 on 3pf. brown	£120	95·00
10B		10pf. carmine	1·50	65
11B	24	15pf. slate-violet	1·00	55
12B	17	20pf. deep blue	1·10	95
		c. Violet-blue	1·10	95
		d. Ultramarine	£2000	£3250
13B	24	25 on 7½pf. orange	18·00	7·75
14B	17	30pf. black and orange/buff	1·30	40
15B		40pf. black and carmine	7·75	7·00
16B		60pf. magenta	2·10	1·30
6B/16B Set of 11			£180	£130

Many of the above exist with inverted or double overprint, with "Pocata" or "Poczto" for "Poczta", or with various letters omitted or inverted.

7

(8)

1918 (5 Dec). Issue for former zone of Austro-Hungarian occupation. Imperial Welfare Fund stamps of Austro-Hungarian Military Post, optd as in T **7**, at Lublin.

17	6	10h. green	13·00	12·50
		a. Opt inverted	£100	90·00
		b. Opt double	£2000	£750
		c. Opt double, one inverted	£2250	£900

18	**7**	20h. claret	9·75	12·50
		a. Opt inverted	65·00	60·00
		b. Opt double, one inverted	£2000	£550
19	**6**	45h. blue	9·75	12·50
		a. Opt inverted	65·00	60·00
		b. Opt double, one inverted	£2000	£550

1918 (19–21 Dec). Second issue for former Austro-Hungarian zone. Emperor Charles stamps of Austro-Hungarian Military Post Surch as in T **8**, at Lublin. P 12½.

(a) With stars

20	**4**	3h. on 3h. olive-green	39·00	31·00
		a. Surch inverted	£4000	£3750
		b. Perf 11½	70·00	44·00
		ba. Surch inverted	£4000	£3750
		c. Perf 11½×12½	39·00	34·00
21		3h. on 15h. rose-pink	9·00	7·50
		a. Surch inverted	29·00	38·00
22		10h. on 30h. deep green	9·00	7·50
		a. Surch inverted	29·00	38·00
		b. Surch in violet	£130	£110
		ba. Surch inverted	£275	£275
23		25h. on 40h. olive	17·00	13·00
		a. Surch inverted	49·00	55·00
		b. Perf 11½	65·00	44·00
		ba. Surch inverted	£200	£190
24		45h. on 60h. carmine	9·00	7·50
		a. Surch inverted	33·00	34·00
25		45h. on 80h. blue	11·00	9·25
		a. Surch inverted	34·00	34·00
26		50h. on 60h. carmine	18·00	16·00
		a. Surch inverted	55·00	41·00

On Nos. 22/7 "HAL." is in capital letters.

Most of the above exist with left-hand star omitted. In such cases it is often replaced by a vertical smudge running right across the stamp. Stamps with cancellations before the date of issue are forged surcharges made on genuine stamps.

(b) With two bars instead of stars

27	**4**	45h. on 80h. blue	13·50	11·00
		a. Surch inverted	46·00	38·00
		b. Surch double, one inverted	£1800	

(c) Optd only (21 Dec)

28	**4**	50h. green	39·00	38·00
		a. Opt inverted	£110	£100
29		90h. violet	9·75	6·25
		a. Opt inverted	£120	£110
20/29 *Set of 10 (cheapest)*			£160	£130

1, 2, 5, 6 and 12h. values with overprint only are private productions.

POCZTA

POLSKA

(9)

POLSKA
POCZTA

(10)

25

11

1919 (10 Jan). Issue for Western Galicia. Austrian stamps of 1916 optd at Cracow.

*(a) Optd with T **9** (Nos. 45/48) or similar type (others)*

30	**49**	3h. violet (Imperial Crown)	£550	£475
31		5h. yellow-green	£700	£500
32		6h. orange	80·00	70·00
		a. Opt inverted	£57000	
33		10h. claret	£550	£475
34		12h. greenish blue	£100	75·00
35	**60**	15h. Venetian red (Charles I)	90·00	38·00
36		20h. deep green	£350	£150
37		25h. blue	£2250	£2000
38		30h. dull violet	£650	£375
39	**51**	40h. olive (Arms)	49·00	33·00
		a. Opt inverted	£400	
		b. Opt double	£2000	£2500
40		50h. deep green	23·00	19·00
		a. Opt inverted		£38000
41		60h. deep blue	20·00	15·00
		a. Opt inverted	£400	
42		80h. red-brown	16·00	15·00
		a. Opt inverted	£350	£275
		b. Opt double	£2000	
43		90h. claret	£1500	£1200
44		1k. red/yellow	34·00	30·00
45	**52**	2k. deep blue (Arms)	19·00	16·00
46		3k. carmine	£225	£190
47		4k. green	£250	£200
48		10k. deep violet	£13000	£14000
		a. Violet	£20000	£23000

*(b) Surch with T **10***

49	**51**	25 on 80h. red-brown	12·50	11·00
		a. Surch inverted	£275	£160

On Nos. 30/44 the overprint has a diamond shape between "POCZTA" and "POLSKA".

The 3k. with inverted overprint is a forgery.

Stamp of Austria

N **53** Mercury

1919 (10 Jan). NEWSPAPER. Newspaper stamps of Austria (Mercury) optd at Cracow similar to T **9** but with diamond shape between "POCZTA" and "POLSKA".

N50	N **53**	2h. brown	23·00	22·00
N51		4h. green	13·00	12·50
N52		6h. blue	13·00	12·50
N53		10h. orange	£275	£250
N54		30h. claret	15·00	17·00
N50/54 *Set of 5*			£300	£275

1919 (10 Jan). POSTAGE DUE. Postage Due stamps of Austria (Numerals) optd at Cracow with T **9** (Nos. D57/9) or similar type (others).

D50	D **55**	5h. carmine	16·00	22·00
D51		10h. carmine	£4750	£9000
D52		15h. carmine	15·00	14·00
		a. Opt inverted	£4000	£3250
D53		20h. carmine	£800	£650
D54		25h. carmine	60·00	50·00
D55		30h. carmine	£2250	£2000
D56		40h. carmine	£500	£475
D57	D **56**	1k. blue (R.)	£6000	£6500
D58		5k. blue (R.)	£6000	£6500
D59		10k. blue (R.)	£26000	£28000
		a. Black opt	£90000	£110000

On Nos. D50/6 the overprint has a diamond shape between "POCZTA" and "POLSKA".

1919 (Jan). POSTAGE DUE. Nos. D287 and D289 of Austria (Francis Joseph I) optd at Cracow similar to T **9** but with diamond shape between "POCZTA" and "POLSKA".

D60	**50**	15 on 36h. violet	£600	£550
D61		50 on 42h. brown	80·00	70·00
		a. Opt double	£4000	£6000

(Des J. Michalski. Litho at Cracow)

1919 (25 Feb). Issue for Western Galicia. Stout wove paper. No gum. Imperf.

50	**11**	2h. grey	1·80	1·30
51		3h. dull violet	1·30	1·10
52		5h. green	1·10	65
53		6h. orange	28·00	34·00
54		10h. lake	1·10	65
55		15h. brown	1·10	65
56		20h. olive-green	1·10	85
57		25h. carmine	1·00	65
58		50h. indigo	1·10	80
59		70h. blue	1·80	1·30
60		1k. carmine and grey	1·80	1·70
50/60 *Set of 11*			37·00	39·00

On the 2 and 3h. the currency is inscribed as "halerze". Stamps printed by typography are forgeries; the 2 and 3h. can be also identified by the inscription "halerzy".

5

Poczta

Polska

(12)

5

5

(13)

10

(14)

1919 (5 Aug). Poznań provisional issue. Stamps of Germany ("Germania") surch as T **12**.

61	**17**	5 on 2pf.grey	41·00	27·00
62	**24**	5 on 7½pf. orange	3·25	2·50
		a. Surch double	£1100	
63	**17**	5 on 20pf. blue	3·25	1·90
64		10 on 25pf. black and red/yellow	9·75	6·25
65		10 on 40pf. black and carmine	4·50	3·95
61/65 *Set of 5*			55·00	37·00

A 10 on 80pf. stamp was prepared for use but was never issued.

KOWEL LOCAL ISSUES. During August 1919 a number of Ukranian postage stamps were overprinted and placed on sale in Eastern Galicia, notably Kowel. The stamps were only on sale between the 20th and 24th of August. They were withdrawn when the Polish Ministry of Posts and Telegraphs took over the area. There is some doubt as to whether the Civilian Commissioner had permission to issue such stamps. Forgeries are also known.

1919 (15 Sept). Gniezno provisional issue. Stamps of Germany ("Germania") surch with T **13** or **14**.

66	**24**	5 on 2pf. yellowish grey (R.)		£600	£325
		a. Surch inverted			£31000
67		10 on 7½pf. orange (G.)		£325	£190

Forgeries of these surcharges exist, including inverts of the "10".

B. ISSUES FOR SOUTHERN POLAND

Austrian Currency

15	**16**	**17** Agriculture

18 Ploughing in Peace	**19** Polish Uhlan	**D 20**

(Des E. Trojanowski (**15**) and E. Bartlomiejczyk (**16/19**). Typo)

1919 (27 Jan). Value in halerzy or korony.

(a) Imperf

68	**15**	3h. brown	35	30 ✓
		a. Ribbed paper	50	50
69		5h. bright green	35	30 ✓
		a. Ribbed paper	50	50
70		10h. orange	35	30 ✓
		a. Ribbed paper	50	50
71		15h. scarlet	35	30 ✓
		a. Ribbed paper	50	50
72	**16**	20h. grey-brown	35	30 ✓
		a. Ribbed paper	50	50
73		25h. pale blue	35	30 ✓
		a. Ribbed paper	50	50
74		50h. red-brown	35	30 ✓
		a. Ribbed paper	50	50
75	**17**	1k. green	65	80 ✓
		a. Ribbed paper	90	95
76		1k.50 brown	7·75	4·00 ✓
77		2k. deep blue	3·25	3·75
		a. Ribbed paper	9·75	6·25 ✓
78	**18**	2k.50 purple	21·00	12·50
		a. Ribbed paper	26·00	15·00 ✓
79	**19**	5k. grey-blue	23·00	19·00
68/79 *Set of 12*			50·00	38·00 ✓

(b) P 10-11½ and compound

80	**15**	3h. brown	35	30
		a. Ribbed paper	1·30	65
81		5h. bright green	35	30
		a. Ribbed paper	40	40
82		10h. orange	35	30
		a. Ribbed paper	40	40
83		15h. scarlet	35	30
		a. Ribbed paper	40	40
84	**16**	20h. grey-brown	35	30
		a. Ribbed paper	40	40
85		25h. pale blue	35	30
		a. Ribbed paper	40	40
86		50h. red-brown	35	30
		a. Ribbed paper	50	40
87	**17**	1k. green	35	30
		a. Ribbed paper	40	40
88		1k.50 brown	90	40
		a. Ribbed paper	5·25	2·75
89		2k. deep blue	1·30	65
		a. Ribbed paper	5·25	2·50
90	**18**	2k.50 purple	1·80	90
		a. Ribbed paper	5·25	2·50

91	**19**	5k. grey-blue	2·30	1·10
		a. Ribbed paper	5·25	2·50
80/91 *Set of 12*			8·25	5·00

1919 (9 Sept). POSTAGE DUE. Value in halerzy. Typo. Wove paper. P 11½.

D92	**D 20**	2h. deep blue	25	15
D93		4h. deep blue	25	15
D94		5h. deep blue	25	15
D95		10h. deep blue	25	15
D96		20h. deep blue	25	15
D97		30h. deep blue	25	15
D98		50h. deep blue	40	15
D99		100h. deep blue	80	1·60
D100		500h. deep blue	2·75	3·75
D92/100 *Set of 9*			5·00	5·75

These stamps were originally issued for use as Postage Dues in former Austrian territory, until superseded by Nos. D126/36. The stock on hand was used for ordinary postage for a time, from February, 1920.

Stamps perforated 11 are forgeries.

See also Nos. D128/36 and D144/7.

C. ISSUES FOR NORTHERN POLAND

Polish Currency

1919 (27 Jan). Value in fenigów or marka. Medium wove paper. Clear impression.

(a) Imperf

92	**15**	3f. brown	50	40
		a. Ribbed paper	2·50	1·90
93		5f. green	50	40
		a. Ribbed paper	65	40
94		10f. purple	50	40
		a. Ribbed paper	50	40
95		15f. lake	50	40
		a. Ribbed paper	50	40
96	**16**	20f. blue	50	40
		a. Ribbed paper	50	40
97		25f. olive	50	40
		a. Ribbed paper	50	40
98		50f. green	50	40
		a. Ribbed paper	65	40
99	**17**	1m. violet	4·00	3·50
		a. Ribbed paper	4·50	3·75
100		1m.50 green	7·75	6·50
		a. Ribbed paper	16·00	12·50
101		2m. brown	7·25	7·75
102	**18**	2m.50 red-brown	33·00	20·00
		a. Ribbed paper	39·00	21·00
103	**19**	5m. purple	39·00	44·00
92/103 *Set of 12*			85·00	75·00

(b) P 11½

104	**15**	3f. brown	40	25
		a. Ribbed paper	50	40
105		5f. yellow-green	35	25
		a. Ribbed paper	40	40
106		10f. purple	25	25
		a. Ribbed paper	40	40
107		15f. scarlet	40	25
		a. Carmine	40	25
		b. Ribbed paper	65	40
108	**16**	20f. blue	25	25
		a. Ribbed paper	50	40
109		25f. olive	25	25
		a. Ribbed paper	40	40
110		50f. green	40	30
		a. Ribbed paper	50	40
111	**17**	1m. violet	65	40
		a. Ribbed paper	65	65
112		1m.50 green	90	40
		a. Ribbed paper	1·30	90
113		2m. brown	1·60	50
114	**18**	2m.50 red-brown	2·00	75
115	**19**	5m. violet	2·30	1·60
104/115 *Set of 12*			8·75	5·00

From 1 February 1920, this series could be used throughout Poland.

See also Nos. 128/43, 146 and 179 etc.

I. POLSKA WYSTAWA MAREK

I. POLSKA WYSTAWA MAREK

5 ✚ 5

(19a)	(19b)

20

21 Prime Minister Paderewski

22 W. Trąmpczynski

23 Eagle and Sailing Ship

1919 (3 May). First Polish Philatelic Exhibition and Polish White Cross Fund. Surch as T **19a** (Nos. 116/118) **19b** (Nos. 119/120), in violet. Imperf.

116	**15**	5+5f. yellow-green	80	65
		b. Perf 11½	65	50
117		10+5f. purple	2·00	3·75
		a. Ribbed paper	9·75	7·50
		b. Perf 11½	1·60	1·30
		ba. Ribbed paper	7·75	6·25
118		15+5f. lake	1·30	65
		a. Ribbed paper	7·75	6·25
		b. Perf 11½	65	50
		ba. Ribbed paper	7·75	6·25
119	**16**	25+5f. olive	1·30	65
		b. Perf 11½	1·30	50
		ba. Ribbed paper	7·75	6·25
120		50+5f. green	1·30	1·30
		a. Ribbed paper	7·75	6·25
		b. Perf 11½	2·50	1·90
		ba. Ribbed paper	7·75	6·25
116/120 *Set of 5*			6·00	6·25
116b/120b *Set of 5*			6·00	4·25

No. 120 is also known with overprint **19a** (*price* £1300 *unused* : £1000 *used*).

(Des E. Bartlomiejczyk (10f., 50f., 1m.), E. Trojanowski (15., 25f.), F. Polkowski (20f.). Typo)

1919 (15 June)–**20**. Opening of First Session of Parliament. Inscr "SEJM 1919". P 11½.

121	**20**	10f. mauve	40	30
122	**21**	15f. red	40	30
123	**22**	20f. brown (21×25 mm)	1·20	65
124		20f. brown (17×20 mm) ('20)	6·50	8·75
125	–	25f. sage-green	80	40
126	**23**	50f. greenish blue	80	40
127	–	1m. violet	1·30	90
121/127 *Set of 7*			10·50	10·50

Designs: Horiz as T **21**—25f. Gen. Pilsudski. As T **23**—1m. Griffin and fasces.

1919 (9 Sept). POSTAGE DUE. Value in fenigów. Typo. Wove paper. P 11½.

D128	D **20**	2f. vermilion	1·00	1·00
D129		4f. vermilion	50	50
D130		5f. vermilion	40	40
D131		10f. vermilion	40	40
D132		20f. vermilion	40	40
D133		30f. vermilion	40	40
D134		50f. vermilion	40	40
D135		100f. vermilion	2·50	1·30
D136		500f. vermilion	4·50	3·00
D128/136 *Set of 9*			9·50	7·00

See also Nos. D144/7.

D. ISSUES FOR THE WHOLE OF POLAND

1 February 1920

O **24**

A

B

(Des E. Bartlomiejczyk. Typo)

1920 (Feb–Nov). OFFICIAL.

(a) Stars as in A on 3 to 50f. Medium wove paper. P 11½, 10 or compound (1 Feb)

O128	O **24**	3f. scarlet	25	55
O129		5f. scarlet	35	55
O130		10f. scarlet	35	55
O131		15f. scarlet	65	55
O132		25f. scarlet	40	55
O133		50f. scarlet	40	55
O134		100f. scarlet	40	55
O135		150f. scarlet	75	55
O136		200f. scarlet	2·30	55
O137		300f. scarlet	2·75	65
O138		600f. scarlet	5·00	1·90
O128/138 *Set of 11*			12·00	6·75

Some stamps in this issue are known imperforate.

(b) Stars as B. Thin laid paper. P 11½ (20 Nov)

O139	O **24**	5f. scarlet	50	40
O140		10f. scarlet	50	35
O141		15f. scarlet	80	75
O142		25f. scarlet	2·00	75
O143		50f. scarlet	1·30	1·00
O139/143 *Set of 5*			4·50	3·00

The stamps on thin paper are printed from new plates in which the stars are inclined outwards instead of inwards, and the figures are larger.

1920 (Feb).

Thin wove paper. Coarse impression. P 10-11½ and compound

128	**15**	5f. green	40	25
129		10f. chocolate	40	25
130		15f. scarlet	40	25
131	**16**	20f. blue	40	25
132		25f. olive	40	25
133		50f. green	40	25
134	**17**	1m. slate-violet	40	25
128/134 *Set of 7*			2·50	1·60

Thin horizontally or vertically laid paper. Coarse impression. P 9 to 11½ and compound

135	**16**	25f. dull olive	40	25
136		50f. dull blue-green	40	25
137	**17**	1m. slate-violet	40	25
138		2m. brown	40	25
139	**18**	3m. red-brown	5·75	40
140	**19**	5m. purple	2·00	45
141		6m. rose-carmine	2·50	40
142		10m. vermilion	1·20	40
143		20m. green	6·50	40
135/143 *Set of 9*			18·00	2·75

Examples of the 20m. in *tête-bêche* pairs are postal forgeries.

Nos. 144/5 are vacant.

1920 (May). POSTAGE DUE. As Nos. D132, etc. but on thin laid paper. P 9 to 11½.

D144	D **20**	20f. deep blue	40	40
D145		100f. deep blue	40	40
D146		200f. deep blue	2·00	40
D147		500f. deep blue	2·00	40
D144/147 *Set of 4*			4·25	1·40

Though Type D **20** in blue was originally sold for Austrian currency, this reissue on thin paper was taken at face value in "fenigów".

24

25

(**26**)

(Des E. Bartlomiejczyk. Typo)

1920 (May). Redrawn value tablet. Thick wove paper. P 10 to 11½ and compounds.

146	**24**	40f. bright violet	50	40

See also Nos. 182 and 184.

(Des E. Trojanowski. Typo)

1920–21. Thin laid or wove paper. P 9 to 14½ and compounds.

147	**25**	1m. carmine	35	40
148		2m. green	35	40
149		3m. pale blue	70	40
150		4m. rose	35	40

151		5m. brown-purple	35	40
152		8m. bistre-brown (1921)	1·10	50
147/152	*Set of 6*		3·00	2·30

The 3m. comes on laid paper (vertical or horizontal) only; the other values exist both on laid paper (8m. horiz only; others vert or horiz) and on wove paper.

1921 (25 Jan). Surch with T **26**.

153	**24**	3m. on 40f. bright violet	65	40
		a. Surch inverted	£1100	
		b. Surch double	49·00	

6 Mk.

dopłata ✚ **30**ₘ

(D **27**)   (**27**)   D **28**

1921 (25 Jan). POSTAGE DUE. Surch as Type D **27**.

D154	**11**	6m. on 15h. brown	1·00	3·50
		a. Surch double	£250	
D155		6m. on 25h. carmine	1·00	2·75
		a. Surch inverted	£200	
D156		20m. on 10h. lake	6·50	12·50
		a. Surch inverted	80·00	
D157		20m. on 50h. indigo	5·25	6·25
D158		35m. on 70h. blue	13·00	31·00
D154/158	*Set of 5*		16·00	30·00

1921 (5 Mar). Red Cross Fund. Surch with T **27**, in red. P 9.

154	**19**	5m. +30m. purple	2·50	10·50
155		5m. +30m. rose-carmine	2·50	10·50
156		10m. +30m. vermilion	7·75	23·00
157		20m. +30m. green	70·00	£150
		a. Opt in carmine	£1100	
154/157	*Set of 4*		75·00	£170

(Des E. Trojanowski. Typo)

1921 (15 Apr). POSTAGE DUE. Wove or laid paper. Size 17×21–22 mm. P 9 to 14½ and compound.

D159	D **28**	1m. indigo	45	40
D160		2m. indigo	45	40
D161		4m. indigo	50	40
D162		6m. indigo	65	40
D163		8m. indigo	65	40
D164		20m. indigo	65	40
D165		50m. indigo	65	40
D166		100m. indigo	90	50
D159/166	*Set of 8*		4·50	3·00

Nos. D159/166 exist on a range of different papers in varying shades. For stamps size 19×24 mm, see Nos. D199/215.

28   **29**   **30**

(Des E. Bartlomiejczyk and W. Huzarski (T **30**). Typo)

1921 (2 May). New Constitution. P 11–11½.

158	**28**	2m. green	2·00	8·75
159		3m. blue	4·00	9·50
160		4m. scarlet	1·30	90
		a. Error. Carmine	£600	
161	**29**	6m. carmine	1·30	1·50
162		10m. slate-green	1·30	1·50
163	**30**	25m. violet	5·25	1·50
164		50m. myrtle green and buff	2·50	90
158/164	*Set of 7*		16·00	22·00

The large labels issued 29 May 1921 (25 and 100m.) inscribed "AERO-TARG: Poznań 1921", with "T.A.B.R.O.M.I.K." at foot are not a Government issue.

31 Sower   **32**

(Des B. Wisniewski. Typo)

1921–22. Peace Treaty with Russia. Laid (No. 165) or wove (all) paper. P 9 to 14½ and compounds.

(a) Size 28×22 mm (May–Aug 1921)

165	**31**	10m. deep turquoise (*shades*)	1·10	30 ✔
166		15m. orange-brown	50	30 ✔
167		20m. red	85	30 ✔

(b) Size 27¼×21½ mm (10m.) or 25½×21 mm (20m.) (Feb 1922)

168	**31**	10m. blue-green	55	30
169		20m. brown-red	80	30
165/169	*Set of 5*		3·50	1·40

(Des E. Trojanowski. Typo)

1921–23.

a) Thick wove paper. P 9 to 14½ and compounds (June 1921)

170	**32**	25m. violet and buff	95	30 ✔
171		50m. carmine and buff	95	30 ✔
172		100m. black-brown and orange	95	30 ✔
173		200m. pink and black	95	30

(b) Thin wove paper. P 10½ to 14½ and compounds (Feb–Apr 1923)

174	**32**	300m. yellow-green	40	30 ✔
175		400m. chocolate	70	30 ✔
176		500m. plum	75	30
177		1000m. orange	2·10	30 ✔
178		2000m. indigo-violet	65	30 ✔
170/178	*Set of 9*		7·50	2·40 ✔

33 Silesian Miner   **34** Copernicus   **35** Konarski

(T **33** des E. Bartlomiejczyk. Typo)

1922 (19 June)–**23**. Issue for districts of Upper Silesia.

(a) P 9 to 14½ and compound

179	**15**	5f. blue	35	1·40
180		10f. mauve	35	1·40
181	**16**	20f. red	50	1·90
182	**24**	40f. purple-brown	35	1·90
183	**16**	50f. red-orange	35	1·90
184	**24**	75f. blue-green	50	2·30 ✔
185	**33**	1m. slate (7.22)	50	1·90 ✔
186		1.25m. deep green (7.22)	80	3·50
187		2m. carmine (7.22)	35	1·90
188		3m. emerald (7.22)	35	1·90
189		4m. deep ultramarine (7.22)	65	3·25
190		5m. yellow-brown (7.22)	50	1·90
191		6m. red-orange (7.22)	1·00	8·25
192		10m. pale chocolate (7.22)	65	2·50
193		20m. deep purple (7.22)	80	2·50
194		50m. olive (7.22)	1·00	3·75

(b) Thicker paper. P 10 to 13½

195 }	**33**	80m. red (3.23)	2·00	30·00
196 {		100m. bright violet (3.23)	1·80	33·00
197		200m. dull orange (3.23)	4·00	44·00
198		300m. pale blue (15.4.23)	7·75	65·00
179/198	*Set of 20*		22·00	£190

Upper Silesia was divided between Germany and Poland after a plebiscite held on 20 March 1921.

1923 (Mar)–**24**. POSTAGE DUE. Wove paper. Size 19×24 mm. P 12½.

D199	D **28**	50m. indigo	30	25
D200		100m. indigo	30	25
D201		200m. indigo	30	25
D202		500m. indigo	45	25
D203		1000m. indigo	45	25
D204		2000m. indigo	55	25
D205		10000m. indigo	45	25
D206		20000m. indigo	55	25
D207		30000m. indigo	55	25
D208		50000m. indigo	80	40
D209		100000m. indigo	55	40
D210		200000m. indigo	85	40
D211		300000m. indigo	9·75	65
D212		500000m. indigo	4·25	90
D213		1000000m. indigo	2·50	1·30
D214		2000000m. indigo	4·25	2·20
D215		3000000m. indigo	6·50	2·50
D199/215	*Set of 17*		30·00	10·00

Nos. D205/215 were issued in the period from January to March 1924.

1923 (June–Nov). 450th Birth Anniv of Copernicus (astronomer) and 150th Death Anniv of Konarski (educationist). Typo. P 10½–12½ and compounds.

199	**34**	1000m. slate	1·70	90

200	**35**	3000m. red-brown	1·70	1·00
		a. Error "KONAPSKI"	26·00	31·00
201	**34**	5000m. carmine	2·00	1·30
199/201	*Set of 3*		4·75	3·00

No. 200a occurs in positions 5 and 15.

(36)

(37)

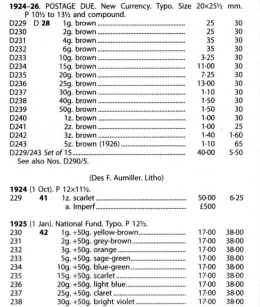

(38)   39

1923–24. Various stamps surch.

(a) With T 36

202	**32**	10,000m. on 25m. violet and buff	3·50	40

(b) As T 37

203	**31**	25,000m. on 20m. red (No. 167)	4·50	3·50
204		25,000m. on 20m. brown-red (169)	1·90	40
205		50,000m. on 10m. deep turquoise (165) .	8·25	40
205a		50,000m. on 10m. blue-green (168)	2·10	40

On No. 204 the surcharge is smaller.

(c) As T 38 (1924)

206	**25**	20,000m. on 2m. green	2·00	90
207		100,000m. on 5m. brown-purple	1·70	65
202/207	*Set of 7*		22·00	6·00

All the above exist with surcharge inverted and surcharge double. Nos. 206/7 exist on both laid and wove paper; for No. 205 only the wove paper printing was surcharged.

1923 (Nov). POSTAGE DUE. Surch in figures.

D216	D **28**	"10000" on 8m. indigo	1·10	35
D217		"20000" on 20m. indigo	1·30	45
D218		"50000" on 2m. indigo	2·00	90
D216/218	*Set of 3*		4·00	1·50

1924 (Jan–Mar). Typo. P 10 to 13½.

208	**39**	10,000m. brown-purple	3·50	65
209		20,000m. sage-green	2·00	45
210		30,000m. scarlet	3·50	65
211		50,000m. apple-green	8·50	65
212		100,000m. chestnut	3·00	65
213		200,000m. light blue	3·50	65
214		300,000m. magenta	8·50	80
215		500,000m. brown	7·00	3·00
216		1,000,000m. pink	1·00	55·00
217		2,000,000m. deep green	1·10	£425
208/217	*Set of 10*		37·00	£450

40

41 President Wojciechowski

42

(Typo State Graphic Institution)

1924 (1 May). New Currency. P 10½ to 13½ and compound.

218	**40**	1g. yellow-brown	1·70	1·60	✓
219		2g. grey-brown	1·70	95	✓
220		3g. orange	1·70	95	✓
221		5g. sage-green	1·70	95	✓
222		10g. blue-green	4·50	1·90	✓
223		15g. scarlet	4·50	1·90	✓
224		20g. light blue	16·00	45	✓
225		25g. claret	40·00	45	✓
		a. Error. *Slate*	£12000	£13000	✓
226		30g. bright violet	55·00	65	✓
		a. Grey-blue	£400	£190	
227		40g. slate	16·00	90	
228		50g. magenta	5·75	65	✓
218/228	*Set of 11*		£130	10·00	

No. 225a came from a cliché of the 25g. in the plate of the 40g.

1924–26. POSTAGE DUE. New Currency. Typo. Size 20×25½ mm. P 10½ to 13½ and compound.

D229	D **28**	1g. brown	25	30
D230		2g. brown	25	30
D231		4g. brown	35	30
D232		6g. brown	35	30
D233		10g. brown	3·25	30
D234		15g. brown	11·00	30
D235		20g. brown	7·25	30
D236		25g. brown	13·00	30
D237		30g. brown	1·10	30
D238		40g. brown	1·50	30
D239		50g. brown	1·50	30
D240		1z. brown	1·00	30
D241		2z. brown	1·00	25
D242		3z. brown	1·40	1·60
D243		5z. brown (1926)	1·10	65
D229/243	*Set of 15*		40·00	5·50

See also Nos. D290/5.

(Des F. Aumiller. Litho)

1924 (1 Oct). P 12×11½.

229	**41**	1z. scarlet	50·00	6·25
		a. Imperf	£500	

1925 (1 Jan). National Fund. Typo. P 12½.

230	**42**	1g. +50g. yellow-brown	17·00	38·00
231		2g. +50g. grey-brown	17·00	38·00
232		3g. +50g. orange	17·00	38·00
233		5g. +50g. sage-green	17·00	38·00
234		10g. +50g. blue-green	17·00	38·00
235		15g. +50g. scarlet	17·00	38·00
236		20g. +50g. light blue	17·00	38·00
237		25g. +50g. claret	17·00	38·00
238		30g. +50g. bright violet	17·00	38·00
239		40g. +50g. slate	17·00	38·00
240		50g. +50g. magenta	17·00	38·00
230/240	*Set of 11*		£325	£425

43 Holy Gate, Vilna

44 Town Hall, Poznań

45 King Sigismund Vasa Column, Warsaw

46 Wawel Castle, Cracow

47 Jan III Sobieski Statue, Lwów

48 Galleon

I.

II.

Nos. 243/6:
I. Coarse printing; background lines touch the figures.
II. Redrawn, clearer design; white surround to figures.

Two types of No. 247:
a. Ornament finishes with 2 points
b. No points

III.

IV.

Nos. 249:
III. Background lines continue through "GR".
IV. Background lines shortened to give white surround to "GR".

V.   VI.

Nos. 250/1:
V. "40" small, 6 mm across.
VI. "40" larger, 6½ mm, nearer to spire.

1925–27. Typo. P 10½×11, 11½×12½, 11½, 12½×13 (13×12½ on 15 and 40g.).

241	**43**	1g. brown	65	20 ✓
242	**47**	2g. brown-olive	90	35
243	**45**	3g. pale blue (I)	3·25	40
		a. Type II	1·70	25
244	**44**	5g. green (I)	2·00	25 ✓
		a. Type II	1·70	25
245	**45**	10g. violet (I)	1·70	25 ✓
		a. Type II	2·00	25 ✓
246	**46**	15g. carmine (I)	1·70	25 ✓
		a. Type II	2·00	25
247	**48**	20g. carmine-red (a)	34·00	25 ✓
		a. Type B	3·50	25
248	**43**	24g. grey-blue	29·00	2·50
249	**47**	30g. dull blue (III)	5·00	25 ✓
		a. Type IV	5·75	25
250	**46**	40g. light blue (V) (1927)	4·50	25 ✓
		a. Type VI	70·00	45
251	**48**	45g. mauve	£100	1·90
241/251		*Set of 11 (cheapest)*	£140	8·00

Use of the 1g. was obligatory on all internal correspondence in payment of a special tax.
The 20g. printed by lithography is a postal forgery.

49 L.V.G. Schneider Biplane   **50** Chopin   **51** Marshal Pilsudski

(Des L. Sowiński. Typo)

1925 (10 Sept). AIR. P 12½.

252	**49**	1g. pale blue	1·60	9·50
253		2g. orange	1·60	9·50
254		3g. yellow-brown	1·60	9·50
255		5g. brown	2·10	1·30
256		10g. blue-green	4·00	1·30
257		15g. bright magenta	13·00	1·90
258		20g. olive-green	22·00	9·50
259		30g. carmine	13·00	3·25
260		45g. deep lilac	22·00	6·25
252/260		*Set of 9*	75·00	47·00

Stamps perforated 11½ are forgeries.

(Des Z. Kamiński. Litho)

1927 (1 Mar). P 11½.

261	**50**	40g. deep ultramarine	30·00	5·00 ✓

1927–28. Typo. P 12½×13.

262	**51**	20g. carmine (*shades*) (19.3.27)	7·75	65 ✓
262a		25g. yellow-brown (*shades*) (1.2.28)	4·50	65 ✓
		b. Perf 11½	5·25	1·00

No. 262 has the shading of the central portrait and background formed of dots (*price* £200) In No. 262a, the shading is made up of lines (*price* £325).

52 President Mościcki   **53**   **54** Dr. K. Kaczkowski

1927 (3 May). P 12×11½.

263	**52**	20g. vermilion	9·75	1·50 ✓

(Des B. Kamiński. Typo)

1927 (3 May). Educational Funds. Background of coloured wavy lines. P 11½.

264	**53**	10g. +5g. purple/*green*	18·00	14·00
265		20g. +5g. indigo/*straw*	20·00	16·00

1927 (27 May). Fourth International Military Medical Congress, Warsaw. Litho (10g.) or typo (others). P 11½ or 12½ (40g.).

266	**54**	10g. grey-green	9·50	5·00
267		25g. carmine	14·00	5·25 ✓
268		40g. blue	23·00	4·00 ✓
266/268		*Set of 3*	42·00	13·00

55 J. Slowacki (poet)   **56** Marshal Pilsudski   **57** Pres. Mościcki

1927 (28 June). Transference of Slowacki's remains to Cracow. Typo. P 12½ or 12½×13.

269	**55**	20g. claret	8·50	1·90 ✓

(Des Z. Kamiński. Eng F. Schirnböck. Recess)

1928 (3 May). Warsaw Philatelic Exhibition. Sheet 117×88 mm. T **56/7** in deep sepia. P 12½.

MS270	50g. and 1z.(+1z.50)	£550	£475

See also Nos. 272/3, 328 and **MS**332b/c.

58 Gen. Joseph Bem   **59** Henryk Sienkiewicz   **60** The ancient Slav God, Swietowit

1928 (May). Typo. P 12½×13.

271	**58**	25g. bright rose	6·50	65

1928 (May)–**31.** T **56** (wove paper) and **57** (vertically laid paper). Various perfs, 10½ to 13½ and compounds.

272	**56**	50g. bluish slate	6·50	40 ✓
272a		50g. blue-green (5.31)	10·50	65 ✓
273	**57**	1z. slate-black/*cream*	20·00	40 ✓
		a. Horiz laid paper (1930)	£110	3·25
272/272a/273		*Set of 3*	33·00	1·30

(Des E. Gaspé. Typo)

1928 (Oct). Henryk Sienkiewicz (author). P 12×12½.

274	**59**	15g. bright blue	3·25	65 ✓

(Des Z. Kamiński. Typo)

1928 (15 Dec). National Exhibition, Poznań. P 12½×12.

275	**60**	25g. red-brown	3·75	65 ✓

61   **62** King Jan III Sobieski   D **63**

(Des Z. Kamiński. Typo)

1928 (15 Dec). P 12×12½.

276	**61**	5g. violet	65	30 ✓
277		10g. green	1·00	30 ✓
278		25g. red-brown	1·30	50 ✓
276/278		*Set of 3*	2·75	1·00

Stamps printed by lithography and the 25g. with vertical edges imperforate are postal forgeries.

(Des F. Schirnböck. Typo)

1930 (July). Birth Tercentenary of King Jan III Sobieski. P 12×12½.
279   **62**   75g. purple ....   6·25   40 ✔

1930 (July). POSTAGE DUE. Typo. P 12½×13.
D280 D **63**   5g. brown   40   40

63   **64** Kościuszko, Washington and Pulaski

(Des T. Gronowski. Typo)

1930 (1 Nov). Centenary of "November Rising" (29 Nov, 1830). P 12½×13.
280   **63**   5g. purple   90   40 ✔
281   15g. blue ....   4·75   75 ✔
282   25g. red-brown ....   1·30   40 ✔
283   30g. rosine .... 12·50   6·25
280/283 *Set of 4* .... 18·00   7·00
  The 25g. perf 11 is a postal forgery.

(Des R. Kleczewski. Eng W. Vacek. Recess)

1932 (3 May). Birth Bicentenary of George Washington. Vert laid paper. P 11½.
284   **64**   30g. chocolate/*cream* ....   4·25   65 ✔

65   **66**

1932–33. Typo. W **66**. P 12×12½.
284*a* **65**   5g. violet (1933)   25   30 ✔
285   10g. green   25   30 ✔
285*a*   15g. claret (1933)   25   30 ✔
286   20g. grey   55   30 ✔
287   25g. bistre   75   30 ✔
288   30g. scarlet ....   2·50   30 ✔
289   60g. cobalt .... 35·00   45 ✔
284*a*/289 *Set of 7* .... 36·00   2·00
  The 25 and 30g. on unwatermarked paper are postal forgeries; the 25g. is line perf 12½, the 30g. perf 13.

1932. POSTAGE DUE. Size 19×24 mm. Typo. P 12½.
D290 D **28** 1g. brown   40   25
D291   2g. brown   40   25
D292   10g. brown ....   1·90   25
D293   15g. brown ....   2·30   25
D294   20g. brown .... 18·00   25
D295   25g. brown .... 44·00   30
D290/295 *Set of 6* .... 60·00   65

> **PRINTER.** The letters "P.W.P.W." below the designs of some stamps from 1933 onwards stand for "Panstwowa-Wytwornia Papierów. Wartosciowych" (the Govt Ptg Wks).

67 Town Hall, Toruń   **68** Franciszek Żwirko (airman), Stanislaw Wigura (aircraft designer) and RWD-6 SP-AHN

1933 (2 Jan). Seventh Centenary of Toruń. Recess. W **66**. P 11½.
290   **67**   60g. blue/*cream* .... 50·00   3·25 ✔

No. 291 is vacant.

(Des R. Kleczewski. Eng W. Vacek. Recess)

1933 (15 Apr). Victory in Flight round Europe Air Race, 1932. W **66**. P 11½ or 12½.
292   **68**   30g. grey-green .... 29·00   3·75

1933 (21 May). Toruń Philatelic Exhibition. Recess. W **66**. P 11½.
293   **67**   60g. scarlet/*cream* .... 31·00 25·00
  No. 293 was sold at 1z., at the Exhibition.

69 Altar piece, St. Mary's Church, Cracow   O **70**

(Des R. Kleczewski. Eng W. Vacek. Recess)

1933 (10 July). Fourth Death Centenary of Veit Stoss (sculptor). Vert laid paper. P 11½.
294   **69**   80g. red-brown/*cream* .... 23·00   3·25

1933 (1 Aug). OFFICIAL. Type O **70** (and similar type). Typo. W **66**. P 12×12½.

(a) Inscr "ZWYCZAJNA" (Ordinary)
O295   (30g.) mauve   80   50

(b) Inscr "POLECONA" (Registered)
O296   (80g.) scarlet   80   50
  See also Nos. O306/7.

70 "The Liberation of Vienna", by J. Matejko   **71** Cross of Independence

(Des R. Kleczewski. Eng W. Vacek. Recess)

1933 (12 Sept). 250th Anniv of Relief of Vienna. Vert laid paper. P 12×11½ or 11½.
295   **70**   1z.20 blue/*cream* .... 65·00 19·00

1933 (11 Nov). 15th Anniv of Proclamation of Republic. Typo. W **66**. P 12½×13.
296   **71**   30g. scarlet .... 13·00   90 ✔

Wyst. Filat. 1934 Katowice   **20 groszy**
    (**72**)   **73** Pilsudski and Legion of Fusiliers' Badge   (D **74**)

1934 (5 May). Katowice Philatelic Exhibition. Optd with T **72**. W **66**. P 12×12½.
297   **65**   20g. grey (R.) .... 50·00 50·00
298   30g. scarlet .... 50·00 50·00
  Overprints reading "1934 r." in the centre are proofs.

(Des R. Kleczewski. Eng W. Vacek. Recess)

1934. 20th Anniv of Formation of Polish Legion. P 11½.
299   **73**   25g. blue (1 Oct) ....   4·50   65 ✔
300   30g. sepia (6 Aug) ....   5·25   65 ✔

1934–38. POSTAGE DUE. Postage Due stamps of 1924–26 surch as Type D **74**.
D301 D **28** 10g. on 2z. brown (1938)   40   40
D302   15g. on 2z. brown (30.11.36)   40   40
D303   20g. on 1z. brown (30.11.36)   40   40
D304   20g. on 5z. brown (6.8.34) .... 10·00   40
D305   25g. on 3z. brown (7.37) ....   1·00   40
D306   30g. on 3z. brown (7.37) ....   1·90   40

D307	50g. on 40g. brown (7.37)		1·90	50
D308	50g. on 3z. brown (1935)		3·25	1·10
D301/308 Set of 8			17·00	3·00

**Challenge
1934** (74)

55 gr. (75) **1 zł.** (76)

DOPŁATA (D 77) **10 GR.**

1934 (28 Aug). International Air Tournament. Optd in red with T **74** or larger overprint (18½×8½ mm).

301	**49**	20g. olive-green	18·00	19·00
302	**68**	30g. grey-green	23·00	6·25

1934 (1 Oct)–**35**. Surch as T **75** (303/4) or **76**.

303	**69**	25g. on 80g. red-brown/cream	9·50	1·30
		a. "gr." lower than "25"	£225	50·00
304	**65**	55g. on 60g. cobalt	6·50	65
		a. Comma instead of full point after 'gr'	75·00	38·00
		b. Full point missing after 'gr'	95·00	44·00
305	**70**	1z. on 1z.20 blue/cream (R.)	30·00	9·50
		a. "l" 4½ mm (1935)	30·00	9·50
303/305 Set of 3			41·00	10·50

No. 303. Surcharge in each of the upper corners over original value.
No. 305. Surcharge in the centre at the foot with bars in upper corners obliterating original value. Figure "1" of surcharge measures 5½ mm.

1934–36. POSTAGE DUE. No. 273a surch as Type D **77** (differing in size and detail for each value). Horiz laid paper.

D309	**57**	10g. on 1z. (R.) (1.6.36)	1·30	65
		a. Vert laid paper	60·00	40·00
D310		20g. on 1z. (Br.) (15.2.36)	2·50	65
D311		25g. on 1z. (B.) (1.10.34)	1·30	65
		a. Vert laid paper	48·00	44·00
		b. Error. "23" instead of "25"	12·50	12·50
D309/311 Set of 3			4·50	1·80

1935 (1 Apr). OFFICIAL. Redrawn types resembling Nos. O295/6.

O306	(30g.) violet-blue ("ZWYCZAJNA")	30	50
O307	(80g.) brown red ("POLECONA")	50	50

77 Marshal Pilsudski

**Kopiec
Marszalka
Piłsudskiego**
(78)

(Des M. R. Polak. Litho (308, 309/10) or typo (others))

1935 (May–July). Mourning for Marshal Pilsudski. P 11½×13 (No. 308) or 11 (others).

306	**77**	5g. black (7.35)	1·30	40
307		5g. black (7.35)	1·30	75
308		25g. black (litho) (16.5.35)	2·50	40
308a		25g. black (typo) (7.35)	2·10	40
309		45g. black (28.5.35)	8·75	3·75
310		1z. black (28.5.35)	18·00	7·50
	Nos. 285a and 299 optd with T **78**			
311	**65**	15g. claret (B.) (31.5.35)	2·10	1·00
312	**73**	25g. blue (R.) (31.5.35)	6·50	4·00
306/312 Set of 8			38·00	16·00

See also No. **MS358a**.

79 Pieskowa Skała (Dog's Rock)

80 President Mościcki

(Des R. Kleczewski (313/5, 324), L. Sowiński (316, 321/3, 325/6), W. Borowski (317/20). Eng W. L. Vacek (313, 315, 322, 324/5, 327), M. R. Polak (314, 316, 317/9, 321, 323, 326), J. Piwczyk (320))

1935–37. As T **79** (various views, ship and buildings) and T **80**.

(a) Typo. P 13×12½

313		5g. violet-blue (16.8.35)	90	25
314		10g. yellow-green (1.12.35)	90	25
315		15g. greenish blue (5.8.35)	4·00	25
316		20g. violet-black (1.12.35)	3·00	25

(b) Recess. P 13×12½ (5 to 20g., 25 (II), 45, 50 (II) g.) or 13 (others). Plate I 28.3×21.3 mm, Plate II 28.5×22 mm

317		5g. violet (1.4.37)	65	30
318		10g. yellow-green (1.4.37)	65	30
319		15g. brown-lake (1.4.37)	75	40
320		20g. brown-orange (1.4.37)	4·50	65
321		25g. deep blue-green (I) (1.12.35)	2·20	25
		a. Plate II (1937)	1·00	25
322		30g. scarlet (1.12.35)	2·75	25
323		45g. magenta (I) (16.1.36)	1·30	25
		a. Plate II (1937)	90	25
324		50g. black (I) (16.1.36)	7·75	40
		a. Plate II (1937)	4·00	40
325		55g. blue (I) (16.1.36)	8·75	75
		a. Plate II (1937)	8·75	75
326		1z. sepia (16.1.36)	7·50	1·50
327		3z. sepia (15.9.35)	4·25	12·50
313/327 Set of 15 (cheapest)			40·00	17·00

Designs: As T **79**—No. 314, Lake Morskie Oko; 315, Piłsudski (liner); 316, Pieniny-Czorsztyn; 317, Monastery of Jasna Góra, Czestochowa; 318, Batory (liner) and Sea passenger terminal, Gdynia; 319, University, Lwów; 320, Administrative Buildings, Katowice; 25g. Belvedere Palace, Warsaw; 30g. Castle at Mir; 45g. Castle at Podhorce; 50g. Cloth Hall, Cracow; 55g. Raczynski Library, Poznań; 1z. Vilna Cathedral.

1936 (3 June). Tenth Anniv of Mościcki Presidency. As T **57** but inscr "1926. 3. VI. 1936" below design. P 12½.

328	**57**	1z. bright blue	8·75	12·50

**GORDON-BENNETT 30.VIII.
1936**
(81)

1936 (15 Aug). Gordon-Bennett International Balloon Race. Optd with T **81**.

329		30g. scarlet (B.) (No. 322)	13·00	10·00
330		55g. blue (R.) (No. 325)	15·00	8·75

82 Marshal Śmigly-Rydz   **83** President Mościcki

(Des S. Chrostowski. Eng M. R. Polak. Recess)

1937 (July–Aug). P 12½.

331	**82**	25g. slate-blue (1 July)	55	40
332		50g. blue (Aug)	80	65

See also No. **MS358a**.

1937 (1 Sept). Visit of King of Rumania. Three sheets each 102×125 mm each containing a block of four of earlier types in new colours. P 12½.

MS332a	**82**	25g.×4, sepia	31·00	41·00
MS332b	**56**	50g.×4, slate-blue	31·00	41·00
MS332c	**57**	1z.×4, black	31·00	41·00

(Eng J. Piwczyk. Recess)

1938 (1 Feb). President's 70th Birthday. P 12½.

333	**83**	15g. greenish slate	80	30
334		30g. purple	1·30	40

84 Kościuszko, Paine and Washington   **84a** Postal Coach

(Des W. Boratyński. Eng W. Vacek. Recess)

1938 (17 Mar). 150th Anniv of U.S. Constitution. P 12×12½.

335	**84**	1z. deep blue	2·75	2·50

(Des W. Boratyński. Eng W. Vacek. Recess)
1938 (3 May). Fifth Philatelic Exhibition, Warsaw. Sheet 130×103 mm.
P 12×12½ or imperf.
MS335a **84a** 45g.(×2) green and 55g.(×2) blue £140 £130

84b Stratosphere Balloon | **85** Boleslaw the Brave | **85a** King Wladislaw Jagiello and Queen Jadwiga

86 Marshal Pilsudski | **87** "Teschen comes to Poland" | D **88**

(Des L. Sowiński. Eng W. Vacek. Recess)
1938 (15 Sept). Proposed Polish Stratosphere Flight. Sheet 75×125 mm. P 12½×12.
MS335b **84b** 75g.(+1z.25) violet £120 £110

(Des W. Boratyński (5g. to 1z.), M. Watorek (2z.) and Z. Rozwadowski (3z.). Eng H. Dutczyński (5g., 45g., 50g., 1z.), J. Piwczyk (10g., 30g., 55g., 75g.) and M. R. Polak (others). Recess)

1938 (11 Nov). 20th Anniv of Independence.
(a) Designs as T **85** and T **85a** (5g. to 2z.) and T **86**. P 12½×13 or 13×12½ (3z.)

336		5g. red-orange	25 ✓	25
337		10g. green	25 ✓	25
338		15g. red-brown	25 ✓	25
339		20g. greenish blue	65 ✓	50
340		25g. purple	40 ✓	25
341		30g. rose-red	95 ✓	25
342		45g. black	1·40 ✓	1·00
343		50g. magenta	1·40 ✓	40
344		55g. bright blue	95 ✓	25
345		75g. blue-green	3·75 ✓	2·20
346		1z. orange	3·75	2·20
347		2z. carmine	16·00	19·00
348		3z. slate-blue	11·50	17·00
336/348	Set of 13		37·00	39·00

(b) Sheet 102×125 mm containing four portraits as T **83** but with value and inscr transposed, all in purple. Recess. P 12½
MS348a 25g. Marshal Pilsudski; 25g. Pres. Narutowicz; 25g. Pres. Mościcki; 25g. Marshal Śmigly-Rydz .... 25·00 38·00
Designs:—10g. Casimir the Great; 20g. Casimir Jagiellon; 25g. Sigismund August; 30g. Stefan Batory; 45g. Chodkiewicz and Żółkiewski; 50g. Jan III Sobieski; 55g. Symbol of Constitution of 3 May, 1791; 75g. Kościuszko, Poniatowski and Dąbrowski; 1z. November Uprising, 1830–31; 2z. Romuald Traugutt.
For stamp as No. 338, but without crossed swords in foreground; see No. 357.

(Des W. Boratyński. Eng W. Vacek. Recess)
1938 (1 Nov). Acquisition of Teschen. P 12½×13.
349 **87** 25g. purple .... 3·75 65

1938 (25 Nov)–**39**. POSTAGE DUE. Typo. P 12½×12.
D350	D **88**	5g. blue-green	40	30
D351		10g. blue-green	40	30
D352		15g. blue-green (1939)	40	30
D353		20g. blue-green (1939)	90	30
D354		25g. blue-green (1939)	65	30
D355		30g. blue-green (1939)	1·10	30
D356		50g. blue-green (1939)	1·70	75

D357		1z. blue-green (1939)	4·75	4·50
D350/357	Set of 8		9·25	3·75

88 "Warmth" | **89** Tatra Mountaineer | **89a** (No. 357)

(Des W. Boratyński. Eng J. Piwczyk. Recess)
1938–39. Winter Relief Fund. P 13×12½.
350	**88**	5g. +5g. red-orange (21.12.38)	50 ✓	3·25
351		25g. +10g. purple (10.1.39)	1·10 ✓	4·50
352		55g. +15g. bright blue (15.3.39)	2·40 ✓	7·50
350/352	Set of 3		3·50	14·00

(Des W. Boratyński. Eng M. Dutczyński. Recess)
1939 (6 Feb). International Ski Championships, Zakopane. P 12½×13.
353	**89**	15g. red-brown	1·50 ✓	1·50
354		25g. purple	2·50 ✓	1·90
355		30g. carmine	3·25 ✓	2·75
356		55g. bright blue	12·50 ✓	9·50
353/356	Set of 4		18·00	14·00

1939 (2 Mar). As No. 338, but crossed swords in foreground replaced by ornamental dais.
357 **89a** 15g. red-brown 65 40

90 Marshal Pilsudski and Polish Legionaries

(Des W. Boratyński. Eng J. Piwczyk. Recess)
1939 (1 Aug). 25th Anniv of Battles of First Polish Legions.
(a) P 12½×13
358 **90** 25g. purple .... 1·40 ✓ 65

(b) Sheet 103×125 mm comprising former types printed in violet-grey. Recess. P 12½
MS358a 25g. T **90**; 25g. T **77**; 25g. T **82** (sold for 1z.75) .... 34·00 55·00

III. GERMAN OCCUPATION

1939–45

German armies invaded Poland on 1 September 1939 and on 17 September Russian troops invaded from the east. On 28 September Poland was divided between Russia and Germany; Germany annexed the territory she had lost in 1919–21 and also parts of the provinces of Łódź, Warsaw, Cracow and Bialystok; on 12 October the rest of the area seized by Germany became a protectorate called the General-Government. Russian stamps were used in the area to the east of River Bug, annexed by the Soviet Union.

16 Groschen 16

Deutsche Post OSTEN
(91)

2 GR 2
General-Gouvernement
(92)

1939 (1–4 Dec). T **94** of Germany (Hindenburg) surch as T **91**.Wmk Swastikas. P 14×14½.
359		6g. on 3pf. bistre-brown	40	65
360		8g. on 4pf. slate-blue	40	65
361		12g. on 6pf. deep green	40	65
362		16g. on 8pf. orange-red (4 Dec)	90	1·90
363		20g. on 10pf. chocolate (4 Dec)	40	65

364	24g. on 12pf. carmine	40	65
365	30g. on 15pf. claret (4 Dec)	90	1·90
366	40g. on 20pf. light blue (4 Dec)	90	65
367	50g. on 25pf. ultramarine	90	1·30
368	60g. on 30pf. bronze-green	90	65
369	80g. on 40pf. magenta (4 Dec)	90	1·30
370	1z. on 50pf. black and green	1·90	2·50
371	2z. on 100pf. black and yellow	3·75	3·75
359/371 *Set of 13*		11·50	15·00

1940 (Feb–Mar). Stamps of Poland, 1937–39, optd as T **92**, at State Ptg Wks, Vienna.

372	2g. on 5g. red-orange (336)	25	50
373	4g. on 5g. red-orange (336)	25	50
374	6g. on 10g. green (337)	25	50
375	8g. on 10g. green (337)	25	50
376	10g. on 10g. green (337)	25	50
377	12g. on 15g. red-brown (I) (357)	25	50
	a. Type II	1·50	3·75
378	16g. on 15g. red-brown (357)	25	50
379	24g. on 25g. slate-blue (331)	1·90	3·75
380	24g. on 25g. purple (340)	25	50
381	30g. on 30g. rose-red (341)	25	50
382	30g. on 5g.+5g. red-orange (350)	40	90
383	40g. on 30g. purple (334)	65	1·30
384	40g. on 25g.+10g. purple (351)	40	90
385	50g. on 50g. magenta (I) (343)	25	90
	a. Type II	4·50	10·50
386	50g. on 55g. blue (332)	50	1·30
387	60g. on 55g. bright blue (344)	10·00	23·00
388	80g. on 75g. blue-green (345)	10·00	44·00
388a	1z. on 55g.+15g. blue (352)	5·75	14·00
389	1z. on 1z. orange (346)	10·50	23·00
390	2z. on 2z. carmine (347)	3·75	8·75
391	3z. on 3z. slate-blue (348)	5·00	12·50
372/391 *Set of 26*		46·00	£110

Two types of 12g. and 50g. Type I is as in T **92**. In Type II the figures of value are very close to the "G" and "l" of "General".

1940 (Feb–Mar). Nos. D353/6 optd with T **92**, at State Ptg Wks, Vienna.

391a	50g. on 20g. blue-green (D353)	1·80	5·00
391b	50g. on 25g. blue-green (D354)	7·50	20·00
391c	50g. on 30g. blue-green (D355)	23·00	44·00
391d	50g. on 50g. blue-green (D356)	1·30	3·75
391e	50g. on 1z. blue-green (D357)	2·50	5·00
391a/e *Set of 5*		32·00	70·00

PRINTER. All stamps from Nos. O392 to 477 were printed at the State Printing Works, Vienna.

O 93

93 Copernicus Memorial, Cracow

(94)

(Des Kreb. Design photo; figures of value typo)

1940 (5 Apr–5 Aug). OFFICIAL. As Type O **93**.

(a) 31×23 mm. P 12½ (5 Apr)

O392	6g. pale brown	95	3·25
O393	8g. grey	95	3·25
O394	10g. pale green	95	3·25
O395	12g. deep green	95	2·50
O396	20g. deep brown	95	3·75
O397	24g. brown-red	15·00	2·50
O398	30g. crimson-lake	1·30	3·75
O399	40g. deep violet	1·30	7·00
O400	48g. pale olive	4·50	7·00
O401	50g. blue	1·30	3·75
O402	60g. deep olive	95	2·50
O403	80g. purple	95	3·25

(b) 35×26 mm. P 13½×14 (5 Apr)

O404	1z. purple and grey	2·50	7·00
O405	3z. red-brown and grey	2·50	7·00
O406	5z. orange and grey	3·75	7·50
O392/406 *Set of 15*		35·00	60·00

(c) Size 21×16 mm

O407	6g. brown (5 Aug)	95	1·90
O408	8g. grey (5 Aug)	95	2·30
O409	10g. blue-green (5 Aug)	1·30	2·50
O410	12g. deep green (5 Aug)	95	2·30
O411	20g. deep brown (22 July)	95	1·90
O412	24g. brown-red (5 Aug)	95	1·90

O413	30g. crimson-lake (22 July)	1·30	2·50
O414	40g. deep violet (22 July)	1·30	2·50
O415	50g. blue (22 July)	1·30	2·50
O407/415 *Set of 9*		9·00	18·00

(Des Prof. Puchinger. Photo)

1940 (5 Aug)–**41**. Views as T **93**. P 14.

392	6g. brown	40	1·00
393	8g. chestnut	40	1·00
394	8g. blue-black (8.9.41)	80	90
395	10g. emerald	25	40
396	12g. deep green	3·25	90
397	12g. violet (8.9.41)	45	50
398	20g. deep brown	25	40
399	24g. lake	25	40
400	30g. reddish violet	25	40
401	30g. purple (8.9.41)	45	90
402	40g. blue-black	25	40
403	48g. red-brown (8.9.41)	95	1·50
404	50g. blue	25	40
405	60g. deep olive	25	40
406	80g. deep violet	65	65
407	1z. reddish purple (9.9.40)	3·25	1·50
408	1z. blue-green (8.9.41)	80	1·50
392/408 *Set of 17*		12·00	12·00

Designs:—6g. Florian Gate, Cracow; 8g. Castle Keep, Cracow; 10g. Cracow Gate, Lublin; 20g. Church of the Dominicans, Cracow; 24g. Wawel Castle, Cracow; 30g. Old Church in Lublin; 40g. Arcade, Cloth Hall, Cracow; 48g. Town Hall, Sandomir; 50g. Town Hall, Cracow; 60g. Courtyard of Wawel Castle, Cracow; 80g. St. Mary's Church, Cracow; 1z. Brühl Palace, Warsaw.

1940 (17 Aug). Red Cross Fund. Pictorial types of 1940–41 (colours changed), surch as T **94**, in red.

409	12g. +8g. greyish olive	2·20	4·50
410	24g. +16g. greyish olive	2·20	4·50
411	50g. +50g. greyish olive	3·25	7·00
412	80g. +80g. greyish olive	3·25	9·50
409/412 *Set of 4*		9·75	23·00

95

96

(Nos. 413/9. Des O. Engelhardt-Kyffhäuser. Eng F. Lorber. Recess)

1940 (26 Oct). First Anniv of German Occupation. T **95** and similar types. Thick straw-coloured paper. P 14½.

413	12g. +38g. deep green	1·80	4·50
414	24g. +26g. red	1·80	4·50
415	30g. +20g. deep violet	2·75	7·50
413/415 *Set of 3*		5·75	15·00

Designs:—24g. Woman with scarf; 30g. Fur-capped peasant (as T **96**).

1940 (1 Dec). Winter Relief Fund. P 12½.

416	**96**	12g. +8g. deep green	75	2·50
417		24g. +16g. red	75	2·75
418		30g. +30g. purple-brown	1·90	3·75
419		50g. +50g.blue	1·90	4·00
416/419 *Set of 4*			4·75	11·50

D 97

97 Cracow

1940 (1 Dec). DELIVERY. Photo. P 14.

D420	D **97**	10g. red-orange	50	1·80
D421		20g. red-orange	50	1·80
D422		30g. red-orange	50	1·80
D423		50g. red-orange	1·50	3·25
D420/423 *Set of 4*			2·75	7·75

Ordinary postage stamps only paid for delivery to the nearest sub-office and the above were applied in addition to pay for delivery to the addressee.

(Des Gessner and W. Kreb. Eng F. Lorber. Recess)

1941 (20 Apr). P 14½.

420	**97**	10z. grey and red	1·60	3·75

Issued in sheets of eight.

98 The Barbican, Cracow **99** Adolf Hitler

(Des Fahringer and Gessner. Eng F. Lorber. Recess)

1941. T **98** and similar horiz design. P 13½×14.

421		2z. blue (22 May)	95	1·30
422		4z. green (10 July)	95	2·20

Design:—4z. Tyniec Monastery.
See also Nos. 465/8.

(Des W. Dachauer. Eng F. Lorber)

1941 (26 Oct)–**44**.

(a) Photo. P 14

423	**99**	2g. grey	20	50
424		6g. yellow-brown	20	50
425		8g. deep grey-blue	20	50
426		10g. yellow-green	20	50
427		12g. deep violet	20	50
428		16g. red-orange	1·90	3·25
429		20g. deep brown	20	50
430		24g. lake	20	50
431		30g. purple	20	50
432		32g. deep blue-green	30	65
433		40g. blue	20	50
434		48g. chocolate	1·60	1·30
435		50g. blue (7.43)	30	90
436		60g. olive (7.43)	30	90
437		80g. deep purple (7.43)	30	90

(b) Recess. P 12½ (7.4.42–44)

438	**99**	50g. deep blue	65	1·30
439		60g. olive	65	1·30
440		80g. reddish purple	65	1·30
441		1z. deep green	65	1·30
		a. Perf 14 (1944)	1·30	19·00
442		1z.20 purple-brown	75	1·90
		a. Perf 14 (1944)	2·75	25·00
443		1z.60 violet-indigo	75	1·90
		a. Perf 14 (1944)	2·75	31·00
423/443	*Set of 21*		9·50	19·00

1942 (20 Apr). Hitler's 53rd Birthday. As T **99**, but premium inserted in design. Recess. Thick straw-coloured paper. P 11.

444		30g. +1z. reddish purple	45	2·50
445		50g. +1z. blue	45	2·50
446		1z.20 +1z. brown	45	2·50
444/446	*Set of 3*		1·20	6·75

100 Modern Lublin

1942 (15 Aug). 600th Anniv of Lublin. T **100** and similar design. Photo. P 12½.

447	–	12g. +8g. purple	25	1·00
448	**100**	24g. +6g. red-brown	25	1·00
449	–	50g. +50g. dull blue	25	1·90
450	**100**	1z. +1z. green	55	2·20
447/450	*Set of 4*		1·20	5·50

Designs:—12g., 50g. Lublin, after an ancient engraving.

101 Copernicus O **102**

(Des W. Dachauer. Eng F. Lorber. Recess)

1942 (20 Nov). Third Anniv of German Occupation. T **101** and similar portraits. P 13½×14.

451		12g. +18g. violet (Veit Stoss (Vit Stvosz))	20	65

452		24g. +26g. lake (Hans Dürer)	20	65
453		30g. +30g. purple (J. Schuch)	20	65
454		50g. +50g. blue (J. Elsner)	20	1·00
455		1z. +1z. green	25	1·30
451/455	*Set of 5*		95	3·75

(Des W. Kreb. Design photo; value typo)

1943 (16 Feb). OFFICIAL. P 14.

O456	O **102**	6g. yellow-brown	25	90
O457		8g. grey-blue	25	90
O458		10g. light green	25	90
O459		12g. violet	25	90
O460		16g. brown-orange	25	90
O461		20g. brown-olive	25	90
O462		24g. brown-lake	25	90
O463		30g. reddish purple	25	90
O464		40g. blue	25	90
O465		60g. olive	25	90
O466		80g. dull purple	25	90
O467		100g. slate	30	1·50
O456/467	*Set of 12*		2·75	10·50

102 Adolf Hitler (102a)

(Des W. Dachauer. Eng F. Lorber. Recess)

1943 (20 Apr). Hitler's 54th Birthday. P 14.

456	**102**	12g. +1z. violet	40	2·10
457		24g. +1z. carmine	40	2·10
458		84g. +1z. green	40	2·10
456/458	*Set of 3*		1·10	5·75

1943 (24 May). 400th Death Anniv of Nicolas Copernicus (astronomer). T **101** (colour changed) optd with T **102a**.

459	**101**	1z. +1z. reddish purple	40	2·50

Issued in sheets of ten.
Examples of the 1z. reddish purple without overprint exist; their status is unclear.

103 Cracow Gate, **103a** Lwòw **104** Adolf Hitler
Lublin

(Des W. Kreb. Frame photo. Centre embossed)

1943 (13 Aug–Sept). Third Anniv of Nazi Party in German-occupied Poland. T **103** and similar designs. P 14.

460		12g. +38g. green	20	75
461		24g. +76g. red	20	75
462		30g. +70g. purple	20	75
463		50g. +1z. blue	20	75
464		1z. +2z. grey	20	75
460/464	*Set of 5*		90	3·50

Designs:—24g. Cloth Hall, Cracow; 30g. Administrative Building, Radom; 50g. Brühl Palace, Warsaw; 1z. Town Hall, Lwòw.

(Des Fahringer (2z., 4z.), F. Prufimeyer (6z.), Gessner (10z.). Eng F. Lorber. Recess)

1943–44. T **103a** and similar horiz designs. P 13½×14 or 14×13½ (10z.).

465		2z. deep green (10.4.44)	20	40
466		4z. slate-violet (10.4.44)	75	1·50
467		6z. agate (11.2.44)	45	1·30
468		10z. grey and chestnut (26.10.43)	50	1·90
465/468	*Set of 4*		1·70	4·50

Designs:—2z. The Barbican, Cracow; 4z. Tyniec Monastery; 10z. Cracow.

(Des W. Kreb. Photo)

1944 (20 Apr). Hitler's 55th Birthday. P 14.

469	**104**	12g. +1z. green	25	1·50
470		24g. +1z. red-brown	25	1·50
471		84g. +1z. violet	25	1·50
469/471	*Set of 3*		70	4·00

105 Konrad Celtis

105a Cracow Castle

(Des W. Dachauer. Eng F. Lorber. Recess)

1944 (15 July). Culture Funds. T **105** and similar portraits. P 14.
472	12g. +18g. green	20	1·90
473	24g. +26g. red	20	1·90
474	30g. +30g. purple	20	2·50
475	50g. +50g. blue	20	3·00
476	1z. +1z. brown	20	3·00
472/476 Set of 5		90	11·00

Designs:—24g. Andreas Schlüter; 30g. Hans Boner; 50g. Augustus the Strong; 1z. Georg Gottlieb Pusch.

(Des P. Stubinger. Eng R. Zenziger. Recess)

1944 (26 Oct). Fifth Anniv of German Occupation. P 13½.
477	**105a**	10z. +10z. greenish black and carmine	10·00	65·00
		a. Grey-black and red	10·00	65·00

Issued in sheets of eight.

IV. ISSUES OF POLISH EXILED GOVERNMENT IN LONDON

1941–44

For correspondence on Polish sea-going vessels and, on certain days, from Polish military camps in Great Britain.

106 Ruins of Ministry of Finance, Warsaw

107 Vickers-Armstrong Wellington and Hawker Hurricanes MK 1 used by Poles in Great Britain

(Eng E. Dawson (5, 25, 75g.), P. S. Hall (10, 80g.), A. B. Hill (25g.), E. Warner (1z.), R. Godbehear (1z.50). Recess Bradbury, Wilkinson)

1941 (15 Dec). T **106/7** and similar designs. P 12½×13 (vert) or 11½×12 (horiz).
478	5g. purple	1·60	2·50
479	10g. myrtle green	2·10	2·50
480	25g. slate-black	2·50	3·75
481	55g. deep blue	3·25	3·75
482	75g. brown-olive	8·50	12·50
483	80g. carmine	8·50	12·50
484	1z. slate-blue	8·50	12·50
485	1z.50 red-brown	8·50	12·50
478/485 Set of 8		39·00	55·00

Designs: As T **106**—5g. Ruins of U.S.A. Embassy, Warsaw; 25g. Destruction of Mickiewicz Monument, Cracow; 1z.50 Polish submarine *Orzel.* As T **107**—55g. Ruins of Warsaw; 75g. Polish machine-gunners; 80g. Polish tank in Great Britain.

108 Vickers-Armstrong Wellington and U-boat

109 Merchant Navy

(Des A. Horowicz. Eng. P. S. Hall (5, 25, 55g.), E. Dawson (10, 75, 80g.), R. Godbehear (12g.), A. B. Hill (1z.50). Recess Bradbury, Wilkinson)

1943 (1 Nov). T **108/9** and similar designs. P 12½×13 (vert) or 11½×12 (horiz).
486	5g. claret	1·10	1·90

487	10g. bright green	1·40	2·50
488	25g. violet	1·40	2·50
489	55g. ultramarine	1·90	3·25
490	75g. red-brown	3·75	5·75
491	80g. carmine	4·50	7·50
492	1z. blackish olive	5·00	8·25
493	1z.50 black	5·00	12·50
486/493 Set of 8		22·00	40·00

Designs: As T **108**—25g. Anti-tank gun in France; 55g. Poles at Narvik; 1z. Saboteurs damaging railway line. As T **109**—75g. The Tobruk road; 80g. Gen. Sikorski visiting Polish troops in Middle East; 1z.50 Underground newspaper office.

(110)

111 Polish Partisans

1944 (27 June). Capture of Monte Cassino. Nos. 482/5 surch as T **110**, or smaller (No. 497).
494	45g. on 75g. olive-green (B.)	17·00	19·00
495	55g. on 80g. carmine (B.)	17·00	19·00
	a. No stop after "18"	24·00	27·00
496	80g. on 1z. slate-blue (B.)	17·00	19·00
497	1z.20 on 1z.50 red-brown (B.)	17·00	19·00
494/497 Set of 4		60·00	70·00

(Des A. Horowicz. Eng W. Vacek. Recess De La Rue)

1945 (3 Feb). Relief Fund for Survivors of Warsaw Rising. P 11½.
498	**111**	1z. +2z. green	7·75	19·00

V. REPUBLIC

In July 1944 a Provisional Government with Soviet sympathies was formed at Lublin, in the part of Poland reconquered by the Red Army. On 28 June 1945 a "Government of National Unity" was formed; by 1948 Poland had gradually been transformed into a Communist state.

112 Romuald Traugutt

113 White Eagle

114 Grunwald Memorial, Cracow

(Des J. Ogórkiewicz. Litho J. Pietrzykowski, Lublin)

1944 (7 Sept). National Heroes. T **112** and similar portraits. No gum. P 11½.
499	25g. rose-red (*shades*)		80·00	£130
	a. Imperf (pair)			£190
	b. Perf 11		£180	£250
500	50g. green (T. Kościuszko)		80·00	£130
	a. Imperf (pair)			£190
	b. Perf 11		£180	£250
501	1z. blue (H. Dąbrowski)		80·00	£150
	a. Imperf (pair)			£190
	b. Perf 11		£180	£275
499/501 Set of 3			£225	£375
499b/501b Set of 3			£475	£700

(Des J. Grubecki. Photo State Ptg Wks, Moscow)

1944 (13 Sept). P 12½.
502	**113**	25g. scarlet	1·90	1·90
503	**114**	50g. slate-green	1·90	1·30

No. 502 was printed in photogravure, but unoverprinted copies also exist from a typographed printing in dull red, which arrived too late for issue in this condition. See Nos. 516a, 536a and 602.

— 1 zł —

31.XII.1943

K. R. N.

31.XII.1944
(115)

— 2 zł —

P. K. W. N.

31.XII.1944
(116)

— 3 zł — 5 zł

31.XII.1944

R. T. R. P.
(117)

22.I.1863.
(118)

"K.R.N."=Krajowa Rada Narodowa (National Federal Council).
"P.K.W.N."=Polski Komitet Wolnosci Narodowej (Polish National Liberation Committee).
"R.T.R.P."=Rzad Tymczasowy Rzeczpospolitej Polskiej (Provisional Government of the Polish Republic).

(Surch typo J. Pietrzykowski, Lublin)

1944–45. No. 502 surch with T **115** to **117**.

504	**113**	1z. on 25g. scarlet (31.12.44)	3·25	8·75
505		2z. on 25g. scarlet (15.1.45)	3·25	8·75
506		3z. on 25g. scarlet (15.1.45)	3·25	8·75
504/506 Set of 3			8·75	24·00

The 1z. with spacing of 5 mm between the second and third and the third and fourth lines of the surcharge are postal forgeries.

1945 (22 Jan). 82nd Anniv of 1863 Revolt against Russia. T **112** surch with T **118**.

507	**112**	5z. on 25g. cinnamon	55·00	£130
		a. Opt double	£13000	
		b. Imperf (pair)	£1300	

— 3 zł —

Bydgoszcz

23. I. 1945
(119)

120 Flag-bearer and War Victim

1945 (12 Feb). Liberation Issue. No. 502 surch as T **119** (various town names with dates of liberation, as shown below), in blue.

508		3z. on 25g. "Bydgoszcz 23.1.1945"	7·00	19·00
509		3z. on 25g. "Częstochowa 17.1.1945"	7·00	19·00
510		3z. on 25g. "Gniezno 22.1.1945"	7·00	19·00
511		3z. on 25g. "Kalisz 24.1.1945"	7·00	19·00
512		3z. on 25g. "Kielce 15.1.1945"	7·00	19·00
513		3z. on 25g. "Kraków 19.1.1 945"	7·00	19·00
514		3z. on 25g. "Łódź 19.1.1945"	7·00	19·00
515		3z. on 25g. "Radom 16.1.1945"	7·00	19·00
516		3z. on 25g. "Warszawa 17.1.1945"	20·00	38·00
		a. Dull red (typo)	£140	£190
517		3z. on 25g. "Zakopane 29.1.1945"	7·00	19·00
508/517 Set of 10			75·00	£190

(T **120/1** des J. Ogórkiewicz. Typo Postal Ptg Inst, Łódź)

1945 (9 Mar). Liberation of Warsaw. White or grey paper. P 11.

518	**120**	5z. scarlet	3·00	3·75

5 zł. ═

121 Łódź Factories

24. III. 1794
(122)

1945 (15 Mar). Liberation of Łódź. P 11.

519	**121**	1z. ultramarine	1·00	65

1945 (9 Apr). 151st Anniv of Kościuszko's Oath of Allegiance. No. 500 surch with T **122**.

520		5z. on 50g. green (R.)	15·00	38·00

123 Grunwald Memorial, Cracow

> **USED PRICES.** From 1945 most commemorative issues were available cancelled-to-order from the Philatelic Bureau and used prices are for stamps in this condition. Postally used stamps may be worth more.

(Des J. Wilczyk. Photo at Cracow)

1945 (10 Apr). Cracow Monuments. T **123** and similar designs. P 11.

521		50g. chocolate	25	30
		a. Perf 11½	25	30
		b. Designer's name omitted (P 11)	1·40	40
522		1z. lake-brown	30	30
		a. Perf 11½	30	30
523		2z. blue	1·40	30
524		3z. plum	1·40	65
525		5z. blue-green	8·50	15·00
521/525 Set of 5			10·50	15·00

Designs: Vert—1z. Kosciuszko Memorial; 3z. Copernicus Memorial. Horiz—2z. Cloth Hall; 5z. Wawel Castle.

Nos. 521/5 are also known imperforate (price £38 per set)

125 Conrad (cruiser)

D **126** Posthorn and Thunderbolts

(Typo at Łódź)

1945 (24 Apr). 25th Anniv of Polish Maritime League. T **125** and similar type inscr "Liga Morska". P 11.

526		50g. +2z. reddish orange	7·25	19·00
527		1z. +3z. royal blue	4·75	11·00
528		2z. +4z. scarlet	3·50	11·00
529		3z. +5z. deep green	3·50	11·00
526/529 Set of 4			17·00	47·00

Designs: Vert—1z. Dar Pomorza (full-rigged cadet ship); 2z. Naval ensigns. Horiz—3z. Crane and Old Grain Tower, Gdańsk.

1945 (20 May). POSTAGE DUE. Litho. Size 26×19½ mm. P 11.

D530	D **126**	1z. orange-brown	25	25
D531		2z. orange-brown	40	25
D532		3z. orange-brown	55	30
D533		5z. orange-brown	95	50
D530/533 Set of 4			1·90	1·10

For stamps in larger size, see Nos. D571/7 and D646/52.

126 Town Hall, Poznań

127 Kościuszko Memorial, Łódź

(Des J. Wilczyk. Photo Postal Ptg Inst, Łódź)

1945 (16 June). Postal Employees' Congress. P 11.

530	**126**	1z. +5z. green	31·00	55·00

(Des Dobrowald. Litho at Łódź)

1945 (1 July). P 11.

531	**127**	3z. purple	3·25	65
		a. Perf 9	14·50	10·00

O **128**

(Des J. Ogórkiewicz. Photo at Cracow)

1945 (1 July)–**46**. OFFICIAL. With control numbers at bottom right.

(a) Control numbers M-01705 (5z.) or M-01706 (10z.). P 11

O532	O **128**	(5z.) deep violet-blue	50	30
O533		(10z.) red	95	40

(b) Redrawn. Control number M-01709 (May 1946). P 11

O534	O **128**	(5z.) deep violet-blue	50	30
		b. Imperf	50	30
O535		(10z.) red	95	40
		b. Imperf	95	40

The blue stamps are inscribed "ZWYKLA" (Ordinary) and the red stamps "POLECONA" (Registered).

Although the control number is the easiest method of identifying the two issues, it is often blurred with the final figure illegible. The redrawn stamps have fewer lines of shading on the eagle and the diagonal lines in each corner are narrower. The 10z. stamps can be further distinguished by the horizontal measurement of the design: No. O533 is 17 mm, No. O535 is 16½ mm.

See also Nos. O748 and O805/6.

128 Grunwald, 1410

129 Eagle and Manifesto

(Des M. Wątorski. Photo at Cracow)

1945 (16 July). 535th Anniv of Battle of Grunwald. P 11.

532	**128**	5z. blue	9·50	25·00
		a. Imperf (pair)	£190	

(Des J. Wilczyk. Photo at Cracow)

1945 (22 July). First Anniv of Liberation. P 11.

533	**129**	3z. carmine	14·50	31·00
		a. Imperf (pair)	£1500	

130 Westerplatte

(Des J. Wilczyk. Photo at Cracow)

1945 (1 Sept). Sixth Anniv of Defence of Westerplatte. P 11.

534	**130**	1z. +9z. slate	29·00	50·00
		a. Imperf (pair)	£110	

The premium was for a fund for sanatoria and rest homes.

(131) **(132)**

1945 (1–10 Sept). Surch with T **131/2**, in brown.

535	**114**	1z. on 50g. slate-green (10 Sept)	65	40
		a. Surch inverted	£110	
536	**113**	1.50z. on 25g. brown-red (1 Sept)	£750	£650
		a. Dull red (typo)	65	40

133 Crane Tower **135** St. John's Cathedral

(Des J. Wilczyk. Photo at Cracow)

1945 (15 Sept). Liberation of Gdańsk. T **133** and similar types inscr "Gdańsk. 30 III 1945". P 11.

537		1z. blackish olive	25	25
538		2z. blue (Stock Exchange)	40	25
539		3z. purple (High Gate (*horiz*))	2·00	1·30
		a. Imperf (pair)	2·30	75
537/539 *Set of 3*			2·40	1·60

(Des J. Wilczyk. Photo at Cracow)

1945–46. "Warsaw, 1939–45". T **135** and similar views of Warsaw before and after destruction. Imperf.

540		1.50z. carmine (Royal Castle) (15.10.45)	25	30
541		3z. blue (St. John's Cathedral) (25.11.45)	1·30	30
542		3.50z. green (City Hall) (5.12.45)	1·60	75
543		6z. slate (G.P.O.) (1.1.46)	1·90	40
544		8z. brown (War Ministry) (1.1.46)	6·25	1·00
545		10z. purple (Church of the Holy Cross) (10.1.46)	1·90	90
540/545 *Set of 6*			12·00	3·25

136 United Workers

(Des J. Wilczyk. Photo at Cracow)

1945 (18 Nov). Trades' Union Congress. P 11.

546	**136**	1.50z. +8.50z. slate	12·50	14·50

137 Soldiers of 1830 and Jan III Sobieski Statue

(Des J. Wilczyk. Photo at Cracow)

1945 (29 Nov). 115th Anniv of 1830 Revolt against Russia. P 11.

547	**137**	10z. slate	15·00	18·00

(138) **139** Insurgent **140** Lisunov Li-2 over ruins of Warsaw

1946 (17 Jan). First Anniv of Liberation of Warsaw. Nos. 540/5 optd with T **138**.

548		1.50z. carmine	3·75	6·25
549		3z. blue	3·75	6·25
		a. Opt inverted	£550	
550		3.50z. green	3·75	6·25
551		6z. slate	3·75	6·25
552		8z. brown	3·75	6·25
		a. Opt inverted	£950	

553		10z. purple	3·75	6·25
548/553	*Set of 6*		20·00	34·00

(Des M. Konarski, after A. Grottger. Photo at Cracow)

1946 (22 Jan). 83rd Anniv of 1863 Revolt. P 11.
554	**139**	6z. blue	12·50	19·00

(Des J. Wilczyk. Photo at Cracow)

1946 (Mar–Nov). AIR. P 11.
555	**140**	5z. slate-grey (25 June)	65 ✓	25 ✓
		a. *Slate-black*	5·50	80
		b. Control Number omitted	12·50	2·50
556		10z. purple (20 May)	1·30 ✓	40 ✓
557		15z. blue (1 Nov)	7·50 ✓	50 ✓
558		20z. claret (5 Mar)	2·50 ✓	40 ✓
559		25z. green (10 Sept)	5·00 ✓	65 ✓
560		30z. red-orange (15 Mar)	8·75 ✓	75
555/560	*Set of 6*		23·00	2·75

Nos. 557 and 559 are without control "M-07741" at foot.

141 Fighting in Spain

142 Bydgoszcz

(Des M. Wątorski. Photo at Cracow)

1946 (10 Mar). Polish Legion in the Spanish Civil War. P 11.
561	**141**	3z. +5z. scarlet	7·75	16·00

(Des M. Wątorski. Photo at Cracow)

1946 (19 Apr). 600th Anniv of Bydgoszcz. P 11.
562	**142**	3z. +2z. grey-black	6·25	17·00

143 "Death" over Majdanek Concentration Camp

144 Shield and Soldiers

145 Infantry

(Des J. Wilczyk. Photo at Cracow)

1946 (29 Apr). Majdanek Concentration Camp. P 11.
563	**143**	3z. +5z. slate-green	12·50	17·00

(Des M. Wątorski. Photo at Cracow)

1946 (2 May). Silesian Uprisings (1919–21 and 1939–45). P 11.
564	**144**	3z. +7z. brown	1·90	4·50 ✓

(Des S. Jasiński. Photo at Cracow)

1946 (9 May). First Anniv of Peace. P 11.
565	**145**	3z. chocolate	1·30	65

146 Polish Coastline

147 Pres Bierut, Premier O. Morawski and Marshal Żymierski

(Des P. Marczewski. Photo)

1946 (21 July). Maritime Festival. P 11.
566	**146**	3z. +7z. blue	4·50	9·75

(Des T. Gronowski. Photo)

1946 (22 July). Second Anniv of Polish Committee of National Liberation Manifesto. P 11.
567	**147**	3z. violet	7·50	19·00

148 Bédzin Castle

149 Crane, Monument and Crane Tower

(Des S. K. Dawski (568/9), S. Żechowski (570). Photo)

1946 (Aug–Dec). T **148** and similar designs. Imperf (5z., 10z.) or P 11 (6z.).
568		5z. olive-black (*shades*) (13.8)	40	30 ✓
568a		5z. chocolate (*shades*) (14.12)	65 ✓	30
569		6z. black (1.9)	90	50 ✓
570		10z. blue (16.12)	1·90	65
568/570	*Set of 4*		3·50	1·60

Designs: Vert—6z. Tombstone of Henry IV. Horiz—10z. Castle at Lanckorona.

1946 (Aug). POSTAGE DUE. Photo. Size 29×21½ mm. Imperf.
D571	D **126**	2z. orange-brown	40	25
D572		3z. orange-brown	40	25
D573		5z. orange-brown	40	25
D574		6z. orange-brown	40	25
D575		10z. orange-brown	40	25
D576		15z. orange-brown	95	30
D577		25z. orange-brown	1·50	40
D571/577	*Set of 7*		2·75	75

See also Nos. D646/52 for perf stamps.

(Des S. Żechowski. Photo)

1946 (14 Sept). The Fallen in Gdańsk. P 11.
571	**149**	3z. +12z.slate	3·75	11·00

150 Schoolchildren at Desk

(Des E. Bartlomiejczyk. Photo Courvoisier)

1946 (10 Oct). Polish Work for Education and Fund for International Bureau of Education. T **150** and similar designs. Granite paper. P 11½.
571a		3z. +22z. vermilion	55·00	£110
571b		6z. +24z. blue	55·00	£110
571c		11z. +19z. green	55·00	£110
571a/571c	*Set of 3*		£150	£300

MS571d 128×80 mm. Nos. 571a/c. Colours slightly changed (sold at 25+75z.) ... £700 £1900

Designs:—6z. Court of Jagiellonian University. Cracow; 11z. Gregor Piramowicz (1735–1801), founder of the Education Commission.

Nos. 571a/c were issued in small sheets of 12.

152 Stojalowski, Bojko, Stapiński and Witos

(Des S. Żechowski. Photo)

1946 (1 Dec). Fiftieth Anniv of Peasant Movement and Relief Fund. P 11.
572	**152**	5z. +10z. blue-green	3·25	12·50
573		5z. +10z. blue	3·25	12·50
574		5z. +10z. brown-olive	3·25	12·50
572/574	*Set of 3*		8·75	34·00

SEJM USTAWODAWCZY 1911947

(153)

1947 (4 Feb). Opening of Polish Parliament. No. 567 surch with T **153**.
575 **147** 3z. +7z.violet (R.) .... 15·00 25·00

XXII MISTRZOSTWA NARCIARSKIE POLSKI 1947

(154)

(155)

1947 (21 Feb). 22nd National Ski Championships, Zakopane. No. 502 surch with T **154**.
576 **113** 5 +15z. on 25g. brown-red (B.) .... 6·25 11·00

1947 (25 Feb). No. 569 surch with T **155**.
577 5z. on 6z. black (R.) .... 1·30 65
  a. Orange surch .... 1·50 65

156 Home of Emil Zegadlowicz

157 Frédéric Chopin (musician)

158 Boguslawski, Modrzejewska and Jaracz (actors)

159 Wounded Soldier, Nurse and Child

(Des F. Suknarowski. Photo)

1947 (1 Mar). Emil Zegadlowicz Commemoration. P 11.
578 **156** 5z. +15z. grey-green .... 5·00 11·50

1947 (1 Mar–10 May). Polish Culture (1st issue). As T **157/8** (Polish Celebrities).

(a) P 11

579A	1z. blue (1 Mar)		65	40
580A	2z. brown (15 Mar)		65	40
581A	3z. turquoise-green (Type **157**) (31 Mar)		65	40
582A	5z. greenish black (Type **158**) (30 Apr)		65	40
583A	6z. greenish grey (30 Apr)		2·50	40
584A	10z. grey (15 Mar)		3·25	40
585A	15z. slate violet (30 Apr)		7·50	65
586A	20z. slate-black (10 May)		10·00	90
579A/586A Set of 8			23·00	3·50

(b) Imperf

579B	1z. blue (1 Mar)		65	65
580B	2z. brown (15 Mar)		1·30	75
581B	3z. turquoise-green (Type **157**) (31 Mar)		1·30	75
582B	5z. greenish black (Type **158**) (30 Apr)		1·30	75
583B	6z. greenish grey (30 Apr)		5·00	75
584B	10z. grey (15 Mar)		5·00	75
585B	15z. slate violet (30 Apr)		7·50	75
586B	20z. slate-black (10 May)		7·50	1·50
579B/586B Set of 8			27·00	6·00

Portraits: Horiz:–1z. Matejko, Malczewski and Chelmoński (painters); 6z. Świętochowski, Żeromski and Prus (writers); 15z. Wyspianski, Slowacki and Kasprowicz (poets).
Vert:–2z. Brother Albert of Cracow (founder of Albertine Social Service Order); 10z. Marie Curie (scientist); 20z. A. Mickiewicz (poet).
See also Nos. 587A/594B and **MS**615a.

1947 (18 May–31 Oct). Polish Culture (2nd issue). Designs as T **157/8** (Polish Celebrities).

(a) P 11

587A	1z. blue-skate (18 May)		65	40
588A	2z. orange (18 May)		65	40
589A	3z. grey-olive (Type **157**) (20 July)		3·75	40
590A	5z. sepia (Type **158**) (2 July)		65	40
591A	6z. carmine (20 July)		65	40
592A	10z. pale blue (25 June)		5·00	65
593A	15z. red-brown (20 July)		4·50	65
594A	20z. dull purple (31 Oct)		4·50	65
587A/594A Set of 8			18·00	3·75

(b) Imperf

587B	1z. blue-skate (18 May)		65	65
588B	2z. orange (18 May)		65	40
589B	3z. grey-olive (Type 157) (20 July)		3·75	65
590B	5z. sepia (Type 158) (2 July)		65	40
591B	6z. carmine (20 July)		65	40
592B	10z. pale blue (25 June)		5·00	65
593B	15z. red-brown (20 July)		4·50	1·00
594B	20z. dull purple (31 Oct)		4·50	1·50
587B/594B Set of 8			18·00	5·00

Portraits: Horiz:–1z. Matejko, Malczewski and Chelmoński (painters); 6z. Świętochowski, Żeromski and Prus (writers); 15z. Wyspiański, Slowacki and Kasprowicz (poets). Vert:– 2z. Brother Albert of Cracow (founder of Albertine Social Service Order); 10z. Marie Curie (scientist); 20z. A. Mickiewicz (poet).

(Des M. Konarski. Photo)

1947 (1 June). Red Cross Fund. Cross in red. P 11.
595 **159** 5z. +5z. grey and red .... 6·25 11·50

161 Steelworker

LOTNICZA zł 50 zł

(162)

(Des S. Żechowski and M. Wątorski (15z.). Eng G. Barlangue, Cottet, Dufresne and Mazelin. Recess Govt Ptg Wks, Paris)

1947 (20 Aug). As T **161** (occupations). P 13.

596	5z. brown-lake		2·50	40
597	10z. emerald-green (Harvester)		65	30
598	15z. blue (Fisherman)		3·25	50
599	20z. black (Miner)		1·90	65
596/599 Set of 4			7·50	1·70

1947 (10 Sept). AIR. Nos. 502/3 surch with T **162** or similar surch.

(a) Design photo, surch typo

600	**114**	40z. on 50g. slate-green (R.)		4·50	1·90
601	**113**	50z. on 25g. scarlet		8·25	6·25
		a. Error. Inscribed "LOFNICZA" (pos. 23)		36·00	

(b) Design and surch typo

602	**113**	50z. on 25g. dull red		7·50	4·50
		a. Error. Inscribed "LOFNICZA" (pos. 23)		45·00	
600/602 Set of 3				18·00	11·50

163 Brother Albert of Cracow

164 Sagittarius

(Des S. Żechowski. Photo)

1947 (21 Dec). Winter Relief Fund. P 11.
603 **163** 2z. +18z. violet .... 3·25 12·00

(Des S. Żechowski. Photo)

1948 (9 Feb–25 Apr). AIR. P 11.

604	**164**	15z. violet (25 Apr)		3·50	65
605		25z. blue (25 Apr)		1·90	30
606		30z. chocolate (25 Apr)		1·50	65
607		50z. green		4·00	90
608		75z. black (15 Mar)		4·00	90

609		100z. red-orange..................................	4·00	90
604/609	*Set of 6*..................................		17·00	3·75

165 Chainbreaker   **166** Generals H. Dembiński and J. Bem

(T **165** des M. Wątorski; others des S. Żechowski. Photo)

1948 (15 Mar–15 July). Revolution Centenaries. T **165** and portraits as T **166**. P 11.

610	15z. sepia...............................		90 ✓	30
611	30z. sepia (15 July)............................		2·30 ✓	65
612	35z. olive-green (15 July)............		6·25 ✓	90
613	60z. scarlet (15 July)............		3·25 ✓	1·30
610/613	*Set of 4*...........................		11·50	2·75

Portraits: 35z. S. Worcell, P. Ściegienny and E. Dembowski; 60z. Friedrich Engels and Karl Marx.

167 Insurgents   **168** Wheel and Streamers

(Des J. Tom. Photo)

1948 (19 Apr). Fifth Anniv of Warsaw Ghetto Defence. P 11.

614	**167**	15z. black............................	4·50	10·00

(Des T. Gronowski. Design photo, blue portion litho)

1948 (1 May). Warsaw–Prague Cycle Race. P 11.

615	**168**	15z. carmine and blue	6·25	3·25

1948 (10 June). Polish Culture (3rd issue). Designs as T **157/8** (Polish Celebrities). P 11½.

MS615a	210×128 mm. Designs and colours as Nos. 587A/94A (sold at 62+438z.)................	£375	£500
	b. Missing control numbers..................	£1000	

169 Cycle Race

(Des N. Jarczewska and K. Witkowski. Photo)

1948 (22 June). Seventh Circuit of Poland Cycle Race. P 11.

616	**169**	3z. grey-black..........................	3·25	7·50 ✓
617		6z. brown...........................	3·50	9·50 ✓
618		15z. green.............................	5·75	11·50
616/618	*Set of 3*		11·50	26·00

170 *Oliwa* under Construction   **173** Firework Display

(Des T. Gronowski. Photo)

1948 (22 June). Merchant Marine, As T **170**. P 11.

619		6z. bight violet........................	2·75	6·25
620		15z. carmine-lake	4·00	7·50
621		35z. slate...........................	5·00	8·25
619/621	*Set of 3*		10·50	20·00

Designs: Horiz—15z. Freighter; 35z. *General M. Zaruski* (cadet ketch).

(Des E. Bartlomiejczyk. Photo)

1948 (15 July). Wroclaw Exhibition. P 11.

622	**173**	6z. greenish blue..................	1·50	90
623		15z. scarlet.........................	1·90	90
624		18z. claret.........................	2·50	90 ✓
625		35z. brown........................	2·50	90
622/625	*Set of 4*...........................		7·50	3·25

174 "Youth"   **175** Roadway, St Anne's Church and Palace

(Des T. Tuszewski. Photo)

1948 (8 Aug). International Youth Conference, Warsaw. P 11.

626	**174**	15z. blue............................	1·30	65

(Des Z. Skibiński. Photo)

1948 (1 Sept). Charity. Warsaw Reconstruction Fund. P 11.

627	**175**	15z. +5z. green..................	90	50 ✓

176 Toruń Ramparts and Mail Coach   **177** Streamlined Steam Locomotive PM36-1, Clock and Winged Wheel

(Des A. Suchanek. Photo)

1948 (4 Sept). Philatelic Congress, Toruń. P 11.

628	**176**	15z. sepia............................	2·50	1·30

(Des E. Bartlomiejczyk. Photo)

1948 (6 Oct). European Railway Conference. P 11½.

629	**177**	18z. blue............................	14·00	38·00

178 President Bierut

(Des M. Wątorski. Photo)

1948–49. P 11½ (6z.) or 11 (others).

629a	**178**	2z. dull orange (15.2.49)	25	15
629b		3z. deep blue-green (15.5.49)..........	25	15
		a. Perf 11½	25	15
630		5z. brown (1.12.48)..................	25	15 ✓
			25	15
631		6z. blue-black (1.12.48).............	1·90	30
631a		10z. violet (15.5.49)................	65	25 ✓
		b. Perf 11½	65	25
632		15z. carmine-red (14.10.48).........	1·30	25 ✓
		a. Perf 11½	1·30	25
633		18z. deep dull green (1.12.48).......	2·50	25
		a. Perf 11½	2·50	25
634		30z. blue (1.12.48).................	3·75	65 ✓
		a. Perf 11½	3·75	65
635		35z. brown-purple (1.12.48).........	8·75	1·30
629a/635	*Set of 9*.............................		18·00	3·00

179 Workers and Flag   **180** Baby

(Des E. John (5z.), T. Gronowski (others). Photo)

1948 (8 Dec). Workers Class Unity Congress. T **179** and similar horiz designs. P 11.

636	5z. carmine-red		1·90	1·30
	a. Perf 11½		1·90	1·30
637	15z. blackish purple		1·90	1·30
	a. Perf 11½		1·90	1·30
638	25z. brown		1·90	1·30
	a. Perf 11½		1·90	1·30
636/638	Set of 3		5·25	2·75

Designs:—15z. Flags and portraits of Engels, Marx, Lenin and Stalin; 25z. Workers marching and portrait of L. Warynski.

1948 (15 Dec). As Nos. 636/8, but colours changed and inscr "XII 1948" instead of "8 XII 1948". P 11 (25z.) or 11½ (others).

639	5z. plum		5·75	3·25
640	15z. blue		5·75	3·25
641	25z. green		5·75	3·25
639/641	Set of 3		16·00	8·75

(Des T. Trepkowski. Photo)

1948 (16 Dec). Anti-tuberculosis Fund. T **180** and similar baby portraits. P 11½ (3z.) or 11 (others).

642	3z. +2z. bronze green		7·50	8·00
643	5z. +5z. reddish brown		7·50	6·75
	a. Perf 11½		7·50	6·75
644	6z. +4z. plum		6·25	6·00
	a. Perf 11½		6·25	6·00
645	15z. +10z. deep rose-red		3·75	5·25
642/645	Set of 4		23·00	23·00

Nos. 642/5 were each issued with se-tenant stamp-sized labels in 10 different designs.

180a President Franklin D. Roosevelt

181 Workers

(Des T. Granowski. Photo Courvoisier)

1948 (30 Dec). AIR. Honouring Presidents Roosevelt, Pulaski and Kościuszko. T **180a** and similar horiz designs. P 11½.

645a	80z. blackish violet		48·00	50·00
645b	100z. purple (Pulaski)		48·00	50·00
645c	120z. blue (Kościuszko)		48·00	50·00
645a/645c	Set of 3		£130	£140

MS645d 160×95 mm. Nos. 645a/c 300+200z. colours changed £550 £900

Nos. 645a/c were issued in small sheets of 16 plus four attached labels.

The sale of this issue was restricted and it is doubtful if many were used, except philatelically.

1949 (15 Feb)–50. POSTAGE DUE. As P 11½ (1, 2z.) or 11 (others).

D646	D **126**	1z. yellow-brown ('50)	30	25
D647		2z. yellow-brown ('50)	30	25
D648		3z. yellow-brown ('50)	30	25
D649		15z. yellow-brown (2.50)	1·10	40
D650		25z. yellow-brown ('50)	90	65
D651		100z. orange-brown	2·00	1·00
D652		150z. orange-brown	2·75	1·10
D646/652	Set of 7		7·00	3·50

(Des E. John. Photo)

1949 (31 May). Trades Union Congress, Warsaw. T **181** and similar types inscr "II./VIII/. KONGRES ZWIAZKOW ZAWODOWYCH. MAJ. 1949". P 11½.

646	3z. carmine		2·10	1·80
647	5z. blue		2·30	1·80
648	15z. green		3·25	3·75
646/648	Set of 3		7·00	6·50

Designs:—5z. Factory, tractor and worker; 15z. Three workers.

182 Banks of R. Vistula

183 Pres. Bierut

(Des W. Borowski (10z., 15z.), R. Kleczewski (35z.). Eng B. Brandt (10z.), M. R. Polak (15z.), S. Lukaszewski (35z.). Litho)

1949 (22 July). Fifth Anniv of National Liberation Committee. T **182/3** and similar vert design. P 13.

649	10z. black		3·50	3·25
650	15z. deep mauve		3·50	3·25
651	35z. grey-blue (Radio station, Raszyn)		3·50	3·25
	a. Perf 11		3·50	3·25
649/651	Set of 3		9·50	8·75

184 Mail Coach and Map   **185** Worker and Tractor

(Des R. Kleczewski. Eng B. Brandt (6z.), S. Lukaszewski (30z.) and M. R. Polak (80z.). Recess)

1949 (10 Oct). 75th Anniv of U.P.U. Various forms of transport as T **184** inscr "75 LAT SWIATOWEGO ZWIAZKU POCZTOWEGO". P 13×12½.

652	6z. slate-purple		1·90	3·25
653	30z. deep blue (Liner)		3·25	3·75
654	80z. myrtle green (Airplane)		6·25	6·25
652/654	Set of 3		10·50	12·00

(Des L. Dąbrowski and D. Piotrowski. Eng S. Lukaszewski. Recess)

1949 (Nov–Dec). Congress of Peasant Movement. P 13×12½.

655	**185**	5z. claret (20.12)	2·00	40 ✔
656		10z. red (20.12)	40	30 ✔
657		15z. green (26.11)	40	30 ✔
658		35z. brown (20.12)	3·25	1·90 ✔
655/658	Set of 4		5·50	2·50

186 Frédéric Chopin   **187** Mickiewicz and Pushkin   **188** Postman

(Des M. Wątorski. Eng M. R. Polak (10z.), S. Lukaszewski (15z.) and B. Brandt (35z.). Recess)

1949 (5 Dec). T **186** and similar portraits. P 12½×13.

659	10z. purple (Adam Mickiewicz)		3·25	2·75
660	15z. brown-red		5·00	4·50
661	35z. blue (Julius Slowacki)		4·50	5·50
659/661	Set of 3		11·50	11·50

(Des M. Milberger. Eng B. Brandt. Recess)

1949 (15 Dec). Polish-Russian Friendship Month. P 12½×13.

662	**187**	15z. slate-violet	4·50	8·00

(Des R. Kleczewski. Eng B. Brandt. Recess)

1950 (21 Jan). Third Congress of Postal Workers. P 12½×13.

663	**188**	15z. bright purple	4·00	5·00

189 Mechanic, Hangar and Aeroplane   **D 190**   **190** President Bierut

(Des W. Borowski. Eng B. Brandt. Recess)

1950 (6 Feb). AIR. P 12½×13.

664	**189**	500z. brown-lake	11·50	12·50

(Des R. Kleczewski. Eng S. Lukaszewski. Recess)

1950 (Feb–Oct). POSTAGE DUE. P 12×12½.

D665	D **190**	5z. brown-red (20.10)	30	30
D666		10z. brown-red (25.2)	30	30
D667		15z. brown-red (5.7)	40	40
D668		20z. brown-red (20.10)	40	40
D669		25z. brown-red (5.7)	55	40

D670		50z. brown-red (24.5)............................		1·30	50
D671		100z. brown-red (20.10).........................		1·90	65
D665/671		Set of 7		4·75	2·75

See also Nos. D701/12, D804/14 and D2699/2702.

(Des W. Borowski. Eng M. R. Polak. Recess)

1950 (22 Feb). P 12×12½.

665	**190**	15z. red....................................	2·50	40

191 Julian Marchlewski   **192** Workers

(Des from photo by W. Kwinta. Photo)

1950 (23 Mar). 25th Death Anniv of Julian Marchlewski (patriot). P 11½.

666	**191**	15z. blue-black	3·25	90
		a. Perf 11	3·25	90

(Des M. Bylina. Photo)

1950 (15 Apr). Reconstruction of Warsaw. P 12.

667	**192**	5z. deep brown............................	65	30 ✓
		a. Perf 11	65	30
		b. Perf 13×11	65	30
		c. Perf 11½×12	65	30
		d. Perf 13×11½	65	30

See also No. 695.

193 Worker and Flag

(Des E. John (10z.), M. Bylina (15z.). Photo)

1950 (26 Apr). 60th Anniv of May Day Manifesto. T **193** and vert type inscr "1 MAJ 1890 1950". P 11½×12 (horiz) or 12×11½ (vert).

668		10z. magenta..............................	3·75	65 ✓
669		15z. olive-green.........................	3·75	1·00 ✓

Design: Vert—15z. Three workers and flag.

194 Statue   **195** Dove and Globe   **195a** President Bierut

(Des J. Wilczyk. Photo)

1950 (27 Apr). 23rd International Fair, Posnań. P 11½.

670	**194**	15z. red-brown	65	40

(Des T. Trepkowski. Photo)

1950 (15 May). International Peace Conference. P 11.

671	**195**	10z. deep green........................	3·25 ✓	40 ✓
672		15z. deep sepia.........................	65 ✓	25 ✓
		a. Perf 11½	65	25

(Des W. Borowski. Eng S. Lukaszewski. Recess)

1950 (25 June–20 Oct). P 12×12½.

673	**195a**	5z. green (25.7)	40	25 ✓
674		10z. scarlet (10.8)......................	40	25 ✓
675		15z. blue (20.10)	4·50	65 ✓
676		20z. violet	1·30	40 ✓
677		25z. red-brown (25.7)................	1·30	40 ✓
678		30z. claret (10.8)	1·30	65 ✓
679		40z. brown	2·50	40 ✓
680		50z. brown-olive	6·25	1·10 ✓
673/680		Set of 8	16·00	3·75 ✓

See also Nos. 687/94.

196 Industrial and Agricultural Worker   **197** Hibner, Kniewski, Rutkowski   **198** Worker and Dove

(Des W. Zakrzewski. Eng M. R. Polak. Recess)

1950 (20 July). Six Year Reconstruction Plan. P 12½×13.

681	**196**	15z. ultramarine (Plate I)	65	40 ✓
		a. Grey-blue (Plate II).............................	2·50 ✓	40

For similar stamps see Nos. 696/e and **MS**721a.

(Des Cz. Kaczmarczyk. Photo at Cracow)

1950 (18 Aug). 25th Death Anniv of Hibner, Kniewski and Rutkowski (revolutionaries). P 11½.

682	**197**	15z. deep blue-grey.................	5·00	1·30

(Des T. Gronowski. Eng M. R. Polak. Recess)

1950 (31 Aug). First Polish Peace Congress. P 12½×13.

683	**198**	15z. grey-green	1·30	65 ✓

Currency Revaluation
100 Old Zlotys = 1 New Groszy

By a decree of 28 October 1950 1 old zloty became worth 1 new groszy and all post offices were empowered to handstamp existing stocks of stamps with the word "Groszy" or "gr". About 50 types of these handstamps are known. These are outside the scope of this catalogue.

The stamps which were authorised for handstamping are Nos. 579/94 perf and imperf, 596/615, 619/645, 646/658, 673/80, D530/3, D571/7, D646/52 and D665/71. Handstamps on other stamps were not authorised.

199 Dove (after Picasso)

I.   II.

In Type II the "5" slopes more, the "R" has a long tail and there are six lines of shading below the "4" instead of nine.

(Eng B. Brandt. Recess)

1950 (13 Nov). Second World Peace Congress, Warsaw. P 13×12½.

684	**199**	40g. grey-blue...........................	3·75	65 ✓
685		45g. claret (I).............................	5·00	75 ✓
		a. Type II	65	40

200 General Bem and Battle of Piski

(Des E. Horvath. Eng M. R. Polak and B. Brandt. Recess)

1950 (10 Dec). Death Centenary of General Bem. P 12½×13.

686	**200**	45g. blue.....................................	5·00	3·75

1950 (16 Dec). Currency revalued. As T **195a**, but values in "groszy". P 12×12½.

687	**195a**	5g. violet	40	25
688		10g. blue-green..........................	40	25
689		15g. yellow-green.......................	40	25
690		25g. Venetian red.......................	55	25

	a. Perf 11½		25·00	12·50
691	30g. scarlet		55	25
692	40g. red-orange		1·30	25
693	45g. blue		3·75	25
694	75g. brown		2·50	25
687/694 Set of 8			8·75	1·80

1950 (16 Dec). Currency revalued. As No. 667, but value in "groszy".
P 11.

695	**192**	15g. green	40	30
		a. Perf 12½×11	40	30
		b. Perf 11½×11	40	30
		c. Perf 13×11½	40	30

1951 (8 Jan–3 June). Currency revalued. As No. 681, but new values.
P 12½×13.

696	**196**	45g. dull ultramarine (Pl. I) (8.1)	50	30
		a. Re-engraved. Plate II	3·75	40
696b		75g. blackish brown (15.4)	85	30
		c. Perf 11½	2·10	40
696d		1z.15 green (15.4)	2·50	50
696e		1z.20 scarlet (3.6)	1·90	40
696/696e Set of 4			5·25	1·40

In No. 696a there is stronger shading in the face and behind the
figures of value and the size is 22.3×28.1 mm instead of 22×27.8 mm.
See also No. **MS**721a.

201 Woman with Doves **202** Battle Scene and J. Dąbrowski **(203)**

(Des B. Brandt. Eng S. Lukaszewski. Recess)

1951 (2 Mar). Women's League Congress. P 12½×13.

697	**201**	45g. carmine	90	65

(Des B. Brandt. Eng M. R. Polak and C. Slania. Recess)

1951 (24 Mar). 80th Anniv of Paris Commune. P 12×12½.

698	**202**	45g. green	90	40 ✔

1951 (20 Apr). Unissued stamp as No. 685, surch with T **203**.

699	**199**	45g. on 15z. claret	1·10	40
		a. Surch double	£900	

204 Worker with Flag  **205** Smelting Works  **206** Pioneer and Badge

(Des S. Lukaszewski. Photo)

1951 (25 Apr). Labour Day. P 13×11.

700	**204**	45g. scarlet	90 ✔	30
		a. Perf 11×14	90	30

1951 (25 Apr)–**52**. POSTAGE DUE. Currency revalued. As Nos. D665/71.

D701	D **190**	5g. brown-red	25	25
D702		10g. brown-red	25	25
D703		15g. brown-red (9.51)	25	25
D704		20g. brown-red	25	25
D705		25g. brown-red (9.51)	25	25
D706		30g. brown-red	25	25
D707		50g. brown-red (10.51)	25	25
D708		60g. brown-red	25	25
D709		90g. brown-red (9.51)	1·90	1·30
D710		1z. brown-red	30	25
D711		2z. brown-red (10.51)	65	30
D712		5z. slate-purple (1952)	1·60	50
D701/712 Set of 12			5·75	4·00

See also Nos. D804/14 and D2699/2702.

(Des B. Brandt. Eng E. Konecki. Recess)

1951 (9 May–15 June). P 13×12½.

701	**205**	40g. blue	40 ✔	25 ✔
		a. Perf 11½	40	25
702		45g. black	55 ∿	25 ✔

702a		60g. brown (15.6)	40 ✔	25 ✔
		b. Perf 11½	40	25
702c		90g. lake (15.6)	2·75 ✔	30 ✔
701/702c Set of 4 (cheapest)			3·75	95

(Des S. Lukaszewski. Photo)

1951 (1 June). International Children's Day. T **206** and similar vert
design. P 12½×13.

703		30g. brown-olive	1·90	1·30
704		45g. turquoise (Boy, girl and map)	12·50	1·90

BLOCKED VALUES. Starting with Nos. 705/10 most commemorative
issues up to 1963 contained one "blocked value" which was not
available at most post offices but could only be obtained in strictly
limited quantities at the Philatelic Bureau. Their relative scarcity is
reflected in the prices quoted. It is understood that this practice was
intended to restrict the export of stamps by private individuals.

---

207 St. Staszic  **208** Wróblewski and Olszewski

(Des M. R. Polak (25g.), S. Lukaszewski (40g.), C. Slania (45g.), B. Brandt
(60g., 1z.20), R. Kleczewski (1z.15). Photo)

1951 (25 June). First Polish Scientific Congress. T **207** and similar vert
designs and T **208**. P 14×10½ (45g.) or 12½×13 (others).

705		25g. carmine	10·00	4·50
706		40g. blue (Marie Curie)	65	40
707		45g. violet	18·00	3·25
708		60g. green (M. Nencki)	90	40
709		1z.15 purple (Copernicus)	90	90
710		1z.20 grey (Dove and book)	2·50	65
705/710 Set of 6			30·00	9·00

209 F. Dzierzyński **210** Pres Bierut, Industry and Agriculture

(Des B. Brandt. Eng S. Lukaszewski. Recess)

1951 (5 July). 25th Death Anniv of Dzierzyński (Russian politician).
P 12×12½.

711	**209**	45g. brown	55 ✔	40 ✔

(Des S. Lukaszewski. Eng M. R. Polak and C. Slania. Recess)

1951 (22 July). Seventh Anniv of People's Republic. P 12½×13.

712	**210**	45g. carmine	3·25 ✔	65
713		60g. grey-green	33·00	12·50
714		90g. deep blue	10·00 ✔	1·90
712/714 Set of 3			42·00	13·50

211 Young People and Globe **45 gr** **(212)**

(Des B. Brandt. Photo)

1951 (5 Aug). Third World Youth Festival, Berlin. P 11.

715	**211**	40g. blue	2·10 ✔	40 ✔
		a. Perf 12½×10½	2·10	40

1951 (1 Sept). Unissued stamp as Nos. 673/80 surch with T **212**.

716	**195a**	45g. on 35z. orange	70	30
		a. Figure "4" shorter than "5"	12·50	6·25
		b. Opt inverted	£2250	

213 Sports Badge **214** Stalin

(Des E. Konecki. Photo)

1951 (8 Sept). Spartacist Games. P 14×11.
717	**213**	45g. green		2·50 ✔	90
		a. Perf 12½×13		6·25	2·50

(Des and eng S. Lukaszewski. Recess)

1951 (30 Oct). Polish–Soviet Friendship. P 12½×13.
718	**214**	45g. brown-carmine		50 ✔	15
719		90g. blackish brown		1·00 ✔	40

(Des and eng E. Konecki. Recess)

1951 (15 Nov). Polish Music Festival. P 13×12½.
720	**215**	45g. black		65 ✔	25
721		90g. red		2·50 ✔	1·00

1951 (15 Nov). Warsaw Stamp Day. Sheet 90×120 mm comprising Nos. 696a/e printed in red-brown. P 12½×13.
MS721a **196**	Sold at 5z	32·00	25·00

216 Mining Machinery **217** Building Modern Flats **218** Installing Electric Cable

(Des and eng C. Slania. Recess)

1951 (4 Dec)–52. Six Year Plan (Mining). P 13×12½.
722	**216**	90g. purple-brown		50 ✔	25
723		1z.20 grey-blue		50 ✔	25
724		1z.20 +15g. red-orange (18.10.52)		65 ✔	40
722/724 Set of 3				1·50	80

(Des R. Kleczewski. Eng B. Brandt. Recess)

1951 (10 Dec)–52. Six Year Plan (Reconstruction). P 12½×13.
725	**217**	30g. green		50	30 ✔
		a. Perf 12×11½		50	30
726		30g. +15g. brown-red (1.6.52)		65 ✔	40
727		1z.15 maroon		50 ✔	25
		a. Perf 12×11½		50	25
725/727 Set of 3				1·50	80

(Des R. Kleczewski. Eng M. R. Polak. Recess)

1951 (15 Dec)–52. Six Year Plan (Electrification). P 12½×13.
728	**218**	30g. black		40 ✔	25
729		45g. scarlet		65 ✔	30
730		45g. +15g. brown (1.6.52)		90 ✔	40
728/730 Set of 3				1·80	85

219 M. Nowotko **220** Women and Banner **221** Gen Świerczewski

(Des C. Slania, eng E. Konecki (45g.); des and eng B. Brandt (90g.); des M. R. Polak, eng S. Lukaszewski (1z.15). Recess)

1952 (18 Jan). Tenth Anniv of Polish Workers' Coalition. T **219** and similar vert portrait designs. P 12½×13.
731		45g. +15g. lake		40 ✔	25
732		90g. chocolate (P. Finder)		75 ✔	50

733		1z.15 orange-red (M. Fornalska)		50 ✔	40
731/733 Set of 3				1·50	1·00

(Des and eng S. Lukaszewski. Recess)

1952 (8 Mar). International Women's Day. P 12½×12.
734	**220**	45g. +15g. purple-brown		65 ✔	40
735		1z.20 scarlet		1·30 ✔	90

(Des and eng C. Slania. Recess)

1952 (28 Mar). Fifth Death Anniv of General Świerczewski. P 12½×13.
736	**221**	45g. +15g. purple-brown		60	25
737		90g. indigo		75	1·00

> **IMPERF STAMPS.** From 1952 until 1961 some sets exist imperf from limited printings and issued at special prices by the Philatelic Bureau. We do not list these but they are mentioned in footnotes.

222 Ilyushin II-12 over Farm **223** President Bierut

(Des C. Slania (55g., 1z.40), B. Brandt (others). Eng B. Brandt (55g.), E. Konecki (90g.), C. Slania (1z.40) and M. R. Polak (5z.). Recess)

1952 (10 Apr). AIR. T **222** and similar horiz designs showing aeroplanes and views. P 12×12½.
738	55g. grey-blue (Tug and freighters)		65	50 ✔
739	90g. deep green		75	50 ✔
740	1z.40 maroon (Warsaw)		1·00	65 ✔
741	5z. black (Steelworks)		2·10	75 ✔
738/741 Set of 4			4·00	2·20

These exist imperforate.

(Des Rolicz. Eng B. Brandt. Recess)

1952 (18 Apr). Pres. Bierut's 60th Birthday. P 13×12½.
742	**223**	45g. +15g. scarlet	65 ✔	65
743		90g. grey-green	2·30	1·90
744		1z.20 +15g. bright blue	1·60	65
742/744 Set of 3			4·00 ✔	3·00

224 Cyclists and City Arms **225** Workers and Banner **226** J. Ignacy. Kraszewski

(Des P. Świątkowski and K. Maleszewski. Photo)

1952 (25 Apr). Fifth Warsaw–Berlin–Prague Peace Cycle Race. P 13×12½.
745	**224**	40g. blue	3·25	1·90

(Des S. Lukaszewski. Eng B. Brandt. Recess)

1952 (1 May). Labour Day. P 12½×13.
746	**225**	45g. +15g. scarlet	50	40
747		75g. green	1·60	1·40

1952–53. OFFICIAL. As No. O534 but no control number and litho. Inscr "ZWYKLA". P 11.
O748	O **128**	(60g.) pale blue	50	40
O749		(1z.55) brown-red (1953)	90	40

See also Nos. O805/6.

(Des and eng M. R. Polak. Recess)

1952 (5 May). 140th Birth Anniv of Józef Ignacy Kraszewski (writer). P 12½×13.
748	**226**	25g. maroon	1·30 ✔	65

227 Maria
Konopnicka

228 H. Kollątaj

229 Leonardo da
Vinci

(Des and eng E. Konecki. Recess)

1952 (10 May). 110th Birth Anniv of Maria Konopnicka (poet).
P 12½×13.
749	**227**	30g. +15g.deep green	1·30	1·50
750		1z.15 brown-red	1·50	1·00

(Des and eng S. Lukaszewski. Recess)

1952 (20 May). 140th Death Anniv of Hugo Kollątaj (educationist and
politician). P 12½×13.
751	**228**	45g.+15g.brown	65	40
752		1z. olive-green	1·30	65

(Des M. R. Polak. Eng B. Brandt. Recess)

1952 (1 June). 500th Birth Anniv of Leonardo da Vinci (artist).
P 12½×13.
753	**229**	30g. +15g.deep blue	1·90	1·30

230 President Bierut and Children   **231** N. V. Gogol

(Des C. Slania. Photo)

1952 (1 June). International Children's Day. P 14.
754	**230**	45g. +15g.blue	5·00	1·90

(Des B. Brandt. Eng C. Slania. Recess)

1952 (5 June). Death Centenary of Nikolai Gogol (Russian writer).
P 12½×13.
755	**231**	25g. deep green	1·90	1·30

232 Cement Works   **233** Swimmers

(Des C. Slania. Eng B. Brandt. Recess)

1952 (17 June). Construction of Cement Works, Wierzbica. P 12½×13.
756	**232**	3z. black	3·25	65
757		10z. scarlet	6·25	2·50

(Des P. Świątkowski. Photo)

1952 (21 June). Sports Day. T **233** and similar vert designs. P 12½×13.
758	30g. +15g. blue	6·25	1·90
759	45g. +15g. violet (Footballers)	1·90	40
760	1z.15 green (Runners)	8·75	3·00
761	1z.20 rose-red (High jumper)	1·90	1·60
758/761	*Set of 4*	17·00	6·25

234 Yachts   **235** Young Workers

(Des B. Brandt (30g.), C. Slania (45g.), R. Kleczewski (90g.). Eng M. R.
Polak (30g.), S. Lukaszewski (45g.). E. Konecki (90g.). Recess)

1952 (28 June). Shipbuilders' Day. T **234** and similar designs.
P 13×12½ (30g.) or 12½×13 (others).
762	30g. +15g. dull blue-green		6·25	2·50
763	45g. +15g. deep violet-blue		1·90	1·30
764	90g. maroon		1·30	2·50
762/764	*Set of 3*		8·50	5·75

Designs: Vert—45g. *Dar Pomorza* (full-rigged cadet ship); 90g.
Brygada Makowskiego (freighter) under construction.

(Des R. Kleczewski (30g.), B. Brandt (45g.) and M. R. Polak (90g.).
Eng B. Brandt (45g.), S. Lukaszewski (others). Recess)

1952 (17 July). Youth Festival, Warsaw. T **235** and similar designs
with flag inscr "20 22 VII WARSZAWA 1952". P 12×12½ (45g.) or
12½×12 (others).
765	30g. +15g. deep green		65	50
766	45g. +15g. scarlet		1·00	40
767	90g. brown		1·30	1·60
765/767	*Set of 3*		2·75	2·30

Designs: Horiz—45g. Girl and boy students. Vert—90g. Boy bugler.

POLISH PEOPLE'S REPUBLIC

The above title was officially adopted on 22 July 1952.

236 "New Constitution"   **237** L. Waryński

(Des T. Gronowski. Photo)

1952 (22 July). Adoption of New Constitution. P 11×11½ (45g.) or
11½×13 (3z.).
768	**236**	45g. +15g. green and purple-brown	5·00	40
769		3z. violet and deep brown	1·30	65

(Des R. Kleczewski. Eng C. Slania. Recess)

1952 (31 July). 70th Anniv of the Party "Proletariat". P 13×12½.
770	**237**	30g. +15g. brown-red	1·00	40
771		45g. +15g. purple-brown	2·30	1·00

238 Jaworzno Power   **239** Frydman   **240** Pilot and Glider
Station

(Des C. Slania. Eng E. Konecki. Recess)

1952 (7 Aug). Electricity Power Station, Jaworzno. P 13×12½.
772	**238**	45g. +15g. red	1·90	40
773		1z. black	5·00	90
774		1z.50 deep green	1·90	40
		a. Perf 11½×12	10·00	2·50
772/774	*Set of 3*		8·00	1·50

(Des Z. Polasińska. Photo)

1952 (18 Aug). Pieniny Mountain Resorts. T **239** and similar vert
designs. P 12½×13.
775	45g. +15g. dull purple	1·30	1·90
776	60g. green (Grywald)	1·30	90
777	1z. rose-red (Niedzica)	5·00	40
	a. Error "NIEDZIGA"	12·50	1·90
775/777	*Set of 3*	6·75	3·00

(Des E. Konecki, eng B. Brandt (30g.). Des C. Slania, eng M. R. Polak
(45g.). Des and eng S. Lukaszewski (90g.). Recess)

1952 (23 Aug). Aviation Day. T **240** and similar horiz designs.
P 13×12½.
778	30g. +15g. deep green	2·00	1·30
779	45g. +15g. scarlet	3·25	1·30
780	90g. deep blue	1·30	65
778/780	*Set of 3*	6·00	3·00

Designs:—45g. Pilot and Yakovlev Yak-18U; 90g. Parachutists
descending.

241 Avicenna   **242** Victor Hugo   **243** Ship-building

(Des and eng C. Slania. Recess)
1952 (1 Sept). Birth Millenary of Avicenna (Arab physician). P 12½×13.
781   **241**   75g. brown-red ....   65 ✔   40

(Des E. Konecki. Eng C. Slania. Recess)
1952 (1 Sept). 150th Birth Anniv of Victor Hugo (French author).
P 12½×13.
782   **242**   90g. chocolate........................   1·30 ✔   40

(Des B. Świderska. Eng E. Konecki. Recess)
1952 (10 Sept). Gdańsk Shipyards. P 12½×13.
783   **243**   5g. deep green ....   40 ✔   25✔
            a. Perf 11½ ....   40 ✔   25✔
784   15g. brown-red   75   25

244 H. Sienkiewicz   **245** Assault on Winter Palace,
(author)   Petrograd

(Des R. Kleczewski. Eng C. Slania. Recess)
1952 (25 Oct). P 12½×13.
785   **244**   45g. +15g. chocolate.....................   65 ✔   40

(Des and eng B. Brandt. Recess)
1952 (7 Nov). 35th Anniv of Russian Revolution. P 12×12½.
786   **245**   45g. +15g. brown-red ....   1·50   40
787   60g. blackish brown ....   1·00   65 ✔
These exist imperforate.

246 Lenin   **247** Miner

(Des and eng M. R. Polak. Recess)
1952 (7 Nov). Polish–Soviet Friendship Month. P 12½×13.
788   **246**   30g. +15g. dull purple....................   65   25
789   45g. +15g. brown ....   1·50   65

(Des E. Konecki. Eng S. Lukaszewski. Recess)
1952 (4 Dec). Miners' Day. P 12½×13.
790   **247**   45g. +15g. brown-black   65   25
791   1z.20 +15g. brown ....   1·30   65

248 H. Wieniawski   **249** Car Factory, Zeran
(violinist)

(Des K. Sopoćko. Photo)
1952 (5 Dec). Second Wieniawski International Violin Competition.
P 12½×13.
792   **248**   30g. +15g. deep green...................   1·30   1·30
793   45g. +15g. violet ....   2·50   90

(Des and eng C. Slania. Recess)
1952 (12 Dec). Zeran Car Workers' Fund. P 13×12½.
794   **249**   45g. +15g. deep grey-green.....................   40 ✔   25
795   1z.15 brown ....   1·30 ✔   50

250 Dove of   **251** Soldier and
Peace   Flag

(Des R. Kleczewski. Photo)
1952 (12 Dec). Peace Congress, Vienna. P 12½×13.
796   **250**   30g. green..............................   1·30 ✔   65
            a. Dot under "P" of "POKOJU".............   4·75   3·25
797   60g. bright blue......................   1·90 ✔   1·30

(Des E. Szancer. Photo)
1953 (2 Feb). Tenth Anniv of Battle of Stalingrad. P 11.
798   **251**   60g. carmine-red and grey-olive.............   10·50   4·50 ✔
799   80g. carmine-red and slate...................   1·90   65

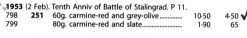

252 Lorry Factory

(Des C. Slania. Eng M. R. Polak. Recess)
1953 (20 Feb). Lublin Lorry Builders' Fund. P 13×12½.
800   **252**   30g. +15g. deep blue...................   1·10   65
801   60g. +20g. dull purple..................   40   25

253 Karl Marx   **254** Globe and
Flag

1953 (14 Mar). 70th Death Anniv of Marx. P 12½×13.
802   **253**   60g. grey-blue................................   35·00   25·00
803   80g. sepia...................................   2·50   65

1953 (Apr). POSTAGE DUE. As Nos. D701/12 but photo and without
imprint at foot. P 12×12½.
D804   D **190**   5g. red-brown   25   20
            a. Perf 11   25   20
D805   10g. red-brown   25   20
            a. Perf 12½×11........................   25   20
D806   15g. red-brown   25   20
D807   20g. red-brown   25   20
D808   25g. red-brown   25   20
D809   30g. red-brown   25   20
D810   50g. red-brown   25   20
D811   60g. red-brown   55   25
D812   90g. red-brown   50   20
D813   1z. red-brown   25   20
            a. Perf 10×13   25   20
D814   2z. red-brown   70   45
D804/814 *Set of 11* ....   3·50   2·30

1953–54. OFFICIAL. As Nos. O534/5 but no control number and litho.
Inscr "ZWYKLA" (60g.) or "POLECONA" (1.55z.). P 11 to 14 and
compound.
O805   (60g.) indigo ('54).....................   70   30
O806   (1.55z.) red..............................   95   30

(Des Cz. Kaczmarczyk. Photo)
1953 (28 Apr). Labour Day. P 12½×13.
804   **254**   60g. dull vermilion.....................   19·00 ✔   7·00
805   80g. carmine-red........................   90 ✔   65

255 Cyclists and Arms of Warsaw   **256** Boxer

(Des Cz. Kaczmarczyk. Photo)

1953 (30 Apr). Sixth International Peace Cycle Race. T **255** and similar vert designs. P 12½×13.

806	–	80g. deep green	1·50	65 ✓
807	**255**	80g. sepia	1·50	65
808	–	80g. brown-red	31·00	18·00
806/808	*Set of 3*		31·00	17·00

Designs:—No. 806, Cyclists and Arms of Berlin; No. 808, Cyclists and Arms of Prague.

(Des C. Borowczyk (95g.), L. Jagodziński (others). Photo)

1953 (17 May). European Boxing Championship, Warsaw. T **256** and similar vert design. P 12½×13.

809	**256**	40g. red-brown	1·50	65 ✓
810	–	80g. orange	31·00	18·00
811	–	95g. dull purple (Boxers in ring)	1·50	65 ✓
809/811	*Set of 3*		31·00	17·00

257 Copernicus (after Matejko)

(Des and eng B. Brandt (20g.). Des J. M. Szancer, eng S. Lukaszewski (80g.). Recess)

1953 (22 May). 480th Birth Anniv of Copernicus. T **257** and similar vert design inscr "1473–1543". P 12×12½ (20g.) or 12½×12 (80g.).

812	20g. brown	3·25	1·30 ✓
	a. Perf 11×11½	3·25	1·30
813	80g. deep blue (Copernicus and diagram)	31·00	24·00

258 *Dalmor* (trawler)   **259** Warsaw Market-place   **260** Students' Badge

(Des and eng B. Brandt (80g.). Des J. Ostrowski. Eng S. Lukaszewski (1z.35). Recess)

1953 (15 July). Merchant Navy Day. T **258** and similar horiz design. P 13×12½.

814	80g. deep dull green	3·25	55 ✓
815	1z.35 deep blue (*Czech* (freighter))	6·25	5·00 ✓

(Des E. John. Photo)

1953 (15 July). Polish National Day. P 12½×13.

816	**259**	20g. deep brown-red	40	25
817		2z.35 blue	9·50	6·25

(Des E. John (40g.), J. Ostrowski (1z.35), Fangor-Tchórzewski (1z.50). Photo)

1953 (24 Aug). Third World Students' Congress, Warsaw.

*(a) POSTAGE. T **260** and other designs. P 13×12½ (40g.) or 12½×13 (others)*

818	–	40g. deep brown	40	25 ✓
819	**260**	1z.35 green	1·30 ✓	40 ✓
820	–	1z.50 blue	6·75	4·25

*(b) AIR. As T **260** but inscr "POCZTA LOTNICZA" instead of dates and with airplane. Imperf*

821	**260**	55g. plum	3·75 ✓	65
822		75g. deep orange-red	3·25 ✓	2·50
818/822	*Set of 5*		14·00	7·25

Designs: Horiz—40g. Students and globe. Vert—1z.35 Woman and dove.

261 Nurse feeding Baby   **262** M. Kalinowski   **263** Jan Kochanowski (poet)

(Des L. Zaturski. Photo)

1953 (21 Sept). Social Health Service. T **261** and similar vert design. P 12½×13.

823	80g. carmine	16·00	12·00
824	1z.75 green (Nurse, mother and baby)	65	50

(Des B. Brandt (45g.), J. Ostrowski (80g.), C. Slania (1z.35). Photo)

1953 (10 Oct). Tenth Anniv of Polish People's Army. T **262** and similar designs. P 13×12½ (80g.) or 12½×13 (others).

825	45g. red-brown	8·75 ✓	6·25
826	80g. carmine-red	1·30	40
827	1z.75 bronze-green	1·30	40
825/827	*Set of 3*	10·00	6·25

Designs: Horiz—80g. Russian and Polish soldiers. Vert—1z.75 R. Paziński.

(Des C. Slania (80g.), M. R. Polak (others). Eng S. Lukaszewski (20g.), C. Slania (80g.), B. Brandt (1z.35). Recess)

1953 (10 Nov). "Renaissance" Commemoration. T **263** and similar designs. P 13×12½ (80g.) or 12½×13 (others).

828	20g. red-brown	25 ✓	25 ✓
	a. Perf 11½	25	25
829	80g. deep reddish purple	1·00	40
	a. Perf 11½	1·00	40
830	1z.35 indigo	5·00	3·25
828/830	*Set of 3*	5·75	3·50

Designs: Horiz—80g. Wawel Castle. Vert—1z.35 Mikolaj Rej (writer).

264 Palace of Science and Culture   **265** Dunajec Canyon, Pieniny Mts.

(Des E. John. Eng S. Lukaszewski (80g.), B. Brandt (1z.75), M. R. Polak (2z.). Recess)

1953 (30 Nov). Reconstruction of Warsaw. T **264** and similar horiz designs inscr "WARSZAWA". P 12×12½.

831	80g. rose-red	19·00	2·50 ✓
832	1z.75 deep blue	3·25	65
833	2z. dull purple	9·50	6·25
831/833	*Set of 3*	29·00	8·50

Designs:—1z.75 Constitution Square; 2z. Old City Market, Warsaw.

(Des B. Brandt (20g.), M. R. Polak (80g.), S. Lukaszewski (others). Recess)

1953 (16 Dec). Tourist Series. Views as T **265**. P 12½×13 (vert) or 13×12½ (horiz).

834	20g. brown-lake and blue	30 ✓	25
	a. Perf 13	30	25
835	80g. deep lilac and blue-green	6·25 ✓	4·50
836	1z.75 slate-green and bistre-brown	1·50 ✓	40
837	2z. black and vermilion	1·50 ✓	40 ✓
834/837	*Set of 4*	8·50	5·00

Designs: Horiz—20g. Krynica Spa; 2z. Ciechocinek Spa. Vert—80g. Morskie Oko Lake, Tatra Mts.

266 Skiing   **267** Infants Playing

(Des J. Rajewicz (80g.), H. Przeżdziecka (95g.), T. Gronowski (2z.85). Litho)

1953 (31 Dec). Winter Sports. T **266** and similar vert designs. P 13×12½ (95g.) or 12½×13 (others).

838	80g. pale blue (Ice-skating)	2·75	75 ✓
839	95g. blue-green	2·30	75 ✓

840	2z.85 brown-red (Ice-hockey)		6·25	2·75 ✓
838/840	Set of 3		10·00	3·75

(Des H. Tomaszewski (1z.50), J. Ostrowski (others). Photo)

1953 (31 Dec). Children's Education. T **267** and similar horiz designs. P 13×12½.

841	10g. violet	30 ✓	25 ✓
842	80g. lake-brown	1·50 ✓	65
843	1z.50 slate-green	14·00 ✓	5·75
841/843	Set of 3	14·00	6·00

Designs:—80g. Girls and school; 1z.50 Two schoolgirls writing.

268 Class EP 02
Electric Locomotive,
1953

(Des Cz. Kaczmarczyk. Eng S. Lukaszewski (60g.), B. Brandt (80g.). Recess)

1954 (26 Jan). Electrification of Railways. T **268** and similar horiz design. P 13×12½.

844	60g. Prussian blue	15·00 ✓	9·50 ✓
845	80g. red-brown	1·30 ✓	65

Design:—60g. Class EW54 electric commuter train 1953.

269 Mill Girl   **270** Flags and Mayflowers   **271** "Warsaw–Berlin–Prague"

(Des S. Lukaszewski (20g.), H. Przezdziecka (others). Photo)

1954 (24 Mar). International Women's Day. T **269** and similar vert designs. P 12½×13.

846	20g. slate-green	4·50 ✓	4·25
847	40g. deep blue (Postwoman)	90 ✓	25
848	80g. chocolate (Woman driving tractor)	1·00 ✓	30
846/848	Set of 3	5·75	4·25

(Des R. Kleczewski. Photo)

1954 (28 Apr). Labour Day. P 12½×13.

849	**270**	40g. chocolate	1·40 ✓	65 ✓
850		60g. blue	2·50 ✓	40 ✓
851		80g. bright carmine-red	1·40 ✓	50 ✓
849/851	Set of 3		4·75	1·40

(Des H. Przezdziecka. Photo)

1954 (29 Apr). Seventh International Peace Cycle Race. T **271** and similar vert design. P 12½×12.

852	80g. brown (Type **271**)	1·40 ✓	25 ✓
853	80g. deep blue (Dove and cycle wheel)	1·60 ✓	1·00 ✓
	a. Perf 12×11	1·60	1·00

272 Symbols of Labour   **272a** Postal Coach and 'Plane

(Des B. Brandt. Eng J. Miller. Recess)

1954 (30 Apr). Third Trades Union Congress, Warsaw. P 12½×11½.

854	**272**	25g. indigo	3·75 ✓	2·50 ✓
855		80g. lake	65 ✓	65 ✓

(Des R. Kleczewski. Eng B. Brandt. Recess)

1954 (23 May). AIR. Third Polish Philatelic Society Congress. Sheet 57×76 mm. P 12½×13.

MS855a **272a** 5z.+(2z.50) greyish green ...... 55·00   50·00
Exists imperforate and blue (*price £450 unused, £500 used*).

273 Glider and Flags

(Des Cz. Kaczmarczyk. Photo)

1954 (31 May). International Gliding Competition. T **273** and similar horiz designs. P 13 (857, 859a) or 13×12½ (others).

856	–	45g. deep green	1·30 ✓	30 ✓
857	**273**	60g. deep lilac	3·25 ✓	2·50 ✓
858		60g. brown	2·75 ✓	30 ✓
859	–	1z.35 dull blue	4·25 ✓	2·50 ✓
		a. Light blue	4·00	65
856/859a	Set of 4 (cheapest)		10·00	3·50

Designs:—45g. Glider with clouds in frame; 1z.35 Glider in large cloud (859 blue clouds, 859a white clouds).

274 Paczków   **275** Fencing

(Des B. Brandt (1z.50), C. Slania (others). Eng J. Miller (60g.), C. Slania (80g., 1z.50), S. Lukaszewski (1z.15), B. Brandt (1z.55), M. R. Polak (1z.95). Recess)

1954 (13 July). AIR. T **274** and similar vert designs. P 12½×13.

860	60g. myrtle green	40	30 ✓
861	80g. scarlet	40	30 ✓
	a. Perf 12×11½	40	30
862	1z.15 black	3·25	3·00
863	1z.50 claret	1·30	30 ✓
864	1z.55 deep blue	1·30	30 ✓
	a. Perf 12×11½	1·30	30
	b. "WARSZAWA" printed double	90·00	3·75
865	1z.95 deep brown	1·90	70 ✓
860/865	Set of 6	7·75	4·50

Designs: Ilyushin Il-12 airplane over—80g. Market-place, Kazimierz Dolny; 1z.15 Wawel Castle, Cracow; 1z.50 Town Hall, Wroclaw; 1z.55 Lazienki Palace, Warsaw; 1z.95 Cracow Tower, Lublin.

(Des H. Przezdziecka (1z.), L. Jagodziński (others). Photo)

1954 (17 July). Second Spartacist Games (1st issue). T **275** and similar designs. P 13 (60g.) or 13×12½ (others).

866	25g. dull purple	2·75	90 ✓
867	60g. greenish blue	2·75	65 ✓
868	1z. ultramarine	5·00	1·60 ✓
866/868	Set of 3	9·50	2·75

Designs: Vert—60g. Gymnastics. Horiz—1z. Running.
See also Nos. 869/70.

276 Spartacist Games Badge

(Des K. Mann. Photo)

1954 (17 July). Second Spartacist Games (2nd issue). P 12×12½.

869	**276**	60g. red-brown	1·30	65 ✓
870		1z.55 deep slate-blue	2·50	1·90 ✓

O **277**   **277** Battlefield

(Des B. Brandt. Eng W. Falkowski. Recess)

1954 (18 Aug). OFFICIAL. P 11×11½.

O871	O **277**	(60g.) deep blue	70	30
O872		(1.55z.) red	95	30
		a. Perf 12×12½	95	30

No. O872 is inscribed "POLECONA".

(Des J. Ostrowski. Photo)

1954 (24 Aug). Tenth Anniv of Liberation and Battle of Studzianki. T **277** and similar horiz design. P 12½×13.

871	60g. green	3·25	65	✓
872	1z. ultramarine	10·50	5·75	✓

Design:—1z. Soldier, airman and tank.

278 Steel Works

279 Steam Train and Signal

(Des Cz. Kaczmarczyk. Eng (b) S. Lukaszewski (10g., 20g., 25g.), J. Miller (20g., 25g.), M. R. Polak (40g., 1z.15), B. Brandt (45g., 2z.10), C. Slania (1z.40, 1z.55). (a) Centres litho. (b) Centres recess. Frames photo)

1954 (Aug)–**55**. Tenth Anniv of Second Republic, T **278** and similar horiz designs. P 12½×12.

873	10g. sepia and red-brown (b) (23.12.54)	1·00	30	✓
874	20g. deep myrtle-green and rose (b) (23.12.54)	65	30	✓
875	25g. grey-black and yellow-brown (a)	8·00	2·50	✓
876	25g. grey-black and yellow-brown (b) ('55)	3·25	1·30	✓
877	40g. purple-brown and orange-yellow (b) (23.12.54)	65	30	
878	45g. dull purple and dull mauve (b) (23.12.54)	65	30	
879	60g. purple-brown and green (a)	3·25	1·00	✓
880	60g. purple-brown and green (b) ('55)	1·30	65	
881	1z.15 black and bright blue-green (b) (23.12.54)	1·90	40	✓
882	1z.40 deep brown and orange (b) (23.12.54)	21·00	5·00	
883	1z.55 deep blue and dull greenish blue (b) (23.12.54)	3·25	1·30	✓
884	2z.10 deep blue and cobalt (b) (23.12.54)	4·00	1·90	
873/884 *Set of 12*		44·00	13·50	

Designs:—10g. Coal mine; 20g. Soldier and flag, 40g. Worker on holiday; 45g. House-builders; 60g. Tractor and binder; 1z.15 Lublin Castle; 1z.40 Customers in bookshop; 1z.55 *Soldek* (freighter) alongside wharf; 2z.10 Battle of Lenino.

(Des T. Gronowski (40g.), E. John, after A. Porebski (60g.). Photo)

1954 (9 Sept). Railway Workers' Day. T **279** and similar vert design. P 13 (40g.) or 12½×13 (60g.).

885	40g. deep blue	9·50	2·50
886	60g. black (steam night express)	7·50	1·50

280 Picking Apples

281 Elblag

(Des H. Przeździecka. Photo)

1954 (15 Sept). Polish–Russian Friendship. P 12½×13.

887	**280** 40g. slate-violet	4·50	2·50
888	60g. black	75	65

(Des S. Żukowski (45g.), K. Górska (1z.40), E. John (1z.55), Cz. Kaczmarczyk (others). Eng B. Brandt (20g.), M. R. Polak (45g.), J. Miller (60g.), S. Lukaszewski (1z.40), C. Slania (1z.55). Recess)

1954 (16 Oct). 500th Anniv of Return of Pomerania to Poland. T **281** and similar horiz designs showing mediaeval views. P 12×12½.

889	20g. carmine/*blue*	3·75	1·60	✓
	a. Perf 11×12	25·00	4·75	
890	45g. brown/*lemon* (Gdańsk)	40	25	✓
891	60g. deep blue-green/*pale green* (Toruń)	45	25	✓
892	1z.40 deep ultramarine/*pink* (Malbork)	90	25	✓
893	1z.55 chocolate/*cream* (Olsztyn)	1·30	25	✓
889/893 *Set of 5*		6·00	2·30	

282 Chopin and Grand Piano

283 Battle Scene

(Des Cz. Kaczmarczyk. Photo)

1954 (8 Nov). Fifth International Chopin Piano Competition, Warsaw (1st issue). P 12½×13.

894	**282** 45g. deep brown	65	20	
895	60g. deep myrtle-green	90	30	
	a. Perf 11	41·00	5·00	
896	1z. blue	4·50	2·30	
894/896 *Set of 3*		5·50	2·50	

See also Nos. 906/7.

(Des after W. Kossak (40g.), after J. Matejko (60g.). Eng S. Lukaszewski (40g.), C. Slania (60g.). Des and eng B. Brandt (1z.40). Recess)

1954 (30 Nov). 160th Anniv of Kosciuszko's Insurrection. T **283** and similar horiz designs. P 14×13.

897	40g. blackish olive	1·00	25
898	60g. deep brown-purple	1·30	40
899	1z.40 slate-black	2·75	1·90
897/899 *Set of 3*		4·50	2·30

Designs:—60g. Kościuszko on horse-back with insurgents; 1z.40 Street battle.

284 European Bison

285 "The Liberator"

(Des C. Borowczyk. Eng B. Brandt (45g.), S. Lukaszewski (60g.), M. R. Polak (1z.90), C. Slania (3z.). Background photo; remainder recess)

1954 (22 Dec). Protected Animals. Vert designs as T **284**. P 12.

900	45g. black-brown and deep yellow-green	65	25
901	60g. brown and bright green	65	25
902	1z.90 black-brown and cobalt	1·50	25
903	3z. brown and deep turquoise-green	2·50	1·50
900/903 *Set of 4*		5·25	2·00

Designs:—60g. Elk; 1z.90 Chamois; 3z. Eurasian Beaver. These exist imperforate.

(Des J. Ostrowski (40g.), T. Trepkowski (60g.). Photo)

1955 (17 Jan). Tenth Anniv of Liberation of Warsaw. T **285** and similar horiz design. P 12½×13.

904	40g. chocolate	3·25	2·30
905	60g. grey-blue ("Spirit of Poland")	3·00	40

286 Bust of Chopin (after L. Isler)

287 Mickiewicz Monument

288 Flags and Tower

(Des K. Podlasiecki. Eng C. Slania. Recess)

1955 (22 Feb). Fifth International Chopin Piano Competition, Warsaw (2nd issue). P 12½×13.

906	**286** 40g. purple-brown	50	25	
907	60g. deep blue	3·75	1·50	

(Des R. Kleczewski (15g., 45g., 1z.55), E. John (others). Eng M. R. Polak (5g.), S. Lukaszewski (10g., 45g.), J. Miller (15g., 20g.), C. Slania (40g.), B. Brandt (60g., 1z.55). Recess)

1955 (Mar–May). Warsaw Monuments. T **287** and similar vert designs. P 12½×13.

908		5g. myrtle green/*olive-yellow*	30	20
		a. Perf 12×11½	30	20
909		10g. maroon/*yellow*	30	20
		a. Perf 12×11½	30	20
910		15g. brownish black/*pale green*	30	20
		a. Perf 12×11½	30	20
911		20g. deep blue/*pink* (31.5)	30	20
		a. Perf 12×11½	30	20
912		40g. deep violet/*reddish lilac* (31.5)	30	20
		a. Perf 12×11½	30	20
913		45g. purple brown/*pale orange*	1·30	40
914		60g. blue/*olive-grey* (31.5)	30	20
		a. Perf 12×11½	30	20
915		1z.55 deep bluish green/*olive-grey*	5·75	3·75
908/915		*Set of 8*	8·00	4·75

Designs: Vert—5g. "Siren"; 10g. Dzerżhiński Statue; 15g. King Sigismund III Statue; 20g. "Brotherhood in Arms"; 40g. Copernicus Monument; 45g. Marie Curie Statue; 1z.55 Kiliński Statue.

(Des E. Kleczewski (40g.), W. Borowczyk (60g.). Photo)

1955 (21 Apr). Tenth Anniv of Russo–Polish Treaty of Friendship. T **288** and similar vert design. P 11½×11.

916	**288**	40g. rose-red	40	20
		a. Perf 12½×12	40	20
917		40g. chestnut	2·10	1·90
		a. Perf 12½×12	2·10	1·90
918	–	60g. turquoise-blue	40	20
		a. Perf 12½×12	40	20
919	–	60g. deep olive-brown	40	20
		a. Perf 12½×12	40	20
916/919		*Set of 4*	3·00	2·30

Design:—60g. Statue of "Friendship".

289

290 Town Hall, Poznań

(Des Cz. Kaczmarczyk (40g.), S. Jasiński (60g.). Photo)

1955 (25 Apr). Eighth International Peace Cycle Race. T **289** and similar vert design. P 12½×13 (40g.) or 13 (60g.).

920		40g. purple-brown	90	90
921		60g. cobalt	40	25

Design:—60g. "VIII" and doves of peace.

(Des Cz. Kazmarczyk. Photo)

1955 (10 June). 24th International Fair, Poznań. P 12½×13.

922	**290**	40g. deep bright blue	65	65
923		60g. red	40	25

See also Nos. **MS926a/b**.

291 Festival Emblem

292 "Peace"

(Des W. Chomicz. Litho)

1955 (16 June). Cracow Festival T **291** and similar design. P 12.

924	**291**	20g. ochre, sepia, red-brown and bluish green	1·50	70
925	–	40g. bluish green, black, chestnut and lilac	65	25
926	**291**	60g. yellow-brown, black, rose and blue	75	65
924/926		*Set of 3*	2·50	1·40

Design: Horiz—40g. Centre as T **291**.

1955 (7 July). Sixth Polish Philatelic Exhibition, Poznań. Two sheets 50×70 mm as T **290**. Imperf.

MS926a	2z.+(1z.) black and blue-green	6·25	6·00
MS926b	3z.+(1z.50) black and carmine	31·00	25·00

(Des J. Woźnicki (Nos. 928, 931), S. Malecki (others). Litho)

1955 (13 July). Fifth International Youth Festival, Warsaw. T **292** and similar vert designs. P 12.

927	–	25g. purple-brown, rose and yellow	30	20
928	–	40g. grey and pale blue	30	20
		a. Perf 11	30	20
929	–	45g. lake, magenta and yellow	65	20
930	**292**	60g. ultramarine and pale blue	65	20
		a. Perf 11	65	20
931	–	60g. black and yellow-orange	65	20
932	**292**	1z. deep slate-purple and pale blue …	1·90	1·30
927/932		*Set of 6*	4·00	2·10

Designs:—25g., 45g. Pansies and dove; 40g., 60g. (No. 931), Dove and tower.

These exist imperforate.

See also Nos. **MS944a/b**.

293 Motor Cyclists    **294** Stalin Palace of Culture and Science, Warsaw

(Des J. Woźnicki. Photo)

1955 (20 July). 13th International Tatra Mountains Motor Cycle Race. P 12½×13.

933	**293**	40g. deep brown	1·50	40
934		60g. green	40	25

(Des K. Podlasiecki. Photo)

1955 (21 July). Polish National Day. P 12½×13.

935	**294**	60g. bright blue	30	20
		a. Pair. Nos. 935/6	65	45
936		60g. bluish grey	30	20
937		75g. turquoise-green	90	75
		a. Pair. Nos. 937/8	1·90	1·60
938		75g. brown	90	75
935/938		*Set of 4*	2·20	1·70

Nos. 935/6 and 937/8 were printed together in sheets containing alternate vertical rows of each colour *se-tenant*.

295 Athletes    **296** Szczecin    **297** Peasants and Flag

(Des J. Karolkiewicz. Photo)

1955 (27 July). Second International Games. T **295** and similar designs. P 13×12½ (60g.) or 12½×13 (others).

939		20g. sepia	25	20
940		40g. brown-purple	40	20
941		60g. dull greenish blue	75	25
942		1z. red-orange	1·00	30
943		1z.35 dull purple	1·40	40
944		1z.55 blue-green	3·25	1·90
939/944		*Set of 6*	6·25	3·00

Designs: Vert—40g. Throwing the hammer; 1z. Netball; 1z.35 Sculling; 1z.55 Swimming. Horiz—60g. Stadium.

These exist imperforate.

1955 (3 Aug). International Philatelic Exhibition, Warsaw. Two sheets 61×84 mm. Imperf.

MS944a	1z.(+1z.) As No. 929	5·00	3·00
MS944b	2z.(+1z.) As No. 932	35·00	27·00

(Des S. Jasiński. Eng B. Brandt (25g.), J. Miller (40g.), M. R. Polak (others). Recess)

1955 (22 Sept). Tenth Anniv of Return of Western Territories. T **296** and similar vert designs. P 12½×13.

945		25g. deep blue-green	25	20
		a. Perf 12×11½	25	20
946		40g. red-brown (Wrocław)	65	25
947		60g. deep violet-blue (Zielona Góra)	90	30
948		95g. brown-black (Opole)	2·75	1·90
945/948		*Set of 4*	4·00	2·40

(Des M. Bylina. Photo)

1955 (30 Sept). 50th Anniv of 1905 Revolution. P 12½×13.

949	**297**	40g. sepia	1·60	1·30
950		60g. carmine-red	40	30

298 Adam Mickiewicz   **299** Statue

(Des H. Przeździecka (20g.), W. Chmielewski (others). Photo)

1955 (10 Oct). Death Centenary of Adam Mickiewicz (poet). T **298** and vert designs as T **299**. P 12×12½ (20g.) or 12½×13 (others).

951	20g. sepia	40	20
952	40g. sepia and brown-orange	40	20
953	60g. sepia and dull green (Sculptured head)	40	20
954	95g. black and brown-red (Statue)	2·75	1·90
951/954	*Set of 4*	3·50	2·30

300 Teacher and Pupil   **301** Rook and Hands   **302** Ice Skates

(Des R. Kleczewski (40g.), H. Przeździecka (60g.). Photo)

1955 (21 Oct). 50th Anniv of Polish Teachers' Union. T **300** and similar vert design. P 12½×13.

955	40g. brown	3·25	65
956	60g. bright blue (Open book and lamp)	6·25	3·25

(Des Cz. Kaczmarczyk. Photo)

1956 (9 Feb). First World Chess Championship for the Deaf and Dumb. T **301** and similar vert design. P 12½×13.

957	40g. brown-red	4·50	3·50
958	60g. dull greenish blue	2·00	40
	Design:—60g. Knight and hands.		

(Des Cz. Kaczmarczyk. Litho)

1956 (7 Mar). 11th World Students' Winter Sports Championship. T **302** and similar vert designs. P 12½×13.

959	20g. black and blue	7·00	5·75
960	40g. ultramarine and bright blue-green	1·00	30
	a. Perf 11	1·00	30
961	60g. claret and mauve	90	30
	a. Perf 11	90	30
959/961	*Set of 3*	8·00	5·75

Designs:—40g. Ice-hockey sticks and puck; 60g. Skis and ski sticks.

303 Officer and *Kiliński* (freighter)   **304** Racing Cyclist

(Des S. Lukaszewski. Eng J. Miller (10g.), M. R. Polak (45g.), S. Lukaszewski (60g.), B. Brandt (others). Recess)

1956 (16 Mar). Merchant Navy. T **303** and similar horiz designs. P 12×12½.

962	5g. deep bluish green	40	20
	a. Perf 11×11½	40	20
963	10g. crimson	40	20
	a. Perf 11×11½	40	20
964	20g. deep blue	40	20
	a. Perf 11×11½	40	20
965	45g. red-brown	2·50	1·90
	a. Perf 11×11½	2·50	1·90
966	60g. deep violet-blue	55	25
	a. Perf 11×11½	55	25
962/966	*Set of 5*	3·75	2·50
962a/966a	*Set of 5*	3·75	2·50

Designs:—10g. Tug and barges; 20g. *Pokój* (freighter) in dock; 45g. Building *Marceli Nowatka* (freighter); 60g. *Fryderyk Chopin* (freighter) and *Rudunia* (trawler).

(Des H. Przeździecka. Photo)

1956 (25 Apr). Ninth International Peace Cycle Race. P 13×12½.

967	**304**	40g. deep blue	2·50	1·00
968		60g. deep green	40	30

40 GR

305 Lodge, Tatra Mountains   **(306)**

(Des Cz. Kaczmarczyk, J. Kończak and S. Jasiński. Photo)

1956 (25 May). Tourist Propaganda. T **305** and similar vert designs. P 12½×13.

969	30g. bottle green	40	25
	a. Perf 13	40	25
970	40g. chestnut	40	25
971	60g. blue	3·25	1·00
972	1z.15 deep dull purple	65	40
969/972	*Set of 4*	4·25	1·70

Designs:—40g. Compass, rucksack and map; 60g. Canoe and map; 1z.15 Skis and mountains.

1956 (6 July). No. 829 surch as T **306**.

973	10g. on 80g. deep reddish purple	1·50	65
974	40g. on 80g. deep reddish purple	40	20
	a. Perf 11½	40	20
975	60g. on 80g. deep reddish purple	65	25
	a. Perf 11½	65	25
976	1z.35 on 80g. deep reddish purple	4·50	3·25
973/976	*Set of 4*	6·25	4·00

307 Ghetto Heroes Monument   **308** "Economic Co-operation"

(Des E. John. Eng C. Slania (30g.), M. R. Polak (40g.), E. Konecki (1z.55). Recess)

1956 (10 July). Warsaw Monuments. T **307** and similar vert designs. P 12½×13.

977	30g. black	40	20
	a. Perf 12×11½	40	20
978	40g. red-brown/*green*	2·50	90
979	1z.55 brown-purple/*pink*	40	25
	a. Perf 12×11½	40	25
977/979	*Set of 3*	3·00	1·30

Designs:—40g. Statue of King Jan III Sobieski; 1z.55 Statue of Prince Joseph Poniatowski.

(Des S. Gospodarek (40g.), S. Malecki (60g.). Litho)

1956 (14 Sept). Russo–Polish Friendship Month. T **308** and similar horiz design. P 12½×12.

980	40g. deep brown and rose-pink	1·30	1·00
	a. Perf 11	1·30	1·00
981	60g. red and bistre	40	25
	Design:—40g. Polish and Russian dancers.		

309 Ludwika Wawrzyńska (teacher)   **310** "Lady with a Weasel" (Leonardo da Vinci)

(Des H. Prreździecka. Photo)

1956 (17 Sept). Ludwika Wawrzyńska Commemoration. P 13.
982	**309**	40g. chocolate	2·30	1·60
983		60g. deep blue	40	25

(Des Cz. Kaczmarczk. Eng E. Konecki (40g.), S. Lukaszewski (60g.), B. Brandt (1z.55). Recess)

1956 (23 Oct–19 Nov). International Campaign for Museums. T **310** and similar vert designs. P 11½×11.
984	40g. myrtle-green (19.11)	5·75	2·50
985	60g. deep violet (19.11)	1·30	40
986	1z.55 blackish chocolate (23.10)	3·25	40
984/986 *Set of 3*		9·25	3·00

Designs:—40g. Niobe (bust); 60g. Madonna (Vit Stvosz).

310a Music Quotation and Profiles of Chopin and Liszt

311 *Apis mellifera* (Bee) and Hive

(Des S. Gospodarek. Photo)

1956 (25 Oct). Stamp Day. Sheet 55×75 mm. Imperf.
MS986a	**310a**	4z.(+2z.) deep bluish green	35·00 28·00

(Des J. Kończak (40g.), S. Gospodarek (60g.). Litho)

1956 (30 Oct). 50th Death Anniv of Jan Dzierzon (apiarist). T **311** and similar vert design. P 12½×13.
987	40g. brown/*orange-yellow*	2·75	75
988	60g. brown/*orange-yellow* (Dr. J. Dżierżon)....	40	20

312 Fencing

313 15th-century Postman

(Des Cz. Kaczmarczyk. Eng E. Konecki (10g.), S. Lukaszewski (20g.), M. R. Polak (25g.), B. Brandt (40g.), C. Slania (60g.), J. Miller (1z.55). Centres recess (except No. 995, photo); frames litho)

1956 (2 Nov–12 Dec). Olympic Games. T **312** and similar designs inscr "MELBOURNE 1956". P 11½.
989	10g. brown and slate	25	20
990	20g. blackish lilac and bistre-brown	30	20
	a. "MELBOURNE 1956" inverted	£32000	
991	25g. black and pale blue	90	30
992	40g. chocolate and blue-green	40	20
993	60g. brown-black and carmine	90	30
994	1z.55 sepia and bright violet	5·00	1·50
995	1z.55 reddish brown and orange (12.12)	1·90	50
989/995 *Set of 7*		8·75	3·00

Designs:—20g. Boxing; 25g. Rowing; 40g. Steeplechase; 60g. Javelin throwing; No. 994, Gymnastics; No. 995, Long jumping (Elizabeth Krzesińska's-Duńska's gold medal).

(Des S. Bernacińsky. Litho)

1956 (30 Nov). Re-opening of Postal Museum, Wroclaw. P 12½×13.
996	**313**	60g. grey-black/*pale blue*	6·25 5·00

314 Snow Crystals and Skier of 1907

315 Apple Tree and Globe

(Des J. Kończak. Photo)

1957 (18 Jan). Fifty years of Skiing in Poland. T **314** and similar designs. P 13.
997	40g. blue	30	20

998	60g. deep bluish green	30	20
999	1z. purple	1·30	1·00
997/999 *Set of 3*		1·70	1·30

Designs: Vert—60g. Snow crystals and skier jumping Horiz—1z. Snow crystals and skier standing.

(Des S. Malecki. Photo)

1957 (26 Feb). United Nations Organization. T **315** and similar designs. P 12½×12 (5g.) or 12×12½ (others).
1000	5g. crimson and deep turquoise-blue	65	30
1001	15g. blue and pale grey	90	30
1002	40g. blue-green and pale grey	1·50	1·30
1000/1002 *Set of 3*		2·75	1·70
MS1002a	55×70 mm. 1z.50 blue and bright blue-green. Imperf	31·00	28·00

Designs: Vert—15g. UNO emblem; 40g., 1z.50 UNO Headquarters, New York.

Nos. 1000/2 exist imperforate.

316 Skier

317 Winged Letter

(Des S. Gospodarek. Photo)

1957 (22 Mar). 12th Death Anniv of Bronislaw Czech and Hanna Marusarzówna (skiers). P 12½×13.
1003	**316**	60g. deep brown	2·10 1·00
1004		60g. blue	65 30

(Des S. Jasiński. Photo)

1957 (28 Mar–18 May). AIR. Seventh Polish National Philatelic Exhibition, Warsaw. P 11½.
1005	**317**	4z. +2z. blue (28.3)	5·00 5·00
MS1005a	55×75 mm. 4z.+2z. violet-blue (T **317**). Imperf (18.5)		10·50 10·00

No. 1005 is printed in sheets of 12 stamps with four labels.

318 Foil, Sword and Sabre on Map

319 Dr. S. Petrycy (philosopher)

320 Cycle Wheel and Flower

(Des J. Kończak (40g.), S. Jasiński (others). Photo)

1957 (20 Apr). World Youth Fencing Championships, Warsaw. T **318** and similar horiz designs. P 13×12½.
1006	40g. purple	90	25
1007	60g. deep rose-red	45	20
	a. Pair. Nos. 1007/8	95	45
1008	60g. bright blue	45	20
1006/1008 *Set of 3*		1·60	60

Designs:—Nos. 1007/8 are arranged in *se-tenant* pairs in the sheet, and together show two fencers duelling.

(Des J. Desselberger. Eng J. Miller (10g.), B. Brandt (20g., 3z.), M. R. Polak (40g.), E. Konecki (60g., 1z.35), S. Lukaszewski (2z.50). Recess and typo)

1957 (27 Apr–30 Sept). Polish Doctors. T **319** and similar designs. P 12×11½.
1009	10g. sepia and ultramarine	25	20
1010	20g. lake and emerald	25	20
1011	40g. black and rose-red	25	20
1012	60g. dull purple and pale blue	1·80	40
1013	1z. blue-grey and yellow-orange (30.9)	40	25
1014	1z.35 black-brown and blue-green	40	25
1015	2z.50 slate-violet and cerise	40	25
1016	3z. deep olive-brown and violet	50	25
1009/1016 *Set of 8*		3·75	1·80

Portraits:—20g. Dr. W. Oczko; 40g. Dr. J. Śniadecki; 60g. Dr. T. Chalubiński; 1z. Dr. W. Biegański; 1z.35 Dr. J. Dietl; 2z.50 Dr. B. Dybowski; 3z. Dr. H. Jordan.

(Des S. Szymański. Photo)

1957 (4 May). Tenth International Peace Cycle Race. T **320** and similar design. P 12½×13.
1017	60g. blue	65	25
1018	1z.50 rose-magenta (Cyclist)	90	40

321 Fair Emblem   **322** Carline Thistle

(Des A. Borys. Litho)

1957 (8 June). 26th International Fair, Poznań. P 13 (60g.) or 12½×13 (2z.50).
1019	**321**	60g. light ultramarine	40	25
1020		2z.50 blue-green	90	40

(Des Cz. Borowczyk. Photo)

1957 (12 Aug). Wild Flowers. T **322** and similar floral designs. P 12×12½.
1021	60g. yellow, blue-green and pale grey	65	25
1022	60g. deep blue-green and pale blue	65	25
1023	60g. olive-green and grey	65	25
1024	60g. yellow, brown-red and pale bluish green	1·60	55
1025	60g. maroon and blue-green	60	25
1021/1025	Set of 5	3·75	1·40

Designs:—No. 1021, T **322**; 1022, Sea Holly; 1023, Edelweiss; 1024, Lady's Slipper Orchid; 1025, Turk's Cap Lily.

323 Fireman   **324** Town Hall, Leipzig   **325** "The Letter" (after Fragonard)

(Des S. Szymański (40g.), S. Gospodarek (60g.), S. Malecki (2z.50). Photo)

1957 (11 Sept). International Fire Brigades Conference, Warsaw. T **323** and similar vert designs. P 12×12½.
1026	40g. black and red	25	20
1027	60g. deep bluish green and orange-red	35	20
1028	2z.50 violet and vermilion	70	35
1026/1028	Set of 3	1·20	70

Designs:—60g. Flames enveloping child; 2z.50 Ear of corn in flames.

(Des H. Macierewicz. Photo)

1957 (25 Sept). Fourth International Trade Unions Congress, Leipzig. P 12½×13.
1029	**324**	60g. violet	40	35

(Des H. Przeździecka. Photo)

1957 (9 Oct). Stamp Day. P 12×12½.
1030	**325**	2z.50 deep myrtle green	1·30	35

326 Red Banner   **327** Karol Libelt (founder)   **328** H. Wieniawski (violinist)

(Des Cz. Kaczmarczyk. Photo)

1957 (7 Nov). 40th Anniv of Russian Revolution. T **326** and similar vert design. P 12½×13.
1031	60g. red and deep blue	35	20
	a. Red (flag) omitted	£250	
1032	2z.50 chestnut and black	40	25

Design: 2z.50 Lenin Monument, Poronin.

(Des J. Skoracki. Photo)

1957 (15 Nov). Centenary of Poznań Scientific Society. P 12½×13.
1033	**327**	60g. crimson	45	35

(Des S. Jasiński. Photo)

1957 (2 Dec). Third Wieniawski International Violin Competition. P 12½×13.
1034	**328**	2z.50 blue	65	40

329 Ilyushin II-14P SP-LAG over Steel Works   **330** Multiple Posthorns   **330a** J. A. Komensky (Comenius)

There are four different types of W **330**, which also come inverted.

(Des J. Miller. Eng S. Lukaszewski (90g.), E. Konecki (1z.50), J. Miller (3z.40, 3z.90), M. R. Polak (4z.), B. Brandt (15z.). Recess, background photo)

1957 (6 Dec)–58. AIR. Pictorial designs as T **329**. W **330** (5, 10, 20, 30, 50z.) or no wmk (others). P 12½.
1035	90g. black and pink	35	20
1036	1z.50 brown and salmon	40	25
1037	3z.40 sepia and buff	80	35
1038	3z.90 deep brown and olive-yellow	1·70	90
1039	4z. Prussian blue and pale green	90	40
1039a	5z. brown-purple and grey (15.12.58)	90	40
1039b	10z. sepia and pale turquoise (15.12.58)	1·60	65
1040	15z. deep bluish violet and turquoise-blue	3·25	80
1040a	20z. slate-violet and pale yellow (15.12.58)	3·25	1·30
1040b	30z. olive-green and buff (15.12.58)	4·50	3·25
1040c	50z. deep blue and pale drab (15.12.58)	10·50	4·50
1035/1040c	Set of 11	25·00	11·50

Designs: Ilyushin II-14P SP-LAG over—1z.50 Castle Square, Warsaw; 3z.40 Market, Cracow; 3z.90 Szczecin; 4z. Karkonosze Mountains; 5z. Old Market, Gdańsk; 10z. Liw Castle; 15z. Lublin; 20z. Cable railway, Kasprowy Wierch; 30z. Porabka Dam; 50z. *Batory* (liner).

For stamp as No. 1039b, but printed in slate-purple only, see No. 1095.

(Des S. Jasiński. Photo)

1957 (11 Dec). 300th Anniv of Publication of Komensky's "Opera Didactica Omnia". P 12.
1041	**330a**	2z.50 bright carmine	65	35

331 A. Strug   **332** Joseph Conrad and *Torrens* (full-rigged sailing ship)

(Des S. Szymański. Photo)

1957 (16 Dec). 20th Death Anniv of Andrzej Strug (writer). P 12½×13.
1042	**331**	2z.50 brown	65	35

(Des S. Lukaszewski. Recess)

1957 (30 Dec). Birth Centenary of Joseph Conrad (Korzeniowski) (author). P 12×12½.
1043	**332**	60g. chocolate/*turquoise*	40	20
1044		2z.50 deep blue/*pink*	1·00	50

333 Postman of 1558

(Des S. Malecki. Litho)

1958 (24 Feb). 400th Anniv of Polish Postal Service (1st issue). P 12½×13.
1045 **333** 2z.50 blackish violet and blue.................... 65 35
  a. Error "00 LAT" instead of "400 LAT"
    (pos. 92)........................ 13·00 10·50
  b. Dot inside "K" of "POLSKA" (pos.
    62)........................
See also Nos. 1063/7.

334 Town Hall, Biecz   **335** Zander (*Lucioperca lucioperca*)

I.   II.

Two types of 20g.:
I. Central part of building more lightly shaded; no stops in engraver's name.
II. Building evenly shaded; stops in engraver's name.

III.   IV.

Two types of 40g.:
III. Second needle from bottom on right-hand side of roof very long; triangular area at top of door unshaded.
IV. Second needle same size as other needles; triangular area shaded.

(Des S. Gospodarek. Eng B. Szymańska (20g., 40g., 2z.10), E. Tirdiszek (others). Recess)

1958 (29 Mar). Ancient Polish Town Halls. Designs as T **334**. P 12×11½ (2z.50), 12½×13 (20, 40g., 2z.10) or 13×12½ (60g.).
1046 20g. blue-green (I)........................ 35 20
  a. Type II........................ 2·00 40
  ab. Perf 12×11½........................ 35 20
1047 40g. brown (Wroclaw) (III)........................ 35 20
  a. Type IV........................ 2·00 40
  ab. Perf 12×11½........................ 35 20
1048 60g. deep blue (Tarnów) (*horiz*)........................ 35 20
1049 2z.10 lake (Gdańsk)........................ 40 20
1050 2z.50 violet (Zamość)........................ 1·00 40
1046/1050 *Set of 5*........................ 2·20 1·10

(Des S. Malecki. Photo)

1958 (22 Apr). Fish. Designs as T **335**. P 12×12½ (vert) or 12½×12 (horiz).
1051 40g. yellow, black and deep turquoise-blue. 45 20
1052 60g. ultramarine, indigo and light green....... 65 25
1053 2z.10 yellow, indigo and blue........................ 1·00 40
1054 2z.50 green, black and reddish violet.............. 2·50 65
1055 6z.40 bistre-brown, vermilion, black and deep turquoise-green........................ 1·30 80
1051/1055 *Set of 5*........................ 5·25 2·10
Designs: Vert—60g. Atlantic Salmon (*Salmo salar*); 2z.10 Northern Pike (*Esox lucius*); 2z.50 Brown Trout (*Salmo trutta m. fario*). Horiz—6z.40 European Grayling (*Thymallus thymallus*).

336 Warsaw University   **337** Fair Emblem

(Des S. Jasiński. Photo)

1958 (14 May). 140th Anniv of Warsaw University. P 12½×13.
1056 **336** 2z.50 deep violet-blue........................ 65 25

(Des Z. Kaja. Litho)

1958 (9 June). 27th International Fair, Poznań. P 12½×13.
1057 **337** 2z.50 red and black........................ 65 25

338

(Des J. Desselberger. Litho)

1958 (14 June). Seventh International Gliding Championships. T **338** and similar vert design. P 12½×13.
1058 60g. black and slate-blue........................ 25 20
1059 2z.50 black and grey........................ 80 35
Design:—2z.50 as T **338** but design in reverse.

339 Armed Postman   **340** Polar Bear on Iceberg

(Des Cz. Kaczmarczyk. Eng E. Konecki. Recess)

1958 (1 Sept). 19th Anniv of Defence of Gdańsk Post Office. P 11×11½.
1060 **339** 60g. deep blue........................ 40 25

(Des S. Jasiński. Photo)

1958 (30 Sept). International Geophysical Year. T **340** and similar vert design. P 12½×12.
1061 60g. black........................ 40 20
1062 2z.50 blue........................ 1·70 40
Design:—2z.50 Sputnik and track of rocket.

341 Tomb of Prosper Prowano (First Polish Postmaster)   **342** Envelope, Quill and Postmark

(Des S. Malecki. Litho)

1958 (8 Oct). 400th Anniv of Polish Postal Service (2nd issue). T **341** and similar vert designs. P 12½×13.
1063 40g. maroon and cobalt........................ 90 25
1064 60g. black and lilac........................ 25 20
1065 95g. violet and yellow-bistre........................ 25 20
1066 2z.10 ultramarine and grey........................ 2·50 80
1067 3z.40 red-brown and turquoise-blue................. 1·30 65
1063/1067 *Set of 5*........................ 4·75 1·90

Designs:—60g. Mail coach and Church of Our Lady, Cracow; 95g. Mail coach (rear view); 2z.10 16th-century postman; 3z.40 Kogge. Nos. 1064/67 show various forms of modern transport in clear silhouette in the background.

(Des S. Gospodarek. Litho)
1958 (9 Oct). Stamp Day. P 12½×13.
1068 **342** 60g. blue-green, red and black................ 2·00 90

343 Partisans' Cross **344** "Mail Coach in the Kielce District" (after painting by A. Kędzierski)

(Des Cz. Kacmarczyk. Photo)
1958 (10 Oct). 15th Anniv of Polish People's Army. Polish decorations as T **343**. P 11.
1069 40g. buff, black and green................ 25 20
1070 60g. brown, yellow, black and blue.................. 40 25
1071 2z.50 yellow, black, red and green..................... 2·00 50
1069/1071 *Set of 3* 2·40 85
Decorations:—60g. Virtuti Military Cross; 2z.50 Grunwald Cross.

(Des H. Przeździecka. Eng S. Lukaszewski. Recess)
1958 (26 Oct). Polish Postal Service 400th Anniv Exhibition. W **330**. P 12½×13.
1072 **344** 2z.50 olive-black/*buff*...................... 2·50 2·00
No. 1072 was printed in sheets of six (*price £20 un*). These sheets normally measure 139 mm in height but examples also exist 20 mm taller with an extra line of perforations in the top margin. These were attached to the fronts of special brochures (*price £160 un*).
See also No. **MS**1078*a*.

345 Galleon **346** UNESCO Headquarters, Paris **347** S. Wyspiański (dramatist and painter)

(Des S. Jasiński. Photo)
1958 (29 Oct). 350th Anniv of Polish Emigration to America. T **345** and similar vert design inscr "1608" etc. P 11.
1073 60g. blackish green................ 40 25
1074 2z.50 carmine-red (Polish emigrants)................ 2·20 65

(Des Cz. Kaczmarczyk. Photo)
1958 (3 Nov). Inauguration of UNESCO Headquarters Buildings, Paris. P 13×12½.
1075 **346** 2z.50 black and green .... 1·30 65

(Des J. Kończak. Eng B. Brandt (60g.), E. Tirdiszek (2z.50). Recess)
1958 (25 Nov). Famous Poles. T **347** and similar vert design. P 12½×13.
1076 60g. violet 40 20
1077 2z.50 deep green 90 40
Portrait:—2z.50 S. Moniuszko (composer).

348 "Human Rights" **348a** Coach and Horses (after A. Kędzierski)

(Des S. Gospodarek. Litho)
1958 (10 Dec). Tenth Anniv of Declaration of Human Rights. P 12½×13.
1078 **348** 2z.50 red-brown and light brown.............. 1·30 40

(Des H. Przeździecka. Eng S. Lukaszewski. Recess on silk)
1958 (12 Dec). 400th Anniv of Polish Postal Service. Sheet 86×76 mm. Imperf.
MS1078*a* **348a** 50z. slate-blue .... 38·00 35·00

349 Party Flag **350** Yacht

(Des A. Balcerzak. Photo)
1958 (16 Dec). 40th Anniv of Polish Communist Party. P 12½×13.
1079 **349** 60g. red and reddish purple..................... 40 20

(Des J. Macierewicz. Photo)
1959 (3 Jan). Sports. T **350** and similar vert designs. P 12½×13.
1080 40g. ultramarine and pale blue................. 65 35
1081 60g. deep purple and salmon................. 65 35
1082 95g. deep purple and green................. 1·30 40
1083 2z. deep blue and pale green................. 65 35
1080/1083 *Set of 4*. 3·00 1·30
Designs:—60g. Archer; 95g. Footballers; 2z. Horseman.

351 The "Guiding Hand" **352** *Amanita phalloides*

(Des J. Kończak (40g.), S. Biernaciński (60g.), S. Malecki (1z.55). Photo)
1959 (10 Mar). Third Polish United Workers' Party Congress. T **351** and similar designs. W **330**. P 13×12½ (60g.) or 12½×13 (others).
1084 40g. black, yellow-brown and red.................. 40 20
1085 60g. black, red, yellow and bluish green.......... 40 20
1086 1z.55 vermilion, grey, purple and black.......... 90 65
1084/1086 *Set of 3*. 1·50 95
Designs: Horiz—60g. Hammer and ears of corn. Vert—1z.55 Nowa Huta foundry.

(Des C. Borowczyk. Photo)
1959 (8 May). Mushrooms. Triangular designs as T **352**. W **330**. P 11½.
1087 20g. yellow, brown and green .... 2·50 2·30
1088 30g. red, olive, brown and orange-yellow ..... 1·30 40
1089 40g. red, green, yellow and dull mauve 90 35
1090 60g. yellow, brown, green and deep green .. 90 35
1091 1z. yellow, brown, green and blue 90 35
1092 2z.50 sepia, green and blue................. 1·60 65
1093 3z.40 red, yellow, green and black................. 2·00 65
1094 5z.60 chocolate, green and olive-yellow.......... 7·25 2·30
1087/1094 *Set of 8*. 16·00 6·50
Mushrooms:—30g. *Suillus luteus* (*Boletus luteus*); 40g. *Boletus edulis*; 60g. *Lactarius deliciosus*; 1z. *Cantharellus cibarius*; 2z.50 *Agaricus campestris* (*Psalliota campestris*); 3z.40 *Amanita muscaria*; 5z.60 *Leccinum scabrum* (*Boletus scaber*).

1959 (23 May). AIR. 65 Years of Philately in Poland and Sixth Polish Philatelic Association Congress, Warsaw. Design as No. 1039*b* but in one colour only. Litho and photo. W **330**. P 12½.
1095 10z. slate-purple................. 6·50 6·25
No. 1095 is printed in sheets of six stamps *se-tenant* with variously inscribed labels in slate-purple and pale green each bearing a premium "+5 zl." (*price £80*).

353 "Storks" (after Chelmonski) **354** Miner **355** Sheaf of Wheat ("Agriculture")

(Des J. Desselberger. Eng E. Konecki (40g.), B. Szymańska (60g.), S. Lukaszewski (1z.), M. R. Polak (1z.50), J. Miller (6z.40). Recess)

1959 (29 June–22 Sept). Polish Paintings. Various designs as T **353**. W **330**. P 13×12 (1z.) or 12 (others).

1096	40g. bronze-green		35	20
1097	60g. deep maroon		50	35
1098	1z. black (22.9)		65	40
1099	1z.50 sepia		1·60	65
1100	6z.40 deep blue		5·25	1·30
1096/1100 *Set of 5*			7·50	2·50

Paintings: Vert—60g. "Motherhood" (after Wyspiański); 1z. "Madame de Romanet" (after Rodakowski); 1z.50 "Death" (after Malczewski). Horiz—6z.40 "The Sandmen" (after Gierymski).

(Des S. Malecki. Litho)

1959 (1 July). Third International Miners' Congress, Katowice. W **330**. P 12½×13.

1101	**354**	2z.50 multicoloured	2·00	40

(Des S. Malecki. Litho)

1959 (21 July). 15th Anniv of People's Republic. T **355** and similar vert designs inscr "XV LAT PRL". W **330**. P 12×12½.

1102	40g. blue-green and black		20	20
1103	60g. red and black		25	25
1104	1z.50 pale blue and black		50	35
1102/1104 *Set of 3*			85	70

Designs:—60g. Crane ("Building"); 1z.50 Corinthian column, and book ("Culture and Science").

356
Dr L. Zamenhof

357 "Flowering Pink" (Map of Austria)

(Des B. Brandt (60g.), R. Dudzicki (1z.50). Litho)

1959 (24 July). International Esperanto Congress, Warsaw, and Birth Centenary of Dr. Ludwig Zamenhof (inventor of Esperanto). T **356** and similar vert design. W **330**. P 12½×13.

1105	60g. black and green/*light olive*	40	25
1106	1z.50 blue-green, red and violet/*grey*	3·50	70

Design:—1z.50 Esperanto Star, and Globe.

(Des E. Konecki. Litho)

1959 (27 July). Seventh World Youth Festival, Vienna. W **330**. P 12½×13.

1107	**357**	60g. multicoloured	40	25
1108		2z.50 multicoloured	1·40	75

358

(Des J. Kończak. Litho)

1959 (24 Aug). 30th Anniv of Polish Airlines "LOT". W **330**. P 13×12½.

1109	**358**	60g. light blue, bluish violet and black.	40	25

359 Parliament House, Warsaw

(Des S. Jasiński. Litho)

1959 (27 Aug). 48th Inter-Parliamentary Union Conference, Warsaw. W **330**. P 12×12½.

1110	**359**	60g. green, red and black	40	25
1111		2z.50 dull purple, red and black	1·50	1·20

BALPEX I - GDAŃSK 1959
(360)

1959 (30 Aug). Baltic States' International Philatelic Exhibition, Gdańsk. No. 890 optd with T **360**.

1112	45g. brown/*lemon* (B.)		1·60	1·30
	a. Error. Missing accent above "n" in "Gdańsk" (pos. 1 and 7)		16·00	16·00

361 Dove and Globe

362 Nurse with Bag

363 Emblem of Polish–Chinese Friendship Society

(Des A. Balcerzak and S. Nargiello. Photo)

1959 (1 Sept). Tenth Anniv of World Peace Movement. W **330**. P 13×12½.

1113	**361**	60g. grey and blue	40	25

(Des Cz. Kaczmarczyk. Litho)

1959 (21 Sept). 40th Anniv of Polish Red Cross. T **362** and similar designs. W **330**. P 11 (2z.50) or 12½×13 (others).

1114	40g. red, black and green		35	20
1115	60g. red, brown and yellow-brown		40	25
1116	2z.50 red, black and light Venetian red		2·75	60
1114/1116 *Set of 3*			3·25	95

Designs: Vert—60g. Nurse with bottle and bandages. Square (23x23 *mm*)—2z.50 J. H. Dunant.

(Des S. Malecki. Litho)

1959 (28 Sept). Polish-Chinese Friendship. W **330**. P 11.

1117	**363**	60g. red, yellow, blue and violet	2·00	1·20
1118		2z.50 red, yellow, blue and blue-green	50	40

364

365 "Sputnik 3"

(Des S. Bernaciński. Litho)

1959 (9 Oct). Stamp Day. W **330**. P 12½×13.

1119	**364**	60g. red, olive-green and light turquoise	35	20
1120		2z.50 violet-blue, blue-green and red	65	35

(Des Cz. Kaczmarczyk. Photo)

1959 (7 Nov). Cosmic Flights. T **365** and similar horiz designs. W **330**. P 12½.

1121	40g. black and turquoise-blue		25	20
1122	60g. black and brown-lake		40	25
1123	2z.50 deep blue and blue-green		2·50	1·00
1121/1123 *Set of 3*			2·75	1·30

Designs:—60g. Rocket "Mieczta" encircling Sun; 2z.50 Moon rocket "Lunik 2".
Nos. 1121/3 exist imperforate.

366 Schoolgirl

367 Charles Darwin

(40g. des W. Górka; eng B. Szymańska. Recess, background photo. 60g. des H. Hilscher; eng E. Tirdiszek. Recess and typo, background photo)

1959 (14 Nov). 1000 Schools for Polish Millennium. T **366** and similar vert design inscr "TYSIAC SZKOL NA TYSIACLECIE". W **330**. P 11½.

1124	40g. sepia and deep green		35	20
1125	60g. red, black and blue		40	25

Designs:—60g. Children going to school.

(Des S. Chludziński. Eng E. Tirdiszek (20g.), E. Konecki (40g.), J. Miller (60g.), B. Brandt (1z.50), B. Kowalska (1z.55), S. Lukaszewski (2z.50). Recess)

1959 (10 Dec). Famous Scientists. Vert portraits as T **367**. W **330**. P 11×11½.

1126	20g. deep blue	15	15
1127	40g. deep olive (Mendeleev)	20	15
1128	60g. brown-purple (Einstein)	25	20
1129	1z.50 chocolate (Pasteur)	40	25
1130	1z.55 deep myrtle-green (Newton)	65	35
1131	2z.50 violet (Copernicus)	2·30	65
1126/1131	Set of 6	3·50	1·60

368 Costumes of Rzeszów   **369** Costumes of Rzeszów   **370** Piano

(Des Cz. Kaczmarczyk. Eng S. Lukaszewski (20g.), B. Konecki (60g.), J. Miller (1z.), B. Brandt (2z.50), M. R. Polak (5z.60). Recess; background photo)

1959 (18 Dec). Provincial Costumes (1st series). T **368/9** and similar vert designs. W **330**. P 12.

1132	20g. greenish black and grey-green	20	15
	a. Pair. Nos. 1132/3	45	35
1133	20g. greenish black and grey-green	20	15
1134	60g. agate and salmon-pink	25	20
	a. Pair. Nos. 1134/5	55	45
1135	60g. agate and salmon-pink	25	20
1136	1z. brown-red and pale blue	35	25
	a. Pair. Nos. 1136/7	75	55
1137	1z. brown-red and pale blue	35	25
1138	2z.50 blue-green and lavender-grey	80	30
	a. Pair. Nos. 1138/9	1·70	65
1139	2z.50 blue-green and lavender-grey	80	30
1140	5z.60 Prussian blue and greenish yellow	2·20	65
	a. Pair. Nos. 1140/1	4·75	1·40
1141	5z.60 Prussian blue and greenish yellow	2·20	65
1132/1141	Set of 10	6·75	2·75

Designs:—Male and female costumes of: Nos. 1134/5, Kurpie; Nos. 1136/7, Silesia; Nos. 1138/9, Górale; Nos. 1140/1, Szamotuly, 1138/9 Górale.

Stamps of the same value were issued together in *se-tenant* pairs within their sheets.

These also exist imperforate.

See also Nos. 1150/9.

(Des S. Malecki. Litho (60g., 1z.50). Eng B. Kowalska. Recess (2z.50))

1960 (22 Feb). 150th Birth Anniv of Chopin. Chopin Music Competition, Warsaw. T **370** and similar vert designs inscr "1810–1960". P 12 (60g., 1z.50) or 12½×12 (2z.50).

1142	60g. black and bright violet	65	25
1143	1z.50 black, red and light blue	1·30	40
1144	2z.50 blackish brown	4·50	2·50
1142/1144	Set of 3	5·75	2·75

Designs: (22×35½ *mm*)—1z.50 Portion of Chopin's music. (25×39½ *mm*)—2z.50 Portrait of Chopin.

371 Polish 10k. Stamp of 1860 and Postmark   **372** Throwing the Discus

(Des A. Balcerzak. Litho)

1960 (21 Mar). Stamp Centenary. T **371** and similar vert designs. W **330**. P 11½×11.

1145	40g. rose, blue, black and light turquoise-blue	25	20
1146	60g. blue, black and violet	40	25
1147	1z.35 blue, red and grey	1·30	80
1148	1z.55 carmine, black and bluish green	2·00	65
	a. Black missing	£800	£650
1149	2z.50 deep myrtle-green, black and light yellow-olive	2·50	90
1145/1149	Set of 5	5·75	2·50

Designs:—1z.35 Emblem inscr "1860 1960". Reproductions of Polish stamps: 60g. No. 356; 1z.55 No. 533; 2z.50 No. 1030; with appropriate postmarks.

A set of five miniature sheets, each containing a value of Nos. 1145/9 in block of four, was presented to subscribers to the first volume of *Polskie Znaki Pocztowe* (price £1000 mint per set).

(Des Cz. Karczmarczyk. Eng M. R. Polak (1150), S. Lukaszewski (1152, 1156), B. Brandt (1154), E. Konecki (1155), B. Szymańska (1157), E. Tirdiszek (1158), J. Miller (others). Recess; background photo)

1960 (28 May). Provincial Costumes (2nd series). Vert designs as T **368/9**. W **330**. P 12.

1150	40g. carmine and light blue	20	15
	a. Pair. Nos. 1150/1	45	35
1151	40g. carmine and light blue	20	15
1152	2z. ultramarine and greenish yellow	25	20
	a. Pair. Nos. 1152/3	55	45
1153	2z. ultramarine and greenish yellow	25	20
1154	3z.10 grey-green and sage green	40	25
	a. Pair. Nos. 1154/5	85	55
1155	3z.10 grey-green and sage green	40	25
1156	3z.40 brown and pale blue	85	40
	a. Pair. Nos. 1156/7	1·70	85
1157	3z.40 brown and pale blue	85	40
1158	6z.50 violet and green	1·60	60
	a. Pair. Nos. 1158/9	3·50	1·30
1159	6z.50 violet and green	1·60	60
1150/1159	Set of 10	6·00	3·00

Designs:—Male and female costumes of Nos. 1150/1, Cracow; Nos. 1152/3, Lowicz; Nos. 1154/5, Kujawy; Nos. 1156/7, Lublin; Nos. 1158/9, Lubski.

Stamps of the same value were issued together in *se-tenant* pairs within their sheets.

These also exist imperforate.

(Des S. Malecki. Litho centres embossed)

1960 (15 June). Olympic Games, Rome. T **372** and similar horiz designs. P 13×13.

1160	60g. greenish blue and black	40	25
	a. Block of 4. Nos. 1160/3	1·70	
1161	60g. magenta and black	40	25
1162	60g. bright violet and black	40	25
1163	60g. bright blue-green and black	40	25
1164	2z.50 ultramarine and black	1·30	65
	a. Block of 4. Nos. 1164/7	5·50	
1165	2z.50 orange-brown and black	1·30	65
1166	2z.50 orange-vermilion and black	1·30	65
1167	2z.50 emerald and black	1·30	65
1160/1167	Set of 8	6·00	3·25

Designs (Polish successes in previous Olympic Games):—No. 1161, Running; 1162, Cycling; 1163, Show jumping; 1164, Trumpeters; 1165, Boxing; 1166, Olympic Flame; 1167, Long jumping.

Stamps of the same value were issued together in *se-tenant* blocks of four stamps within the sheet, each block illustrating a complete circuit of the stadium track.

These also exist imperforate.

373 King Wladislaw Jagiello's Tomb, Wawel Castle   **374** 1860 Stamp and Postmark   **375** I. Lukasiewicz (inventor of paraffin lamp)

(Des Cz. Kaczmarczyk. Eng E. Konecki (60g.), S. Lukaszewski (90g.), J. Miller (2z.50). Recess)

1960 (15 July). 550th Anniv of Battle of Grunwald. T **373** and other designs inscr "GRUNWALD 1410–1960". W **330**. P 11×11½.

1168	60g. chocolate	65	40
1169	90g. deep bronze-green	1·30	65

1170	2z.50 black	5·75	2·20
1168/1170	*Set of 3*	7·00	3·00

Designs: Vert—90g. Proposed Grunwald monument. Horiz (78×35½ mm)—"Battle of Grunwald" (after Matejko).

(Des A. Balcerzak. Litho)

1960 (4 Sept). International Philatelic Exhibition, Warsaw. W **330**. P 11×11½.

1171	**374**	10z. +10z. red, black and blue	11·50	11·50
		a. Balck omitted		£500

Printed in sheets of four and sold only at the Exhibition (*price £85*). Sheets of four with black omitted are also known (*price £2500*).

(Des J. Desselberger. Eng E. Konecki. Recess; background photo)

1960 (14 Sept). Lukasiewicz Commemoration and Fifth Pharmaceutical Science Congress, Poznań. W **330**. P 11×11½.

1172	**375**	60g. black and olive-yellow	40	25

376 "The Annunciation"

377 Paderewski

(Des R. Kleczewski. Eng E. Konecki (20g., 2z.50), E. Tirdiszek (30g.), B. Brandt (40g.), B. Szymańska (60g.), J. Miller (5z.60), S. Lukaszewski (10z.). Recess)

1960 (20 Sept). Altar Wood Carvings of St. Mary's Church, Cracow, by Veit Stoss. T **376** and similar horiz designs. W **330**. P 12½×12 or imperf (10z.).

1173	20g. slate-blue	40	20
1174	30g. red-brown	40	20
1175	40g. violet	40	25
1176	60g. deep grey-green	40	35
1177	2z.50 deep claret	2·00	65
1178	5z.60 sepia	11·50	8·50
1173/1178	*Set of 6*	13·50	9·25
MS1178a	86×107 mm. 10z. grey-black	17·00	13·00

Designs:—30g. "The Nativity"; 40g. "Homage of the Three Kings"; 60g. "The Resurrection"; 2z.50 "The Ascension"; 5z.60 "The Descent of the Holy Ghost". Vert (72×95 mm)—10z. "The Assumption of the Virgin".

(Des J. Desselberger. Eng E. Konecki. Recess)

1960 (26 Sept). Birth Centenary of Paderewski. W **330**. P 13×12½.

1179	**377**	2z.50 black	65	40

DZIEŃ ZNACZKA
1960
(378)

379 Gniezno

1960 (9 Oct). Stamp Day. Optd with T **378**.

1180	**371**	40g. rose, blue, black and light turquoise-blue	2·50	1·30

(Des W. Chomicz. Eng S. Lukaszewski (5g., 1z.15, 3z.10), A. Szklarczyk (10g., 50g., 5z.60), B. Kowalska (20g., 60g. (1187)), E. Tirdiszek (40g., 95g., 1z.50, 2z.10), E. Konecki (60g. (1186), 90g., 1z.35, 1z.55, 2z.50), B. Brandt (80g.), J. Miller (1z., 2z.). Recess)

1960 (15 Nov)–**61**. Old Polish Towns. Horiz designs as T **379**. P 13×12½ (95g.) or 11½×12 (others).

1181	5g. red-brown	15	15
	a. Perf 13×12½	15	15
1182	10g. blue-green	15	15
	a. Perf 13×12½	15	15
1183	20g. sepia	20	15
	a. Perf 13×12½	20	15
1184	40g. vermilion	20	15
	a. Perf 13×12½	20	15
1185	50g. violet	65	40
1186	60g. brown-lilac	25	20
	a. Perf 13×12½	25	20
1187	60g. dull ultramarine (12.5.61)	25	20
1188	80g. deep violet-blue	25	20
	a. Perf 13×12½	35	25
1189	90g. brown (12.5.61)	1·30	40
1190	95g. blackish olive	35	25
1191	1z. orange-red and pale lilac	35	25

1192	1z.15 bottle green and pale orange (28.12.60)	35	25
1193	1z.35 magenta and pale green (28.12.60)	35	25
1194	1z.50 bistre-brown and pale blue (28.12.60)	35	25
1195	1z.55 brown-lilac and pale yellow (28.12.60)	35	25
1196	2z. deep blue and pale lilac (28.12.60)	40	35
1197	2z.10 agate and pale yellow (28.12.60)	40	35
1198	2z.50 violet and pale green (28.12.60)	50	40
1199	3z.10 bright scarlet and pale grey (28.12.60)	1·00	75
1200	5z.60 slate and light grey-green (28.12.60)	4·00	1·80
1181/1200	*Set of 20*	10·50	6·50

Towns:—10g. Cracow; 20g. Warsaw; 40g. Poznań; 50g. Plock; 60g. (1186) Kalisz; 60g. (1187) Tczew; 80g. Frombork; 90g. Toruń; 95g. Puck; 1z. Slupsk; 1z.15 Gdańsk; 1z.35 Wroclaw; 1z.50 Szczecin; 1z.55 Opole; 2z. Kolobrzeg; 2z.10 Legnica; 2z.50 Katowice; 3z.10 Lódź; 5z.60 Walbrzych.

380 Great Bustard (*Otis tarda*)

381 Front page of newspaper *Prolètaryat* (1883)

(Des J. Desselberger. Photo)

1960 (26 Nov). Birds. T **380** and similar square designs. Multicoloured. P 11½.

1201	10g. Type **380**	40	20
1202	20g. Common Raven (*Corvus corax*)	40	20
1203	30g. Great Cormorant (*Phalacrocorax carbo*)	40	20
1204	40g. Black Stork (*Ciconia nigra*)	65	25
1205	50g. Eagle Owl (*Bubo bubo*)	65	25
1206	60g. White-tailed Sea Eagle (*Haliaeetus albicilla*)	90	35
1207	75g. Golden Eagle (*Aquila chrysaëtos*)	90	35
1208	90g. Short-toed Eagle (*Circaëtus gallicus*)	1·30	40
1209	2z.50 Rock Thrush (*Montccla saxatilis*)	6·50	3·00
1210	4z. River Kingfisher (*Alcedo atthis*)	5·25	1·60
1211	5z.60 Wallcreeper (*Tichodroma muraria*)	9·75	2·00
1212	6z.50 European Roller (*Coracias garrulus*)	13·00	4·50
1201/1212	*Set of 12*	36·00	12·00

(Des Cz. Kaczmarczyk. Litho; "300" embossed)

1961 (3 Jan). 300th Anniv of Polish Newspaper Press. T **381** and similar vert designs. W **330**. P 12.

1213	40g. green, blue and black	65	40
1214	60g. yellow, brown-red and black	65	40
1215	2z.50 blue, violet and black	7·25	5·25
1213/1215	*Set of 3*	7·75	5·50

Designs:—As T **381** but showing front page of newspapers; 40g. *Merkuriusz* (first issue, 1661); 2z.50 *Rzeczpospolita* (1944).

382 Ice-hockey

383 Congress Emblem

(Des J. Grabiański. Litho)

1961 (1 Feb). First Winter Military Spartakiad. T **382** and similar vert designs. W **330**. P 12.

1216	40g. black, olive-yellow and lilac	65	40
1217	60g. black, carmine, violet-blue and cobalt	65	50
1218	1z. olive, black, red, deep blue and light blue	13·00	4·50
1219	1z.50 black, yellow and light turquoise-blue	65	50
1216/1219	*Set of 4*	13·50	5·50

Designs:—60g. Ski jumping; 1z. Rifle-shooting; 1z.50 Slalom.

(Des S. Jasiński. Litho)

1961 (11 Feb). Fourth Polish Engineers' Conference. W **330**. P 12½×13.

1220	**383**	60g. black and red	40	35

384 Yuri Gagarin

385 Fair Emblem

(Des A. Heidrich. Photo)

1961 (27 Apr). World's First Manned Space Flight. T **384** and similar horiz design inscr "12.1V.1961". W **330**. P 12.

1221	40g. black, red and brown-red	1·00	40
1222	60g. red, black and blue	1·30	65

Design:—60g. Globe and star.

(Des Z. Kaja. Litho)

1961 (25 May). 30th International Fair, Poznań. W **330**. P 12½.

1223	**385** 40g. black, orange-red and blue	25	20
1224	1z.50 black, blue and orange-red	65	35

See also No. **MS**1245*a*.

386 King Mieszko I

(Des A. Heidrich. Eng A. Szklarczyk (1225), S. Lukaszewski (1226), J. Miller (1227), E. Tirdiszek (1228), E. Konecki (1229), B. Kowalska (1230). Recess; background photo)

1961 (15 June). Famous Poles (1st series). T **386** and similar horiz portrait designs. W **330**. P 11×12.

1225	60g. black and blue	40	25
1226	60g. black and claret	40	25
1227	60g. black and grey-green	40	25
1228	60g. black and violet	1·30	40
1229	60g. black and light brown	40	25
1230	60g. black and olive-brown	40	25
1225/1230 *Set of 6*		3·00	1·50

Portraits:—No. 1225, T **386**; No. 1226, King Casimir the Great; No. 1227, King Casimir Jagiellon; No. 1228, Copernicus; No 1229, A. F. Modrzewski; No. 1230, Kościuszko.

See also Nos. 1301/6 and 1398/1401.

387 *Leskov* (trawler support ship)

(Des J. Desselberger. Litho)

1961 (24 June). Shipbuilding Industry. T **387** and similar horiz designs. Multicoloured. P 11.

1231	60g. Type **387**	40	20
1232	1z.55 *Severodvinsk* (depot ship)	80	35
1233	2z.50 *Rambutan* (coaster)	1·30	50
1234	3z.40 *Krynica* (freighter)	2·00	65
1235	4z. Type B54 (freighter)	3·25	1·30
1236	5z.60 *Baysk* (tanker)	8·50	3·50
1231/1236 *Set of 6*		14·50	5·75

Sizes: As T **387**—2z.50 81×21 mm; 1z.55 3z.40, 4z. 108×21 mm 5z.60.

388 Posthorn and Telephone Dial

389 Opole Seal

390 Beribboned Paddle

(Des S. Malecki. Litho)

1961 (26 June). Communications Ministers' Conference, Warsaw. T **388** and similar designs. No wmk or W **330** (No. **MS**1239*a*). P 11.

1237	40g. orange-red, deep green and slate-blue	35	20
1238	60g. brown, violet, yellow and light slate-purple	35	20
1239	2z.50 ultramarine, light blue and bistre-brown.	1·20	40
1237/1239 *Set of 3*		1·70	70
MS1239*a* 108×66 mm. Nos. 1237/9 (sold at 5z.)		13·00	6·50

Designs: Posthorn and 60g. Radar screen; 2z.50 Conference emblem.

(Des Cz. Kaczmarczyk. Eng A. Szklarczyk (1240), E. Konecki (1241, 1243*b*), S. Lukaszewski (1242), B. Kowalska (1243), E. Tirdiszek (1243*a*, 1244), J. Miller (1245). Recess and photo)

1961 (21 July)–**62**. Polish Western Provinces. T **389** and similar designs. W **330**. P 11.

1240	40g. deep chocolate and grey-brown	25	15
	a. Pair. Nos. 1240/1 plus label	55	35
1241	40g. deep chocolate and grey-brown	25	15
1242	60g. deep reddish violet and pink	35	20
	a. Pair. Nos. 1242/3 plus label	75	45
1243	60g. deep reddish violet and pink	35	20
1243*a*	95g. myrtle green and turquoise-blue (23.2.62)	50	35
	ab. Pair. Nos. 1243*a*/b plus label	1·10	75
1243*b*	95g. myrtle green and turquoise-blue (23.2.62)	50	35
1244	2z.50 bronze green and yellow-olive	1·20	65
	a. Pair. Nos. 1244/5 plus label	2·50	1·40
1245	2z.50 bronze green and yellow-olive	1·20	65
1240/1245 *Set of 8*		4·25	2·40

Designs: Vert—No. 1240, Type **389**; 1242, Henry IV's tomb; 1243*a*, Seal of Conrad II; 1244, Prince Barnim's seal. Horiz—No. 1241, Opole cement-works; 1243, Wroclaw apartment-house; 1243*b*, Factory interior, Zielona Góra; 1245, Szczecin harbour.

Stamps of the same value were issued together *se-tenant* with ⅔ stamp-size inscribed label.

See also Nos. 1308/13.

1961 (29 July). "Intermess II" Stamp Exhibition. Sheet 121×51 mm containing pair of No. 1224 but imperf.

MS1245*a* 1z.50 (×2) (sold at 4z.50+2z.50)		10·50	6·50

(Des R. Dudzicki. Litho)

1961 (18 Aug). Sixth European Canoeing Championships. T **390** and similar designs. W **330**. P 12½.

1246	40g. red, yellow, green, blue and turquoise..	35	20
1247	60g. red, yellow, violet and blue	35	20
1248	2z.50 red, yellow, violet, grey-green and slate	2·50	1·00
1246/1248 *Set of 3*		3·00	1·30

Designs: Horiz—40g. Two canoes within letter "E"; 60g. Two four-seater canoes at finishing post.

These also exist imperforate.

391 Titov and Orbit within Star

392 Monument

(Des S. Bernaciński. Photo)

1961 (24 Aug). Second Russian Manned Space Flight. T **391** and similar horiz design inscr "700,000 KM W KOSMOSIE" etc. P 12×13.

1249	40g. black, red and pale pink	80	25
1250	60g. blue and black	90	40

Design:—60g. Dove and spaceman's orbit around globe.

(Des J. Desselberger. Litho)

1961 (15 Sept). 40th Anniv of Third Silesian Uprising. T **392** and similar vert design inscr "40 ROCZNICA TRZECIEGO" etc. W **330**. P 12.

1251	60g. grey and emerald	25	20
1252	1z.55 grey and light blue	50	25

Design:—1z.55 Cross of Silesian uprisers.

393 P.K.O. Emblem and Ant

(Des S. Malecki. Litho)

1961 (30 Sept). Savings Month. T **393** and similar horiz designs. W **330**. P 12.

1253	40g. orange-red, yellow and black	25	20
1254	60g. brown, yellow and black	35	25
1255	60g. blue, violet and pink	35	25
1256	60g. green, orange-red and black	50	25
1257	2z.50 magenta, grey and black	4·00	2·00
1253/1257 Set of 5		5·00	2·75

Designs:—No. 1253, Savings Bank motif; 1254, T **393**; 1255, Bee; 1256, Squirrel; 1257, Savings Bank book.

394 "Mail Cart"
(after J. Chelmonski)

(Des Cz. Kaczmarczyk. Eng J. Miller. Recess)

1961 (9 Oct). Stamp Day and 40th Anniv of Postal Museum. W **330**. P 12×12½.

1258	**394** 60g. chocolate	50	35
1259	60g. deep green	50	35

395 Congress Emblem   **396** Emblem of Kopasyni mining family, 1284   **397** Child and Syringe

(Des S. Jasiński. Eng B. Kowalska. Recess)

1961 (20 Nov). Fifth World Federation of Trade Unions' Congress, Moscow. W **330**. P 12×12½.

1260	**395** 60g. black	40	25

(Des S. Miklaszewski. Litho)

1961 (4 Dec). Millenary of Polish Mining Industry. As T **396**, inscr "TYSIACLECIE GORNICTWA POLSKIEGO". W **330**. P 11×11½.

1261	40g. brown-purple, orange and light orange	20	15
1262	60g. grey-blue, ultramarine and light blue	25	20
1263	2z.50 green, black and light green	1·30	40
1261/1263 Set of 3		1·60	70

Designs:—60g. 14th-century seal of Bytom; 2z.50 Emblem of International Mine Constructors' Congress, Warsaw, 1958.

(Des S. Gospodarek. Litho)

1961 (11 Dec). 15th Anniv of UNICEF. T **397** and similar designs inscr "1961 XV ROCZNICA POWSTANIA UNICEF". W **330**. P 12×12½ (60g.) or 12½×12 (others).

1264	40g. black and light blue	25	20
1265	60g. black and yellow-orange	35	25
1266	2z.50 black and turquoise-green	1·30	40
1264/1266 Set of 3		1·70	75

Designs: Horiz—60g. Children of three races. Vert—2z.50 Mother and child, and feeding bottle.

398 Cogwheel and Wheat   **399** *Calosoma sycophanta*

(Des Cz. Kaczmarczyk. Litho)

1961 (12 Dec). 15th Economic Co-operative Council Meeting, Warsaw. T **398** and similar horiz design. W **330**. P 12.

1267	40g. crimson, yellow and black	35	25
1268	60g. red, light blue and ultramarine	40	35

Design:—60g. Oil pipeline map, E. Europe.

(Des J. Desselberger (1269/74), A. Balcerzak (1275/8), A. Heidrich (1279/80). Photo)

1961 (30 Dec). Insects. T **399** and similar multicoloured designs. P 13×12 (20g. to 80g.) or 11½ (1z.15 to 5z.60).

1269	20g. Type **399**	30	20
1270	30g. *Carabus violaceus*	30	20
1271	40g. *Rosalia alpina*	30	20
1272	50g. *Cerambyx cerdo*	30	20
1273	60g. *Carabus auronitens*	35	25
1274	80g. *Lucanus cervus*	35	25
1275	1z.15 *Parnassius mnemosyne*	65	35
1276	1z.35 *Acherintia atropos*	65	35
1277	1z.50 *Iphiclides podalirius (Papilio podalirius)*	1·30	40
1278	1z.55 *Parnassius apollo*	90	40
1279	2z.50 *Formica rufa*	2·50	80
1280	5z.60 *Bombus lucorum*	13·00	5·75
1269/1280 Set of 12		19·00	8·50

Sizes: As T **399**—20g. to 80g. 36½×36½ mm—1z.15 to 5z.60.

400 Worker with Flag and Dove   **401** Two Skiers Racing

(Des J. Desselberger. Litho)

1962 (5 Jan). 20th Anniv of Polish Workers' Coalition. T **400** and similar vert designs. P 12½×12.

1281	60g. sepia, black and vermilion	30	20
1282	60g. bistre, black and vermilion	30	20
1283	60g. violet, black and vermilion	30	20
1284	60g. slate-green, black and vermilion	30	20
1285	60g. grey-blue, black and vermilion	30	20
1281/1285 Set of 5		1·40	90

Designs:—1282, helmsman; 1283, Worker with hammer; 1284, Soldier with weapon; 1285, Worker with trowel and rifle.

(Des S. Toepfer. Litho. Central figures embossed in colour)

1962 (14 Feb). F.I.S. International Ski Championships, Zakopane. T **401** and similar designs. P 12×12½ (1z.50), 12½×12 (40, 60g.) or imperf (10z.).

1286	**401**	40g. slate-blue, grey and red	25	20
1287		40g. grey-blue, bistre-brown and red	1·30	40
1288	–	60g. slate-blue, grey and red	35	25
1289	–	60g. indigo, bistre-brown and red	2·00	90
1290	–	1z.50 slate-blue, grey and red	40	35
1291		1z.50 violet, grey and red	4·00	2·00
1286/1291 Set of 6			7·50	3·75
MS1291a 67×80 mm. 10z.(+5z.) slate-blue, grey and red			9·00	7·75

Designs: Horiz—60g. Skier racing. Vert—1z.50 Ski-jumper; 10z. F.I.S. emblem.

Nos. 1286, 1288 and 1290 also exist in sheets of four, perf 11×11½ or 11½×11 (*price per set of 3 sheets £400 un*).

402 Majdanek Monument   **403** Racing Cyclist

(Des S. Jasiński. Eng J. Miller (40g.), E. Konecki (60g.), B. Kowalska (1z.50). Recess)

1962 (2 Apr). Concentration Camp Monuments. T **402** and similar designs. W **330**. P 11½.

1292	40g. deep blue	25	20
1293	60g. black	40	25
1294	1z.50 violet	90	40
1292/1294 Set of 3		1·40	75

Designs: Vert (20×31 *mm*)—40g. Broken carnations and portion of prison clothing (Oswiecim or Auschwitz Camp); 1z.50 Treblinka Monument.

(Des S. Malecki. Litho)

1962 (27 Apr). 15th International Peace Cycle Race. T **403** and similar horiz designs. W **330**. P 12.

1295	60g. black and blue	40	25
1296	2z.50 black and yellow	1·00	40
1297	3z.40 black and light reddish violet	2·20	90
1295/1297 *Set of 3*		3·25	1·40

Designs:—(74½×22 *mm*) 2z.50 Cyclists and "XV"; (As T **403**) 3z.40 Arms of Berlin, Prague and Warsaw, and cycle wheel.

405 Lenin walking   **406** General K. Świerczewski-Walter (monument)   **407** *Crocus scepusiensis* (Borb)

(Des S. Malecki. Eng E. Tirdiszek (40g.), A. Szklarczyk (60g.), B. Kowalska (2z.50). Recess)

1962 (25 May). 50th Anniv of Lenin's Sojourn in Poland. T **405** and similar vert designs inscr "1912–1962". W **330**. P 11×11½.

1298	40g. deep bluish green and pale green	65	40
1299	60g. lake and pale pink	40	25
1300	2z.50 sepia and pale yellow	1·30	50
1298/1300 *Set of 3*		2·10	1·00

Designs:—60g. Lenin; 2z.50 Lenin wearing cap, and St. Mary's Church, Cracow.

(Des A. Heidrich; eng S. Lukaszewski (1301), J. Miller (1302). Recess; background photo. Des A. Heidrich. Litho (others))

1962 (20 June). Famous Poles (2nd series). Portrait designs as T **386**. W **330**. P 11×12 (Nos. 1301/2) or 12×12½ (others).

1301	60g. black and light grey-green	40	25
1302	60g. black and orange-brown	40	25
1303	60g. black and blue	40	25
1304	60g. black and brown-bistre	40	25
1305	60g. black and reddish purple	40	25
1306	60g. black and deep bluish green	40	25
1301/1306 *Set of 6*		2·20	1·40

Portraits:—1301, A. Mickiewicz (poet); 1302, J. Slowacki (poet); 1303, F. Chopin (composer); 1304, R. Traugutt (patriot); 1305, J. Dąbrowski (revolutionary); 1306, Maria Konopnicka (poet).

(Des S. Jasiński. Eng J. Miller. Recess)

1962 (14 July). 15th Anniv of Death of General K. Świerczewski-Walter (patriot). P 11×11½.

1307	**406** 60g. black	40	35

(Des Cz. Kaczmarczyk. Eng E. Tirdszek (1308), A. Szklarczyk (1309), Z. Kowalski (1310), E. Konecki (1311, 1312), J. Miller (1313). Recess and photo)

1962 (21 July). Polish Northern Provinces. Designs as T **389**. P 11.

1308	60g. deep violet-blue and bluish grey	25	20
	a. Pair. Nos. 1308/9 plus label	55	45
1309	60g. deep violet-blue and bluish grey	25	20
1310	1z.55 sepia and pale yellow	40	25
	a. Pair. Nos. 1310/1 plus label	85	55
1311	1z.55 sepia and pale yellow	40	25
1312	2z.50 greenish slate and greenish grey	90	40
	a. Pair. Nos. 1312/13 plus label	1·90	85
1313	2z.50 greenish slate and greenish grey	90	40
1308/1313 *Set of 6*		2·75	1·50

Designs: Vert—No. 1308, Princess Elizabeth's seal; 1310, Gdańsk Governor's seal; 1312, Frombork Cathedral. Horiz—No. 1309, Insulator factory, Szczecinek; 1311, Gdańsk shipyard; 1313, Laboratory of Agricultural College, Kortowo.

Stamps of the same value were issued together *se-tenant* with ⅔ stamp-size inscribed label.

(Des A. Balcerzak. Photo)

1962 (8 Aug). Polish Protected Plants. T **407** and similar vert designs. Plants in natural colours. P 12.

1314	60g. yellow	25	20
1315	60g. cinnamon	1·30	65
1316	60g. pink	25	20
1317	90g. yellow-green	40	25
1318	90g. yellow-olive	40	25
1319	90g. green	40	25
1320	1z.50 grey-blue	65	40
1321	1z.50 light green	65	40

1322	1z.50 bluish green	65	40
1323	2z.50 grey-green	1·60	90
1324	2z.50 turquoise	2·00	90
1325	2z.50 violet-blue	2·20	1·10
1314/1325 *Set of 12*		9·75	5·25

Plants:—No. 1314, T **407**; 1315, *Platanthera bifolia* (Rich); 1316, *Aconitum callibotryon* (Rchb); 1317, *Gentiana clusii* (Perr. et Song); 1318, *Dictamnus albus* (L); 1319, *Nymphaea alba* (L.); 1320, *Daphne mezereum* (L.); 1321, *Pulsatilla vulgaris* (Mill.); 1322, *Anemone Silvestris* (L.); 1323, *Trollius europaeus* (L.); 1324, *Galanthus nivalis* (L.); 1325, *Adonis vernalis* (L.).

408 "The Poisoned Well", after J. Malczewski   **409** Pole Vault

(Des J. Desselberger. Eng E. Tirdiszek. Recess)

1962 (25 Aug). F.I.P. Day (1st Sept—Fédération Internationale de Philatélie). W **330**. P 11½.

1326	**408** 60g. black/cream	90	65

No. 1326 was printed in sheets of 40 stamps *se-tenant* with labels inscribed "FILA-TELISTYKA ZBLIZA LUDZI WSZYSTKICH KRAJOW" ("Philately unites people of all countries").

It also exists in sheets of four stamps and four labels (*price* £65).

(Des R. Dudzicki. Litho)

1962 (12 Sept). Seventh European Athletic Championships, Belgrade. T **409** and similar horiz designs. Multicoloured. P 11.

1327	40g. Type **409**	20	15
1328	60g. 400-metres relay	20	15
1329	90g. Throwing the javelin	25	20
1330	1z. Hurdling	25	20
1331	1z.50 High-jumping	35	25
1332	1z.55 Throwing the discus	35	25
1333	2z.50 100-metres	40	35
1334	3z.40 Throwing the hammer	2·00	40
1327/1334 *Set of 8*		3·50	1·80

The above exist imperforate.

410 *Anopheles* sp (mosquito)   **411** Cosmonauts "in Flight"

(Des S. Malecki. Litho)

1962 (1 Oct). Malaria Eradication. T **410** and similar vert designs. W **330**. P 13×12 or imperf (3z.).

1335	60g. olive-brown and deep bluish green	25	20
1336	1z.50 pink, grey, violet and red	35	25
1337	2z.50 orange, yellow-green, ultramarine and greenish grey	1·60	65
1335/1337 *Set of 3*		2·00	1·00
MS1337*a* 60×81 mm. 3z. multicoloured		2·50	1·60

Designs:—1z.50 Malaria parasites in blood; 2z.50 Cinchona plant; 3z. *Anopheles* mosquito.

(Des J. Desselberger. Litho)

1962 (6 Oct). First "Team" Manned Space Flight. T **411** and similar vert design. W **330**. P 12½×12 or 11½×11 (10z.).

1338	60g. yellow-green, black and bluish violet	40	25
1339	2z.50 red, black and turquoise-blue	1·00	40
	a. "PWPW" missing (pos. 11)	26·00	13·00
MS1339*b* 70×94 mm. 10z. red, black and turquoise-blue		5·75	4·00

Design:—2z.50, 10z. Two stars (representing space-ships) in orbit.

412 "A Moment of Determination" (after painting by A. Kamiński)

413 Mazovian Princes' Mansion, Warsaw

(Des H. Przeździecka. Eng B. Kowalska. Recess)

1962 (9 Oct). Stamp Day. W **330**. P 13×12.
1340	**412**	60g. black	40	25
1341		2z.50 red-brown	1·20	40

(Des Cz. Kaczmarczyk. Litho)

1962 (13 Oct). 25th Anniv of Polish Democratic Party. W **330**. P 13×12.
1342	**413**	60g. black/red	40	25

414 *Aurora* (Russian cruiser)

415 J. Korczak (bust after Dunikowski)

(Des S. Malecki. Eng Z. Kowalski. Recess and photo)

1962 (3 Nov). 45th Anniv of Russian Revolution. W **330**. P 11.
1343	**414**	60g. grey-blue and orange-red	40	25

(Des J. Srokowski. Litho)

1962 (12 Nov). 20th Death Anniv of Janusz Korczak (child educator). T **415** and similar vert designs. P 13×12.
1344	40g. sepia, light bistre and red-brown	25	20
1345	60g. multicoloured	40	25
1346	90g. multicoloured	90	40
1347	1z. multicoloured	90	40
1348	2z.50 multicoloured	1·30	90
1349	5z.60 multicoloured	4·00	1·60
1344/1349 *Set of 6*		7·00	3·50

Designs:—60g. to 5z.60 Illustrations from Korczak's children's books.

416 Old Town, Warsaw

417 Master Buncombe

(Des A. Heidrich. Litho)

1962 (26 Nov). Fifth Trade Unions Congress, Warsaw. W **330**. P 11.
1350	**416**	3z.40 grey-blue, red, black and cream	1·60	65

Also printed in sheets of four (*price* £13.00).

(Des J. M. Szancer. Litho)

1962 (31 Dec). Maria Konopnicka's Fairy Tale "The Dwarfs and Orphan Mary". T **417** and similar vert designs. Multicoloured. P 12½×12.
1351	40g. Type **417**	90	25
1352	60g. Lardie the Fox and Master Buncombe	4·00	1·30
1353	1z.50 Bluey and the frog	1·00	40
1354	1z.55 Peter's kitchen	1·00	65
1355	2z.50 Saraband's concert	1·30	65
1356	3z.40 Orphan Mary and Subearthy	4·50	3·25
1351/1356 *Set of 6*		11·50	5·75

418 R. Traugutt (insurgent leader)

(Des A. Heidrich. Litho)

1963 (31 Jan). Centenary of January (1863) Rising. W **330**. P 11½×11.
1357	**418**	60g. black, pale pink and turquoise-blue	40	25

419 Tractor and Wheat

(Des A. Heidrich. Litho)

1963 (25 Feb). Freedom from Hunger. T **419** and similar horiz designs. Multicoloured. W **330**. P 12×12½.
1358	40g. Type **419**	25	20
1359	60g. Millet and hoeing	1·30	40
1360	2z.50 Rice and mechanical harvester	2·30	80
1358/1360 *Set of 3*		3·50	1·30

420 Cocker Spaniel

(Des J. Grabiański. Litho)

1963 (25 Mar). Dogs. Designs as T **420**. P 12½.
1361	20g. orange, red, black and lilac	20	15
1362	30g. black and carmine	25	20
1363	40g. yellow-ochre, black and lilac	35	25
1364	50g. yellow-ochre, black and blue	40	35
1365	60g. black and light blue	65	40
1366	1z. black and yellow-green	90	45
1367	2z.50 brown, yellow and black	2·00	80
1368	3z.40 black and vermilion	4·50	2·00
1369	6z.50 black and greenish yellow	10·50	7·75
1361/1369 *Set of 9*		18·00	11·00

Dogs: Horiz—30g. Sheep-dog; 40g. Boxer; 2z.50 Gun-dog "Ogar"; 6z.50 Great Dane. Vert—50g. Airedale terrier; 60g. French bulldog; 1z. French poodle; 3z.40 Podhale sheep-dog.

421 Egyptian Galley (15th Century, B.C.)

(Des S. Malecki. Eng Z. Kowalski (5g., 1z.15), A. Szklarczyk (10g., 60g.), J. Miller (20g.), B. Kowalska (30g., 40g.), E. Tirdiszek (1z.). Recess and photo)

1963 (5 Apr). Sailing Ships (1st series). Horiz designs as T **421**. P 11½×12.
1370	5g. red-brown/light bistre	15	15
1371	10g. deep bluish green/light green	15	15
1372	20g. ultramarine/light violet	15	15
1373	30g. black/yellow-olive	20	15
1374	40g. blue/light blue	25	20
1375	60g. purple/light grey-brown	35	25
1376	1z. black/light blue	40	35
1377	1z.15 green/light pink	80	40
1370/1377 *Set of 8*		2·20	1·60

Ships:—10g. Phoenician merchantman (15th cent. B.C.); 20g. Greek trireme (5th cent. B.C.); 30g. Roman merchantman (3rd cent. A.D.); 40g. *Mora* (Norman ship, 1066); 60g. Hanse kogge (14th cent.); 1z. Holk (14th cent.); 1z.15 Carrack (15th cent.).
See also Nos. 1451/66.

422 Insurgent

423 Centenary Emblem

(Des S. Jasiński. Eng J. Miller. Recess and photo)

1963 (19 Apr). 20th Anniv of Warsaw Ghetto Uprising. W **330**. P 11½×11.
1378 **422** 2z.50 deep purple-brown and pale blue 65 40

(Des F. Winiarski. Litho)

1963 (8 May). Red Cross Centenary. P 12½×12.
1379 **423** 2z.50 red, blue and greenish yellow .... 1·60 40
      a. *Tête-bêche* (pair) .... 6·50 4·00
No. 1379 is arranged in sheets with alternate horizontal rows inverted.

424 Lizard

425 Epée, Foil, Sabre and Knight's Helmet

(Des J. Desselberger. Photo)

1963 (10 June). Protected Reptiles and Amphibians. T **424** and similar designs. Reptiles in natural colours; inscriptions and values black; background colours given. P 11½.
1380   30g. grey-green 20 15
1381   40g. olive 25 15
1382   50g. light brown 25 15
1383   60g. drab 25 15
1384   90g. myrtle 35 20
1385   1z.15 grey 35 20
1386   1z.35 grey-blue 45 25
1387   1z.50 turquoise-green 50 35
1388   1z.55 pale grey-blue 65 40
1389   2z.50 lavender 65 40
1390   3z. myrtle-green .... 2·00 65
1391   3z.40 slate-purple .... 4·50 4·00
1380/1391 *Set of 12* .... 9·25 6·25
Reptiles:—40g. Copperhead (snake); 50g. Marsh tortoise; 60g. Grass snake; 90g. Blindworm; 1z.15 Tree toad; 1z.35 Mountain newt; 1z.50 Crested newt; 1z.55 Green toad; 2z.50 "Bombina" toad; 3z. Salamander; 3z.40 "Natterjack" (toad).

(Des K. Tarkowska. Litho)

1963 (29 June). World Fencing Championships. Gdańsk. T **425** and similar designs. P 11×11½ (**MS**1397a), 13×12 (6z.50) or 12×13 (others).
1392   20g. orange-yellow and red-brown 15 15
1393   40g. light blue and blue 20 15
1394   60g. light red and carmine-red 25 20
1395   1z.15 light green and green 40 25
1396   1z.55 reddish violet and violet 90 40
1397   6z.50 yellow, brown-purple and light bistre-brown .... 2·75 90
1392/1397 *Set of 6* .... 4·25 1·80
MS1397a 110×93 mm. Nos. 1393/6 .... 80·00 80·00
Designs: Horiz—Fencers with background of 40g. Knights jousting; 60g. Dragoons in sword-fight; 1z.15 18th-century duellists; 1z.55 Old Gdańsk. Vert—6z.50 Inscription and Arms of Gdańsk.

(Des A. Heidrich. Litho)

1963 (20 July). Famous Poles (3rd series). Portrait designs as T **386**. W **330**. P 12×12.
1398   60g. black and brown-red 40 25

1399   60g. black and sepia 40 25
1400   60g. black and light greenish blue 40 25
1401   60g. black and green 40 25
1398/1401 *Set of 4* .... 1·40 90
Portraits:—No. 1398, L. Waryński (patriot), 1399, L. Krzywicki, (economist); 1400, M. Skłodowska-Curie (scientist); 1401, K. Świerczewski (patriot).

426 Bykovsky and "Vostok 5"

1963 (26 Aug). Second "Team" Manned Space Flights. T **426** and similar horiz designs. P 11.
1402   40g. black, green and blue 25 20
1403   60g. black, blue and bluish green 40 25
1404   6z.50 green, blue, black and red .... 2·20 65
1402/1404 *Set of 3* .... 2·50 1·00
Designs:—60g. Tereshkova and "Vostok 6"; 6z.50 "Vostoks 5 and 6" in orbit.

427 Basketball

428 Missile

(Des T. Michaluk. Litho)

1963 (16 Sept). 13th European (Men's) Basketball Championships, Wroclaw. T **427** and similar designs. P 11½ or imperf (10z.).
1405   40g. green, brown black and yellow 15 15
1406   50g. green, black and pink 20 15
1407   60g. black, light green and red 25 20
1408   90g. violet, red-brown, black and light emerald 35 25
1409   2z.50 black, orange, red-brown and cobalt 40 35
1410   5z.60 black, cream, light green and blue .... 2·75 40
1405/1410 *Set of 6* .... 3·75 1·40
MS1410a 76×86 mm 10z.(+5z.) multicoloured .... 4·00 2·20
Designs:—50g. to 2z.50, As T **427** but with ball, players and hands in various positions; 5z.60 Hands placing ball in net; 10z. Town Hall, People's Hall and Arms of Wroclaw.

(Des R. Dudzicki. Litho)

1963 (1 Oct). 20th Anniv of Polish People's Army. T **428** and similar horiz designs. Multicoloured. P 12×12½.
1411   20g. Type **428** 15 15
1412   40g. *Błyskawica* (destroyer) 15 15
1413   60g. Mikoyan Gurevich MiG-21C 20 15
1414   1z.15 Radar scanner 25 20
1415   1z.35 Tank 35 25
1416   1z.55 Missile carrier 40 25
1417   2z.50 Amphibious troop carrier 65 35
1418   3z. Ancient warrior, modern soldier and two swords .... 1·30 40
1411/1418 *Set of 8* .... 3·00 1·70

429 "A Love Letter" (after Czachórski)

23–28. X. 1963
W. F. Bykowski
w Polsce
(**430**)

(Des Cz. Kaczmarczyk. Eng E. Konecki. Recess)

1963 (9 Oct). Stamp Day. P 11½.
1419 **429** 60g. red-brown 40 25

1963 (23 Oct). Visit of Soviet Cosmonauts to Poland. Nos. 1402/4 optd diagonally as T **430**, or horiz in small capitals at foot (6z.50).

1420	40g. black, green and blue (R.)	65	40
1421	60g. black, blue and bluish green	65	40
1422	6z.50 green, blue, black and red	3·25	2·00
1420/1422 Set of 3		4·00	2·50

431 Tsiolkovsky's Rocket and Formula

432 Mazurian Horses

(Des J. Desselberger. Litho)

1963 (25 Nov). "The Conquest of Space". T **431** and similar vert designs. P 13×12.

1423	30g. deep turquoise-green and black	15	15
1424	40g. yellow-olive and black	20	15
1425	50g. violet-blue and black	25	15
1426	60g. orange brown and black	25	15
1427	1z. blue-green and black	35	20
1428	1z.50 brown-red and black	40	20
1429	1z.55 blue and black	40	20
1430	2z.50 purple and black	65	25
1431	5z.50 yellow-green and black	1·30	35
1432	6z.50 turquoise-blue and black	2·50	40
1423/1432 Set of 10		5·75	2·00
MS1432a 78×106 mm. Nos. 1431/2 (two of each)		85·00	85·00

Designs:—40g. "Sputnik 1"; 50g. "Explorer 1"; 60g. Banner carried by "Lunik 2"; 1z. "Lunik 3"; 2z.50 "Vostok 1"; 1z.55 "Friendship 7"; 2z.50 "Vostoks 3 and 4"; 5z.60 "Mariner 2"; 6z.50 "Mars 1".

The perforations on **MS**1432a extend top and bottom. No. **MS**1432a also exists without perforations extending into the margins at the top of the sheet (price £140 us., £140 un).

(Des L. Maciąg. Photo)

1963 (31 Dec). Polish Horse-breeding. Designs as T **432**. Multicoloured. P 11½×11 (20, 30, 40g.), 12½×12 (50, 90g., 4z.) or 13×12 (others).

1433	20g. Arab stallion "Comet"	15	15
1434	30g. Wild horses	15	15
1435	40g. Sokólski horse	20	15
1436	50g. Arab mares and foals	25	20
1437	60g. Type **432**	25	20
1438	90g. Steeplechasers	40	25
1439	1z.55 Arab stallion "Witez II"	90	35
1440	2z.50 Head of Arab horse (facing right)	1·60	40
1441	4z. Mixed breeds	4·00	90
1442	6z.50 Head of Arab horse (facing left)	5·25	4·25
1433/1442 Set of 10		12·00	6·25

Sizes:—Triangular (55×27½ mm), 20g., 30g., 40g. Horiz (75×26 mm), 50g., 90g., 4z. Vert as T **432**, 60g., 1z.55, 2z.50, 6z.50.

433 Ice Hockey

434 "Flourishing Tree"

(Des F. Winiarski. Litho)

1964 (25 Jan). Winter Olympic Games, Innsbruck. Horiz designs as T **433**. Multicoloured. P 12×13 or 11×11½ (No. **MS**1450a).

1443	20g. Type **433**	15	15
1444	30g. Slalom	20	15
1445	40g. Downhill skiing	25	20
1446	60g. Speed skating	40	25
1447	1z. Ski-jumping	50	35
1448	2z.50 Tobogganing	1·00	40
1449	5z.60 Cross-country skiing	2·20	90
1450	6z.50 Pairs, figure-skating	3·25	1·30
1443/1450 Set of 8		7·25	3·25
MS1450a 110×94 mm. Nos. 1448 and 1450 (two of each)		46·00	46·00

(Des S. Malecki 5g. to 1z.15 eng as Nos. 1370/7; others eng E. Konecki (1z.35, 3z.40), E. Tirdiszek (1z.50), A. Szklarczyk (1z.55), Z. Kowalski (2z., 2z.50), J. Miller (2z.10), B. Kowalska (3z.). Recess)

1964 (19 Mar)–**65**. Sailing Ships (2nd series). Designs as T **421** but without coloured backgrounds. P 12½×13 (vert) or 13×12½ (horiz).

1451	5g. reddish brown (25.1.65)	15	15
1452	10g. deep dull green (25.1.65)	15	15
1453	20g. slate-blue (25.1.65)	15	15
	a. Perf 11½×12	15	15
1454	30g. bronze green (25.1.65)	20	15
1455	40g. grey-blue (25.1.65)	25	15
1456	60g. deep claret (25.1.65)	25	15
	a. Perf 11½×12	25	15
1457	1z. chestnut (25.1.65)	25	15
	a. Perf 11½×12	25	15
1458	1z.15 red-brown (25.1.65)	25	15
1459	1z.35 blue	25	20
	a. Perf 12×11½	25	20
1460	1z.50 maroon	25	20
1461	1z.55 black	25	20
	a. Perf 12×11½	25	20
1462	2z. deep reddish violet	40	25
1463	2z.10 blue-green	50	25
	a. Perf 11½×12	50	25
1464	2z.50 magenta	65	35
1465	3z. deep olive	90	35
	a. Perf 11½×12	90	35
1466	3z.40 brown	1·40	40
	a. Perf 12×11½	1·40	40
1451/1466 Set of 16		5·75	3·00

Ships: Horiz—5g. to 1z.15 As Nos. 1370/7; 1z.50 Ark Royal (English galleon, 1587); 2z.10 Ship of the line (18th cent); 2z.50 Sail frigate (19th cent.); 3z. Flying Cloud (clipper, 19th cent.). Vert—1z.35 Santa Maria (Columbus's ship); 1z.55 Wodnik (17th-century Polish warship); 2z. Dutch fleute (17th cent.); 3z.40 Dar Pomorza (cadet ship).

(Des A. Heidrich. Litho)

1984 (15 Apr). 20th Anniv of People's Republic (1st issue). T **434** and similar horiz design. P 12×12½.

1467	60g. red, ochre, blue, black and green (T **434**)	40	25
1468	60g. black, orange-yellow and red	40	25

Design:—No. 1468, Emblem composed of symbols of agriculture and industry.

See also Nos. 1497/1506.

435 European Cat

436 King Casimir the Great (founder)

(Des J. Grabiański. Litho)

1964 (30 Apr). Domestic Cats. T **435** and similar designs. P 12½.

1469	30g. black and greenish yellow	25	15
1470	40g. light grey-green, pink, black and orange	35	15
1471	50g. black, turquoise-green and yellow	40	20
1472	60g. multicoloured	45	20
1473	90g. multicoloured	60	25
1474	1z.35 yellow-ochre, yellow-orange, black and emerald	65	35
1475	1z.55 sepia, light blue, black and ultramarine	80	40
1476	2z.50 greenish yellow, black and violet	1·00	65
1477	3z.40 grey-violet, orange, black and rose-carmine	5·25	1·60
1478	6z.50 black, yellow-green, cerise and violet	9·00	4·00
1469/1478 Set of 10		17·00	7·25

Cats: Vert (European)—40g., 2z.50, 6z.50 (Siamese)—50g. (Persian)—3z.40. Horiz (European)—60g., 1z.55 (Persian)—90g. 1z.35.

(Des S. Malecki. Eng E. Tirdiszek (1479), J. Miller (1480), E. Konecki (1481), Z. Kowalski (1482), B. Kowalska (1483). Recess)

1964 (5 May). 600th Anniv of Jagiellonian University, Cracow. T **436** and similar designs. P 11½ (2z.50) or 11×11½ (others).

1479	40g. purple (T **436**)	25	15
1480	40g. deep green	25	15
1481	60g. Violet	40	20

1482	60g. deep violet-blue	80	25
1483	2z.50 sepia	90	40
1479/1483 Set of 5		2·30	1·00

Portraits:—No. 1480, Hugo Kollątaj (educationist and politician); No. 1481, Jan Dlugosz (geographer and historian); No. 1482, Copernicus (astronomer); No. 1483, (36×37 mm), King Wladyslaw Jagiello and Queen Jadwiga.

437 Northern Lapwing
(*Vanellus vanellus*)

(Des J. Desselberger. Photo)

1964 (5 June). Birds. Designs as T **437**. Multicoloured. P 11½.

1484	30g. Type **437**	20	15
1485	40g. Bluethroat (*Luscinia svecica*)	25	15
	a. Blue omitted	£200	
1486	50g. Black-tailed Godwit (*Limosa limosa*)	35	20
1487	60g. Osprey (*Pandion haliaëtus*)	40	25
1488	90g. Grey Heron (*Ardea cinerea*)	65	25
1489	1z.35 Little Gull (*Larus minutus*)	90	35
1490	1z.55 Common Shoveler (*Spatula clypeata*)	90	40
1491	5z.60 Black-throated Diver (*Gavia arctica*)	2·20	90
1492	6z.50 Great Crested Grebe (*Podiceps cristatus*)	3·50	1·60
1484/1492 Set of 9		8·50	3·75

Nos. 1487/9 are vert (35×48 mm), the rest as T **437**.

438 Red Flag on Brick Wall

(Des A. Heidrich (1493), R. Dudzicki (others). Litho)

1964 (15 June). Fourth Polish United Workers' Party Congress, Warsaw. T **438** and similar horiz designs. Multicoloured. P 11.

1493	60g. Type **438**	40	25
	a. Black omitted	£160	
1494	60g. Beribboned hammer	40	25
1495	60g. Hands reaching for Red Flag	40	25
1496	60g. Hammer and corn emblems	40	25
1493/1496 Set of 4		1·40	90

439 Factory and Cogwheel
440 Gdańsk Shipyard

(Des T. Michaluk. Photo (1497/1500). Des S. Malecki (others).
Eng E. Tirdiszek (1501), J. Miller (1502), B. Kowalska (1503), Z. Kowalski (1504). E. Konecki (1505/6). Recess and photo)

1964 (21 July). 20th Anniv of People's Republic (2nd issue). Various designs. P 11.

*(a) As T **439***

1497	60g. black and blue (T **439**)	40	25
1498	60g. black and green	40	25
1499	60g. red and orange	40	25
1500	60g. ultramarine and grey	40	25

Designs: Vert—No. 1498, Tractor and ear of wheat; No. 1499, Mask and symbols of the arts; No. 1500, Atomic symbol and book.

*(b) As T **440***

1501	60g. ultramarine and turquoise-green	40	25
1502	60g. reddish violet and magenta	40	25
1503	60g. sepia and slate-violet	40	25
1504	60g. bronze-green and green	40	25
1505	60g. reddish purple and salmon-red	40	25
1506	60g. sepia and olive-yellow	40	25
1497/1506 Set of 10		3·50	2·30

Designs: Horiz—No. 1501, T **440**; 1502, Lenin Foundry. Nowa Huta; 1503, Cement works, Chelm; 1504, Turoszów power station; 1505, Petro-chemical plant, Plock; 1505, Tarnobrzeg sulphur mine.

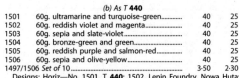

441 Battle Scene
442 Relay-racing

(Des R. Dudzicki. Litho)

1964 (1 Aug). 20th Anniv of Warsaw Insurrection. P 12½×12.

1507	**441**	60g. multicoloured	40	25

(Des J. Korolkiewicz and J. Jaworowski (**MS**1515b). Litho)

1964. Olympic Games, Tokyo.

*(a) T **442** and similar designs. Multicoloured. P 11×11½ (5z.60, 6z.50) or 11½ (others) (25 Aug)*

1508	20g. Triple-jumping	15	15
1509	40g. Rowing	20	15
1510	60g. Weightlifting	25	20
1511	90g. Type **442**	35	25
1512	1z. Boxing	40	25
1513	2z.50 Football	65	40
1514	5z.60 Highjumping (women)	2·00	65
1515	6z.50 High-diving	2·75	90
1508/1515 Set of 8		6·00	2·75
MS1515a 83×111 mm. Nos. 1514/5 (two of each) (31 Aug)		70·00	65·00

Sizes: Diamond—20g. to 60g.; Square—90g. to 2z.50: Vert (23×36 mm) 5z.60, 6z.50.

(b) Sheet 79×106 mm containing four diamond-shaped stamps. Multicoloured. Imperf (31 Aug)

MS1515b 2z.50 Rifle-shooting; 2z.50 Canoeing; 5z. Fencing; 5z. Basketball	5·25	2·75

443 Congress Emblem
444 Hand holding Hammer

(Des T. Michaluk. Litho)

1964 (7 Sept). 15th International Astronautical Congress, Warsaw. P 13×12.

1516	**443**	2z.50 black and bright violet	90	40

(Des F. Winiarski. Litho)

1964 (21 Sept). Third Congress of Fighters for Freedom and Democracy Association, Warsaw. P 11×11½.

1517	**444**	60g. red, black and blue-green	40	25

445 S. Żeromski

(Des M. Żeromska. Photo)

1964 (21 Sept). Birth Centenary of Stefan Żeromski (writer).
P 12½×13.
1518 **445** 60g. olive-brown 40 25

446 Globe and Red Flag   **447** 18th-Century Stage Coach (after J. Brodowski)

(Des J. Desselberger. Photo)

1964 (28 Sept). Centenary of "First International". P 12½.
1519 **446** 60g. black and orange-red 40 25

(Des A. Heidrich. Eng B. Kowalska. Recess)

1964 (9 Oct). Stamp Day. P 11½.
1520 **447** 60g. green 40 25
1521 60g. bistre-brown 40 25

448 Eleanor Roosevelt   **449** Battle of Studzianki (after S. Żółtowski)

(Des A. Heidrich. Eng E. Konecki. Recess)

1964 (10 Oct). 80th Birth Anniv of Eleanor Roosevelt. P 12½×13.
1522 **448** 2z.50 sepia 65 40

(Des S. Malecki. Eng J. Miller (1523), E. Konecki (1524), E. Tirdiszek (1525, 1527), Z. Kowalski (1526). Recess)

1964 (16 Nov). "Poland's Struggle" (World War II) (1st issue). T **449** and similar designs. P 11×11½ (horiz) or 11½×11 (vert).
1523 40g. black 25 20
1524 40g. slate-violet 25 20
1525 60g. deep blue 40 25
1526 60g. deep bluish green 40 25
1527 60g. bronze-green (T **449**) 40 25
1523/1527 Set of 5 .... 1·50 1·00
Designs: Vert—No. 1523, Virtuti Militari Cross; 1524, Westerplatte Memorial, Gdańsk; 1525, Bydgoszcz Memorial. Horiz—1526. Soldiers crossing the Oder (after S. Żółtowski).
Printed in sheets of 50 stamps and 20 inscribed labels or 56 stamps and 14 labels.
See also Nos. 1610/12.

449a W. Komarov   **450** Cyclamen

(Des A. Heidrich. Litho)

1964 (20 Nov). Russian Three-manned Space Flight. Sheet 114×63 mm depicting crew. P 11½.
MS1527a 60g. black and red (T **449a**); 60g. black and green (Feoktistov); 60g. black and blue (Yegorov) ...... 2·50 1·30

(Des A. Balcerzak. Photo)

1964 (30 Nov). Garden Flowers. T **450** and similar designs. Multicoloured. P 11½ (20g. to 90g.) or 13×12 (others).
1528 20g. Type **450** 15 15
1529 30g. Freesia 15 15
1530 40g. Rose 20 15
1531 50g. Peony 25 15
1532 60g. Lily 35 20
1533 90g. Poppy 35 20
1534 1z.35 Tulip 40 25
1535 1z.50 Narcissus .... 1·30 65
1536 1z.55 Begonia 40 25
1537 2z.50 Carnation .... 1·40 40
1538 3z.40 Iris .... 2·00 65
1539 5z.60 Japanese Camelia .... 3·50 1·60
1528/1539 Set of 12 .... 9·50 4·25
Sizes: As T **450**—20g. to 90g.; Vert (26½×37 mm)—others.
Nos. 1528/39 were also available in individual sheets of ten stamps (price for set of 12 sheets £160).

451 Spacecraft of the Future   **452** "Siren" of Warsaw

(Des T. Michaluk. Litho)

1964 (30 Dec). Space Research. T **451** and similar designs. Multicoloured. P 13×12.
1540 20g. Type **451** 15 15
1541 30g. Launching rocket 20 15
1542 40g. Dog "Laika" and rocket 25 20
1543 60g. "Lunik 3" and Moon 35 25
1544 1z.55 Satellite 40 35
1545 2z.50 "Elektron 2" 80 40
1546 5z.60 "Mars I" .... 2·00 80
1547 6z.50 +2z. Gagarin seated in capsule .... 2·50 1·40
1540/1547 Set of 8 .... 6·00 3·25

(Des T. Michaluk. Eng E. Konecki. Recess)

1965 (15 Jan). 20th Anniv of Liberation of Warsaw. P 11×11½.
1548 **452** 60g. grey-green 40 25

453 Edaphosaurus

(Des A. Heidrich. Litho)

1965 (5 Mar). Prehistoric Animals (1st series). T **453** and similar designs. Multicoloured. P 12½.
1549 20g. Type **453** 20 15
1550 30g. Cryptocleidus (vert) 25 15
1551 40g. Brontosaurus 25 20
1552 60g. Mesosaurus (vert) 25 20
1553 90g. Stegosaurus 35 25
    a. Error. Missing face value
1554 1z.15 Brachiosaurus (vert) 40 25
    a. Error. Missing face value
1555 1z.35 Styracosaurus 40 35
1556 3z.40 Corythosaurus (vert) .... 1·60 50
1557 5z.60 Rhamphorhynchus (vert) .... 2·75 90
1558 6z.50 Tyrannosaurus .... 4·50 1·30
1549/1558 Set of 10 .... 9·75 3·75
See also Nos. 1639/47.
Nos. 1549/58 were also aavailable in individual sheetlets of ten stamps (price for set of 10 sheets £200).

454 Petro-chemical Works, Plock, and Polish and Soviet Flags

(Des S. Malecki. Litho)

1965 (21 Apr). 20th Anniv of Polish–Soviet Friendship Treaty. T **454** and similar design. P 13×12 (No. 1559) or 13×12½ (No. 1560).
1559   60g. carmine, black, yellow and grey-green .   40   25
1560   60g. black, carmine, red and yellow-olive......   40   25
   Design: Vert (27×38½ mm)—No. 1559, Seal.

455 Polish Eagle and Civic Arms   **456** Dove of Peace

(Des T. Michaluk. Eng E. Konecki. Recess)

1965 (8 May). 20th Anniv of Return of Western and Northern Territories to Poland. P 11½.
1561   **455**   60g. carmine-red...................   40   25

(Des S. Jasiński. Litho)

1965 (8 May). 20th Anniv of Victory. P 12×12½.
1562   **456**   60g. red and black.....................   40   25

457 I.T.U. Emblem   **458** Clover-leaf Emblem and The Friend of the People (journal)

(Des S. Malecki. Litho)

1965 (17 May). Centenary of International Telecommunications Union. P 13×12.
1563   **457**   2z.50 black, reddish violet and new blue........................   1·00   40

(Des A. Kalczyńska. Litho)

1965 (5 June). 70th Anniv of Peasant Movement. T **458** and similar design. P 11×11½ (40g.) or 11½×11 (60g.).
1564   40g. green, black, drab and light bluish violet........................   25   20
1565   60g. yellow-orange, ultramarine, black and bluish green........................   40   25
   Design: Horiz—60g. Ears of corn and industrial plant.

459 "Dragon" Class Yachts   **460** Marx and Lenin

(Des J. Jaworowski and R. Dudzicki (15z.). Litho)

1965 (14 June). World Finn Class Sailing Championships, Gdynia. T **459** and similar designs. Multicoloured. P 12 or 11 (15z.).
1566   30g. Type 459   15   15
1567   40g. "5.5 m" class   20   15
1568   50g. "Finn" dinghies (horiz)...........   25   20
1569   60g. "V" dinghies (horiz).................   35   25
1570   1z.35 "Cadet" dinghies (horiz)......   40   35
1571   4z. "Star" yachts.............................   1·60   65
1572   5z.60 "Flying Dutchman" class.......   2·75   1·00

1573   6z.50 "Amethyst" dinghies (horiz) ....   4·25   1·40
1566/1573 Set of 8...............................   9·00   3·75
MS1573a 79×59 mm 15z. "Finn" dinghies.........................   4·50   2·50
   Nos. 1566/73 were also available in individual sheetlets of ten stamps (price for set of 8 sheets £225).

(Des J. Desselberger. Eng E. Konecki. Recess and photo)

1965 (14 June). Postal Ministers' Congress, Peking. P 11½×11.
1574   **460**   60g. black/red.............................   40   25

461 17th-Century Arms of Warsaw   **462** "Nike" Memorial and Old Warsaw Seal

(Des Cz. Kaczmarczyk. Eng E. Konecki (5g.), B. Kowalska (10g., 2z.50), E. Tirdiszek (20g., 60g.), J. Miller (40g., 1z.55), Z. Kowalski (1z.50). Recess. Des S. Malecki. Eng E. Konecki (3z.40). Recess and photo)

1965 (21 July). 700th Anniv of Warsaw. T **461** and similar designs and T **462**. P 11½×12 (5, 10g.) or 12×11½ (others).
1575   5g. carmine   15   15
   a. Perf 12×12½.............................   15   15
1576   10g. myrtle green......................   15   15
   a. Perf 12×12½.............................   15   15
1577   20g. deep blue..........................   20   15
   a. Perf 12½×12.............................   20   15
1578   40g. red-brown.........................   25   15
   a. Perf 12½×12.............................   25   15
1579   60g. orange-red........................   25   20
   a. Perf 12½×12.............................   25   20
1580   1z.50 black...............................   35   25
   a. Perf 12½×12.............................   35   25
1581   1z.55 greenish blue..................   40   35
   a. Perf 12½×12.............................   40   35
1582   2z.50 reddish purple................   80   40
   a. Perf 12½×12.............................   80   40
1575/1582 Set of 8...............................   2·30   1·60
MS1583 51×62 mm 3z.40 black and bistre................   2·00   1·20
   Designs: Vert—10g. 13th-century antiquities. Horiz—20g. Tombstone of last Masovian dukes; 40g. Old Town Hall; 60g. Barbican; 1z.50 Arsenal; 1z.55 National Theatre; 2z.50 Staszic Palace; 3z.40 T **462**.

463 I.Q.S.Y. Emblem   **464** Odontoglossum grande

(Des T. Michaluk. Litho)

1965 (9 Aug). International Quiet Sun Year. T **463** and similar designs. Multicoloured; background colours given. P 11½.
1584   60g. ultramarine......................   40   20
1585   60g. bluish violet......................   40   20
1586   2z.50 red.................................   65   25
1587   2z.50 brown-red.......................   65   25
1588   3z.40 orange............................   1·00   40
1589   3z.40 greyish olive....................   1·00   40
1584/1589 Set of 6...............................   3·75   1·50
   Designs:—2z.50 Solar scanner; 3z.40 Solar System.

(Des G. Dokalski. Photo)

1965 (6 Sept). Orchids. T **464** and similar vert designs. Multicoloured. P 13×12.

1590	20g. Type **464**	15	15
1591	30g. Cypripedium hibridum	20	15
1592	40g. Lycaste skinneri	25	20
1593	50g. Cattleya warszewicza	35	25
1594	60g. Vanda sanderiana	40	25
1595	1z.35 Cypripedium hibridum (different)	65	40
1596	4z. Sobralia	2·00	65
1597	5z.60 Disa grandiflora	2·20	80
1598	6z.50 Cattleya labiata	4·00	2·20
1590/1598 Set of 9		9·25	4·50

Nos. 1590/8 were also available in individual sheetlets of ten stamps (*price for set of 9 sheets £130*).

465 Weightlifting

466 "The Post Coach"
(after P. Michalowski)

(Des S. Malecki. Photo)

1965 (8 Oct). Olympic Games, Tokyo. Polish Medal Winners. T **465** and similar vert designs. Multicoloured with backgrounds of bronze (7z.10), silver (50g., 90g.) or gold (others), according to medals. P 13×12.

1599	30g. Type **465**	15	15
1600	40g. Boxing	20	15
1601	50g. Relay-racing	25	20
1602	60g. Fencing	35	25
1603	90g. Hurdling (women's 80-m)	40	35
1604	3z.40 Relay-racing (women's)	1·00	40
1605	6z.50 "Longjump"	2·10	90
1606	7z.10 Volleyball (women's)	2·50	1·30
1599/1606 Set of 8		6·25	3·25

Nos. 1599/1606 were each issued in sheets of eight, two panes of four being divided by two *se-tenant* labels showing the reverse and obverse of the medals (price for each sheet £70).

Nos. 1599/1606 were also available in individual sheetlets of ten stamps (*price for set of 8 sheets £70*).

(Des A. Balcerzak. Eng B. Kowalska (60g.), E. Tirdiszek (2z.50). Recess)

1965 (9 Oct). Stamp Day. T **466** and similar horiz design. P 11×11½.

1607	60g. brown	40	25
1608	2z.50 bronze-green	65	40

Design:—2z.50 "Coach about to leave" (after P. Michalowski).

Nos. 1607/8 were each in sheets of 50 with attached *se-tenant* labels inscr "DZIEN ZNACZKA 1965 R."

467 UN Emblem

468 Memorial, Holy
Cross Mountains

(Des A. Kalczyńska. Litho)

1966 (24 Oct). 20th Anniv of UNO. P 13×12.

1609	**467** 2z.50 bright blue	65	40

(Des S. Malecki. Eng E. Tirdiszek (1610), B. Kowalska (1611), J. Miller (1612). Recess)

1965 (29 Nov). "Poland's Struggle" (World War II) (2nd issue). T **468** and similar designs. P 11×11½ (No. 1612) or 11½×11 (others).

1610	**468** 60g. deep brown	40	25
1611	– 60g. bronze-green	40	25
1612	– 60g. blackish brown	40	25
1610/1612 Set of 3		1·10	70

Designs: Vert—No. 1611, Memorial, Plaszow. Horiz—1612, Memorial, Chelm-on-Ner.

Nos. 1610/11 were each printed in sheets of 56 stamps and 14 inscribed labels, and No. 1612 in sheets of 50 stamps and 20 labels.

469 Wolf

(Des J. Desselberger. Photo)

1965 (30 Nov). Forest Animals. T **469** and similar designs. Multicoloured. P 11½.

1613	20g. Type **469**	20	15
1614	30g. Lynx	25	15
1615	40g. Red Fox	25	20
1616	50g. Eurasian Badger	35	25
1617	60g. Brown Bear	40	25
1618	1z.50 Wild Boar	65	35
1619	2z.50 Red Deer	90	40
1620	5z.60 European Bison	2·00	50
1621	7z.10 Elk	4·00	90
1613/1621 Set of 9		8·00	2·75

470 Gig

(Des J. Miller. Litho)

1965 (30 Dec). Horse-drawn Carriages in Lancut Museum. T **470** and similar horiz designs. Multicoloured. P 11.

1622	20g. Type **470**	20	15
1623	40g. Coupe	25	15
1624	50g. Ladies' "basket" (trap)	25	15
1625	60g. "Vis-à-vis"	25	20
1626	90g. Cab	35	25
1627	1z.15 Berlinka	40	35
1628	2z.50 Hunting brake	1·00	40
1629	6z.50 Barouche	2·75	90
1630	7z.10 English brake	4·25	2·20
1622/1630 Set of 9		8·75	4·25

Nos. 1627/9 are 77×22 mm and No. 1630 is 10×22 mm.

471 Congress Emblem and Industrial Products

(Des A. Heidrich. Litho)

1966 (10 Feb). Fifth Polish Technicians Congress. Katowice. P 11.

1631	**471** 60g. multicoloured	40	25

No. 1631 was printed in sheets of 20 stamps and 20 *se-tenant* commemorative labels.

(Des A. Heidrich. Litho)

1966 (10 Feb–21 May). 20th Anniv of Industrial Nationalisation. Designs similar to T **471**. Multicoloured. P 11.

1632	60g. Pithead gear (10.2)	40	25
1633	60g. Henryk Jedza (freighter)	40	25
1634	60g. Petrochemical works, Plock	40	25
1635	60g. Combine-harvester	40	25
1636	60g. Class EN 57 electric train	40	25
1637	60g. Exhibition Hall, 35th Poznań Fair	40	25
1638	60g. Crane	40	25
1632/1638 Set of 7		2·50	1·60

Nos. 1632 and 1638 are vertical. Each stamp has *se-tenant* commemorative label.

(Des A. Heidrich. Litho)

1966 (5 Mar). Prehistoric Animals (2nd series). Designs as T **453**. Multicoloured. P 12½.

1639	20g. Terror fish (Dinichthys) (fossil)	20	15

1640	30g. Lobefin (Eusthenopteron) (fossil)	25	15
1641	40g. Ichthyostega	35	20
1642	50g. Mastodonsaurus	40	25
1643	60g. Cynognathus	65	35
1644	2z.50 Archaeopteryx (vert)	90	35
1645	3z.40 Brontotherium	1·30	40
1646	6z.50 Machairodus	2·75	90
1647	7z.10 Mammuthus	4·50	1·60
1639/1647	Set of 9	10·00	4·00

472 H. Sienkiewicz (novelist)

473 Footballers (Montevideo, 1930)

475 Soldier with Flag and Dove of Peace

476 Women's Relay-racing

477 Long-distance Running

(Des T. Michaluk. Eng E. Konecki. Typo, litho and recess)

1966 (9 May). 21st Anniv of Victory Day. P 11×11½.

1658	**475**	60g. red and black/silver	40	25

(Des S. Malecki. Litho)

1966 (18 June). Eighth European Athletic Championships, Budapest. T **476** and similar designs. Multicoloured. P 11½×11 (vert) or 11×11½ (horiz).

1659	20g. Runner starting race	15	15
1660	40g. Type **476**	20	15
1661	60g. Throwing the javelin	25	20
1662	90g. Women's hurdles	35	25
1663	1z.35 Throwing the discus	40	35
1664	3z.40 Finish of race	1·20	40
1665	6z.50 Throwing the hammer	2·10	80
1666	7z.10 High-jumping	2·30	1·20
1659/1666	Set of 8	6·25	3·25
MS1667	**477** 110×66 mm. 5z. Imperf	4·00	2·00

The 20g., 60g., 1z.35 and 6z.50 are vert.

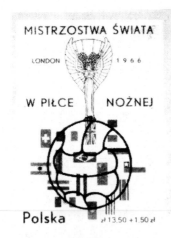

474 Jules Rimet Cup, Flags and Football

(Des T. Michaluk. Eng E. Tirdiszek. Recess)

1966 (30 Mar). 50th Death Anniv of Henryk Sienkiewicz. P 11½×11.

1648	**472**	60g. blackish brown/light buff	40	25

(Des J. Jaworowski. Litho)

1966 (6 May). World Cup Football Championship.

(a) T **473** and similar vert designs showing football scenes representing World Cup finals. Multicoloured. P 13×12

1649	20g. Type **473**	15	15
1650	40g. Rome, 1934	20	15
1651	60g. Paris, 1938	25	20
1652	90g. Rio de Janeiro, 1950	40	25
1653	1z.50 Berne, 1954	1·60	40
1654	3z.40 Stockholm, 1958	1·70	50
1655	6z.50 Santiago, 1962	2·50	1·30
1656	7z.10 "London", 1966 (elimination match Glasgow 1965)	4·00	2·50
1649/1656	Set of 8	9·75	5·00

(b) Sheet 61×81 mm. Litho. Multicoloured. Imperf

MS1657	**474**	13z.50+1z.50	6·50	3·25

Nos. 1649/50 were also available in individual sheetlets of ten stamps (price for set of 8 sheets £160).

478 White Eagle

479 Flowers and Produce

(Des F. Winiarski. Photo and embossed)

1966 (21 July). Polish Millenary (1st issue). Each printed in red and black on gold. P 12½×12.

1668	60g. Type **478**	40	25
	a. Pair. Nos. 1668/9	85	55
1669	60g. Polish flag	40	25
1670	2z.50 Type **478**	65	40
	a. Pair. Nos. 1670/1	1·40	85
1671	2z.50 Polish flag	65	40
1668/1671	Set of 4	1·90	1·20

Nos. 1668/9 and 1670/1 were issued respectively in se-tenant pairs within sheets of ten stamps.

See also Nos. 1717/18.

(Des H. Matuszewska. Photo)

1966 (15 Aug). Harvest Festival. T **479** and similar designs. Multicoloured. P 11.

1672	40g. Type **479**	50	25
1673	60g. Woman and loaf	65	40
	a. Silver (value and bottom inscr) omitted	£160	

1674	3z.40 Festival bouquet	1·30	80
1672/1674	Set of 3	2·20	1·30

The 60g. is vert as Type **479** and the 3z.40 is 49×48 mm.

480 Chrysanthemum

481 Tourist Map

(Des S. Malecki. Photo)

1966 (1 Sept). Flowers. T **480** and similar designs. Multicoloured. P 11½.

1675	10g. Type **480**	15	15
1676	20g. Poinsettia	20	15
1677	30g. Centaury	25	20
1678	40g. Rose	35	25
1679	60g. Zinnia	40	35
1680	90g. Nasturtium	60	40
1681	5z.60 Dahlia	2·00	65
1682	6z.50 Sunflower	2·50	90
1683	7z.10 Magnolia	4·00	1·00
1675/1683	Set of 9	9·50	3·75

(Des T. Michaluk. Eng J. Miller (10g., 60g.—No. 1688,
1z.35), B. Kowalska (20g., 1z.15), Z Kowalski (40g., 2z.), E. Tirdiszek
(60g.—No. 1687), B. Brandt (1z.55). Recess)

1966 (15 Sept). Tourism. T **481** and similar horiz designs. P 13×12½.

1684	10g. rose	15	15
	a. Perf 11½×12	15	15
1685	20g. drab	15	15
	a. Perf 11½×12	15	15
1686	40g. slate-blue	15	15
	a. Perf 11½×12	15	15
1687	60g. brown	20	15
	a. Perf 11½×12	20	15
1688	60g. black	20	15
	a. Perf 11½×12	20	15
1689	1z.15 deep green	25	20
	a. Perf 11½×12	25	20
1690	1z.35 vermilion	35	25
	a. Perf 11½×12	35	25
1691	1z.55 deep reddish violet	40	25
	a. Perf 11½×12	40	25
1692	2z. slate-green	80	40
	a. Perf 11½×12	80	40
1684/1692	Set of 9	2·40	1·70
1684a/1692a	Set of 9	2·40	1·70

Designs:—20g. Hela Lighthouse; 40g. Yacht; 60g.
(No. 1687), Poniatowski Bridge, Warsaw; 60g. (No. 1688), Mining
Academy, Kielce; 1z.15 Dunajec Gorge; 1z.35 Old oaks, Rogalin; 1z.55
Silesian Planetarium; 2z. *Batory* (liner).

482 Roman Capital

(Des R. Dudzicki. Eng E. Tirdiszek. Recess and photo)

1966 (7 Oct). Polish Culture Congress. P 11½.

1693	**482**	60g. cerise and deep chocolate	40	25

483 Stable-man with Percherons

(Des J. Miklaszewski (after paintings by P. Michalowski). Eng E. Konecki
(60g.), E. Tirdiszek (2z.50). Recess)

1966 (8 Oct). Stamp Day. T **483** and similar horiz design. P 11×12.

1694	60g. sepia	40	25

1695	2z.50 myrtle-green	80	40

Design:—2z.50 Stable-men with horses and dogs.

484 Soldier in Action

485 Woodland Birds

(Des A. Heidrich. Litho)

1966 (20 Oct). 30th Anniv of Jaroslav Dąbrowski Brigade in Spain.
P 11×11½.

1696	**484**	60g. black, olive-green and red	40	25

(Des T. Michaluk (10g.), J. Desselberger (others). Photo)

1966 (17 Nov). Woodland Birds. T **485** and similar square designs.
Multicoloured. P 11½.

1697	10g. Type **485**	30	15
1698	20g. Green Woodpecker (*Picus viridis*)	30	15
1699	30g. Jay (*Garrulus glandarius*)	30	15
1700	40g. Golden Oriole (*Oriolus oriolus*)	35	20
1701	60g. Hoopoe (*Upupa epops*)	40	25
1702	2z.50 Common Redstart (*Phoenicurus phoenicurus*)	90	50
1703	4z. Spruce Siskin (*Carduelis spinus*)	2·30	65
1704	6z.50 Chaffinch (*Fringilla coelebs*)	2·75	1·30
1705	7z.10 Great Tit (*Parus major*)	3·50	1·40
1697/1705	Set of 9	10·00	4·25

Type **485** shows the species depicted on Nos. 1698/1705.

486 Ram (ritual statuette)

487 "Vostok 1"

(Des K. Tarkowska. Eng E. Konecki (1706), Z. Kowalski
(1707), B. Kowalska (1708). Recess)

1966 (10 Dec). Polish Archaeological Research. T **486** and similar
designs. P 11½×11 (No. 1708) or 11×11½ (others).

1706	60g. slate-blue	40	25
1707	60g. myrtle-green	40	25
1708	60g. brown	40	25
1706/1708	Set of 3	1·10	70

Designs: Vert—No. 1706, T **486**; 1707, Plan of Biskupin settlement.
Horiz—1708, Brass implements and ornaments.

(Des T. Michaluk. Litho)

1966 (20 Dec). Space Research. T **487** and similar vert designs
showing spacecraft. Multicoloured. P 11½×11.

1709	20g. Type **487**	15	15
1710	40g. "Gemini"	20	15
1711	60g. "Ariel 2"	20	15
1712	1z.35 "Proton 1"	40	20
1713	1z.50 "FR 1"	65	25
1714	3z.40 "Alouette"	90	35
1715	6z.50 "San Marco 1"	2·50	40
1716	7z.10 "Luna 9"	3·00	80
1709/1716	Set of 8	7·25	2·20

488 Polish Eagle and Hammer

(Des S. Malecki. Litho)

1966 (20 Dec). Polish Millenary (2nd issue). T **488** and similar horiz design. P 11.

1717	40g. purple-brown, lilac and light red............	25	20
1718	60g. purple-brown, sage-green and light red...	40	25

Design:—60g. Polish eagle and agricultural and industrial symbols.

489 Dressage

(Des B. Kamiński. Photo)

1967 (25 Feb). 150th Anniv of Racehorse Breeding in Poland. T **489** and similar horiz designs. Multicoloured. P 12½.

1719	10g. Type **489**	20	15
1720	20g. Cross-country racing	25	20
1721	40g. Horse-jumping	35	25
1722	60g. Jumping fence in open country........	50	35
1723	90g. Horse-trotting................................	65	40
1724	5z.90 Playing polo.................................	2·00	90
1725	6z.60 Stallion "Ofir"...............................	3·25	1·30
1726	7z. Stallion "Skoworenk"........................	5·25	1·60
1719/1726 Set of 8..		11·00	4·75

490 Black-wedged Butterflyfish (*Chaetodon melanotus*)

491 Auschwitz Memorial

(Des J. Desselberger. Litho)

1967 (1 Apr). Exotic Fish. T **490** and similar horiz designs. Multicoloured. P 11×11½.

1727	5g. Type **490**	15	15
1728	10g. Emperor Angelfish (*Pomacanthus imperator* juv.)	20	15
1729	40g. Racoon Butterflyfish (*Chaetodon fasciatus*)	20	15
1730	60g. Clown Triggerfish (*Balistoides conspicillum*)	25	20
1731	90g. Undulate Triggerfish (*Balistapus undulatus*)......................................	25	20
1732	1z.50 Picasso Triggerfish (*Rhinecanthus aculeatus*)	40	35
1733	4z.50 Black-finned Melon Butterflyfish (*Chaetodon melapterus*)	2·10	40
1734	6z.60 Semicircle Angelfish (*Pomacanthus semicirculatus*)	3·00	1·60
1735	7z. Saddle Butterflyfish (*Chaetodon ephippium*)	2·75	65
1727/1735 Set of 9..		8·50	3·50

(Des K. Rogaczewska. Eng E. Tirdiszek (1736, 1738), B. Kowalska (1737). Recess)

1967 (10 Apr). Polish Martyrdom and Resistance, 1939–45 (1st series). T **491** and similar designs. P 11½×11 (No. 1736) or 11×11½ (others).

1736	**491**	40g. olive-brown	40	25
1737	–	40g. black..	40	25
1738	–	40g. deep reddish purple..................	40	25
1736/1738 Set of 3......................................			1·10	70

Designs: Vert—No. 1737, Auschwitz-Monowitz Memorial; 1738, Memorial guide's emblem.

See also Nos. 1770/2, 1798/9, 1865/9.

492 Cyclists

(Des T. Michaluk. Litho)

1967 (2 May). 20th International Peace Cycle Race. P 11.

1739	**492**	60g. multicoloured.......................	40	25

493 Running

494 Socialist Symbols

(Des F. Winiarski. Litho)

1967 (24 May). Olympic Games (1968). T **493** and similar horiz designs. Multicoloured. P 11.

1740	20g. Type **493**	15	15
1741	40g. Horse-jumping................................	20	15
1742	60g. Relay-running	20	15
1743	90g. Weightlifting	25	20
1744	1z.35 Hurdling.......................................	40	25
1745	3z.40 Gymnastics	1·20	40
1746	6z.60 High-jumping................................	1·60	80
1747	7z. Boxing...	2·50	1·30
1740/1747 Set of 8...		5·75	3·00
MS1748 65×86 mm. 10z.+5z. multicoloured. Imperf....		4·50	2·50

Design: Diamond (30×30 *mm*)—10z. Kusociński winning 10,000 metres race at Olympic Games, Los Angeles, 1932.

The face value is expressed outside the "stamp" which has facsimile perforations. Nos. 1740/7 are each in sheets of eight (2×4) with intervening *se-tenant* labels showing the Olympic torch and rings.

(Des A. Heidrich. Litho)

1967 (2 June). Polish Trade Unions Congress, Warsaw. P 11.

1749	**494**	60g. multicoloured.......................	50	40

No. 1749 was issued with *se-tenant* label showing Congress emblem, both in sheets in 20 and sheets of four.

495 *Arnica montana*

496 Katowice Memorial

(Des A. Heidrich. Litho)

1967 (14 June). Protected Plants. T **495** and similar vert designs. Multicoloured. P 11½×11.

1750	40g. Type **495**	20	15
1751	60g. *Aquilegia vulgaris*.........................	25	20
1752	3z.40 *Gentiana punctata*	80	25
1753	4z.50 *Lycopodium clavatum*	90	25
1754	5z. *Iris sibirica*	1·30	40
1755	10z. *Azalea pontica*	2·50	50
1750/1755 Set of 6...		5·25	1·60

(Des R. Dudzicki. Litho)

1967 (21 July). Inauguration of Katowice Memorial. P 11½.

1756	**496**	60g. multicoloured.......................	40	25

497 Marie Curie

498 "Fifth Congress of the Deaf" (sign language)

(Des S. Malecki. Eng J. Miller (1757), E. Tirdiszek (1758), B. Kowalska (1759). Recess)

1967 (1 Aug). Birth Centenary of Marie Curie. T **497** and similar vert designs. P 11½×11.

1757	**497**	60g. lake	40	25
1758	–	60g. sepia.....................................	40	25

1759	– 60g. violet		40	25
1757/1759	*Set of 3*		1·10	70

Designs:—No. 1758, Marie Curie's Nobel Prize diploma; No. 1759, Statue of Marie Curie, Warsaw.

(Des Cz. Kaczmarczyk. Litho)

1987 (1 Aug). Fifth World Federation of the Deaf Congress, Warsaw. P 11×12.

1760	**498**	60g. black and new blue	40	25

499 Bouquet   **500** "Wilanów Palace" (from painting by W. Kasprzycki)

(Des T. Michaluk. Photo)

1967 (5 Sept). Flowers of the Meadow. T **499** and similar square designs. Multicoloured. P 11½.

1761	20g. Type **499**	20	15
1762	40g. Red Poppy	20	15
1763	60g. Field Bindweed	20	20
1764	90g. Wild Pansy	25	20
1765	1z.15 Tansy	40	25
1766	2z.50 Corn Cockle	65	40
1767	3z.40 Field Scabious	1·20	60
1768	4z.50 Scarlet Pimpernel	3·25	65
1769	7z.90 Chicory	3·50	1·30
1761/1769	*Set of 9*	8·75	3·50

(Des K. Rogaczewska. Eng B. Kowalska (1770), J. Miller (1771), E. Tirdiszek (1772). Recess)

1967 (9 Oct). Polish Martyrdom and Resistance, 1939–45 (2nd series). Designs as T **491**. P 11½×11 (No. 1770) or 11×11½ (others).

1770	40g. ultramarine	35	25
1771	40g. bronze green	35	25
1772	40g. black	35	25
1770/1772	*Set of 3*	95	70

Designs: Horiz—No. 1770, Stutthof Memorial. Vert—1771, Walcz Memorial; 1772, Lódź-Radogoszcz Memorial.

(Des S. Malecki. Eng J. Miller. Recess and photo)

1967 (9 Oct). Stamp Day. P 11½.

1773	**500**	60g. olive-brown and pale blue	40	35

501 *Aurora* (Russian Cruiser)

(Des K. Tarkowska. Litho)

1967 (9 Oct). 50th Anniv of October Revolution. T **501** and similar horiz designs. All in black, grey and brown-red. P 11.

1774	60g. Type **501**	40	35
1775	60g. Lenin	40	35
1776	60g. "Luna 10"	40	35
1774/1776	*Set of 3*	1·10	95

502 *Inachis io* (*Vanessa io*)   **503** Kościuszko

(Des J. Desselberger. Litho)

1967 (14 Oct). Butterflies. T **502** and similar square designs. Multicoloured. P 11½.

1777	10g. Type **502**	20	15

1778	20g. *Papilio machaon*	25	20
1779	40g. *Aglais urticae* (*Vanessa urticae*)	35	25
1780	60g. *Nymphalis antiopa* (*Vanessa antiopa*)	40	25
1781	2z. *Apatura iris*	50	30
1782	2z.50 *Vanessa atlanta* (*Pyrameis atalanta*)	65	35
1783	3z.40 *Colias hyale*	80	40
1784	4z.50 *Melanargia galathea*	4·00	1·30
1785	7z.90 *Maculinea arion*	4·25	1·60
1777/1785	*Set of 9*	10·50	4·25

(Des R. Dudzicki. Eng E. Konecki. Recess and photo)

1967 (14 Oct). 150th Death Anniv of Tadeusz Kościuszko (national hero). P 12×11.

1786	**503**	60g. chocolate and light yellow-brown	40	25
1787		2z.50 myrtle-green and carmine	50	40

504 "The Lobster" (Jean de Heem)   **505** W. S. Reymont

(Des J. S. Miklaszewski. Photo)

1967 (15 Nov). Famous Paintings. T **504** and similar designs. P 11×11½ (4z.50, 6z.60) or 11½×11 (others).

1788	20g. multicoloured	25	15
1789	40g. multicoloured	35	25
1790	60g. multicoloured	40	35
1791	2z. multicoloured	80	40
1792	2z.50 multicoloured	90	60
1793	3z.40 multicoloured	1·30	65
1794	4z.50 multicoloured	2·20	1·30
1795	6z.60 multicoloured	3·25	1·60
1788/1795	*Set of 8*	8·50	4·75

Paintings from the National Museums, Warsaw and Cracow: Vert—20g. "Lady with a Weasel" (Leonardo da Vinci); 40g. "The Polish Lady" (Watteau); 60g. "Dog Fighting Heron" (A. Hondius); 2z. "Fowler Tuning Guitar" (J.-B. Greuze); 2z.50 "The Tax Collectors" (M. van Reymerswaele); 3z.40 "Daria Fiodorowna" (F. S. Rokotov). Horiz—6z.60 "Parable of the Good Samaritan" (landscape, Rembrandt).

Printed in sheets of five stamps with one stamp-size *se-tenant* label.

(Des R. Dudzicki. Litho)

1967 (12 Dec). Birth Centenary of W. S. Reymont (novelist). P 11×11½.

1796	**505**	60g. sepia, red and ochre	40	35

506 J. M. Ossoliński (medallion), Book and Flag

(Des R. Dudzicki. Litho)

1967 (12 Dec). 150th Anniv of Ossolineum Foundation. P 11.

1797	**506**	60g. yellow-brown, red, greenish blue and light blue	40	35

(Des K. Rogaczewska. Eng B. Kowalska (1798), E. Tirdiszek (1799). Recess)

1967 (28 Dec). Polish Martyrdom and Resistance, 1939–45 (3rd series). Designs as T **491**. P 11×11½ (No. 1798) or 11½×11 (1799).

1798	40g. claret	35	25
1799	40g. brown	35	25

Designs: Vert—No. 1798, Żagań Memorial. Horiz—1799, Lambinowice Memorial.

507 Ice Hockey

(Des F. Winiarski. Litho)

1968 (10 Jan). Winter Olympic Games, Grenoble. T **507** and similar horiz designs. Multicoloured. P 11×11½.

1800	40g. Type **507**	15	15
1801	60g. Downhill	20	15
1802	90g. Slalom	25	20
1803	1z.35 Speed-skating	35	25
1804	1z.55 Ski-walking	40	25
1805	2z. Tobogganing	65	40
1806	7z. Rifle-shooting on skis	1·30	80
1807	7z.90 Ski-jumping	2·50	1·00
1800/1807	Set of 8	5·25	3·00

508 "Puss in Boots"   **509** *Passiflora quadrangularis*

(Des H. Matuszewska. Litho)

1968 (15 Mar). Fairy Tales. T **508** and similar vert designs. Multicoloured. P 12½.

1808	20g. Type **508**	20	15
1809	40g. "The Raven and the Fox"	35	20
1810	60g. "Mr. Twardowski"	40	25
1811	2z. "The Fisherman and the Fish"	65	25
1812	2z.50 "Little Red Riding Hood"	80	35
1813	3z.40 "Cinderella"	1·20	40
1814	5z.50 "The Waif"	2·75	90
1815	7z. "Snow White"	3·50	1·30
1808/1815	Set of 8	8·75	3·50

(Des T. Michaluk. Litho)

1968 (15 May). Flowers. T **509** and similar square designs. Multicoloured. P 11½.

1816	10g. *Clianthus dampieri*	15	15
1817	20g. Type **509**	20	15
1818	30g. *Strelitzia reginae*	25	20
1819	40g. *Coryphanta vivipara*	30	20
	a. Error. "POISKA"	49·00	
1820	60g. *Odontonia*	35	25
1821	90g. *Protea cynaroides*	40	35
1822	4z. +2z. *Abutilon*	2·10	90
1823	8z.+4z. *Rosa polyantha*	4·50	2·10
1816/1823	Set of 8	7·50	3·75

510 "Peace" (poster   **511** Zephyr Glider SP-1127
by H. Tomaszewski)

(Des A. Heidrich. Litho)

1968 (29 May). Second International Poster Biennial, Warsaw. T **510** and similar vert design. Multicoloured. P 11½×11.

1824	60g. Type **510**	35	25
1825	2z.50 Gounod's "Faust" (poster by Jan Lenica)	50	40

(Des J. Jaworowski. Litho)

1968 (29 May). 11th World Gliding Championships, Leszno. T **511** and similar horiz designs showing gliders. Multicoloured. P 12½.

1826	60g. Type **511**	20	15
1827	90g. Stork glider SP-1135	35	25
1828	1z.50 Swallow glider SP-1050	40	35
1829	3z.40 Fly glider	90	40
1830	4z. Seal glider SP-1201	2·00	50
1831	5z.50 Pirate glider SP-250	2·30	65
1826/1831	Set of 6	5·50	2·10

512 Child with "Stamp"   **513** Part of Monument

(Des T. Michaluk. Litho)

1968 (2 July). 75 Years of Polish Philately. T **512** and similar vert design. Multicoloured. P 11½×11.

1832	60g. Type **512**	40	35
	a. Pair. Nos. 1832/3	85	75
1833	60g. Balloon over Poznań	40	35

Nos. 1832/3 were printed together *se-tenant* in sheets of 12.

(Des W. Chrucki. Eng B. Brandt. Recess and photo)

1968 (20 July). Silesian Insurrection Monument, Sosnowiec. P 11×11½.

1834	**513**	60g. black and bright purple	40	35

514 Relay-racing

(Des T. Michaluk. Litho)

1968 (2 Sept). Olympic Games, Mexico. T **514** and similar horiz designs. Multicoloured. P 11×11½ or 11½ (10z.).

1835	30g. Type **514**	15	15
1836	40g. Boxing	20	15
1837	60g. Basketball	25	20
1838	90g. Long-jumping	35	20
1839	2z.50 Throwing the javelin	40	25
1840	3z.40 Gymnastics	50	35
1841	4z. Cycling	65	40
1842	7z.90 Fencing	1·30	65
1843	10z. +5z. Torch Runner and Aztec bas-relief (56×45 *mm*)	4·00	1·30
1835/1843	Set of 9	7·00	3·25

515 "Knight on a Bay Horse"   **516** "September, 1939" (Bylina)
(P. Michalowski)

(Des A. Heidrich. Photo)

1968 (10 Oct). Polish Paintings. T **515** and similar multicoloured designs. P 11½×11 (vert) or 11×11½ (horiz).

1844	40g. Type **515**	20	15
1845	60g. "Fisherman" (L. Wyczółkowski)	25	20
1846	1z.15 "Jewish Woman with Lemons" (A. Gierymski)	35	25
1847	1z.35 "Eliza Parenska" (S. Wyspiański)	45	35
1848	1z.50 "Manifesto" (W. Weiss)	65	40
1849	4z.50 "Stanczyk" (Jan Matejko)	90	50
1850	5z. "Children's Band" (T. Makowski)	1·60	65
1851	7z. "Feast II" (Z. Waliszewski)	2·50	90
1844/1851	Set of 8	6·25	3·00

The 4z.50, 5z. and 7z. are horiz designs.
Printed in sheets of four stamps and two labels.

(Des S. Malecki. Eng E. Konecki (1852, 1854, 1860, 1861), E. Tirdiszek (1853, 1856, 1859), B. Brandt (1855), B. Kowalska (1857), J. Miller (1858). Recess, typo and photo)

1968 (12 Oct). 25th Anniv of Polish People's Army. T **516** and similar horiz designs, showing paintings. P 11½.

1852	40g. reddish violet and olive/*pale yellow*	25	20
1853	40g. deep ultramarine and reddish violet/*pale lilac*	25	20
1854	40g. olive-green and deep blue/*pale grey*	25	20
1855	40g. black and orange-brown/*pale orange*	25	20
1856	40g. purple and bronze-green/*pale green*......	25	20
1857	60g. blackish brown and ultramarine/*pale blue*	40	25
1858	60g. maroon and olive-green/*pale yellow-green*........	40	25
1859	60g. blackish olive and carmine-red/*pale pink*........	40	25
1860	60g. emerald-green and chocolate/*pale rose*	40	25
1861	60g. indigo and turquoise/*pale greenish blue*	40	25
1852/1861 *Set of 10*		3·00	2·00

Paintings and painters:—No. 1852, T **516**; 1853, "Partisans" (Maciąg); 1854 "Lenino" (Bylina); 1855, "Monte Cassino" (Boratyński); 1856, "Tanks before Warsaw" (Garwatowski); 1857, "Neisse River" (Bylina); 1858, "On the Oder" (Mackiewicz); 1859, "In Berlin" (Bylina); 1860, *"Blyskawica"* (destroyer) (Mokwa); 1861, "Pursuit" (Mikoyan Gurevich MiG-17 aircraft) (Kulisiewicz).

517 "Party Members" (F. Kowarski)

(Des F. Winiarski. Litho)

1968 (11 Nov). Fifth Polish United Workers' Party Congress, Warsaw. T **517** and similar multicoloured designs showing paintings. P 11×11½ (horiz) or 11½×11 (vert).

1862	60g. Type **517**	40	25
1863	60g. "Strike" (S. Lentz) (*vert*)	40	25
1864	60g. "Manifesto" (W. Weiss) (*vert*)......	40	25
1862/1864 *Set of 3*		1·10	70

(Des K. Rogaczewska. Eng E. Tirdiszek (1865, 1867), J. Miller (1866), B. Kowalska (1868), B. Brandt (1869). Recess)

1968 (15 Nov). Polish Martyrdom and Resistance, 1939–45 (4th series). Designs as T **491**. P 11½×11 (horiz) or 11×11½ (vert).

1865	40g. slate-grey	25	20
1866	40g. blackish brown	25	20
1867	40g. sepia	25	20
1868	40g. deep ultramarine	25	20
1869	40g. lake-brown	25	20
1865/1869 *Set of 5*........		1·10	90

Designs: Horiz—No. 1865, Tomb of Unknown Soldier, Warsaw; 1866, Partisans' Monument, Kartuzy. Vert—1867, Insurgents' Monument, Poznań; 1868, People's Guard Insurgents' Monument, Polichno; 1869, Rotunda, Zamość.

518 "Start of Hunt" (W. Kossak)

(Des S. Malecki. Litho)

1968 (20 Nov). Paintings. Hunting Scenes. T **518** and similar horiz designs. Multicoloured. P 11.

1870	20g. Type **518**	15	15
1871	40g. "Hunting with Falcon" (J. Kossak)........	20	15
1872	60g. "Wolves' Raid" (A. Wierusz-Kowalski).......	25	20
1873	1z.50 "Home-coming with a Bear" (J. Falat)	40	25
1874	2z.50 "The Fox-hunt" (T. Sutherland)........	50	35
1875	3z.40 "The Boar-hunt" (F. Snyders)........	80	40
1876	4z.50 "Hunters' Rest" (W. G. Pierov)........	2·30	80
1877	8z.50 "Hunting a Lion in Morocco" (Delacroix)........	2·50	1·00
1870/1877 *Set of 8*........		6·50	3·00

519 Maltese Terrier **520** House Sign

(Des J. Grabiański. Litho)

1969 (2 Feb). Pedigree Dogs. Multicoloured designs as T **519**. P 11½×11 (vert) or 11×11½ (horiz).

1878	20g. Type **519**	25	15
1879	40g. Wire-haired Fox-terrier (*vert*)........	40	20
1880	60g. Afghan Hound........	50	25
1881	1z.50 Rough-haired Terrier........	65	25
1882	2z.50 English Setter........	90	35
1883	3z.40 Pekinese........	1·30	40
1884	4z.50 Alsatian (*vert*)........	2·50	65
1885	8z.50 Pointer (*vert*)........	4·50	1·30
1878/1885 *Set of 8*........		10·00	3·25

(Des K. Rogaczewska. Litho)

1969 (23 Feb). Ninth Polish Democratic Party Congress. P 11½×11.

1886	**520**	60g. carmine-red, black and grey...........	40	25

521 "Dove" and Wheat-ears **522** Running

(Des K. Śliwka. Litho)

1969 (29 Mar). Fifth Congress of United Peasants' Party. P 11½.

1887	**521**	60g. multicoloured........	40	25

(Des J. Jaworowski. Litho)

1969 (25 Apr). 75th Anniversary of International Olympic Committee and 50th Anniv of Polish Olympic Committee. T **522** and similar vert designs. Multicoloured. P 11½×11.

1888	10g. Type **522**	15	15
1889	20g. Gymnastics	20	15
1890	40g. Weightlifting	25	20
1891	60g. Throwing the javelin	35	20
1892	2z.50 +50g. Throwing the discus	40	25
1893	3z.40 +1z. Running	65	35
1894	4z. +1z.50 Wrestling	1·30	40
1895	7z. +2z. Fencing........	2·00	65
1888/1895 *Set of 8*........		4·75	2·10

523 Pictorial Map of Świętokrzyski National Park

(Des A. Heidrich. Litho)

1969 (20 May). Tourism (1st series). T **523** and similar multicoloured designs. P 11.

1896	40g. Type **523**	15	15
1897	60g. Niedzica Castle (*vert*)........	20	15
1898	1z.35 Kolobrzeg Lighthouse and yacht........	25	20
1899	1z.50 Szczecin Castle and Harbour	35	25
1900	2z.50 Toruń and River Vistula........	40	35
1901	3z.40 KLodźko, Silesia (*vert*)........	65	40
1902	4z. Sulejów........	90	50
1903	4z.50 Kazimierz Dolny marketplace (*vert*)	1·00	60
1896/1903 *Set of 8*........		3·50	2·30

Nos. 1896/1903 were each issued with *se-tenant* half stamp-size labels showing either flora or arms.

See also Nos. 1981/5.

524 Route Map and *Opty*

525 Copernicus (after woodcut by T. Stimer) and Inscription

(Des A. Heidrich. Litho)

1969 (21 June). Leonid Teliga's World Voyage in Yacht *Opty*. P 11×11½.
1904	**524**	60g. multicoloured	40	35

(Des H. Chyliński. Eng Z. Kowalski (40g.), E. Konecki (60g.), B. Kowalska (2z.50). Recess and litho)

1969 (26 June). 500th Birth Anniversary of Copernicus (1973) (1st issue). T **525** and similar horiz designs. P 11½.
1905	40g. blackish brown, red and yellow	35	25
1906	60g. deep slate-blue, red and light grey-green	40	35
	a. Full point after "GR"	7·25	4·25
1907	2z.50 olive, red and light brown-purple	90	40
1905/1907 *Set of 3*		1·50	90

Designs:—60g. Copernicus (after J. Falck) and 15th-century globe; 2z.50 Copernicus (after painting by J. Matejko) and diagram of heliocentric system.

See also Nos. 1995/7, 2069/72, 2167/**MS**2171, 2213/4, 2217/2221.

526 "Memory" Flame and Badge

527 Frontier Guard and Arms

528 Coal-miner

529 Astronauts and Module on Moon

(Des T. Michaluk. Eng E. Tirdiszek. Recess, litho and typo)

1969 (19 July). Fifth National Alert of Polish Boy Scout Association. T **526** and similar vert designs. P 11×11½.
1908	60g. black, red and light blue	40	35
1909	60g. red, black and green	40	35
1910	60g. black, green and rose	40	35
1908/1910 *Set of 3*		1·10	95

Designs:—No. 1908, Type **526**; No. 1909, "Defence" eagle and badge; No. 1910, "Labour" map and badge.

(Des I. Michaluk. Litho and embossed (Nos. 1911/15). Des F. Winiarski. Litho (others))

1969 (21 July). 25th Anniv of Polish People's Republic. Multicoloured. P 11.

(a) Vert designs as T **527**
1911	60g. Type **527**	40	35
	a. Horiz strip of 5. Nos. 1911/15	2·10	
1912	60g. Łódź petro-chemical plant	40	35
1913	60g. Combine-harvester	40	35
1914	60g. Grand Theatre, Warsaw	40	35
1915	60g. Curie statue and University, Lublin	40	35

(b) Horiz designs as T **528**
1916	60g. Type **528**	40	35
	a. Horiz strip of 4. Nos. 1916/19	1·70	
1917	60g. Sulphur worker	40	35
1918	60g. Steel worker	40	35
1919	60g. Shipbuilder	40	35
1911/1919 *Set of 9*		3·25	2·75

Nos. 1911/15 and 1916/19 respectively were issued in vertical and horizontal *se-tenant* strips within their sheets.

(Des A. Balcerzak. Litho)

1969 (21 Aug). First Man on the Moon. P 12×12½.
1920	**529**	2z.50 multicoloured	1·60	90

Issued in sheets of eight stamps and two different stamp-size *se-tenant* labels.

530 "Motherhood" (S. Wyspiański)

(Des R. Dudzicki. Photo)

1969 (4 Sept). Polish Paintings. Multicoloured designs as T **530**. P 11½×11 (vert) or 11×11½ (horiz).
1921	20g. Type **530**	15	15
1922	40g. "Hamlet" (J. Malczewski)	20	15
1923	60g. "Indian Summer" (J. Chelmoński)	25	20
1924	2z. "Two Girls" (O. Boznańska) (*vert*)	35	25
1925	2z.50 The Sun of May (J. Mehoffer) (*vert*)	40	35
1926	3z.40 "Woman combing her Hair" (W. Ślewiński)	65	50
1927	5z.50 "Still Life" (J. Pankiewicz)	1·60	65
1928	7z. "Abduction of the King's Daughter" (W. Wojtkiewicz)	2·50	90
1921/1928 *Set of 8*		5·50	2·75

Issued in sheets of four stamps and two *se-tenant* labels inscribed with the artist's name.

531 "Nike" Statue

(Des K. Śliwka. Litho)

1969 (19 Sept). Fourth Congress of Fighters for Freedom and Democracy Association. P 11½×11.
1929	**531**	60g. red, black and bistre	40	35

532 Majdanek Memorial

533 Krzczonów (Lublin) Costumes

(Des K. Rogaczewska. Litho)

1969 (20 Sept). Inauguration of Majdanek Memorial. P 11.
1930	**532**	40g. black and bright mauve	35	25

(Des S. Malecki. Litho)

1969 (30 Sept). Provincial Costumes. T **533** and similar vert designs. Multicoloured. P 11½×11.
1931	40g. Type **533**	15	15
1932	60g. Łowicz (Łódź)	20	15
1933	1z.15 Rozbark (Katowice)	25	20
1934	1z.35 Lower Silesia (Wrocław)	40	25
1935	1z.50 Opoczno (Łódź)	65	35
1936	4z.50 Sącz (Cracow)	1·00	45
1937	5z. Highlanders (Cracow)	1·30	65
1938	7z. Kurpie (Warsaw)	1·80	80
1931/1938 *Set of 8*		5·25	2·75

534 "Pedestrians—
Keep Left"

535 Welding and
I.L.O. Emblem

(Des K. Śliwka. Litho)

1969 (4 Oct). Road Safety. T **534** and similar red designs.
Multicoloured. P 11.

1939	40g. Type **534**	35	20
1940	60g. "Drive Carefully" (horses on road)	40	25
1941	2z.50 "Do Not Dazzle" (cars on road at night)	50	40
1939/1941	Set of 3	1·10	75

(Des J. Desselberger. Litho)

1969 (20 Oct). 50th Anniv of International Labour Organization.
P 11×11½.

1942	**535**	2z.50 chalky blue and gold	40	35

536 "The Bell-founder"

537 "Angel"
(19th-century)

(Des J. Rapnicki and F. Winiarski. Litho)

1969 (12 Nov). Miniatures from *Behem's Code* of 1505. T **536** and
similar vert designs. Multicoloured. P 12½.

1943	40g. Type **536**	15	15
1944	60g. "The Painter"	20	15
1945	1z.35 "The Woodcarver"	25	20
1946	1z.55 "The Shoemaker"	40	25
1947	2z.50 "The Cooper"	50	35
1948	3z.40 "The Baker"	80	40
1949	4z.50 "The Tailor"	1·30	65
1950	7z. "The Bowyer"	2·20	80
1943/1950	Set of 8	5·25	2·75

(Des S. Malecki. Litho)

1969 (19 Dec). Polish Folk Sculpture. T **537** and similar vert designs.
Multicoloured. P 11½×11 (5z.50, 7z.) or 12½ (others).

1951	20g. Type **537**	15	15
1952	40g. "Sorrowful Christ" (19th-century)	20	15
1953	60g. "Sorrowful Christ" (19th-century) (different)	25	20
1954	2z. "Weeping Woman" (19th-century)	35	25
1955	2z.50 "Adam and Eve" (F. Czajkowski)	40	35
1956	3z.40 "Girl with Birds" (L. Kudla)	65	40
1957	5z.50 +1z.50 "Choir" (A. Zegadlo)	1·80	80
1958	7z. +1z.50 "Organ-grinder" (Z. Skrętowicz)	2·50	1·00
1951/1958	Set of 8	5·75	3·00

Nos. 1957/8 are larger, 25×35 mm.

538 Leopold Staff

(Des R. Dudzicki. Eng B. Kowalska (40g.), J. Miller (60g., 2z.50,
3z.40), E. Konecki (others). Recess, typo and photo)

1969 (30 Dec). Modern Polish Writers. T **538** and similar horiz
portraits. P 11×11½.

1959	40g. black, olive-green and pale sage-green	15	15
1960	60g. black, carmine-red and pale pink	20	15
1961	1z.35 black, royal blue and pale blue	25	15
1962	1z.50 black, deep bluish violet and pale lilac	35	20
1963	1z.55 black, deep emerald and pale turquoise-green	40	25
1964	2z.50 black, ultramarine and pale blue	50	35
1965	3z.40 black, red-brown and pale brown	80	40
1959/1965	Set of 7	2·40	1·50

Dcsigns:—60g. Władysław Broniewski; 1z.35 Leon Kruczkowski;
1z.50 Julian Tuwim; 1z.55 Konstanty Ildefons Galczyński; 2z.50 Maria
Dąbrownka; 3z.40 Zofia Nalkowska.

539 Nike Monument

(Des F. Bąracz. Photo)

1970 (17 Jan). 25th Anniversary of Liberation of Warsaw. P 11½.

1966	**539**	60g. multicoloured	40	35

540 Early Printing
Works and Colour Dots

541 Mallard

(Des A. Heidrich. Litho)

1970 (20 Jan). Centenary of Printers' Trade Union. P 11½×11.

1967	**540**	60g. multicoloured	40	35

(Des J. Desselberger. Litho)

1970 (28 Feb). Game Birds. T **541** and similar square designs.
Multicoloured. P 11½.

1968	40g. Type **541**	15	15
1969	60g. Common Pheasant	20	15
1970	1z.15 Eurasian Woodcock	35	20
1971	1z.35 Ruff	40	25
1972	1z.50 Wood Pigeon	50	35
1973	3z.40 Black Grouse	65	40
1974	7z. Grey Partridge	4·50	1·30
1975	8z.50 Western Capercaillie	5·25	1·70
1968/1975	Set of 8	11·00	4·00

542 Lenin at Desk

(Des K. Tarkowska. Eng J. Miller (40g.), E. Konecki (60g.), B. Brandt
(2z.50). Recess and typo)

1970 (22 Apr–10 Oct). Birth Centenary of Lenin. T **542** and similar
horiz designs. P 11.

1976	40g. deep olive-grey and brown-red	35	25
1977	60g. sepia and magenta	40	35
1978	2z.50 black and vermilion	65	40
1976/1978	Set of 3	1·30	90
MS1979	134×81 mm. No. 1977×4 (10 Oct)	5·25	2·00

Designs:—60g. Lenin addressing meeting; 2z.50 Lenin at Party
Conference.

No. **MS**1979 was issued for Cracow Philatelic Exhibition.

543 Polish and Russian Soldiers in Berlin

544 Polish "Flower"

(Des A. Heidrich. Litho)

1970 (9 May). 25th Anniversary of Liberation. P 11×11½.
1980 **543** 60g. multicoloured............................. 40 ✓ 35

(Des A. Heidrich. Litho)

1970 (9 May). Tourism (2nd series). Multicoloured designs as T **523**. P 11.

1981	60g. Town Hall, Wrocław (*vert*)...............	40	35
1982	60g. View of Opole	40	35
1983	60g. Legnica Castle	40	35
1984	60g. Bolków Castle	40	35
1985	60g. Town Hall, Brzeg	40	35
1981/1985 *Set of 5*..		1·80	1·60

Issued with *se-tenant* labels as described for the first series.

(Des K. Rogaczewska. Eng E. Konecki. Recess, litho and typo)

1970 (9 May). 25th Anniv of Return of Western Territories. P 11½.
1986 **544** 60g. red, silver and deep bluish green.. 40 35

545 Movement Flag

546 U.P.U. Emblem and New Headquarters

(Des K. Syta. Litho)

1970 (15 May). 75th Anniversary of Peasant Movement. P 11½.
1987 **545** 60g. multicoloured........................... 40 35

(Des H. Chyliński. Litho)

1970 (20 May). New UPU Headquarters Building, Berne. P 11½.
1988 **546** 2z.50 bright blue and light greenish blue.. 45 40

547 Footballers

548 Hand with "Lamp of Learning"

(Des H. Matuszewska. Litho)

1970 (30 May). Górnik Zabrze v. Manchester City, Final of European Cup-winners Cup Championship. P 11½×11.
1989 **547** 60g. multicoloured........................ 65 50

No. 1989 was issued with *se-tenant* stamp-size label with inscription giving results of previous matches.

(Des H. Chyliński. Litho)

1970 (3 June). 150th Anniversary of Plock Scientific Society. P 11½.
1990 **548** 60g. yellow-olive, red and black............... 40 35

549 "Olympic Runners" (from Greek amphora)

(Des F. Winiarski (Nos. 1991 and 1993), W. Skoczylas (No. 1992), Z. Kamiński (**MS**1994). Photo)

1970 (16 June). Tenth Session of International Olympic Academy. T **549** and similar horiz designs. P 11×12.

1991	60g. vermilion, orange-yellow and black	40	35
1992	60g. deep violet-blue, bright blue and black..	40	35
1993	60g. multicoloured.................................	40	35
1991/1993 *Set of 3*..		1·10	95
MS1994 71×101 mm. 10z.+5z. multicoloured. Imperf..		4·50	2·20

Designs:—No. 1992, "The Archer"; No. 1993, Modern runners; No. **MS**1994, "Horse of Fame" emblem of Polish Olympic Committee.

550 Copernicus (after miniature by Bacciarelli), and Bologna

(Des H. Matuszewska. Eng E. Tirdiszek (40g.), B. Kowalska (60g.), B. Brandt (2z.50). Recess, photo and typo)

1970 (26 June). 500th Birth Anniv of Copernicus (1973) (2nd issue). Vert designs as T **550**. P 11½.

1995	40g. bronze-green, red-orange and reddish lilac...	35	25
1996	60g. reddish lilac, bronze-green and orange-yellow..................................	40	35
1997	2z.50 brown, ultramarine and light emerald ..	1·00	40
1995/1997 *Set of 3*..		1·60	90

Designs:—60g. Copernicus (after miniature by Lesseur), and Padua; 2z.50 Copernicus (by Zinck after lost Goluchowska portrait), and Ferrara.

551 "Aleksander Orlowski" (self-portrait)

552 UN Emblem within "Eye"

(Des T. Michaluk. Litho and photo)

1970 (27 Aug). Polish Miniatures. T **551** and similar vert portraits. Multicoloured. P 11½×11.

1998	20g. Type **551**	15	15
1999	40g. "Jan Matejko" (self-portrait)...............	20	15
2000	60g. "Stefan Batory" (unknown artist).............	25	20
2001	2z. "Maria Leszczyńska" (unknown artist)	35	25
2002	2z.50 "Maria Walewska" (Marie-Victoire Jacquetot)...................................	40	35
2003	3z.40 "Tadeusz Kościuszko" (J. Rustem)...............	50	40
2004	5z.50 "Samuel Linde" (G. Landolfi)...............	1·60	80
2005	7z. "Michał Ogiński" (Nanette Windisch)	3·25	90
1998/2005 *Set of 8*..		6·00	3·00

Issued in sheets of four stamps and two inscribed stamp-sized *se-tenant* labels.

(Des F. Bąracz. Photo)

1970 (8 Sept). 25th Anniv of United Nations. P 11½.
2006 **552** 2z.50 multicoloured 50 40

553 Piano Keyboard and Chopin's Signature

554 Population Pictograph

(Des S. Malecki. Eng E. Tirdiszek. Recess and photo)

1970 (8 Sept). Eighth International Chopin Piano Competition. P 11.
2007 **553** 2z.50 black and violet 50 40

(Des K. Rogaczewska. Litho)

1970 (15 Sept). National Census. T **554** and similar vert design. Multicoloured. P 11½×11.
2008 40g. Type **554** 35 25
2009 60g. Family in "house" 40 35

555 *Piorun* (destroyer)

(Des K. Rogaczewska. Eng B. Kowalska (40g.), E. Tirdiszek (60g.), B. Brandt (2z.50). Recess and photo)

1911 (25 Sept). Polish Warships of World War II. T **555** and similar horiz designs. P 11½×11.
2010 40g. blackish brown 35 25
2011 60g. black 40 35
2012 2z.50 deep brown 90 40
2010/2012 *Set of 3* .... 1·50 90
Designs:—60g. *Orzel* (submarine); 2z.50 H.M.S. *Garland* (destroyer loaned to Polish Navy).

556 "Expressions" (Maria Jarema)

557 "Luna 16" landing on Moon

(Des S. Malecki. Photo)

1970 (9 Oct). Stamp Day. Contemporary Polish Paintings. T **556** and similar multicoloured designs. P 11½×12 (vert) or 12×11½ (horiz).
2013 20g. "The Violin-cellist" (J. Nowosielski)
(*vert*) 15 15
2014 40g. "View of Lódź" (B. Liberski) (*vert*) 20 15
2015 60g. "Studio Concert" (W. Taranczewski)
(*vert*) 25 20
2016 1z.50 "Still Life" (Z. Pronaszko) (*vert*) 35 20
2017 2z. "Hanging-up Washing" (A. Wróblewski)
(*vert*) 40 25
2018 3z.40 Type **556** 50 35
2019 4z. "Canal in the Forest" (P. Potworowski) ... 1·30 40
2020 8z.50 "The Sun" (W. Strzemiński) .... 2·50 90
2013/2020 *Set of 8* .... 5·00 2·30

(Des Z. Stasik. Litho)

1970 (20 Nov). Moon Landing of "Luna 16". P 11½×11.
2021 **557** 2z.50 multicoloured 80 40
Issued in sheets of eight stamps and two different stamp-size *se-tenant* labels, showing Space scenes.

558 "Stag" (detail from "Daniel" tapestry)

559 Cadet Ship *Dar Pomorza*

(Des H. Matuszewska. Photo)

1970 (23 Dec). Tapestries in Wawel Castle. T **558** and similar vert designs. Multicoloured. P 11½.
2022 60g. Type **558** 20 15
2023 1z.15 "White Stork" (detail) 25 15
2024 1z.35 "Panther fighting Dragon" 40 20
2025 2z. "Man's Head" (detail, "Deluge" tapestry) ... 50 25
2026 2z.50 "Child with Bird" (detail, "Adam Tilling
the Soil" tapestry) 65 35
2027 4z. "God, Adam and Eve" (detail,
"Happiness in Paradise" tapestry) .... 1·30 40
2028 4z.50 Royal Monogram tapestry .... 1·70 65
2022/2028 *Set of 7* .... 4·50 1·90
MS2029 Two sheets, each 62×89 mm. (a) 5z.50 Polish
coat-of-arms; (b) 7z.+3z. Monogram and satyrs.
Imperf *Set of 2 sheets* .... 5·25 4·00
The designs on the miniature sheets are larger, 45×55 mm.

(Des S. Malecki. Photo)

1971 (20 Feb). Polish Ships. T **559** and similar horiz designs. Multicoloured. P 11.
2030 40g. Type **559** .... 15 ✔ 15
2031 60g. Liner *Stefan Batory* .... 20 ✔ 15
2032 1z.15 Ice-breaker *Perkun* .... 30 ✔ 20
2033 1z.35 Lifeboat *R-1* .... 35 ✔ 25
2034 1z.50 Bulk carrier *Ziemia Szczecińska* .... 40 ✔ 35
2035 2z.50 Tanker *Beskidy* .... 55 ✔ 40
2036 5z. Fast freighter *Hel* .... 1·40 55
2037 8z.50 Ferry *Gryf* .... 2·75 1·20
2030/2037 *Set of 8* .... 5·50 3·00

560 Chęciny Castle

(Des T. Michaluk. Litho)

1971 (5 Mar). Polish Castles. T **560** and similar horiz designs. Multicoloured. P 11×12.
2038 20g. Type **560** .... 15 ✔ 15
2039 40g. Wiśnicz .... 20 ✔ 15
2040 60g. Bedzin .... 30 ✔ 20
2041 2z. Ogrodzieniec .... 35 ✔ 20
2042 2z.50 Niedzica .... 40 ✔ 25
2043 3z.40 Kwidzyń .... 55 ✔ 35
2044 4z. Pieskowa Skala .... 1·00 ✔ 40
2045 8z.50 Lidzbark Warmiński .... 2·10 ✔ 95
2038/2045 *Set of 8* .... 4·50 2·40

561 Battle of Pouilly, J. Dąbrowski and W. Wróblewski

562 Plantation

(Des H. Matuszewska. Litho)

1971 (10 Mar). Centenary of Paris Commune. P 12½.
2046 **561** 60g. purple-brown, bright blue and
rosine 40 35

(Des Z. Stasik. Photo)

1971 (30 Mar). Forestry Management. T **562** and similar vert designs.
Multicoloured. P 12½ (60g.) or 11½×11 (others).

2047	40g. Type **562**	35	25
2048	60g. Forest (27×47 *mm*)	40	35
2049	1z.50 Tree-felling	70	40
2047/2049 *Set of 3*		1·30	90

563 "Bishop Marianos"

(Des H. Chyliński. Photo)

1971 (20 Apr). Fresco Discoveries made by Polish Expedition at Faras,
Nubia. T **563** and similar vert designs. Multicoloured. P 11½×11.

2050	40g. Type **563**	15	15
2051	60g. "St. Anne"	20	15
2052	1z.15 "Archangel Michael"	30	20
2053	1z.35 "The Hermit, Anamon"	35	25
2054	1z.50 "Head of Archangel Michael"	40	35
2055	4z.50 "Evangelists' Cross"	1·10	40
2056	5z. "Christ protecting a nobleman"	1·30	55
2057	7z. "Archangel Michael" (half-length)	1·70	95
2050/2057 *Set of 8*		5·00	2·75

564 Revolutionaries

(Des J. W. Brzoza. Photo)

1971 (3 May–17 June). 50th Anniversary of Silesian Insurrection. P 11.

2058	**564** 60g. red-brown and gold	55	40
MS2059 108×106 mm. No. 2058×3 (17 June)		5·50	2·30

No. 2058 was issued in sheets of 15 stamps with half stamp-size *se-
tenant* labels dated "1971".

No. **MS**2059 also contains three such labels, and was issued in
connection with a Philatelic Exhibition at Katowice.

565 "Soldiers"   **566** Fair Emblem

(Des H. Matuszewska from children's drawings. Photo)

1971 (29 May). 25th Anniversary of UNICEF Children's
Drawings. T **565** and similar multicoloured designs. P 11½×11
(vert) or 11×11½ (horiz).

2060	20g. "Peacock" (*vert*)	15	15
2061	40g. Type **565**	20	15
2062	60g. "Lady Spring" (*vert*)	30	20
2063	2z. "Cat and Ball"	40	25
2064	2z.50 "Flowers in Jug" (*vert*)	55	35
2065	3z.40 "Friendship"	70	40
2066	5z.50 "Clown" (*vert*)	1·40	70
2067	7z. "Strange Planet"	2·10	95
2060/2067 *Set of 8*		5·25	2·75

(Des H. Chyliński. Photo)

1971 (1 June). 40th International Fair, Poznań. P 11½×11.

2068	**566** 60g. multicoloured	40	35

567 Copernicus's   **568** Folk Art
House, Toruń   Pattern

(Des A. Heidrich. Litho)

1971 (1 June). 500th Birth Anniv of Copernicus (1973) (3rd
series). T **567** and similar multicoloured designs. P 11.

2069	40g. Type **567**	35	20
2070	60g. Collegium Maius, Jagiellonian University, Cracow (*horiz*)	40	25
2071	2z.50 Olsztyn Castle (*horiz*)	70	35
2072	4z. Frombork Cathedral	1·00	40
2069/2072 *Set of 4*		2·20	1·10

Each value issued with different half stamp-size *se-tenant* label
showing Copernicus (40g.) or aspects of his work.

(Des J. Jaworowski. Recess and photo)

1971 (12 July). Folk Art Paper "Cut-outs". T **568** and similar vert
designs showing different patterns. P 12×11½.

2073	20g. black, emerald and pale blue	35	25
2074	40g. indigo, deep olive and pale cream	35	25
2075	60g. deep brown, greenish blue and pale grey	35	25
2076	1z.15 maroon, yellow-brown and pale buff	35	25
2077	1z.35 deep bluish green, vermilion and pale yellow-green	35	25
2073/2077 *Set of 5*		1·60	1·10

569 "Head of Worker"
(X. Dunikowski)

(Des J. W. Brzoza. Photo)

1971 (21 July–27 Oct). Modern Polish Sculpture. T **569** and similar
vert designs. Multicoloured. P 11½×11.

2078	40g. Type **569**	35	25
2079	40g. "Foundryman" (X. Dunikowski)	35	25
2080	60g. "Miners" (M. Więcek)	40	35
2081	60g. "Harvester" (S. Horno-Poplawski)	40	35
2078/2081 *Set of 4*		1·40	1·10
MS2082 158×85 mm. Nos. 2078/81. P 12½×12 (27 Oct)		7·00	2·75

No. **MS**2082 was issued in connection with a Philatelic Exhibition at
Szczecin.

570 Congress Emblem and   **571** "Angel" (J. Mehoffer)
Computer Tapes

(Des H. Chyliński. Litho)

1971 (2 Sept). Sixth Polish Technical Congress, Warsaw. P 11×11½.

2083	**570** 60g. violet and red	40	35

(Des K. Tarkowska. Photo)

1971 (15 Sept). Stained-glass Windows. T **571** and similar vert designs. Multicoloured. P 11½×11.

2084	20g. Type **571**	15	15
2085	40g. "Lilies" (S. Wyspiański)	20	15
2086	60g. "Iris" (S. Wyspiański)	30	20
2087	1z.35 "Apollo" (S. Wyspiański)	35	25
2088	1z.55 "Two Wise Men" (14th century)	40	35
2089	3z.40 "The Flight into Egypt" (14th century)	70	40
2090	5z.50 "Jacob" (14th-century)	1·40	55
2091	8z.50 +4z. "Madonna" (15th-century)	2·10	1·40
2084/2091 Set of 8		5·00	3·00

The 40g., 60g., 1z.35 and 8z.50 are larger, 26×39 mm.

572 "Mrs. Fedorowicz" (W. Pruszkowski)

573 PZL P-11C Fighters

(Des K. Śliwka. Litho)

1971 (25 Sept). Contemporary Art from National Museum, Cracow. T **572** and similar multicoloured designs. P 11×11½.

2092	40g. Type **572**	15	15
2093	50g. "Woman with Book" (T. Czyżewski)	20	15
2094	60g. "Girl with Chrysanthemums" (O. Bożnańska)	30	20
2095	2z.50 "Girl in Red Dress" (J. Pankiewicz) (*horiz*)	40	25
2096	3z.40 "Reclining Nude" (L. Chwistek) (*horiz*)	70	25
2097	4z.50 "Strange Garden" (J. Mehoffer)	1·00	35
2098	5z. "Wife in White Hat" (Z. Pronaszko)	1·10	40
2099	7z. +1z. "Seated Nude" (W. Weiss)	1·50	1·40
2092/2099 Set of 8		4·75	2·75

Issued in sheets of four stamps and two stamp-size *se-tenant* labels bearing inscription.

(Des J. Brodowski. Photo)

1971 (14 Oct). Polish Aircraft of World War II. T **573** and similar horiz designs. Multicoloured. P 11×11½.

2100	90g. Type **573**	40	25
2101	1z.50 PZL 23A Karaś fighters	70	35
2102	3z.40 PZL P-37 Loś bomber	85	40
2100/2102 Set of 3		1·80	90

574 Royal Castle, Warsaw (pre-1939)

(Des K. Śliwka. Photo)

1971 (14 Oct). Reconstruction of Royal Castle, Warsaw. P 11×11½.

2103	**574**	60g. black, red and gold	40	35

575 Astronauts in Moon Rover

576 "Lunokhod 1"

(Des A. Balcerzak. Photo)

1971 (17 Nov). Moon Flight of "Apollo 15". P 11×11½.

2104	**575**	2z.50 multicoloured	1·10	40

MS2105 122×157 mm. No. 2104×6 plus two stamp-size *se-tenant* labels, showing Space scenes .... 14·00 6·75

(Des Z. Stasik. Photo)

1971 (17 Nov). Moon Flight of "Lunik 17" and "Lunokhod 1". P 11½×11.

2106	**576**	2z.50 multicoloured	1·10	40

MS2107 158×118 mm. No. 2106×6 plus two stamp-size *se-tenant* labels, showing Space scenes .... 14·00 6·75

577 Worker at Wheel

578 Shipbuilding

(Des S. Malecki (Nos. 2108/9) or J. W. Brzoza (others). Photo)

1971 (16 Dec)–**72**. Sixth Polish United Workers' Party Congress.

*(a) Party Posters. T **577** and similar vert design. P 11½×11*

2108	**577**	60g. red, violet-blue and pale grey	40	35
		a. Strip. Nos. 2108/9 plus label	85	75
2109	–	60g. red and pale grey (Worker's head)	40	35

*(b) Industrial Development. T **578** and similar horiz designs. Each gold, black and red. P 11×11½*

2110	60g. Type **578**	40	35
	a. Block of 6. Nos. 2110/15	2·50	
2111	60g. Building construction	40	35
2112	60g. Combine harvester	40	35
2113	60g. Motor-car production	40	35
2114	60g. Pithead	40	35
2115	60g. Petro-chemical plant	40	35
2108/2115 Set of 6		3·00	2·50

MS2116 102×115 mm. Nos. 2110/15 (4.72) .... 3·50 2·00

Nos. 2108/9 were issued *se-tenant* within the sheet with an intervening stamp-size label inscr "PZPR".

Nos. 2110/15 were issued together *se-tenant* in blocks of six within the sheet, forming an outline map of Poland.

579 Prunus cerasus

(Des A. Balcerzak. Litho)

1971 (28 Dec). Flowers of Trees and Shrubs. T **579** and similar horiz designs. Multicoloured. P 12½.

2117	10g. Type **579**	15	15
2118	20g. *Malus niedzwetzkyana*	15	15
2119	40g. *Pyrus L.*	15	15
2120	60g. *Prunus persica*	20	15
2121	1z.15 *Magnolia kobus*	30	20
2122	1z.35 *Crataegus oxyacantha*	35	25
2123	2z.50 *Malus M.*	40	35
2124	3z.40 *Aesculus carnea*	70	40
2125	5z. *Robinia pseudoacacia*	1·70	70
2126	8z.50 *Prunus avium*	3·50	1·40
2117/2126 Set of 10		6·75	3·50

580 "Worker" (sculpture, J. Januszkiewicz)

(Des J. Brzoza. Recess and photo)

1972 (5 Jan). 30th Anniversary of Polish Workers' Coalition. P 11½.
2127 **580** 60g. black and red 40 35

581 Tobogganing

(Des H. Matuszewska. Photo)

1972 (12 Jan). Winter Olympic Games, Sapporo, Japan. T **581** and similar multicoloured designs. P 11.
2128	40g. Type **581**	30	20
2129	60g. Slalom (vert).............................	40	25
2130	1z.65 Biathlon (vert)........................	70	35
2131	2z.50 Ski jumping............................	1·00	40
2128/2131	Set of 4...............................	2·20	1·10
MS2132	85×68 mm. 10z.+5z. Downhill skiing. Imperf.	5·50	3·00

582 "Heart" and   **583** Running
Cardiogram Trace

(Des K. Śliwka. Photo)

1972 (28 Mar). World Heart Month. P 11½×11.
2133 **582** 2z.50 multicoloured........................ 55 40

(Des W. Świerzy. Photo)

1972 (25 Apr). Olympic Games, Munich. T **583** and similar vert designs. Multicoloured. P 11½×11.
2134	20g. Type **583**	15	15
2135	30g. Archery....................................	15	15
2136	40g. Boxing.....................................	20	15
2137	60g. Fencing....................................	30	20
2138	2z.50 Wrestling...............................	35	25
2139	3z.40 Weightlifting..........................	40	35
2140	5z. Cycling......................................	1·00	40
2141	8z.50 Shooting................................	1·70	70
2134/2141	Set of 8...............................	3·75	2·10
MS2142	70×80 mm. 10z.+5z. As 30g............	3·50	1·60

584 Cyclists   **585** Polish War
Memorial, Berlin

(Des T. Michaluk. Photo)

1972 (2 May). 25th International Peace Cycle Race. P 11.
2143 **584** 60g. multicoloured........................ 40 35

(Des S. Malecki. Eng E. Tirdiszek. Recess)

1972 (9 May). "Victory Day, 1945". P 11½×11.
2144 **585** 60g. blackish green........................ 40 35

586 "Rodlo" Emblem   **587** Polish Knight of
972 A.D.

(Des J. Klopocka. Photo)

1972 (28 May). 50th Anniv of Polish Posts in Germany. P 11½×11.
2145 **586** 60g. scarlet, myrtle-green and pale
bistre 40 35

(Des J. Wysocki. Photo)

1972 (12 June). Millenary of Battle of Cedynia. P 11½×11.
2146 **587** 60g. multicoloured........................ 40 35

588 Cheetah (Acinonyx jubatus)   **589** L. Waryński
(founder)

(Des J. Grabiański. Litho)

1972 (21 Aug). Zoo Animals. T **588** and similar multicoloured designs on pale buff paper. P 12½.
2147	20g. Type **588**	20	15
2148	40g. Giraffe (Giraffa camelopardalis) (vert)......	30	15
2149	60g. Toco Toucan............................	35	20
2150	1z.35 Chimpanzee (Pan troglodytes)..................	40	25
2151	1z.65 Common Gibbon (Hylobates lar)............	70	35
2152	3z.40 Crocodile...............................	1·00	40
2153	4z. Red Kangaroo (Macropus rufus)...............	1·70	80
2154	4z.50 Tiger (Panthera tigris sumatrae) (vert)......	5·50	2·75
2155	7z. Mountain Zebra (Equus zebra)...............	7·00	3·50
2147/2155	Set of 9...............................	15·00	7·75

(Des K. W. Brzoza. Photo)

1972 (1 Sept). 90th Anniv of Proletarian Party. P 11.
2156 **589** 60g. multicoloured........................ 40 35
No. 2156 was issued together with se-tenant stamp-sized labels showing a facsimile of the front page of Proletaryat.

590 F. Dzierżyński   **591** Global Emblem

(Des Z. Stasik. Photo)

1972 (11 Sept). 95th Birth Anniv of Feliks Dzierżyińsky (Russian politician). P 11×11½.
2157 **590** 60g. black and red 40 35

(Des M. Wieczorek. Photo)

1972 (15 Sept). 25th International Co-operative Federation Congress. P 11½×11.
2158 **591** 60g. multicoloured........................ 40 35

592 Scene from *In Barracks* (ballet)

593 "Copernicus the Astronomer"

(Des J. Desselberger. Eng B. Kowalska (10g., 2z.50), B. Brandt (20g., 1z.35, 1z.55), E. Tirdiszek (40g., 60g.) and E. Konecki (1z.15). Recess and photo)

1972 (15 Sept). Death Centenary of Stanislaus Moniuszko (composer). Scenes from Works. T **592** and similar vert designs. P 11½.

2159	10g. violet and gold	15	15
2160	20g. black and gold	15	15
2161	40g. myrtle-green and gold	20	15
2162	60g. indigo and gold	30	20
2163	1z.15 deep blue and gold	35	20
2164	1z.35 deep blue and gold	40	25
2165	1z.55 olive-grey and gold	55	35
2166	2z.50 blackish brown and gold	1·00	40
2159/2166 *Set of 8*		2·75	1·70

Designs:—20g. *The Countess* (opera); 40g. *The Haunted Manor* (opera); 60g. *Halka* (opera); 1z.15 *New Don Quixote* (ballet); 1z.35 *Verbum Nobile* (opera); 1z.55 *Ideal* (operetta); 2z.50 *Pariah* (opera).

(Des W. Andrzejewski. Eng B. Kowalska (10z.). Litho or recess and typo (10z.))

1972 (28 Sept). 500th Birth Anniv of Nicolas Copernicus (1973) (4th issue), and "Polska 73" Stamp Exhibition, Poznań. T **593** and similar designs. P 11×11½ or 11½ (10z.).

2167	40g. black and bright blue	35	25
2168	60g. black and yellow-orange	40	35
2169	2z.50 black and bright red	85	40
2170	3z.40 black and yellow-green	1·40	70
2167/2170 *Set of 4*		2·75	1·50
MS2171 62×102 mm 10z.+5z. multicoloured		5·50	2·75

Designs: Horiz—60g. Copernicus and Medal of 1530; 2z.50 Copernicus and Polish eagle; 3z.40 Copernicus and page of book. Vert (29×48 *mm*)—10z.+5z. Copernicus charting the planets.

594 "Amazon" (P. Michalowski)   **(595)**

(Des T. Michaluk. Photo)

1972 (28 Sept). Stamp Day. Polish Paintings. T **594** and similar multicoloured designs. P 11.

2172	30g. Type **594**	20	15
2173	40g. "Ostafi Laskiewicz" (J. Metejko)	20	15
2174	60g. "Summer Idyll" (W. Gerson)	20	15
2175	2z. "The Neapolitan Woman" (A. Kotsis)	30	20
2176	2z.50 "Girl Bathing" (P. Szyndler)	35	25
2177	3z.40 "The Princess of Thum" (A. Grottger)	40	35
2178	4z. "Rhapsody" (S. Wyspiański)	2·40	40
2179	8z.50 +4z. "Young Woman" (J. Malczewski) (*horiz*)	3·00	70
2172/2179 *Set of 8*		6·25	2·10

1972 (2 Oct–17 Nov). Provisionals. Nos. 1578/9 surch as T **595**.

2180	50g. on 40g. red-brown (R.) (17.11)	20	15
2181	90g. on 40g. red-brown (R.) (17.11)	25	15
2182	1z. on 40g. red-brown (R.)	30	15
2183	1z.50 on 60g. orange-red	35	20
2184	2z.70 on 60g. red-brown (R.)	40	20
2185	4z. on 60g. orange-red	55	25
2186	4z.50 on 60g. orange-red	70	35

2187	4z.90 on 60g. orange-red	1·00	40
2180/2187 *Set of 8*		3·50	1·70

On Nos. 2180/2 and 2184 the old denominations are obliterated by crosses.

596 "The Little Soldier" (E. Piwowarski)

597 "Royal Castle, Warsaw" (E. J. Dahlberg, 1656)

(Des T. Michaluk. Litho)

1972 (16 Oct). Children's Health Centre. P 11½.

2188	**596**	60g. black and pink	40	35

(Des A. Heidrich. Photo)

1972 (16 Oct). Restoration of Royal Castle, Warsaw. P 11×11½.

2189	**597**	60g. black, reddish violet and light blue	40	35

598 Chalet, Chocholowska Valley

599 Trade Union Banners

600 Congress Emblem

(Des A. Balcerzak. Photo)

1972 (13 Nov). Tourism. Mountain Chalets. T **598** and similar multicoloured designs. P 11.

2190	40g. Type **598**	15	15
2191	60g. Hala Ornak (*horiz*)	20	15
2192	1z.55 Hala Gąsienicowa	30	20
2193	1z.65 Valley of Five Lakes (*horiz*)	35	25
2194	2z.50 Morskie Oko	40	35
2190/2194 *Set of 5*		1·30	1·00

(Des K. Śliwka. Photo)

1972 (13 Nov). Seventh Polish Trade Unions Congress. P 11½×11.

2195	**599**	60g. multicoloured	40	35

(Des A. Heidrich. Photo)

1972 (15 Dec). Fifth Socialist Youth Union Congress. P 11½.

2196	**600**	60g. multicoloured	40	35

601 Japanese Azalea

602 Piast Knight (10th-century)

(Des A. Balcerzak. Litho)

1972 (15 Dec). Flowering Shrubs. T **601** and similar horiz designs. Multicoloured. P 12½.

2197	40g. Type **601**	15	15

2198	50g. Alpine rose	20	15
2199	60g. Pomeranian Honeysuckle	30	15
2200	1z.65 Chinese Quince	35	20
2201	2z.50 Korean Cranberry	40	25
2202	3z.40 Pontic Azalea	70	35
2203	4z. Delavay's White Syringa	2·10	40
2204	8z.50 Common Lilac ("Massena")	3·00	1·40
2197/2204 *Set of 8*		6·50	2·75

(Des L. Maciąg. Photo)

1972 (28 Dec). Polish Cavalry Through the Ages. T **602** and similar multicoloured designs. P 11.

2205	20g. Type **602**	20	15
2206	40g. 13th-century knight	30	15
2207	60g. Knight of Władysław Jagiełło's Army (15th-century) (*horiz*)	35	20
2208	1z.35 17th-century hussar	40	25
2209	4z. Lancer of the National Guard (18th-century)	1·30	35
2210	4z.50 Congress Kingdom cavalry officer (1831)	1·40	40
2211	5z. Trooper of Light Cavalry (1939) (*horiz*)	2·20	70
2212	7z. Trooper of People's Army (1945)	2·75	95
2205/2212 *Set of 8*		8·00	2·75

603 Copernicus | **604** Couple with Hammer and Sickle | **605** "Copernicus as a Young Man" (Bacciarelli)

(Des A. Heidrich. Photo)

1972 (28 Dec). Coil Stamps. 500th Birth Anniv of Copernicus (1973) (5th issue). P 14.

2213	**603**	1z. brown-lake	35	25
2214		1z.50 deep ochre	40	35

(Des T. Konarski and J. Wysocki. Photo)

1972 (30 Dec). 50th Anniv of USSR. T **604** and similar vert design. P 11½×11.

2215	**604**	40g. multicoloured	35	25
2216	–	60g. vermilion, ultramarine and black	40	35

Design:—60g. Red Star and globe.

(Des H. Chyliński. Photo)

1973 (18 Feb). 500th Birth Anniv of Copernicus (6th issue). T **605** and similar multicoloured portraits. P 11×11½ (4z.90) or 11½×11 (others).

2217	1z. Type **605**	15	15
2218	1z.50 "Copernicus" (anon.)	30	20
2219	2z.70 "Copernicus" (Nora Zinck)	70	35
2220	4z. "Copernicus" (from Strasbourg clock)	85	40
2221	4z.90 "Copernicus" (Jan Matejko) (*horiz*)	1·40	70
2217/2221 *Set of 5*		3·00	1·60

606 Coronation Sword | **607** Statue of Lenin

(Des S. Malecki. Photo)

1973 (28 Mar). Polish Art. T **606** and similar vert designs. Multicoloured. P 11½×11.

2222	50g. Type **606**	15	15
2223	1z. Krużlowa Madonna (detail)	30	20
2224	1z. Armour of hussar	30	20
2225	1z.50 Carved head from Wawel Castle	40	25
2226	1z.50 Silver cockerel	40	25
2227	2z.70 Armorial eagle	70	40
2228	4z.90 Skarbimierz Madonna	1·40	70

2229	8z.50 "Portrait of Tenczyński" (anon)	2·40	1·20
2222/2229 *Set of 8*		5·50	3·00

(Des S. Malecki. Litho)

1973 (28 Apr). Unveiling of Lenin's Statue, Nowa Huta. P 11×11½.

2230	**607**	1z. multicoloured	40	35

608 Coded Letter | **610** "Salyut"

609 Wolf (*Canis lupus*)

(Des H. Chyliński. Photo)

1973 (5 May). Introduction of Postal Codes. P 11×11½.

2231	**608**	1z.50 multicoloured	40	35

(Des I. Konarski and J. Wysocki. Photo)

1973 (21 May). International Hunting Council Congress and 50th Anniv of Polish Hunting Association. Game Animals. T **609** and similar horiz designs. Multicoloured. P 11.

2232	50g. Type **609**	20	15
2233	1z. Mouflon (*Ovis ammon musimon*)	20	15
2234	1z.50 Elk (*Alces alces*)	30	15
2235	2z.70 Western Capercaillie (*Tetrao urogallus*)	35	20
2236	3z. Roe Deer (*Capreolus capreolus*)	40	30
2237	4z.50 Lynx (*Lynx lynx*)	1·00	40
2238	4z.90 Red Deer (*Cervus elaphus*)	3·75	75
2239	5z. Wild Boar (*Sus scrofa*)	4·50	1·00
2232/2239 *Set of 8*		9·75	2·75

(Des Z. Stasik. Photo)

1973 (20 June). Cosmic Research. T **610** and similar horiz design. Multicoloured. P 11×11½.

2240	4z.90 Type **610**	1·00	40
2241	4z.90 "Copernicus" (US satellite)	1·00	40

Nos. 2240/1 were respectively issued in sheets of six stamps plus two *se-tenant* stamp-sized labels depicting (No. 2240) "Soyuz 11" or Soviet astronauts; (2241) Copernicus or constellations.

611 Open Book and Flame | **612** Ancient Seal of Poznań

(Des R. Dudzicki. Litho)

1973 (26 June). Second Polish Science Congress, Warsaw. P 11½.

2242	**611**	1z.50 multicoloured	40	35

(Des W. Andrzejewski. Eng E. Konecki (10z.). Litho or recess and litho (10z.))

1973 (30 June–19 Aug). Polska 73 Philatelic Exhibition, Poznań. T **612** and similar multicoloured designs. P 11×11½ (4z.) or 11½×11 (others).

2243	1z. Type **612**	20	15
2244	1z.50 Tombstone of N. Tomicki	30	20
2245	2z.70 Kalisz paten	40	30
2246	4z. Bronze gates, Gniezno Cathedral (*horiz*)	70	40
2243/2246 *Set of 4*		1·40	95

MS2247 91×66 mm. 10z.+5z. deep purple and pale olive. Imperf .... 4·25 2·10
MS2248 91×66 mm. 10z.+5z. deep purple and pale lilac. Imperf .... 14·00 9·00
Design: 68×32 mm—10z. Poznań in 1740.
No. **MS**2248 was sold only with entrance tickets to the exhibition.

613 M. Nowotko   **614** Cherry Blossom

(Des J. Wysocki. Litho)

1973 (8 Aug). 80th Birth Anniv of Marceli Nowotko (party leader). P 11½×11.
2249   **613**   1z.50 black and vermilion 40 35

(Des H. Matuszewska. Photo)

1973 (20 Aug). Protection of the Environment. T **614** and similar horiz designs. Multicoloured. P 11.
2250   50g. Type **614** 20 15
2251   90g. Cattle in meadow 20 15
2252   1z. White stork on nest 30 20
2253   1z.50 Fresh water life 35 30
2254   2z.70 Meadow flora 40 35
2255   4z.90 Ocean fauna 70 40
2256   5z. Forest life .... 3·50 70
2257   6z.50 Agricultural produce .... 4·50 1·10
2250/2257 Set of 8 .... 9·25 3·00

615 Motor-cyclist

(Des W. Andrzejewski. Photo)

1973 (2 Sept). World Speedway Championships, Chorzów. P 11½.
2258   **615**   1z.50 multicoloured 40 35

616 "Copernicus" (M. Bacciarelli)

(Des A. Heidrich. Photo)

1973 (27 Sept). Stamp Day. P 11×11½.
2259   **616**   4z. +2z. multicoloured .... 1·30 55

617 Tank

(Des T. Michaluk. Litho)

1973 (4 Oct). 30th Anniv of Polish People's Army. T **617** and similar horiz designs. Multicoloured. P 12½.
2260   1z. Type **617** 35 30
2261   1z. Mikoyan Gurevich MiG-21D airplane 35 30

2262   1z.50 Guided missile 40 35
2263   1z.50 Puck (missile boat) 40 35
2260/2263 Set of 4 .... 1·40 1·20

618 G. Piramowicz and Title Page

(Des S. Malecki. Eng E. Tirdiszek (1z.) and B. Brandt (1z.50). Recess and photo)

1973 (13 Oct). Bicentenary of National Education Commission. T **618** and similar horiz design. P 12×11½.
2264   1z. blackish brown and pale yellow 30 20
2265   1z.50 bronze-green and pale grey-green 40 35
Design:—1z.50 J. Śniadecki, H. Kollątaj and J. U. Niemcewicz.

619 Pawel Strzelecki (explorer)   **620** Polish Flag
and Red Kangaroo

(Des T. Michaluk. Photo)

1973 (30 Nov). Polish Scientists. T **619** and similar vert designs. Multicoloured. P 11.
2266   1z. Type **619** 30 15
2267   1z. Henryk Arctowski (polar explorer) and Adelie Penguins 30 15
2268   1z.50 Stefan Rogoziński (explorer) and Lucy-Margaret (schooner) 35 20
2269   1z.50 Benedykt Dybowski (zoologist) and Sable, Lake Baikal 35 20
2270   2z. Bronislaw Malinowski (anthropologist) and New Guinea dancers 40 30
2271   2z.70 Stefan Drzewiecki (oceanographer) and submarine 55 35
2272   3z. Edward Strasburger (botanist) and classified plants 85 40
2273   8z. Ignacy Domeyko (geologist) and Chilean desert landscape .... 2·50 70
2266/2273 Set of 8 .... 5·00 2·20

(Des K. Śliwka. Photo)

1973 (15 Dec). 25th Anniv of Polish United Workers' Party. P 11½×11.
2274   **620**   1z.50 red, ultramarine and gold 55 40

621 Jelcz-Berliet Coach   **622** Iris

(Des T. Konarski and J. Wysocki. Photo)

1973 (28 Dec). Polish Motor Vehicles. T **621** and similar horiz designs. Multicoloured. P 11×11½.
2275   50g. Type **621** 20 15
2276   90g. Jelcz "316" truck 30 20
2277   1z. Polski Fiat "126p" saloon 35 30
2278   1z.50 Polski Fiat "125p" saloon 40 35
2279   4z. Nysa "M-521" utility van 85 40
2280   4z.50 Star "660" truck .... 1·40 55
2275/2280 Set of 6 .... 3·25 1·80

(Des J. Brodowski. Eng B. Kowalska (50g., 1z.), E. Konecki (1z.50, 3z.), A. Ostrowska (4z., 4z.50). Recess)

1974 (22 Jan). Flowers. Drawings by S. Wyspiański. T **622** and similar vert designs. P 12×11½.

2281	50g. purple	30	15
2282	1z. turquoise-green	35	15
2283	1z.50 vermilion	40	20
2284	3z. violet	55	30
2285	4z. ultramarine	85	35
2286	4z.50 blue-green	1·00	40
2281/2286 Set of 6		3·00	1·40

Flowers:—1z. Dandelion; 1z.50 Rose; 3z. Thistle; 4z. Cornflower; 4z.50 Clover.

623 Cottage, Kurpie

624 19th-century Mail Coach

(Des F. Winiarski. Photo)

1974 (5 Mar). Wooden Architecture. T **623** and similar horiz designs. Multicoloured. P 11×11½.

2287	1z. Type **623**	20	15
2288	1z.50 Church, Sękowa	30	20
2289	4z. Town Hall, Sulmierzyce	55	35
2290	4z.50 Church, Lachowice	70	40
2291	4z.90 Windmill, Sobienie-Jeziory	1·10	55
2292	5z. Orthodox Church, Ulucz	1·40	70
2287/2292 Set of 6		3·75	2·10

(Des T. Michaluk. Photo)

1974 (30 Mar). Centenary of Universal Postal Union. P 11½.

2293	**624**	1z.50 multicoloured	40	35

625 Cracow Motif

626 Association Emblem

(Des H. Matuszewska. Photo)

1974 (7–19 May). "SOCPHILEX IV" International Stamp Exhibition, Katowice. Regional Floral Embroideries. T **625** and similar vert designs. Multicoloured. P 11½×11.

2294	50g. Type **625**	20	15
2295	1z.50 Lowicz motif	40	30
2296	4z. Silesian motif	70	40
2294/2296 Set of 3		1·20	75

MS2297 69×171 mm. No. 2296×3. Imperf (sold at 17z.) (19.5) 2·75 2·10

The normal, imperforate, version of No. **MS**2297 has bluish violet borders, showing a lace pattern in white. The miniature sheet also exists perforated from a limited printing with white borders and the lace pattern in silver.

(Des K. Śliwka. Litho)

1974 (8 May). Fifth Congress of Fighters for Freedom and Democracy Association, Warsaw. P 11½.

2298	**626**	1z.50 red and brownish grey	40	35

627 Soldier and Dove

628 "Comecon" Headquarters, Moscow

(Des T. Michaluk. Litho)

1974 (9 May). 29th Anniv of Victory over Fascism in Second World War. P 11½×11.

2299	**627**	1z.50 multicoloured	40	35

(Des Z. Stasik. Litho)

1974 (15 May). 25th Anniv of Council for Mutual Economic Aid. P 11×11½.

2300	**628**	1z.50 ochre, red and cobalt	40	35

629 World Cup Emblem

(Des H. Chyliński. Photo)

1974 (6 June). World Cup Football Championship, West Germany. T **629** and similar horiz design. Multicoloured. P 11×11½.

2301	4z.90 Type **629**	1·00	40
2302	4z.90 Players and Olympic Gold Medal of 1972	1·00	40

MS2303 116×83 mm. Nos. 2301/2×2 16·00 14·00

See also No. **MS**2315.

630 Model of 16th-century Galleon

631 Title page of *Chess* by Jan Kochanowski, 1564

(Des W. Andrzejewski. Litho)

1974 (29 June). Sailing Ships. T **630** and similar vert designs. Multicoloured. P 11½×11.

2304	1z. Type **630**	20	15
2305	1z.50 Trans-Atlantic sloop *Dal* (1934)	30	20
2306	2z.70 Yacht *Opty* (Teliga's circumnavigation, 1969)	40	30
2307	4z. *Dar Pomorza* (full-rigged cadet ship)	70	35
2308	4z.90 Yacht *Polonez* (Baranowski's circumnavigation 1973)	1·40	40
2304/2308 Set of 5		2·75	1·30

(Des A. Heidrich. Litho)

1974 (15 July). Tenth International Chess Festival, Lublin. T **631** and similar vert design. Multicoloured. P 11½×11.

2309	1z. Type **631**	35	30
2310	1z.50 "Education" (1790s engraving by D. Chodowiecki)	40	35

632 Lazienkowska Road Junction

633 Face on Map of Poland

(Des M. Wieczorek. Litho)

1974 (21 July). Opening of Lazienkowska Road Junction. P 11×11½.

2311	**632**	1z.50 multicoloured	40	35

(Des J. W. Brzoza. Photo)

1974 (21 July). 30th Anniv of Polish People's Republic. T **633** and similar designs. P 11½×11.

2312	1z.50 black, gold and vermilion	40	35

2313	1z.50 multicoloured (silver background)	40	35
2314	1z.50 multicoloured (scarlet background)	40	35
2312/2314 Set of 3		1·10	95

Designs: 31×43 mm—Nos. 2313 and 2314, Polish "Eagle".

(Des H. Chyliński. Photo)

1974 (21 July). Poland—Third Place in World Cup Football Championship. Sheet 107×121 mm containing four stamps as No. 2301, but with inscr in silver instead of black, and two labels. P 11×11½.

MS2315	**629**	4z.90×4 multicoloured	8·50	3·50

634 Strawberries

635 Civic Militia and Security Service Emblem

(Des K. Śliwka. Photo)

1974 (10 Sept). 19th International Horticultural Congress, Warsaw. T **634** and similar vert designs. Multicoloured. P 11½.

2316	50g. Type **634**	20	15
2317	90g. Blackcurrants	20	15
2318	1z. Apples	30	20
2319	1z.50 Cucumbers	35	30
2320	2z.70 Tomatoes	40	35
2321	4z.50 Peas	1·00	40
2322	4z.90 Pansies	2·40	50
2323	5z. Nasturtiums	2·75	70
2316/2323 Set of 8		6·75	2·50

(Des W. Surowiecki. Photo)

1974 (3 Oct). 30th Anniv of Polish Civic Militia and Security Service. P 11½×11.

2324	**635**	1z.50 multicoloured	40	35

636 "Child in Polish Costume" (L. Orlowski)

637 "The Crib", Cracow

(Des W. Andrzejewski. Photo)

1974 (9 Oct). Stamp Day. Polish Paintings of Children. T **636** and similar vert designs. Multicoloured. P 11½×11.

2325	50g. Type **636**	15	15
2326	90g. "Girl with Pigeon" (anon.)	15	15
2327	1z. "Portrait of Girl" (S. Wyspiański)	20	15
2328	1z.50 "Orphan from Poronin" (W. Slewiński)	30	20
2329	3z. "Peasant Boy" (K. Sichulski)	40	30
2330	4z.50 "Florence Page" (A. Gierymski)	70	35
2331	4z.90 "Tadeusz and Dog" (P. Michalowski)	1·00	40
2332	6z.50 "Boy with Doe" (A. Kotsis)	1·50	85
2325/2332 Set of 8		4·00	2·30

(Des S. Malecki. Litho)

1974 (2 Dec). Polish Art. T **637** and similar vert designs. Multicoloured. P 11½×11.

2333	1z. Type **637**	15	15
2334	1z.50 "The Flight to Egypt" (15th-century polyptych)	30	20
2335	2z. "King Sigismund III Vasa" (16th-century miniature)	40	30
2336	4z. "King Jan Olbracht" (16th-century title-page)	1·80	40
2333/2336 Set of 4		2·40	95

638 Angler and Fish

639 "Pablo Neruda" (O. Guayasamin)

(Des T. Michaluk. Eng B. Kowalska (1z.), M. Kopecki (1z.50). Recess)

1974 (30 Dec). Polish Folklore. 16th-century wood-carvings (1st series). T **638** and similar horiz design. P 12×11.

2337	1z. black	30	15
2338	1z.50 blue-black	35	20

Design:—1z.50 Hunter and wild animals.

(Des H. Chyliński. Litho)

1974 (31 Dec). 70th Birth Anniv of Pablo Neruda (Chilean poet). P 11½×11.

2339	**639**	1z.50 multicoloured	40	35

640 "Nike" Memorial and National Opera-house

(Des H. Chyliński. Photo)

1975 (17 Jan). 30th Anniv of Liberation of Warsaw. P 11.

2340	**640**	1z.50 multicoloured	40	35

641 Male Lesser Kestrel (Falco naumanni)

642 Broken Barbed Wire

(Des J. Desselberger. Photo)

1975 (23 Jan). Birds of Prey. T **641** and similar vert designs. Multicoloured. P 11½×12.

2341	1z. Type **641**	30	15
	a. Pair. Nos. 2341/2	65	35
2342	1z. Female Lesser Kestrel	30	15
2343	1z.50 Male Western Red-footed Falcon (Falco vespertinus)	40	20
	a. Pair. Nos. 2343/4	85	45
2344	1z.50 Female Western Red-footed Falcon	40	20
2345	2z. Northern Hobby (Falco subbuteo)	70	30
2346	3z. Common Kestrel (Falco tinnunculus)	1·10	40
2347	4z. Merlin (Falco columbarius)	3·00	1·00
2348	8z. Peregrine Falcon (Falco peregrinus)	5·00	1·70
2341/2348 Set of 8		10·00	3·75

Nos. 2341/2 and 2343/4 were issued in se-tenant pairs within their sheets.

(Des Z. Stasik. Recess and photo)

1975 (27 Jan). 30th Anniv of Auschwitz Concentration Camp Liberation. P 11½×11.

2349	**642**	1z.50 black and red	40	35

643 Hurdling

(Des W. Andrzejewski. Litho (Nos. 2350/3) or recess and photo
(**MS**2354))

1975 (8 Mar). Sixth European Indoor Athletics Championships,
Katowice. T **643** and similar horiz designs. Multicoloured.
P 11×11½.

2350	1z. Type **643**	30	15
2351	1z.50 Pole vaulting	40	20
2352	4z. Triple jump	70	30
2353	4z.90 Running	1·00	40
2350/2353	Set of 4	2·20	95

MS2354 72×63 mm. 10z.+5z. deep turquoise-green
and silver (Montreal Olympics emblem) (26×31
mm). P 11½ .... 5·00 2·10
No. **MS**2354 has both the stamp and the outer edges of the sheet
perforated.

644 "St Anne" (Veit Stoss)   **645** Globe and "Radio Waves"

(Des A. Heidrich. Photo)

1975 (15 Apr). Arphila 1975 International Stamp Exhibition, Paris.
P 11×11½.

2355	**644** 1z.50 multicoloured	40	35

(Des S. Malecki. Litho)

1975 (15 Apr). International Amateur Radio Union Conference,
Warsaw. P 11½.

2356	**645** 1z.50 multicoloured	40	35

646 Stone Pine and   **647** Hands holding   **648** Flags of Member
Tatra Mountains   Tulips and Rifle   Countries

(Des A. Balcerzak. Photo)

1975 (30 Apr). Centenary of National Mountain Guides'
Association. T **646** and similar multicoloured designs. P 11.

2357	1z. Type **646**	20	15
	a. Pair. Nos. 2357/8	45	35
2358	1z. Gentian and Tatra Mountains	20	15
2359	1z.50 Sudety Mountains (horiz)	40	30
	a. Pair. Nos. 2359/60	85	65
2360	1z.50 Yew-tree branch (horiz)	40	30
2361	4z. Beskidy Mountains	70	40
	a. Pair. Nos. 2361/2	1·50	85
2362	4z. Arnica blossoms	70	40
2357/2362	Set of 6	2·30	1·50

Designs of the same value were issued in se-tenant pairs forming
composite designs.

(Des H. Chyliński. Photo)

1975 (9 May). 30th Anniv of Victory over Fascism. P 11½×11.

2363	**647** 1z.50 multicoloured	40	35

(Des W. Surowiecki. Photo)

1975 (14 May). 20th Anniv of Warsaw Treaty Organisation. P 11½×11.

2364	**648** 1z.50 multicoloured	40	35

649 Hens

(Des A. Balcerzak. Photo)

1975 (23 June). 26th European Zootechnical Federation Congress,
Warsaw. T **649** and similar horiz designs. Multicoloured. P 11½.

2365	50g. Type **649**	15	15
2366	1z. Geese	20	15
2367	1z.50 Cattle	30	20
2368	2z. Cow	35	30
2369	3z. Wielkopolska horse	40	35
2370	4z. Arab horses	85	40
2371	4z.50 Pigs	3·50	55
2372	5z. Sheep	3·75	1·20
2365/2372	Set of 8	8·50	3·00

650 "Apollo" and "Soyuz"
Spacecraft linked

(Des R. Dudzicki. Photo)

1975 (30 June). "Apollo-Soyuz" Space Link. T **650** and similar horiz
designs. Multicoloured. P 11×11½.

2373	1z.50 Type **650**	40	30
2374	4z.90 "Apollo" spacecraft	1·30	40
	a. Pair. Nos. 2374/5	2·75	85
2375	4z.90 "Soyuz" spacecraft	1·30	40
2373/2375	Set of 3	2·75	1·00

MS2376 119×156 mm. Nos. 2373×2, 2374×2 and
2375×2 .... 11·00 7·00
Nos. 2374/5 were issued together in se-tenant pairs within the
sheet.

651 Organisation   **652** UN Emblem
Emblem

(Des K. Tarkowska. Photo)

1975 (12 July). National Health Protection Fund. P 11½×11.

2377	**651** 1z.50 blue, black and silver	40	35

(Des A. Heidrich. Litho)

1975 (25 July). 30th Anniv of United Nations Organisation. P 11×11½.

2378	**652** 4z. multicoloured	85	40

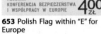

653 Polish Flag within "E" for   **654** "Bolek and Lolek"
Europe

(Des H. Chyliński. Litho)

1975 (30 July). European Security and Co-operation Conference, Helsinki. P 11×11½.
2379 **653** 4z. multicoloured.............................. 85 70

(Des H. Matuszewska. Photo)

1975 (30 Aug). Children's Television Characters. T **654** and similar horiz designs. Multicoloured. P 11×11½.
2380 50g. Type **654**................................. 20 15
2381 1z. "Jacek and Agatka".................... 30 20
2382 1z.50 "Reksio"................................... 40 30
2383 4z. "Telesfor".................................. 1·00 40
2380/2383 Set of 4................................. 1·70 95

655 Institute Emblem   **656** Women's Faces

(Des K. Rogaczewska. Litho)

1975 (1 Sept). 40th Session of International Institute of Statistics. P 11½×11.
2384 **655** 1z.50 multicoloured..................... 40 35

(Des S. Malecki. Photo)

1975 (8 Sept). International Women's Year. P 11.
2385 **656** 1z.50 multicoloured..................... 40 35

657 Albatros Biplane   **658** *Mary and Margaret* (emigrant ship) and Polish Settlers

(Des J. Brodowski. Litho)

1975 (25 Sept). 50th Anniv of First Polish Airmail Stamps. T **657** and similar horiz design. Multicoloured. P 11×11½.
2386 2z.40 Type **657**.............................. 40 35
2387 4z.90 Tail of Ilyushin Il-62M airplane of LOT ... 85 40

(Des T. Michaluk. Litho)

1975 (26 Sept). Bicentenary of American Revolution. T **658** and similar horiz designs. Multicoloured. P 11×11½.
2388 1z. Type **658**................................ 20 15
2389 1z.50 Polish Glass-works, Jamestown................ 30 20
2390 2z.70 H. Modrzejewska (actress).................. 40 30
2391 4z. K. Pulaski (soldier)....................... 70 40
2392 6z.40 T. Kościuszko (soldier)................... 1·10 70
2388/2392 Set of 5.............................. 2·40 1·60
MS2393 117×102 mm. 4z.90 Washington; 4z.90 Kościuszko; 4z.90 Pulaski. P 12.............. 2·75 1·70
No. **MS**2393 was issued with three *se-tenant* labels.

659 Frédéric Chopin   **660** "Self-Portrait"

(Des S. Malecki. Photo)

1975 (7 Oct). Ninth International Chopin Piano Competition. P 11½.
2394 **659** 1z.50 black, lavender and gold................ 40 35
No. 2394 was issued with *se-tenant* stamp-size label.

(Des H. Matuszewska. Photo)

1975 (9 Oct). Stamp Day and Birth Centenary of Xawery Dunikowski (sculptor). T **660** and similar vert designs. Multicoloured. P 11½×11.
2395 50g. Type **660**.............................. 20 15
2396 1z. "Breath"................................. 30 20
2397 1z.50 "Maternity"........................... 40 35
2398 8z. +4z. "Silesian Insurrectionists"........ 2·10 85
2395/2398 Set of 4............................. 2·75 1·40

661 Market Place, Kazimierz Dolny

(Des S. Malecki. Photo)

1975 (11 Nov). European Architectural Heritage Year. T **661** and similar design. P 14.
2399 1z. deep olive............................. 35 30
2400 1z.50 lake................................ 40 35
Design: Vert—1z.50 Town Hall, Zamość.

662 "Łódź" (W. Strzeminski)   **663** Henry IV's Eagle Gravestone Head (14th-century)

(Des Z. Stasik. Litho)

1975 (22 Nov). Łódź 1975 National Stamp Exhibition. P 12½.
2401 **662** 4z.50 multicoloured..................... 70 40
MS2402 80×101 mm. No. 2401..................... 2·75 1·70

(Des H. Matuszewska. Eng M. Kopecki (1z.). Des H. Matuszewska and K. Tarkowska. Eng M. Kopecki (1z.50). Des K. Tarkowska. Eng W. Morycińska (4z.))

1975 (29 Nov). Piast Dynasty of Silesia. T **663** and similar horiz designs. P 11½×12.
2403 1z. deep dull green........................ 20 15
2404 1z.50 sepia................................ 30 20
2405 4z. deep lilac............................. 70 40
2403/2405 Set of 3............................. 1·10 70
Designs:—1z.50 Prince Boleslaw seal (14th-century); 4z. Prince Jerzy Wilhelm coin (17th-century).

664 Symbolised figure "7"   **665** Ski Jumping

(Des W. Surowiecki (1z.), Z. Horodecki (1z.50). Photo)

1975 (8 Dec). Seventh Polish United Workers' Party Congress. T **664** and similar design. P 11½×11.
2406 1z. multicoloured.......................... 35 30
2407 1z.50 vermilion, ultramarine and silver............. 40 35
Design: 32×43 mm—1z.50 Party Initials ("P.Z.P.R.").

(Des H. Matuszewska. Photo)

1976 (10 Jan). Winter Olympic Games, Innsbruck. T **665** and similar horiz designs. Multicoloured. P 11×11½.
2408 50g. Type **665**.............................. 15 15
2409 1z. Ice-hockey............................. 20 15
2410 1z.50 Skiing............................... 30 15

2411	2z. Skating	40	20
2412	4z. Tobogganing	70	30
2413	6z.40 Shooting (Biathlon)	1·40	40
2408/2413	Set of 6	2·75	1·20

666 R. Trevithick's Steam Railway Locomotive, 1803

(Des S. Malecki. Photo)

1976 (13 Feb). History of the Railway Locomotive. T **666** and similar horiz designs. Multicoloured. P 11½.

2414	50g. Type **666**	20	15
2415	1z. Murray and Blenkinsop's steam locomotive and carriage, 1810	20	15
2416	1z.50 George Stephenson's locomotive *Rocket*, 1829	20	15
2417	1z.50 Polish "Universal" electric locomotive No. ET22-001, 1969	30	20
2418	2z.70 Robert Stephenson's locomotive *North Star*, 1837	35	20
2419	3z. Joseph Harrison's locomotive, 1840	40	30
2420	4z.50 Thomas Rogers, Locomotive 1855, USA	1·70	35
2421	4z.90 A. Xiężopolski (locomotive engineer) and series Ok22 steam locomotive, 1922	2·10	40
2414/2421	Set of 8	5·00	1·70

667 Flags of Member Countries

(Des Z. Stasik. Litho)

1976 (8 Mar). 20th Anniv of International Nuclear Research Institute. P 11½.

2422	**667** 1z.50 multicoloured	40	35

668 Early Telephone, Satellites and Radar   **669** Jantar Glider

(Des Z. Stasik. Photo)

1976 (10 Mar). Telephone Centenary. P 11.

2423	**668** 1z.50 multicoloured	40	35

(Des J. Brodowski. Recess)

1976 (27 Mar)–**78**. AIR. Contemporary Aviation. T **669** and similar vert designs. P 11½.

2424	5z. deep blue-green	85	30
2425	10z. sepia	1·70	35
2425a	20z. blackish olive (15.2.77)	3·75	40
2425b	50z. brown-lake (2.2.78)	7·00	1·40
2424/2425b	Set of 4	12·00	2·20

Designs:—10z. Mil Mi-6 helicopter; 20z. PZL-106 Kruk spraying crops; 50z. PZL-Mielec TS-11 Iskra jet trainer over Warsaw Castle.

670 Player   **671** Polish UN Soldier

(Des T. Michaluk. Photo)

1976 (8 Apr). World Ice Hockey Championships, Katowice. T **670** and similar vert design. Multicoloured. P 11½×11.

2426	1z. Type **670**	35	30
2427	1z.50 Player (*different*)	40	35

(Des B. Berg. Photo)

1976 (30 Apr). Polish United Nations Troops in Sinai. P 11×11½.

2428	**671** 1z.50 multicoloured	70	55

No. 2428 was issued with a *se-tenant* stamp-size label.

672 "Glory to the Sappers" (S. Kulon)   **673** "Interphil 76"

(Des K. Tarkowska. Photo)

1976 (8 May). War Memorials. T **672** and similar vert design. Multicoloured. P 11½.

2429	1z. Type **672**	40	40
2430	1z. 1st Polish Army Monument, Sandau/ Laba (B. Koniuszy)	40	40

(Des T. Michaluk. Litho)

1976 (20 May). Interphil 1976 International Stamp Exhibition, Philadelphia. P 11½×11.

2431	**673** 8z.40 multicoloured	1·50	75

674 Wielkopolski and Tawny Owl

(Des J. Brodowski. Photo)

1976 (22 May). National Parks. T **674** and similar horiz designs. Multicoloured. P 11½.

2432	90g. Type **674**	20	15
2433	1z. Wolinski and White-tailed Sea Eagle	30	15
2434	1z.50 Slowinski and Seagull	40	25
2435	4z.50 Bieszczadzki and Lynx	70	30
2436	5z. Ojcowski and Bat	85	40
2437	6z. Kampinoski and Elk	1·10	45
2432/2437	Set of 6	3·25	1·50

675 Peace Dove within Globe   **676** Fencing

(Des S. Malecki. Litho)

1976 (29 June). 25th Anniv of United Nations Postal Administration. P 11×11½.
2438 **675** 8z.40 multicoloured .... 1·50 45

(Des T. Michaluk. Photo (Nos. 2439/44). Eng M. Kopecki. Recess and photo (**MS**2445))

1976 (30 June). Olympic Games, Montreal. T **676** and similar horiz designs. Multicoloured. P 11×11½.
2439 50g. Type **676** 15 15
2440 1z. Cycling 15 15
2441 1z.50 Football 30 15
2442 4z.20 Boxing 70 25
2443 6z.90 Weight-lifting .... 1·10 45
2444 8z.40 Athletics .... 1·50 60
2439/2444 *Set of 6* .... 3·50 1·60
MS2445 78×94 mm. 10z.+5z. black and bright rose-red (Volleyball) (23×29 *mm*). P 11½ .... 4·25 2·30
No. **MS**2445 has both the stamp and the outer edges of the sheet perforated.

677 National Theatre

678 Aleksander Czekanowski and Baikal landscape

(Des S. Malecki. Litho)

1976 (12 July). Centenary of National Theatre, Poznań. P 11×11½.
2446 **677** 1z.50 deep yellow-green and orange 40 30

(Des T. Michaluk. Photo)

1976 (3 Sept). Death Centenary of Aleksander Czekanowski (geologist). P 11×11½.
2447 **678** 1z.50 multicoloured 40 30

679 "Sphinx"

(Des H. Matuszewska. Photo)

1976 (30 Sept). Stamp Day. Corinthian Vase Paintings (7th century B.C.). T **679** and similar multicoloured designs. P 11×11½ (vert) or 11×11½ (horiz).
2448 1z. Type **679** 20 15
2449 1z.50 "Siren" (*horiz*) 30 25
2450 2z. "Lion" (*horiz*) 40 30
2451 4z.20 "Bull" (*horiz*) 70 40
2452 4z.50 "Goat" (*horiz*) 85 45
2453 8z.+4z. "Sphinx" (*different*) .... 2·20 90
2448/2453 *Set of 6* .... 4·25 2·20

680 Warszawa "M-20"

(Des W. Surowiecki. Photo)

1976 (6 Nov). 25th Anniv of Żerań Motor-car Factory, Warsaw, T **680** and similar horiz designs. Multicoloured. P 11.
2454 1z. Type **680** 20 15
2455 1z.50 Warszawa "223" 30 25
2456 2z. Syrena "104" 40 30
2457 4z.90 Polski-Fiat "125-P" 85 60
2454/2457 *Set of 4* .... 1·60 1·20

MS2458 137×109 mm. Nos. 2454/7 .... 5·50 3·00
No. **MS**2458 was issued with two *se-tenant* labels.

681 Molten Steel Ladle

682 Congress Emblem

683 "Wirzbieto Epitaph" (painting on wood, 1425)

(Des M. Zabaglo. Litho)

1976 (26 Nov). Huta Katowice Steel Works. P 11.
2459 **681** 1z.50 multicoloured 40 30

(Des S. Malecki. Photo)

1976 (6 Dec). Eighth Polish Trade Unions Congress. P 11.
2460 **682** 1z.50 red-orange, bistre and sepia 40 30

(Des S. Malecki. Litho)

1976 (15 Dec). Polish Art. T **683** and similar vert design. Multicoloured. P 11×11½.
2461 1z. Type **683** 30 25
2462 6z. "Madonna and Child" (painted carving, *c* 1410) .... 1·00 45

684 *Zawrat* (tanker) at Oil Terminal, Gdańsk

685 Nurse and Patient

(Des S. Malecki. Photo)

1976 (29 Dec). Polish Ports. T **684** and similar horiz designs. Multicoloured. P 11.
2463 1z. Type **684** 20 15
2464 1z. *Gryf* (ferry) at Gdańsk 20 15
2465 1z.50 Loading *General Bem* (container ship), Gdynia 30 25
2466 1z.50 *Stefan Batory* (liner) leaving Gdynia 30 25
2467 2z. *Ziemia Szczecinska* (bulk carrier) loading at Szczecin 40 30
2468 4z.20 Loading coal, Świnoujscie 85 40
2469 6z.90 Hydrofoil and river boat, Kolobrzeg .... 1·30 45
2470 8z.40 Bulk carrier, tanker and coastal map....... 1·40 75
2463/2470 *Set of 8* .... 4·50 2·40

(Des E. Nozko-Paprocka. Litho)

1977 (24 Jan). Polish Red Cross. P 11½×11.
2471 **685** 1z.50 multicoloured 40 30

686 Order of Civil Defence Service

687 Ball in Road

(Des E. Nożko-Paprocka. Litho)

1977 (26 Feb). Polish Civil Defence. P 11.
2472 **686** 1z.50 multicoloured 40 30

(Des J. Raczko. Photo)

1977 (12 Mar). Child Road Safety Campaign. P 11.
2473 **687** 1z.50 multicoloured 40 30

688 Dewberries (*Rubus caesius*)

689 Computer Tape

(Des A. Balcerzak. Photo)

1977 (17 Mar). Wild Fruits. T **688** and similar vert designs. Multicoloured. P 11½×11.

2474	50g. Type **688**	15	15
2475	90g. Cowberries (*Vaccinium vitis-idaea*)	20	15
2476	1z. Wild Strawberries (*Fragaria vesca*)	30	15
2477	1z.50 Bilberries (*Vaccinium myrtillus*)	35	15
2478	2z. Raspberries (*Rubus idaeus*)	40	25
2479	4z.50 Sloes (*Prunus spinosa*)	70	25
2480	6z. Rose hips (*Rosa canina*)	1·00	30
2481	6z.90 Hazelnuts (*Corylus avellana*)	1·70	45
2474/2481 *Set of 8*		4·25	1·70

(Des W. Surowiecki. Litho)

1977 (4 Apr). 30th Anniv of Russian-Polish Technical Co-operation. P 11½×11.

2482	**689**	1z.50 multicoloured	40	30

690 Pendulum Traces and Emblem

691 "Toilet of Venus"

(Des K. Śliwka. Litho)

1977 (22 Apr). Seventh Polish Congress of Technology. P 11½×11.

2483	**690**	1z.50 multicoloured	40	30

(Des T. Michaluk. Recess (8z.), litho (others))

1977 (30 Apr). 400th Birth Anniv of Peter Paul Rubens (artist). T **691** and similar designs. Multicoloured. P 11½.

2484	1z. Type **691**	20	15
2485	1z.50 "Bathsheba at the Fountain" (detail)	30	25
2486	5z. "Hélèna Fourment with Fur Coat"	85	30
2487	6z. "Self-portrait"	1·00	45
2484/2487 *Set of 4*		2·10	1·00
MS2488 76×62 mm. 8z.+4z. sepia ("The Stoning of St. Stephen") (21×26 *mm*). P 11½		3·50	1·80

No. **MS**2488 has both the stamp and the outer edges of the sheet perforated. It also exists printed in black with the face value obliterated with wavy lines; this was not valid for postage.

692 Dove

693 Cyclist

(Des W. Freudenreich. Litho)

1977 (6 May). World Peace Congress, Warsaw. P 11×11½.

2489	**692**	1z.50 bright blue, black and lemon	40	30

(Des T. Michaluk. Photo)

1977 (6 May). 30th International Peace Cycle Race. P 11×11½.

2490	**693**	1z.50 multicoloured	40	30

694 Wolf (*Canis lupus*)

695 "The Violinist" (Jacob Toorenvliet)

(Des H. Matuszewska. Photo)

1977 (12 May). Endangered Animals. T **694** and similar vert designs. Multicoloured. P 11½×11.

2491	1z. Type **694**	35	25
2492	1z.50 Great Bustard (*Otis tarda*)	50	30
2493	1z.50 Common Kestrel (*Falco tinnunculus*)	50	30
2494	6z. European Otter (*Lutra lutra*)	1·00	45
2491/2494 *Set of 4*		2·10	1·20

1977 (16 May). Amphilex 77 International Stamp Exhibition, Amsterdam. P 11½×11.

2495	**695**	6z. multicoloured	1·00	75
Printed in sheets of six.				

696 Midsummer's Day Bonfire

(Des K. Tarkowska. Photo)

1977 (13 June). Folk Customs. T **696** and similar designs from 19th-century wood engravings. Multicoloured. P 11×11½ (horiz) or 11½×11 (vert).

2496	90g. Type **696**	20	15
2497	1z. Easter cock (*vert*)	30	15
2498	1z.50 "Smigus" (dousing of women on Easter Monday, Miechów district) (*vert*)	35	15
2499	3z. Harvest Festival, Sandomierz district (*vert*)	40	25
2500	6z. Children with Christmas crib (*vert*)	1·00	30
2501	8z.40 Mountain wedding dance	1·70	45
2496/2501 *Set of 6*		3·50	1·30

697 H. Wieniawski and Music Clef

698 *Parnassius apollo*

(Des Z. Kaja. Litho)

1977 (30 June). Wieniawski International Music Competition, Poznań. P 11½×11.

2502	**697**	1z.50 black, gold and red-orange	40	30

(Des J. Wysocki. Photo)

1977 (22 Aug). Butterflies. T **898** and similar horiz designs. Multicoloured. P 11.

2503	1z. Type **698**	30	15
2504	1z. *Nymphalis polychloros*	30	15
2505	1z.50 *Nymphalis antiopa*	40	30
2506	1z.50 *Papilio machaon*	40	30
2507	5z. *Fabriciana adippe*	1·40	45
2508	6z.90 *Argynnis paphia*	2·75	1·10
2503/2508 *Set of 8*		5·00	2·20

699 Keyboard and Arms of Slupsk

700 Feliks Dzierżyński

(Des S. Malecki. Litho)

1977 (3 Sept). Piano Festival, Slupsk. P 11½.
2509 **699** 1z.50 bright mve, black and grey-green. 40 30

(Des W. Surowiecki. Litho)

1977 (10 Sept). Birth Centenary of Feliks E. Dzierżyński (Russian politician). P 11½×11.
2510 **700** 1z.50 bistre-brown and deep brown-ochre....................... 40 30

701 "Sputnik" circling Earth

702 Silver Dinar (11th century)

(Des Z. Stasik. Litho)

1977 (1 Oct). 60th Anniv of Russian Revolution and 20th Anniv of First Artificial Satellite (1st issue). P 11×11½.
2511 **701** 1z.50 ultramarine and cerise..................... 55 45
MS2512 99×125 mm. No. 2511×3 plus three labels. P 12 2·10 1·50
No. 2511 was issued *se-tenant* with a label depicting the Winter Palace, Leningrad.
See also No. 2527.

(Des Z. Horodecki. Photo)

1977 (9 Oct). Stamp Day. Polish Coins. T **702** and similar vert designs. Multicoloured. P 11½×11.
2513 50g. Type **702** 20 15
2514 1z. Cracow grosz, 14th century 30 25
2515 1z.50 Legnica thaler, 17th century 40 25
2516 4z.20 Gdańsk guilder, 18th century 70 30
2517 4z.50 Silver 5z. coin, 1936.................. 85 40
2518 6z. Millenary 100z. coin, 1966.................. 1·00 45
2513/2518 *Set of 6*.................. 3·00 1·60

703 Wolin Gate, Kamień Pomorski

704 "Sputnik 1" and "Mercury" Capsule

(Des J. Brodowski. Photo)

1977 (21 Nov). Architectural Monuments. T **703** and similar designs. Multicoloured. P 11½×11 (vert) or 11×11½ (horiz).
2519 1z. Type **703** 30 25
2520 1z. Larch church, Dębno......................... 30 25
2521 1z.50 Monastery, Przasnysz (*horiz*) 40 30
2522 1z.50 Plock cathedral (*horiz*)..................... 40 30
2523 6z. Kórnik Castle (*horiz*).................... 1·00 40
2524 6z.90 Palace and garden, Wilanów (*horiz*)...... 1·10 45
2519/2524 *Set of 6*..................... 3·25 1·80

1977 (12 Dec). Polish Folklore. 16th-century Wood-carvings (2nd series). Horiz designs as T **638**. Recess. P 11½×11.
2525 4z. blackish olive......................... 70 40
2526 4z.50 deep brown......................... 85 45
Designs:—4z. Bird snaring; 4z.50 Beekeeper and hives.

1977 (28 Dec). 20th Anniv of First Artificial Satellite (2nd issue). Photo. P 11×11½.
2527 **704** 6z.90 multicoloured........................ 1·10 75
  a. Tête-bêche (horiz pair)........................ 2·50 2·00
  b. Sheet of 6. No. 2527, plus 2 labels 8·50 6·00
No. 2527 was issued in sheets of six stamps and two different labels, depicting "Sputnik 1" or "Explorer 1". The sheet was arranged in four rows of two, the labels being in the top right and bottom left positions. The latter label and the three stamps of the right-hand vertical row were printed inverted.

705 DN Category Iceboats

(Des M. Raducki. Litho)

1978 (6 Feb). Sixth World Ice Sailing Championships. T **705** and similar horiz design. P 11.
2528 1z.50 black, pale grey-blue and azure.............. 40 30
  a. Vert strip. Nos. 2528/9 plus label.............. 85 65
2529 1z.50 black, pale grey-blue and azure.............. 40 30
Design:—No. 2529, Close-up of DN iceboat.
Nos. 2528/9 were issued together *se-tenant* with an intervening label bearing the Championships emblem, within sheets of 16 stamps and eight labels.

706 Electric Locomotive and Katowice Railway Station

(Des S. Malecki. Photo)

1978 (28 Feb). Railway Engines. T **706** and similar horiz designs. Multicoloured. P 11½.
2530 50g. Type **706**...................... 20 15
2531 1z. Steam locomotive No. Py 27 and tender No. 731, Żnin-Gąsawa railway 30 15
2532 1z. Streamlined steam locomotive No. Pm36-1 (1936) and Cegielski's factory, Poznań.................. 30 15
2533 1z.50 Electric locomotive and Otwock station.................. 40 25
2534 1z.50 Steam locomotive No. 17KDM and Warsaw Stalowa station.................. 40 25
2535 4z.50 Steam locomotive No. Ty51 and Gdynia station.................. 70 30
2536 5z. Steam locomotive No. Tr21 and locomotive factory, Chrzanów 85 40
2537 6z. Cockerill steam locomotive and Vienna station.................. 1·40 45
2530/2537 *Set of 8*.................. 4·00 1·90

707 Czeslaw Tański and Glider

708 Tackle

(Des J. Brodowski. Photo)

1978 (15 Apr). Aviation History and 50th Anniv of Polish Aero Club. T **707** and similar multicoloured designs. P 11½×11 (horiz) or 11½×11 (vert).
2538 50g. Type **707**.......................... 20 15
2539 1z. Franciszek Żwirko and Stanislaw Wigura with RWD-6 SP-AHN aircraft (*vert*).................. 30 15
2540 1z.50 Stanislaw Skarżyński and RWD-5 bis SP-AJU monoplane (*vert*).................. 40 25
2541 4z.20 Mil Mi-2 helicopter SP-WXA (*vert*).......... 70 30
2542 6z.90 PZL-104 Wilga 35 monoplane .... 1·80 40

2543	8z.40 SZD-45 Ogar powered glider....................	1·70	45
2538/2543 Set of 6..		4·50	1·50

1978 (12 May). World Cup Football Championship, Argentina. T **708** and similar horiz design. Multicoloured. P 11½×11 (1z.50) or 11×11½ (6z.90).

2544	1z.50 Type **708**	40	30
2545	6z.90 Ball on field	1·00	45

709 Biennial Emblem

710 Kazimierz Stanislaw Gzowski (bridge engineer)

(Des W. Jankowski. Litho)

1978 (1 June). Seventh International Poster Biennial, Warsaw. P 11½.

2546	**709** 1z.50 magenta, greenish yellow and bluish violet....................................	40	30

(Des H. Matuszewska. Photo)

1978 (6 June). Capex 78 International Stamp Exhibition, Toronto. Sheet 68×79 mm. P 11½×11.

MS2547	**710** 8z.40+4z. multicoloured	2·75	1·50

711 Polonez Saloon Car

1978 (10 June). Car Production. Photo. P 11.

2548	**711** 1z.50 multicoloured	40	30

712 Fair Emblem

(Des W. Freudenreich. Litho)

1978 (10 June). 50th International Fair, Poznań. P 11.

2549	**712** 1z.50 multicoloured	40	30

713 Miroslaw Hermaszewski

714 Globe containing Face

1978 (27 June). First Pole in Space. T **713** and similar horiz design. Multicoloured. P 11½×11 (1z.50) or 11×11½ (6z.90).

A. With date "27.6.1978"

2550A	1z.50 Type **713**	40	30
2551A	6z.90 Hermaszewski and globe	1·10	45

B. Without date

2550B	1z.50 Type **713**	40	30
2551B	6z.90 Hermaszewski and globe	1·70	75

Nos. 2550B/1B were each printed in sheets of six stamps and two different labels (*price* £25).

A similar set of stamps portraying Major Jankowski, the stand-by cosmonaut, was prepared but not issued.

(Des S. Malecki. Litho)

1978 (12 July). 11th World Youth and Students' Festival. Havana. P 11½.

2552	**714** 1z.50 multicoloured	40	30

715 Flowers

716 Anopheles maculipennis and Malaria Organisms

(Des S. Malecki. Photo)

1978 (20 July). 30th Anniv of Polish Youth Union. Sheet 69×79 mm. P 11½×11.

MS2553	**715** 1z.50 multicoloured........................	1·00	75

(Des T. Konarski. Litho)

1978 (19 Aug). Fourth International Congress of Parasitologists, Warsaw and Cracow. T **716** and similar vert design. Multicoloured. P 11½×11.

2554	1z.50 Type **716**	40	30
2555	6z. *Gossina palpalis* and sleeping sickness organisms........................	1·00	45

717 Pedunculate Oak (*Quercus robur*)

(Des J. Towpik. Photo German Bank Note Ptg Co, Leipzig)

1978 (6 Sept). Environment Protection. Trees. T **717** and similar vert designs. Multicoloured. P 14.

2556	50g. Norway Maple (*Acer platanoides*).............	20	15
2557	1z. Type **717**	30	15
2558	1z.50 White Poplar (*Populus alba*).......................	40	25
2559	4z.20 Scots Pine (*Pinus silvestris*)........................	65	30
2560	4z.50 White Willow (*Salix alba*)........................	70	40
2561	6z. Birch (*Betula verrucosa*)..................................	1·00	45
2556/2561 Set of 6..		3·00	1·50

718 "The Battle of Grunwald" (detail, Jan Matejko)

719 Communications

(Des K. Tarkowska. Photo)

1978 (8 Sept). PRAGA 1978 International Stamp Exhibition. Sheet 69×79 mm. P 11½×11.

MS2562	**718** 6z. multicoloured	2·75	1·50

(Des Z. Stasik. Litho)

1978 (20 Sept). 20th Anniv of Socialist Countries' Communications Organization. P 11.

2563	**719** 1z.50 dull vermilion, greenish blue and royal blue	40	30

720 "Peace" (André Le Brun)

721 Polish Unit of UN Middle East Force

(Des J. Brodowski. Litho)

1978 (30 Sept)–79. P 12½.
2564	**720**	1z. deep reddish violet	30	15
		a. Perf 11	30	15
2565		1z.50 deep turquoise-blue (28.4.79)	35	25
2565a		2z. deep brown (30.11.79)	40	30
2565b		2z.50 ultramarine (5.11.79)	70	45
2564/2565b Set of 4			1·60	1·20

(Des T. Michaluk. Photo)

1978 (6 Oct). 35th Anniv of Polish People's Army. T **721** and similar horiz designs. Multicoloured. P 11½.
2566		1z.50 Colour party of Tadeusz Kosciuszko 1st Warsaw Infantry Division	40	30
2567		1z.50 Colour party of Mechanized Unit	40	30
2568		1z.50 Type **721**	40	30
2566/2568 Set of 3			1·10	80

722 "Portrait of a Young Man" (Raphael)

723 Janusz Korczak with Children

(Des J. Wysocki. Photo)

1978 (9 Oct). Stamp Day. P 11.
2569	**722**	6z. multicoloured	1·00	75

(Des T. Konarski. Litho)

1978 (11 Oct). Birth Centenary of Janusz Korczak (pioneer of children's education). P 11½x11.
2570	**723**	1z.50 multicoloured	55	45

724 Wojciech Boguslawski

725 Polish Combatants' Monument and Eiffel Tower

(Des S. Malecki. Litho)

1978 (1 Nov). Polish Dramatists. T **724** and similar square designs. Multicoloured. P 11½.
2571		50g. Type **724**	15	15
2572		1z. Aleksander Fredro	20	15
2573		1z.50 Juliusz Slowacki	30	25
2574		2z. Adam Mickiewicz	40	30
2575		4z.50 Stanislaw Wyspiański	85	40
2576		6z. Gabriela Zapolska	1·00	45
2571/2576 Set of 6			2·50	1·50

(Des A. Heidrich. Photo)

1978 (2 Nov). Monument to Polish Combatants in France, Paris. P 11x11½.
2577	**725**	1z.50 multicoloured	55	45

726 Wild Horses (*Equus przewalskii*)

727 Party Flag

(Des J. Towpik. Photo)

1978 (10 Nov). 50th Anniv of Warsaw Zoo. T **726** and similar horiz designs. Multicoloured. P 11x11½.
2578		50g. Type **726**	15	15
2579		1z. Polar Bears (*Thalarctos maritimus*)	20	15
2580		1z.50 Indian Elephants (*Elaphas maximus*)	30	15
2581		2z. Jaguars (*Panthera onca*)	40	25
2582		4z.20 Grey Seals (*Halichoerus grypus*)	65	30
2583		4z.50 Hartebeests (*Alcelaphus caama*)	70	40
2584		6z. Mandrills (*Mandrillus sphinx*)	1·70	45
2578/2584 Set of 7			3·75	1·70

(Des W. Freudenreich. Photo)

1978 (15 Dec). 30th Anniv of Polish United Workers' Party. P 11x11½.
2585	**727**	1z.50 orange-vermilion, gold and black.	40	30

728 Stanislaw Dubois

729 Ilyushin Il-62M and Fokker F.VIIb/3m P-POZM

(Des J. Brodowski. Photo)

1978 (15 Dec). Leaders of Polish Workers' Movement. T **728** and similar vert designs. P 11½x11.
2586		1z.50 steel blue and cerise	40	30
2587		1z.50 blackish lilac and cerise	40	30
2588		1z.50 deep brown-olive and cerise	40	30
2589		1z.50 reddish brown and cerise	40	30
2586/2589 Set of 4			1·40	1·10

Portraits:—No. 2586, Type **728**; 2587, Aleksander Zawadzki; 2588, Julian Leński; 2589, Adolf Warski.

(Des J. Bokiewicz. Photo)

1979 (2 Jan). 50th Anniv of LOT Polish Airlines. P 11x11½.
2590	**729**	6z.90 multicoloured	1·10	45

730 Train

(Des K. Tarkowska. Photo)

1979 (13 Jan). International Year of the Child. T **730** and similar horiz designs showing children's paintings. Multicoloured. P 11.
2591		50g. Type **730**	20	15
2592		1z. Mother with children	30	25
2593		1z.50 Children playing	40	30
2594		6z. Family group	1·10	45
2591/2594 Set of 4			1·80	1·00

731 "Portrait of Artist's Wife with Foxgloves" (Karol Mondrala)

732 A. Frycz Modrzewski (political writer), King Stefan Batory and J. Zamoyski (chancellor)

(Des S. Malecki. Recess)

1979 (5 Mar). Contemporary Graphics. T **731** and similar designs. P 11½.

2595	50g. deep lilac	20	15
2596	1z. blackish olive	30	25
2597	1z.50 indigo	40	30
2598	4z.50 purple-brown	85	40
2595/2598 Set of 4		1·60	1·00

Designs: Horiz—50g. "Lightning" (Edmund Bartlomiejczyk). Vert—1z.50 "The Musicians" (Tadeusz Kulisiewicz); 4z.50 "Head of a Man" (Wladyslaw Skoczylas).

(Des T. Michaluk. Recess and photo)

1979 (12 Mar). 400th Anniv of Royal Tribunal in Piotrków Trybunalski (1978). P 11½.

2599	**732**	1z.50 pale grey-brown and blackish brown	40	30

733 Pole Vaulting

(Des E. Nożko-Paprocka (10z.), M. Raducki (others). Recess and photo (10z.), photo (others))

1979 (26 Mar–19 May). 60th Anniv of Polish Olympic Committee. T **733** and similar horiz designs. P 11½.

2600	1z. brown-lilac, deep brown and bright crimson	30	15
2601	1z.50 brown-lilac, deep brown and bright crimson	40	25
2602	6z. brown-lilac, deep brown and bright crimson	70	30
2603	8z.40 brown-lilac, deep brown and bright crimson	1·10	45
2600/2603 Set of 4		2·30	1·00
MS2604	102×61 mm. 110z.+5z. blackish brown. Imperf (19 May)	2·10	1·80

Designs:—1z.50 High jumping; 6z. Skiing; 8z.40 Horse riding; 10z. Olympic rings.

734 European Flounder (*Platichthys flesus*)

(Des J. Brodowski. Photo)

1979 (26 Apr). Centenary of Polish Angling. T **734** and similar horiz designs. Multicoloured. P 11½.

2605	50g. Type **734**	15	15
2606	90g. Eurasian Perch (*Perca fluviatilis*)	20	15
2607	1z. European Greyling (*Thymallus thymallus*)	20	15
2608	1z.50 Atlantic Salmon (*Salmo salar*)	30	15
2609	2z. Brown Trout (*Salmo trutta*)	40	25
2610	4z.50 Northern Pike (*Esox lucius*)	70	30
2611	5z. Common Carp (*Cyprinus carpio*)	1·00	40
2612	6z. Wels (*Silurus glanis*)	1·40	45
2605/2612 Set of 8		4·00	1·80

735 "30 Years of RWPG"

736 Soldier, Civilian and Congress Emblem

(Des W. Freudenreich. Litho)

1979 (30 Apr). 30th Anniv of Council for Mutual Economic Aid. P 11×11½.

2613	**735**	1z.50 orange-vermilion, ultramarine and greenish blue	40	30

(Des S. Malecki. Litho)

1979 (7 May). Sixth Congress of Association of Fighters for Liberty and Democracy, Warsaw. P 11.

2614	**736**	1z.50 orange-vermilion and black	40	30

737 St. George's Church, Sofia

738 Pope and Auschwitz Concentration Camp Memorial

(Des Z. Stasik. Photo)

1979 (15 May). Philaserdica '79 International Stamp Exhibition, Sofia, Bulgaria. P 11×11½.

2615	**737**	1z.50 pale orange, reddish brown and carmine-vermilion	40	30

(Des S. Malecki. Photo)

1979 (2 June). Visit of Pope John Paul II. T **738** and similar vert design. Multicoloured. P 11½×11 (50z.) or 11 (others).

2616	1z.50 Pope and St. Mary's Church, Cracow	70	40
2617	8z.40 Type **738**	1·40	45
MS2618	68×79 mm. 50z. Framed portrait of Pope (26×35 mm)	14·00	10·50

No. **MS**2618 has a gold frame. A version with a silver frame exists from a limited printing (*price £70*).

739 *Książę Ksawery* (river paddle-steamer) and Old Warsaw

740 Statue of Tadeusz Kosciuszko (Marian Konieczny)

(Des S. Malecki. Litho)

1979 (15 June). 150th Anniv of Navigation on River Vistula. T **739** and similar horiz designs. Multicoloured. P 11.

2619	1z. Type **739**	30	15
2620	1z.50 *General Świerczewski* (river paddle-steamer) and Gdańsk	40	25
2621	4z.50 *Żubr* (river tug) and Plock	70	30
2622	6z. *Syrena* (passenger launch) and modern Warsaw	85	45
2619/2622 Set of 4		2·00	1·00

(Des J. Brodowski. Photo)

1979 (1 July). Monument to Tadeusz Kosciuszko in Philadelphia. P 11½.

2623	**740**	8z.40 multicoloured	1·00	60

741 Mining Machinery

742 Heraldic Eagle

(Des Z. Stasik. Photo German Bank Note Ptg Co, Leipzig)

1979 (14 July). Wieliczka Salt Mine. T **741** and similar horiz design. P 14.
2624   1z. orange-brown and black............................. 30   25
2625   1z.50 deep turquoise-green and black.............. 40   30
Design:—1z.50 Salt crystals.

(Des J. Brodowski. Photo)

1979 (21 July–2 Sept). 35th Anniv of Polish People's Republic. T **742** and similar vert design. P 11½×11.
2626   1z.50 vermilion, black and silver......................... 40   30
2627   1z.50 vermilion, silver and greenish blue......... 40   30
MS2628 120×84 mm. Nos. 2626/7 plus label (2.9.79).. 1·00   90
Design:—No. 2626, Girl and stylized flag.
No **MS**2628 was sold at the Katowice '79 Stamp Exhibition for 10z. including admission.

743 Rowland Hill and 1860 Stamp

(Des S. Malecki. Litho)

1979 (16 Aug). Death Centenary of Rowland Hill. P 11½×11.
2629   **743**   6z. dull blue, black and orange............ 1·10   45

744 "The Rape of Europa"   **745** Wojciech
(Bernardo Strozzi)   Jastrzebowski

(Des Z. Stasik. Photo)

1979 (20 Aug). International Stamp Exhibitions. Sheet 86×63 mm. P 11×11½.
MS2630 **744** 10z. multicoloured...................................... 2·10   1·50

(Des J. Wysocki. Photo)

1979 (27 Aug). Seventh Congress of International Ergonomic Association, Warsaw. P 11½×11.
2631 **745** 1z.50 multicoloured............................... 40   30

746 Monument (Wincenty Kućma)

(Des A. Heidrich. Photo)

1979 (1 Sept). Unveiling of Monument to Defenders of Polish Post, Gdańsk, and 40th Anniv of German Occupation. P 11×11½.
2632 **746** 1z.50 brownish grey, sepia and orange-
             vermilion... 40   30
MS2633 79×69 mm. **746** 10z.+5z. brownish grey,
sepia and orange-vermilion. Imperf............... 2·75   2·30

747 Radio Mast and Telecommunications Emblem

(Des W. Freudenreich. Photo)

1979 (24 Sept). 50th Anniv of International Radio Communication Advisory Committee. P 11×11½.
2634 **747** 1z.50 multicoloured............................... 40   30

748 Violin

749 Statue of Kazimierz Pulaski, Buffalo (K. Danilewicz)

(Des W. Freudenreich. Photo)

1979 (25 Sept). Wieniawski Young Violinists' Competition, Lublin. P 11×11½.
2635 **748** 1z.50 deep ultramarine, red-orange and
             emerald...................................... 40   30

(Des J. Brodowski. Photo)

1979 (1 Oct). Death Bicentenary of Kazimierz Pulaski (American Revolution hero). P 11½.
2636 **749** 8z.40 multicoloured.............................. 1·50   45

750 Franciszek Jóźwiak (first Commander)

(Des W. Surowiecki. Photo)

1979 (3 Oct). 35th Anniv of Civic Militia and Security Force. P 11½×11.
2637 **750** 1z.50 blue and gold.................................... 40   30

751 Post Office in Rural Area

(Des A. Balcerzak. Photo)

1979 (9 Oct). Stamp Day. T **751** and similar horiz designs. Multicoloured. P 11½.
2638   1z. Type **751** 30   15
2639   1z.50 Parcel sorting machinery..................... 35   25
2640   4z.50 Loading mail onto train....................... 85   30
2641   6z. Mobile post office.................................. 1·00   45
2638/2641 *Set of 4*....................................... 2·30   1·00

752 "The Holy Family" (Ewelina Pękasowa)

753 "Soyuz 30–Salyut 6" Complex and Crystal

(Des H. Matuszewska. Photo)

1979 (4 Dec). Polish Folk Art. Glass Paintings. T **752** and similar horiz design. Multicoloured. P 11½×11 (2z.) or 11×11½ (6z.90).
2642   2z. Type **752** 40   30
2643   6z.90 "The Nativity" (Zdzisław Walczak)........... 1·00   45

(Des Z. Stasik. Photo)

1979 (28 Dec). Space Achievements. T **753** and similar vert designs. Multicoloured. P 11½×11.

2644	1z. Type **753** (First anniv of first Pole in space)	20	15
2645	1z.50 "Kopernik" and "Copernicus" satellites ...	30	15
2646	2z. "Lunik 2" and "Ranger 7" spacecraft (20th anniv of first unmanned Moon landing)	40	25
2647	4z.50 Yuri Gagarin and "Vostok 1"	70	30
2648	6z.90 Neil Armstrong, lunar module and "Apollo 11" (10th anniv of first man on Moon)	1·10	45
2644/2648 Set of 5		2·40	1·20
MS2649 120×103 mm. Nos. 2644/8, plus label (*sold at* 20z.90)		3·00	2·50

754 Coach and Four

755 Slogan on Map of Poland

1980 (31 Jan). 150th Anniv of Sieraków Stud Farm. T **754** and similar vert designs. Multicoloured. Photo. P 11½.

2650	1z. Type **754**	20	15
2651	2z. Horse and groom	30	15
2652	2z.50 Sulky racing	40	15
2653	3z. Hunting	55	25
2654	4z. Horse-drawn sledge	70	30
2655	6z. Haywain	90	40
2656	6z.50 Grooms exercising horses	1·00	40
2657	6z.90 Show jumping	1·10	45
2650/2657 Set of 8		4·75	2·00

(Des A. Barecki and Z. Stasik. Photo)

1980 (11 Feb). Eighth Polish United Workers' Party Congress. T **755** and similar vert design. Multicoloured. P 11½×11 (No. 2658) or 11½.

2658	2z.50 Type **755**	40	40
2659	2z.50 Poster by Janusz Stannby (26×46 *mm*).	40	40

756 Horse Jumping

1980 (31 Mar). Winter Olympic Games, Lake Placid, and Olympic Games, Moscow. T **756** and similar horiz designs. Multicoloured. Photo. P 12×11½.

2660	2z. Type **756**	35	15
2661	2z.50 Archery	40	25
2662	6z.50 Skiing	85	30
2663	8z.40 Volleyball	1·50	45
2660/2663 Set of 4		2·75	1·00
MS2664 87×69 mm. 10z.50+5z. Kayak (42×30 *mm*). P 11×11½		3·25	3·00

757 Town Plan and Old Town Hall

(Des Z. Stasik. Litho)

1980 (3 Apr). 400th Anniv of Zamość. P 11½.

2665	**757** 2z.50 buff, reddish brown and deep green	40	30

758 Satellite orbiting Earth

759 Seals of Poland and Russia

1980 (12 Apr). Intercosmos Space Programme. Sheet 63×79 mm. Photo. P 11½×11.

MS2666 **758** 6z.90+3z. multicoloured	1·80	1·70

Stamps of a similar design were issued by Bulgaria, Czechoslovakia, East Germany and Russia.

(Des A. Barecki. Litho)

1980 (21 Apr). 35th Anniv of Soviet–Polish Friendship Treaty. P 11½.

2667	**759** 2z.50 multicoloured	40	40

760 "Lenin in Cracow" (Zbigniew Pronaszko)

761 Workers with Red Flag

(Des J. Brodowski. Photo)

1980 (22 Apr). 110th Birth Anniv of Lenin. P 11.

2668	**760** 2z.50 multicoloured	40	40

(Des K. Tarkowska. Photo)

1980 (1 May). 75th Anniv of Russian 1905 Revolution. P 11½×11.

2669	**761** 2z.50 vermilion, black and lemon	40	40

762 Dove

763 Shield with Crests of Member Nations

(Des H. Matuszewska. Photo)

1980 (9 May). 35th Anniv of Liberation. P 11½.

2670	**762** 2z.50 multicoloured	40	40

(Des Z. Stasik. Litho)

1980 (14 May). 25th Anniv of Warsaw Pact. P 11½×11.

2671	**763** 2z. grey-black and orange-red	40	30

For a full range of Stanley Gibbons catalogues, please visit **www.stanleygibbons.com**

764 Speleological Expedition, Cuba   **765** School and Arms

(Photo German Bank Note Ptg Co, Leipzig)

1980 (22 May). Polish Scientific Expeditions. T **764** and similar horiz designs. Multicoloured. P 14.

2672	2z. Type **764**	30	25
2673	2z. Antarctic	30	25
2674	2z.50 Archaeology, Syria	40	30
2675	2z.50 Ethnology, Mongolia	40	30
2676	6z.50 Mountaineering, Nepal	1·00	40
2677	8z.40 Palaeontology, Mongolia	1·70	45
2672/2677	Set of 6	3·75	1·80

(Des A. Heidrich. Photo)

1980 (7 June). 800th Anniv of Malachowianka School, Plock. P 11×11½.
2678	**765**	2z. dull yellowish green and black	40	30

766 Clathrus cancellatus (Clathrus ruber)   **767** T. Ziółkowski and Lwów

(Des A. Balcerzak. Photo)

1980 (30 June). Fungi. T **766** and similar vert designs. Multicoloured. P 11½×11.

2679	2z. Type **766**	30	25
2680	2z. Xerocomus parasiticus	30	25
2681	2z.50 Strobilomyces floccopus	40	30
2682	2z.50 Phallus hadriani	40	30
2683	8z. Sparassis crispa	1·10	45
2684	10z.50 Langermannia gigantea	1·40	55
2679/2684	Set of 6	3·50	1·90

(Des S. Malecki. Litho)

1980 (21 July). Polish Merchant Navy School. Cadet Ships and their Captains. T **767** and similar horiz designs. P 11.

2685	2z. black, bright mauve and bright violet	30	15
2686	2z.50 black, greenish blue and new blue	35	15
2687	6z. black, pale green and blue-green	70	25
2688	6z.50 black, olive-yellow and yellow-olive	85	30
2689	6z.90 black, brownish grey and slate-green	1·00	40
2690	8z.40 black, cobalt and blue-green	1·40	45
2685/2690	Set of 6	4·25	1·50

Designs:—2z.50 A. Garnuszewski and *Antoni Garnuszewski*; 6z. A. Ledóchowski and *Zenit*; 6z.50 K. Porębski and *Jan Turlejski*; 6z.90 G. Kański and *Horyzont*; 8z.40 K. Maciejewicz and *Dar Pomorza*.

768 Town Hall   **769** Atropa belladonna   **770** Jan Kochanowski

(Des S. Malecki. Photo)

1980 (26 July). Millenary of Sandomir. P 11×11½.
2691	**768**	2z.50 olive-brown and black	55	45

1980 (15 Aug). Medicinal Plants. T **769** and similar vert designs. Multicoloured. Photo. P 11½×11.

2692	2z. Type **769**	20	15
2693	2z.50 Datura innoxia	30	15
2694	3z.40 Valeriana officinalis	40	25
2695	5z. Mentha piperita	70	30
2696	6z.50 Calendula officinalis	1·00	40
2697	8z. Salvia officinalis	1·70	45
2692/2697	Set of 6	3·75	1·50

(Des W. Chomicz. Litho)

1980 (20 Aug). 450th Birth Anniv of Jan Kochanowski (poet). P 11.
2698	**770**	2z.50 multicoloured	55	45

1980 (2 Sept). POSTAGE DUE. As Type D **190** but redrawn without imprint at foot. Litho. P 12½.

D2699	D **190**	1z. Venetian red	30	25
D2700		2z. drab	40	30
D2701		3z. slate-lilac	55	45
D2702		5z. brown	1·00	60
D2699/2702	Set of 4		2·00	1·40

771 UN General Assembly

(Des J. Bokiewicz. Photo)

1980 (19 Sept). 35th Anniv of United Nations Organization. P 11×11½.
2703	**771**	8z.40 deep brown, light blue and vermilion	1·50	75

772 Chopin and Trees

1980 (2 Oct). Tenth International Chopin Piano Competition, Warsaw. Litho. P 11½.
2704	**772**	6z.90 multicoloured	1·00	45

773 Postman emptying Post Box

(Des A. Balcerzak. Photo)

1980 (9 Oct). Stamp Day. T **773** and similar horiz designs. Multicoloured. P 11½.

2705	2z. Type **773**	35	25
2706	2z.50 Mail sorting	40	30
2707	6z. Loading mail on to airplane	1·00	40
2708	6z.50 Letter boxes	1·40	45
2705/2708	Set of 4	2·75	1·30
MS2709	123×94 mm. Nos. 2705/8	8·50	4·25

774 Child embracing Dove

(Des W. Freudenreich, Litho)

1980 (21 Nov). United Nations Declaration on Preparation of Societies for Life in Peace. P 11×11½.
2710　**774**　8z.40 multicoloured .... 1·50　50

775 "Battle of Olszynka Grochowska"
(Wojciech Kossak)

1980 (29 Nov). 150th Anniv of Battle of Olszynka Grochowska. Photo. P 11.
2711　**775**　2z.50 multicoloured .... 60　40

776 Fire Engine

777 "Honour to Silesian Rebels" (statue, Jan Borowczak)

(Des J. Miller. Photo)

1980 (16 Dec). Warsaw Horse-drawn Vehicles. T **776** and similar horiz designs. Multicoloured. P 11.
2712	2z. Type **776**	30	15
2713	2z.50 Omnibus	35	15
2714	3z. Brewery dray	45	25
2715	5z. Sledge-cab	75	30
2716	6z. Horse tram	1·00	50
2717	6z.50 Droshky cab	1·50	65
2712/2717 Set of 5		4·00	1·80

(Des A. Heidrich. Recess)

1981 (22 Jan). 60th Anniv of Silesian Rising. P 11½.
2718　**777**　2z.50 deep green .... 60　50

778 Picasso

779 Jean-François Pilâtre de Rozier and Jules Romain in Hydrogen/hot-air Balloon, 1785*

(Des W. Freudenreich. Photo)

1981 (10 Mar). Birth Centenary of Pablo Picasso (artist). P 11½×11.
2719　**778**　8z.40 multicoloured .... 1·50　65
MS2720 95×130 mm. No. 2719×2 plus two labels (sold at 20z.80) .... 6·50　3·25
No. 2719 was issued *se-tenant* with a label depicting Picasso's work "Weeping Woman".

(Des R. Dudzicki. Photo)

1981 (25 Mar). Balloons. T **779** and similar vert designs. Multicoloured. P 11½.
2721	2z. Type **779**	30	15
2722	2z. Balloon of J. Blanchard and J. Jeffries, 1785	30	15
2723	2z.50 Eugène Godard's quintuple "acrobatic" balloon, 1850	35	15

2724	3z. F. Hynek and Z. Burzyński's SP-ADS *Kościuszko*, 1933	45	25
2725	6z. Z. Burzyński and N. Wysocki's *Polonia II*, 1935	1·00	30
2726	6z.50 Ben Abruzzo, Max Anderson and Larry Newman's *Double Eagle II*, 1978	1·70	50
2721/2726 Set of 6		3·75	1·40
MS2727 59×98 mm. 10z.50 Balloon SP-BCU L.O.P.P. and Gordon Bennett, statuette. Imperf		2·20	1·90

*No. 2721 is wrongly inscr "Pilatre de Rozier D'Arlandes 1783".

780 "Iphigenia" (Anton Maulbertsch)

(Des A. Barecki. Litho)

1981 (11 May). WIPA 1981 International Stamp Exhibition, Vienna. P 11½.
2728　**780**　10z.50 multicoloured .... 2·50　80

781 Wroclaw, 1493

(Des A. Barecki. Photo)

1981 (15 May–28 July). Towns. T **781** and similar designs. P 11×11½ (4, 5z.), 11½×11 (6, 8z.) or 14 (6z.50).
2729	4z. reddish violet (28.7.81)	85	15
2730	5z. bright blue-green (28.7.81)	1·20	30
2731	6z. red-orange (28.7.81)	1·30	40
2732	6z 50 bistre-brown	1·50	50
2733	8z. blue (28.7.81)	1·90	65
2729/2733 Set of 5		6·00	1·90

Designs: Vert—4z. Gdańsk, 1652; 5z. Cracow, 1493. Horiz—6z. Legnica, 1744; 8z. Warsaw, 1618.

Nos. 2734/43 are vacant.

782 Sikorski

783 Faience Vase

(Des A. Balcerzak. Photo)

1981 (20 May). Birth Centenary of Gen. Wladyslaw E. Sikorski (statesman). P 11½×11.
2744　**782**　6z.50 multicoloured .... 1·50　50

(Des K. Tarkowska (1, 5z., 8z.40), H. Matuszewska (others). Photo)

1981 (15 June). Pottery. T **783** and similar vert designs. Multicoloured. P 11½×11.
2745	1z. Type **783**	30	15
2746	2z. Porcelain cup and saucer in "Baranówka" design	45	15
2747	2z.50 Porcelain jug, Korzec manufacture	60	25
2748	5z. Faience plate with portrait of King Jan III Sobieski by Thiele	1·20	40
2749	6z.50 Faience "Secession" vase	1·50	65
2750	8z.40 Porcelain dish, Ćmielów manufacture	1·90	65
2745/2750 Set of 6		5·25	1·90

784 Congress Emblem

785 Wild Boar (*Sus scrofa*), Rifle and Oak Leaves

(Des W. Freudenreich. Litho)

1981 (15 June). Architects' Congress. P 11½×11.
2751　**784**　2z.50 lemon, black and bright scarlet......　60　40

(Des W. Surowiecki. Litho)

1981 (30 June). Game Shooting. T **785** and similar multicoloured designs. P 11×11½ (6z.50) or 11½×11 (others).
2752　2z. Type **785** ....　45　25
2753　2z. Elk (*Alces alces*), rifle and fir twigs...........　45　25
2754　2z.50 Red Fox (*Vulpes vulpes*), shotgun, cartridges and fir branches ....　60　30
2755　2z.50 Roe Deer (*Capreolus capreolus*), feeding rack, rifle and fir branches....................　60　30
2756　6z.50 Mallards, shotgun, basket and reeds......　1·50　80
2757　6z.50 Barnacle goose, shotgun and reeds (*horiz*) ....　1·50　80
2752/2757 *Set of 6*...　4·50　2·40

786 European Bison

787 Tennis Player

(Des K. Śliwka. Photo)

1981 (27 Aug). Protection of European Bison (*Bison bonasus*). T **786** and similar vert designs. Multicoloured. P 11½×11.
2758　6z.50 Type **786** ....　1·70　65
　　　a. Strip of 5. Nos. 2758/62 ....　8·75
2759　6z.50 Two Bison (one grazing) ....　1·70　65
2760　6z.50 Bison with Calf ....　1·70　65
2761　6z.50 Calf feeding ....　1·70　65
2762　6z.50 Two Bison (both looking towards right)..　1·70　65
2758/2762 *Set of 5*...　7·75　3·00
　Nos. 2758/62 were printed together in *se-tenant* strips of five within the sheet each strip forming a composite design.

(Des W. Świerzy. Photo)

1981 (17 Sept). 60th Anniv of Polish Tennis Federation. P 11×11½.
2763　**787**　6z.50 multicoloured ....　1·50　50

788 Boy with Model Airplane

(Des J. Brodowski. Photo German Bank Note Ptg Co, Leipzig)

1981 (24 Sept). Model Making. T **788** and similar horiz designs. Multicoloured. P 14.
2764　1z. Type **788** ....　30　15
2765　2z. *Atlas 2* (tug).......................................　45　15
2766　2z.50 Cars..　60　25
2767　4z.20 Man with gliders...............................　85　30
2768　6z.50 Racing cars.......................................　1·50　50
2769　8z. Man with yachts....................................　1·90　65
2764/2769 *Set of 6*...　5·00　1·80

789 Disabled Pictogram

790 17th-century Flint-lock Pistol

(Des. R. Dudzicki. Litho)

1981 (25 Sept). International Year of Disabled Persons. P 11½×11.
2770　**789**　8z.40 blue-green, light yellowish green and black...　1·90　65

(Des H. Chyliński. Photo German Bank Note Ptg Co, Leipzig)

1981 (9 Oct). Stamp Day. Antique Weapons. T **790** and similar vert design. Multicoloured. P 14.
2771　2z.50 Type **790** ....　60　40
2772　8z.40 17th-century gala sabre.....................　1·90　65

791 H. Wieniawski and Violin Head

792 Bronislaw Wesolowski

(Des S. Malecki. Photo)

1981 (10 Oct). Wieniawski Young Violinists' Competition. P 11½.
2773　**791**　2z.50 multicoloured ....　60　30

(Des Z. Stasik. Litho)

1981 (15 Oct). Activists of Polish Workers' Movement. T **792** and similar horiz designs. P 11½.
2774　50g. green and black ....　20　15
2775　2z. blue and black ....　45　15
2776　2z.50 light brown and black ....　60　25
2777　6z.50 magenta and black.............................　1·50　50
2774/2777 *Set of 4*...　2·50　95
　Designs:—2z. Malgorzata Fornalska; 2z.50 Maria Koszutska; 6z.50 Marcin Kasprzak.

793 F.A.O. Emblem and Globe

(Des Z. Stasik. Litho)

1981 (16 Oct). World Food Day. P 11½×11.
2778　**793**　6z.90 bistre-brown, dull orange and pale yellow ....　1·60　50

794 Helena Modrzejewska (actress)

(Des J. Brodowski. Recess and photo)

1981 (17 Oct). Bicentenary of Cracow Old Theatre. T **794** and similar horiz designs. P 12×11½.

2779	2z. maroon, pale grey and bluish violet......	45	15
2780	2z.50 deep blue, pale stone and olive-sepia ..	60	25
2781	6z.50 dull violet, pale grey-blue and brown-olive......................................	1·50	30
2782	8z. bistre-brown, pale sage green and brown-lake....................................	1·90	50
2779/2782 Set of 4..		4·00	1·10

Designs:—2z.50 Stanislaw Koźmian (politician, writer and theatre director); 6z.50 Konrad Swinarski (stage manager and scenographer); 8z. Old Theatre building.

795 Cracow and Vistula River   **796** Gdańsk Memorial

(Des S. Malecki. Litho)

1981 (20 Nov). Vistula River Project. Sheet 62×51 mm. P 11½.
MS2783 **795** 10z.50 multicoloured.................................. 3·75   2·75

(Des S. Malecki. Litho)

1981 (16 Dec). Memorials to Victims of 1970 Uprising. T **796** and similar vert design. P 11½×12 (2z.50) or 11½×11 (6z.50).

2784	2z.50 +1z. olive-grey, black and orange-vermilion..................................	75	30
2785	6z.50 +1z. olive-grey, black and violet-blue....	1·70	65

Design: 26×37 mm—6z.50 Gdynia memorial.

797 Epyphyllopsis gaertneri   **798** Writing on Wall

(Des A. Balcerzak. Photo German Bank Note Ptg Co, Leipzig)

1981 (22 Dec). Succulent Plants. T **797** and similar square designs. Multicoloured. P 13.

2786	90g. Type **797**	20	15
2787	1z. Cereus tonduzii	30	15
2788	2z. Cylindropuntia leptocaulis	45	15
2789	2z.50 Cylindropuntia fulgida....................	60	25
2790	2z.50 Caralluma lugardi............................	60	25
2791	6z.50 Nopalea chochenillifera	1·50	50
2792	6z.50 Lithops helmutii	1·50	50
2793	10z.50 Cylindropuntia spinosior..................	2·50	80
2786/2793 Set of 8..		7·00	2·50

UNDERGROUND POST. Between 1982 and 1989, following the imposition of martial law, a large number of unofficial stamps were printed and circulated by the Solidarity Movement, camp internees, and similar organizations. Although most of these were used on clandestine mail some did pass through the normal mail network.

(Des A. Barecki. Photo)

1982 (5 Jan). 40th Anniv of Polish Workers' Coalition. P 11½×11.
2794   **798**   2z.50 salmon-pink, rosine and black.......   60   40
No. 2794 with overprint "13. XII. 1981r. WOJNA WRON Z NARODEM 13. XII. 1982r." is a private issue.

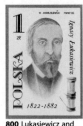

799 Faience Plate, Wloclawek   **800** Lukasiewicz and Lamp

(Des K. Tarkowska (6z.), H. Matuszewska (others). Photo)

1982 (20 Jan). Polish Ceramics. T **799** and similar vert designs. Multicoloured. P 11½×11.

2795	1z. Type **799**	20	15
2796	2z. Porcelain cup and saucer, Korzec	45	15
2797	2z.50 Porcelain tureen and sauce-boat, Barnówka..............................	60	25
2798	6z. Porcelain inkpot, Horodnica..............	1·30	50
2799	8z. Faience "Hunter's Tumbler", Lubartów....	1·90	65
2800	10z.50 Faience figurine of nobleman, Biala Podlaska..................................	2·50	95
2795/2800 Set of 6................................		6·25	2·40

(Des W. Andrzejewski. Photo)

1982 (22 Mar). Death Centenary of Ignacy Lukasiewicz (inventor of paraffin lamp). T **800** and similar vert designs. Multicoloured. P 11½×11.

2801	1z. Type **800**	25	15
2802	2z. Lamp with green shade...................	45	25
2803	2z.50 Lamp with pink shade...................	60	40
2804	3z.50 Two lamps.....................................	75	50
2805	9z. Lamp with decorated shade	2·10	65
2806	10z. Lamp with globe	2·40	80
2801/2806 Set of 6................................		6·00	2·50

801 Karol Szymanowski   **802** RWD-6 SP-AHN, 1932

(Des K. Sliwka. Photo)

1982 (8 Apr). Birth Centenary of Karol Szymanowski (composer). P 11½×11.
2807   **801**   2z.50 deep bistre-brown and gold...........   60   30

(Des J. Brodowski. Photo)

1982 (5 May). 50th Anniv of First Polish Victory in Tourist Aircraft Challenge Competition. T **802** and similar horiz design. Multicoloured. P 11½×11½.

2808	27z. Type **802**	1·80	50
2809	31z. RWD-9 SP-ORO (winner of 1934 Challenge)	2·30	80
MS2810 89×101 mm. Nos. 2808/9................		5·50	4·25

803 Henryk Sienkiewicz (literature, 1905)   **804** Football as Globe

(Des W. Freudenreich. Litho)

1982 (10 May). Polish Nobel Prize Winners. T **803** and similar vert designs. P 11½×11.
2811   3z. blackish olive and black.............   30   15

2812	15z. sepia and black		75	40
2813	25z. blue-black		90	50
2814	31z. grey and black		2·50	80
2811/2814 Set of 4			4·00	1·70

Designs:—15z. Wladyslaw Reymont (literature, 1924); 25z. Marie Curie (physics, 1903, and chemistry, 1911); 31z. Czeslaw Milosz (literature, 1980).

(Des J. Konarzewski (25z.), K. Kosmowski (27z.). Photo)

1982 (28 May). World Cup Football Championship, Spain. T **804** and similar horiz design. Multicoloured. P 11½×11 (25z.) or 11×11½ (27z.).

2815	25z. Type **804**		1·80	65
2816	27z. Bull and football (35×28 mm)		2·00	95

805 "Maria Kazimiera Sobieska"

806 Stanislaw Sierakowski and Boleslaw Domański (former Association presidents)

(Des J. Brodowski. Photo)

1982 (11 June). Philexfrance 82 International Stamp Exhibition, Paris. Sheet 69×86 mm. P 11½×11.

MS2817	**805**	65z. multicoloured	6·75	6·50

(Des S. Malecki. Litho)

1982 (20 July). 60th Anniv of Association of Poles in Germany. P 11½×11.

2818	**806**	4z.50 orange-vermilion and bronze-green	90	50

807 Text around Globe   **(808)**

(Des H. Chyliński. Photo)

1982 (9 Aug). Second United Nations Conference on the Exploration and Peaceful Uses of Outer Space, Vienna. P 11½×11.

2819	**807**	31z. multicoloured	2·30	80

1982 (20 Aug). No. 2732 surch with T **808**.

2820	**781**	10z. on 6z.50 bistre-brown	75	50

809 Father Augustyn Kordecki (prior)

(Des R. Dudzicki. Photo)

1982 (26 Aug). 600th Anniv of "Black Madonna" (icon) of Jasna Góra. T **809** and similar multicoloured designs. P 11.

2821		2z.50 Type **809**	45	15

2822	25z. "Siege of Jasna Góra by Swedes, 1655" (detail) (horiz)		1·10	50
	a. Missing accent under first E of OBLĘŻENIE (pos. 32)		15·00	
2823	65z. "Black Madonna"		3·00	80
2821/2823 Set of 3			4·00	1·30
MS2824 122×108 mm. No. 2823×2 (sold at 140z.)			18·00	24·00

The premium on No. **MS**2824 was for benefit of the Polish Philatelic Federation.

810 Marchers with Banner

811 Norbert Barlicki

(Des K. Kosmowski. Photo)

1982 (3 Sept). Centenary of Proletarian Party. P 11½×11.

2825	**810**	6z. multicoloured	75	50

(Des Z. Stasik. Photo)

1982 (10 Sept). Activists of Polish Workers' Movement. T **811** and similar vert designs. P 12×11½.

2826	5z. light new blue, bright blue and black		25	20
2827	6z. greenish grey, dull blue-green and black		30	25
2828	15z. salmon-pink, deep carmine and black		45	30
2829	20z. mauve, reddish violet and black		75	40
2830	29z. buff, orange-brown and black		1·10	50
2826/2830 Set of 5			2·50	1·50

Designs:—6z. Pawel Finder; 15z. Marian Buczek; 20z. Cezaryna Wojnarowska; 29z. Ignacy Daszyński.

812 Dr. Robert Koch

(Des K. Syta. Photo)

1982 (22 Sept). Centenary of Discovery of Tubercle Bacillus. T **812** and similar vert design. Multicoloured. P 11½×10.

2831	10z. Type **812**		90	50
2832	25z. Dr. Odo Bujwid		2·40	65

813 Head of Woman

813a Head of Ruler

814 Maximilian Kolbe (after M. Koscielniak)

(Des S. Skiba (2833/4), J. Konarzewski (others). Eng W. Zajdel (2840), B. Kowalska (2842), M. Kopecki (2843a). Photo German Bank Note Ptg Co, Leipzig (2836, 2841, 2843); recess (2840, 2842, 2843a) or photo (others) Govt Ptg Wks, Warsaw)

1982 (25 Sept)–**89**. Carved Heads from Wawel Castle.

(a) T **813** and similar vert design. P 12×11½

2833	60z. salmon and brown		3·75	1·30
2834	100z. ochre and sepia		6·00	1·90

Design:—100z. Man.

(b) T **813a** and similar vert designs. P 14 (2836, 2841, 2843) or 11×12 (others)

2835	3z.50 reddish brown (24.1.85)		30	15
2836	5z. deep bluish green (10.7.84)		30	15

2837	5z. crimson (8.7.85)	30	15
2838	10z. ultramarine (8.7.85)	40	15
2839	15z. lake-brown (22.9.88)	45	15
2840	20z. olive-grey (30.7.86)	75	30
2841	20z. deep dull blue (31.3.89)	30	15
2842	40z. agate (30.7.86)	2·30	50
2843	60z. deep green (15.12.89)	45	25
2843a	200z. black (11.11.86)	6·00	1·30
2833/2843a	Set of 12	19·00	5·75

Designs:—Nos. 2835, 2841, Type **813a**; 2836, Warrior; 2837, 2839, Woman wearing chaplet; 2838, Man in cap; 2840, Thinker; 2842, Man in beret; 2843, Young man; 2843a, Man.

Nos. 2836, 2841 and 2843 were issued in coils, with every fifth stamp numbered on the back.

(Des K. Kosmowski. Photo)

1882 (10 Oct). Sanctification of Maximilian Kolbe (Franciscan concentration camp victim). P 11½×11.
2844	**814**	27z. multicoloured	2·50	80

815 Polar Research Station

(Des H. Matuszewska. Litho)

1982 (25 Oct). 50th Anniv of Polish Polar Research. P 11½.
2845	**815**	27z. multicoloured	2·75	80

816 "Log Floats on Vistula River" (drawing by J. Telakowski)

(Des M. Piekarski. Photo)

1982 (2 Nov). Views of Vistula River. T **816** and similar horiz designs. P 11½×12.
2846	12z. ultramarine	40	15
2847	17z. cobalt	45	25
2848	25z. deep blue	60	40
2846/2848	Set of 3	1·30	70

Designs:—17z. "Kazimierz Dolny" (engraving by Andriollo); 25z. "Danzig" (18th-century engraving).

817 Stanislaw Zaremba

(Des H. Chyliński. Photo)

1982 (23 Nov). Mathematicians. T **817** and similar horiz designs. P 11×11½.
2849	5z. reddish purple, ultramarine and black	45	15
2850	6z. orange, violet and black	60	25
2851	12z. cobalt, olive-brown and black	1·20	40
2852	15z. olive-yellow, deep chestnut and black	1·50	40
2849/2852	Set of 4	3·50	1·20

Designs:—6z. Waclaw Sierpiński; 12z. Zygmunt Janiszewski; 15z. Stefan Banach.

818 Military Council Medal

1982 (13 Dec). First Anniv of Military Council. Photo. P 12×11½.
2853	**818**	2z.50 black, yellow and rosine	60	30

819 Deanery Gate   **820** Bernard Wapowski Map, 1526

(Des A. Heidrich. Eng M. Kopecki (65z.). Recess and photo (65z.), litho (others))

1982 (20 Dec). Renovation of Cracow Monuments (1st series). T **819** and similar vert design. P 11½×11.
2854	15z. black, yellow-olive and emerald	1·10	40
2855	25z. black, dull purple and deep magenta	1·80	50
MS2856	75×93 mm. 65z. pale blue-green, dull purple and sepia (22×27 mm). Imperf	3·75	2·40

Designs:—25z. Gateway of Collegium Iuridicum; 65z. Street plan of Old Cracow.

See also Nos. 2904/5, 2968/9, 3029/30, 3116 and 3153.

(Des J. Brodowski. Litho)

1982 (28 Dec). Polish Maps. T **820** and similar square designs. P 11½.
2857	5z. multicoloured	30	15
2858	6z. pale cinnamon, black and maroon	40	25
2859	8z. multicoloured	45	30
2860	25z. multicoloured	1·70	65
2857/2860	Set of 4	2·50	1·20

Designs:—6z. Map of Prague, 1839; 8z. Map of Poland from Eugen Romer's Atlas, 1908; 25z. Plan of Cracow by A. Buchowiecki, 1703, and astrolabe.

821 The Last of the Resistance (Artur Grottger)

1983 (22 Jan). 120th Anniv of January Rising. Photo. P 12×11½.
2861	**821**	6z. deep brown	45	25

822 "Grand Theatre, Warsaw, 1838" (Maciej Zaleski)

1983 (24 Feb). 150th Anniv of Grand Theatre, Warsaw. Photo. P 11.
2862	**822**	6z. multicoloured	45	25

823 Wild Flowers   **824** Karol Kurpiński (composer)

(Des S. Malecki. Litho)

1983 (24 Mar). Environmental Protection. T **823** and similar square designs. Multicoloured. P 11½.

2863	5z. Type **823**	40	15
2864	6z. Mirror Carp, European Eel and Mute Swan	45	25
2865	17z. Hoopoe and trees	1·40	65
2866	30z. Redfish, Lumpsucker, Sailfish, Flying-fish and Trunkfish	2·40	1·00
2867	31z. European Bison and Roe Deer	2·50	1·10
2868	38z. Fruit	3·00	1·40
2863/2868	*Set of 6*	9·25	4·00

(Des H. Chyliński. Photo)

1983 (25 Mar). Celebrities. T **824** and similar vert designs. P 11½×11.

2869	5z. cinnamon and reddish brown	40	15
2870	6z. pale magenta and bluish violet	45	25
2871	17z. pale bluish green and slate-green	1·10	50
2872	25z. pale yellow-orange and deep orange-brown	1·50	65
2873	27z. new blue and deep ultramarine	1·80	70
2874	31z. reddish lilac and bright violet	2·30	80
2869/2874	*Set of 6*	6·75	2·75

Designs:—6z. Maria Jasnorzewska-Pawlikowska (poet); 17z. Stanislaw Szober (linguist); 25z. Tadeusz Banachiewicz (astronomer and mathematician); 27z. Jaroslaw Iwaszkiewicz (writer); 31z. Wladyslaw Tatarkiewicz (philosopher and historian).

825 3000 Metres Steeplechase

826 Ghetto Heroes Monument (Natan Rappaport)

(Des W. Freudenreich. Photo)

1983 (5 Apr). Sports Achievements. T **825** and similar horiz designs. P 11×11½.

2875	5z. pale pink and bright violet	40	15
2876	6z. chestnut, pale pink and black	45	25
2877	15z. stone and deep olive	1·10	50
2878	27z. +5z. dull violet-blue, deep blue and black	2·50	80
2875/2878	*Set of 4*	4·00	1·50

Designs:—6z. Show jumping; 15z. Football; 27z.+5z. Pole vaulting. The 5, 6 and 27z. commemorate gold medals won by Polish athletes at the Moscow Olympic Games, the 15z. third place in World Cup Football Championship, Spain.

(Des M. Piekarski. Photo)

1983 (19 Apr). 40th Anniv of Warsaw Ghetto Uprising. P 11½×11.

2879	**826**	6z. buff and deep bistre-brown	60	40

No. 2879 was issued with *se-tenant* label showing the anniversary medal by K. Danielewicz.

827 Customs Officer and Suitcases

828 John Paul II and Jasna Góra Sanctuary

(Des K. Kosmowski. Photo)

1983 (28 Apr). 30th Anniv of Customs Co-operation Council. P 11½×11.

2880	**827**	5z. multicoloured	45	30

(Des R. Dudzicki. Photo)

1983 (16 June). Papal Visit. T **828** and similar horiz design. Multicoloured. P 11.

2881	31z. Type **828**	2·50	80

2882	65z. Niepokalanów Church and John Paul holding crucifix	5·00	1·90
MS2883	107×81 mm. No. 2882	5·50	5·00

829 Dragoons

830 Arrow piercing "E"

(Des R. Dudzicki. Photo)

1983 (5 July). 300th Anniv of Polish Relief of Vienna (1st issue). Troops of King Jan III Sobieski. T **829** and similar vert designs. Multicoloured. P 11½×11.

2884	5z. Type **829**	40	15
2885	5z. Armoured cavalryman	40	15
2886	6z. Infantry non-commissioned officer and musketeer	45	25
2887	15z. Light cavalry lieutenant	1·20	50
2888	27z. "Winged" hussar and trooper with carbine	2·10	95
2884/2888	*Set of 5*	4·00	1·80

See also Nos. 2893/**MS**2897.

(Des A. Barecki. Litho)

1983 (16 Aug). 50th Anniv of Deciphering "Enigma" Machine Codes. P 11½×11.

2889	**830**	5z. vermilion, grey and black	45	25

831 Toruń

832 Child's Painting

(Des S. Malecki. Photo)

1983 (25 Aug). 750th Anniv of Toruń. P 11.

2890	**831**	6z. multicoloured	45	25
MS2891	142×116 mm. No. 2890×4	6·75	7·25

The gutter of No. **MS**2891 is inscribed for 14th Polish Philatelic Exhibition, Toruń.

(Des H. Matuszewska. Photo)

1983 (9 Sept). "Order of the Smile" (politeness publicity campaign). P 11½×12.

2892	**832**	6z. multicoloured	45	25

833 King Jan III Sobieski

834 Wanda Wasilewska

(Des S. Malecki. Photo)

1983 (12 Sept). 300th Anniv of Polish Relief of Vienna (2nd issue). T **833** and similar vert designs. Multicoloured. P 11.

2893	5z. Type **833**	40	15
2894	6z. King Jan III Sobieski (*different*)	45	25

2895	6z. "King Jan III Sobieski on Horseback" (Francesco Trevisani).....................	45	25
2896	25z. "King Jan III Sobieski" (Jerzy Eleuter)	2·30	50
2893/2896 *Set of 4*..		3·25	1·00
MS2897 97×75 mm. 65z.+10z. "King Jan III Sobieski at Vienna" (Jan Matejko). Imperf		5·25	4·00

(Des W. Surowiecki (2898/9). Photo)

1983 (12 Oct). 40th Anniv of Polish People's Army. T **834** and similar designs. P 12×11½ (2901) or 11½×12 (others).

2898	5z. multicoloured	40	15
2899	5z. greenish black, blue-green and black....	40	15
2900	6z. multicoloured	45	25
2901	6z. multicoloured	45	25
2898/2901 *Set of 4*..		1·50	70

Designs: Vert—No. 2899, General Zygmunt Berling, 2900, "The Frontier Post" (S. Poznański). Horiz—No. 2901, "Taking the Oath" (S. Poznański).

835 Profiles and W.C.Y. Emblem

(Des N. Chyliński. Photo)

1983 (18 Oct). World Communications Year. P 11×11½.

2902	**835**	15z. black, greenish blue and rosine	1·10	50

836 Boxing

(Des J. Brodowski. Litho)

1983 (19 Nov). 60th Anniv of Polish Boxing Federation. P 11½×11.

2903	**836**	8z. multicoloured	60	30

(Des A. Heidrich. Litho)

1983 (25 Nov). Renovation of Cracow Monuments (2nd series). Designs as T **819**. P 11×11½ (5z.) or 11½×11 (6z.).

2904	5z. brown, purple and black	40	15
2905	6z. black, olive-green and new blue	45	25

Design: Horiz—5z. Cloth Hall. Vert—6z. Town Hall tower.

837 Biskupiec Costume

838 Hand with Sword (poster by Zakrzewski and Krolikowski, 1945)

(Des W. Świerzy. Photo)

1983 (16 Dec). Women's Folk Costumes. T **837** and similar vert designs. Multicoloured. P 11½×11.

2906	5z. Type **837**	40	15
2907	5z. Rozbark	40	15
2908	6z. Warmia and Mazuria	45	25
2909	6z. Cieszyń	45	25
2910	25z. Kurpie	2·30	80
2911	38z. Lubsko	3·25	1·10
2906/2911 *Set of 6*..		6·50	2·40

(Des Z. Stasik. Photo)

1983 (31 Dec). 40th Anniv of National People's Council. P 11½×11.

2912	**838**	6z. multicoloured	45 ✓	30

839 Badge of "General Bem" Brigade

840 Dulcimer

(Des W. Surowiecki. Litho)

1983 (31 Dec). 40th Anniv of People's Army. P 11½.

2913	**839**	5z. multicoloured	45 ✓	30

(Des Z. Stasik. Photo)

1984 (10 Feb). Musical Instruments (1st series). T **840** and similar vert designs. Multicoloured. P 11½×11.

2914	5z. Type **840**	40	15
2915	6z. Kettle drum and tambourine..................	45	25
2916	10z. Accordion	90	30
2917	15z. Double bass	1·40	50
2918	17z. Bagpipe	1·50	55
2919	29z. Country band (wood carvings by Tadeusz Zak)	2·50	80
2914/2919 *Set of 6*..		6·50	2·30

See also Nos. 2994/9.

841 Wincenty Witos

842 *Clematis lanuginosa*

(Des S. Malecki. Litho)

1984 (2 Mar). 110th Birth Anniv of Wincenty Witos (leader of Peasants' Movement). P 11½×11.

2920	**841**	6z. purple-brown and bright emerald	45	30

(A. Balcerzak. Photo)

1984 (26 Mar). Clematis. T **842** and similar horiz designs. Multicoloured. P 11×11½.

2921	5z. Type **842**	40	15
2922	6z. *Clematis tangutica*	45	25
2923	10z. *Clematis texensis*	90	30
2924	17z. *Clematis alpina*	1·50	50
2925	25z. Travellers' joy (*Clematis vitalba*)................	2·30	70
2926	27z. *Clematis montana*	2·40	80
2921/2926 *Set of 6*..		7·25	2·40

843 "The Ecstasy of St. Francis" (El Greco)

844 Handball

(Des J. Konarzewski. Photo)

1984 (21 Apr). España 84 International Stamp Exhibition, Madrid. P 11.

2927	**843**	27z. multicoloured	2·40	80

(Des J. Brodowski. Litho)

1984 (25 Apr). Olympic Games, Los Angeles, and Winter Olympics, Sarajevo. T **844** and similar horiz designs. Multicoloured. P 11×11½.

2928	5z. Type **844**	40	15
2929	6z. Fencing	45	25
2930	15z. Cycling	1·20	40
2931	16z. Janusz Kusociński winning 10,000 metres race, 1932 Olympics, Los Angeles	1·40	50
2932	17z. Stanislawa Walasiewiczówna winning 100 metres race, 1932 Olympics, Los Angeles	1·50	55
2933	31z. Women's slalom (Winter Olympics)	2·75	95
2928/2933	Set of 6	7·00	2·50

MS2934 129×78 mm. Nos. 2931/2. P 12×13 (*sold at 43z.*) .... 3·75 3·25

The 10z. premium on No. **MS**2934 was for benefit of the Polish Olympic Committee.

845 Monte Cassino Memorial Cross and Monastery

846 "German Princess" (Lucas Cranach)

(Des S. Malecki. Photo)

1984 (18 May). 40th Anniv of Battle of Monte Cassino. P 11½×11.
2935	**845**	15z. blackish olive and orange-vermilion	1·40	50

(Des R. Dudzicki. Photo)

1984 (15 June). 19th Universal Postal Union Congress, Hamburg. P 11½×12.
2936	**846**	27z. +10z. multicoloured	3·25	1·30

No. 2936 was issued with *se-tenant* label bearing text and UPU emblem.

847 "Warsaw from Praga Bank" (detail) (Canaletto)

848 Order of Grunwald Cross

(Des J. Wysocki. Photo)

1984 (20 June). Paintings of Vistula River. T **847** and similar horiz designs. Multicoloured. P 11.

2937	5z. Type **847**	40	25
2938	6z. "Trumpet Festivity" (Aleksander Gierymski)	45	30
2939	25z. "The Vistula River near Bielany District" (Józef Rapacki)	2·30	80
2940	27z. "Steamship Harbour in Powiśle District" (Franciszek Kostrzewski)	2·40	90
2937/2940	Set of 4	5·00	2·00

(Des J. Desselberger. Photo)

1984 (21 July). 40th Anniv of Polish People's Republic. T **848** and similar vert designs. Multicoloured. P 11½.

2941	5z. Type **848**	40	15
2942	6z. Order of Revival of Poland	45	25
2943	10z. Order of Banner of Labour, First Class	75	30
2944	16z. Order of Builders of People's Poland	1·50	50
2941/2944	Set of 4	2·75	1·10
MS2945	156×101 mm. Nos. 2941/4	11·50	8·75

849 Group of Insurgents

(Des W. Freudenreich. Photo)

1984 (1 Aug). 40th Anniv of Warsaw Uprising. T **849** and similar horiz designs. Multicoloured. P 11×11½.

2946	4z. Type **849**	30	15
2947	5z. Insurgent on postal duty	40	25
2948	6z. Insurgents fighting	45	30
2949	25z. Tending wounded	2·30	50
2946/2949	Set of 4	3·00	1·10

850 Defence of Oksywie Holm and Col. Stanislaw Dąbek

(Des A. Balcerzak. Photo)

1984 (1 Sept). 45th Anniv of German Invasion. T **850** and similar horiz design. Multicoloured. P 12×11½.

2950	5z. Type **850**	40	25
2951	6z. Battle of Bzura River and Gen. Tadeusz Kutrzeba	45	30

See also Nos. 3004/5, 3062, 3126/8, 3172/4 and 3240/3.

851 "Broken Heart" (monument, Łódź Concentration Camp)

852 Militiaman and Ruins

(Des W. Surowiecki. Photo)

1984 (17 Sept). Child Martyrs. P 11½×11.
2952	**851**	16z. deep bistre-brown, bright blue and blackish brown	1·10	50

(Des J. Kroll. Photo)

1984 (29 Sept). 40th Anniv of Civic Militia and Security Force. T **852** and similar horiz design. Multicoloured. P 11×11½.

2953	5z. Type **852**	40	25
2954	6z. Militiaman in control centre	45	30

853 First Balloon Flight, 1784 (after Chrostowski)

854 Weasel (*Mustela nivalis*)

(Des A. Balcerzak. Photo)

1984 (5 Nov). Polish Aviation. T **853** and similar horiz designs. P 11×11½.

2955	5z. black, apple green and mauve	40	15
2956	5z. multicoloured	40	15
2957	6z. multicoloured	45	25
2958	10z. multicoloured	75	30
2959	16z. multicoloured	1·20	50
2960	27z. multicoloured	2·40	80

2961 31z. multicoloured................................ 2·50 95
2955/2961 *Set of 7*.. 7·25 2·75
Designs:—No. 2956, Michal Scipio del Campo and biplane (first flight over Warsaw, 1911); 2957, Balloon *Polonez* (winner, Gordon Bennett Cup, 1983); 2958, PWS 101 and Jantar gliders (Lilenthal Medal winners); 2959, PZL-104 Wilga SP-APV airplane (world precise flight champion, 1983); 2960, Jan Nagórski and Farman M.F.7 floatplane (Arctic zone flights, 1914); 2961, PZL P-37 Loś and PZL P-7 aircraft.

(Des J. Brodowski. Photo)

1984 (4 Dec). Fur-bearing Animals. T **854** and similar multicoloured designs. P 11×11½ (horiz) or 11½×11 (vert).
2962 4z. Type **854**................................. 25 15
2963 5z. Stoat (*Mustela erminea*)............ 30 25
2964 5z. Beech Marten (*Martes foina*)...... 30 25
2965 10z. Eurasian Beaver (*Castor fiber*) (*vert*)....... 45 30
2966 10z. Eurasian Otter (*Lutra lutra*) (*vert*)..... 45 30
2967 65z. Alpine Marmot (*Marmota marmota*) (*vert*)......... 4·75 1·10
2962/2967 *Set of 6*.. 5·75 2·10

(Des A. Heidrich. Litho)

1984 (10 Dec). Renovation of Cracow Monuments (3rd series). Designs as T **819**. P 11½×11 (5z.) or 11×11½ (15z.).
2968 5z. lake-brown, black and deep bluish green.................. 45 30
2969 15z. turquoise-blue, chestnut and black.... 75 50
Designs: Vert—5z. Wawel cathedral. Horiz—15z. Wawel Castle (royal residence).

855 Protestant Church, Warsaw

856 Steam Fire Hose (late 19th century)

(Des J. Wysocki. Photo)

1984 (28 Dec). Religious Architecture. T **855** and similar multicoloured designs. P 11½×12 (vert) or 12×11½ (horiz).
2970 5z. Type **855**................................. 25 15
2971 10z. Saint Andrew's Roman Catholic church, Cracow........ 45 25
2972 15z. Greek Catholic church, Rychwald.... 75 30
2973 20z. St. Maria Magdalena Orthodox church, Warsaw........... 1·10 40
2974 25z. Tykocin synagogue, Kaczorów (*horiz*).... 1·50 50
2975 31z. Tatar mosque, Kruszyniany (*horiz*)... 1·80 55
2970/2975 *Set of 6*.. 5·25 1·90

(Des Z. Stasik. Photo)

1985 (25 Feb). Fire Engines. T **856** and similar horiz designs. Multicoloured. P 11×11½.
2976 4z. Type **856**................................. 25 15
2977 10z. "Polski Fiat", 1930s.................. 45 25
2978 12z. "Jelcz 315" fire engine............. 60 25
2979 15z. Manual fire hose, 1899............. 75 30
2980 20z. "Magirus" fire ladder on "Jelcz" chassis.. 1·10 40
2981 30z. Manual fire hose (early 18th century) ... 2·30 50
2976/2981 *Set of 6*.. 5·00 1·70

857 "Battle of Raclawice" (Jan Styka and Wojciech Kossak)

858 Wincenty Rzymowski

(Des A. Heidrich. Photo)

1985 (4 Apr). P 11.
2982 **857** 27z. multicoloured................ 1·50 65

(Des Z. Stasik. Litho)

1985 (11 Apr). 35th Death Anniv of Wincenty Rzymowski (founder of Polish Democratic Party). P 11½×11.
2983 **858** 10z. deep blue-violet and dull vermilion........ 60 30

859 Badge on Denim

860 Boleslaw III, the Wry-mouthed, and Map

(Des H. Matuszewska and K. Tarkowska. Photo)

1985 (25 Apr). International Youth Year. P 11½×11.
2984 **859** 15z. multicoloured................ 1·10 50

(Des. S. Malecki. Litho)

1985 (8 May). 40th Anniv of Return of Western and Northern Territories to Poland. T **860** and similar square designs. Multicoloured. P 11½.
2985 5z. Type **660**................................. 30 15
2986 10z. Wladyslaw Gomulka (vice-president of first post-war government) and map..... 60 25
2987 20z. Piotr Zaremba (Governor of Szczecin) and map......... 1·40 50
2985/2987 *Set of 3*.. 2·10 80

861 "Victory, Berlin 1945" (Józef Mlynarski)

862 Warsaw Arms and Flags of Member Countries

(Des W. Surowiecki. Photo)

1985 (9 May). 40th Anniv of Victory over Fascism. P 12×11½.
2988 **861** 5z. multicoloured................. 45 30

(Des S. Tolodziecki. Litho)

1985 (14 May). 30th Anniv of Warsaw Pact. P 11½.
2989 **862** 5z. multicoloured................. 45 30

863 Wolves in Winter

864 *Iskra* (cadet ship)

(Des J. Brodowski. Photo)

1985 (25 May). Protected Animals. The Wolf (*Canis lupus*). T **863** and similar horiz designs. Multicoloured. P 11×11½.
2990 5z. Type **863**................................. 1·10 40
2991 10z. She-wolf with cubs.................... 1·70 70
2992 10z. Close-up of wolf....................... 1·70 70
2993 20z. Wolves in summer.................... 3·50 2·10
2990/2993 *Set of 4*.. 7·25 3·50

(Des Z. Stasik. Photo)

1985 (25 June). Musical Instruments (2nd series). Vert designs as T **840**. Multicoloured. P 11½×11.
2994 5z. Rattle and tarapata..................... 30 15
2995 10z. Stick rattle and berlo................. 60 25

2996	12z. Clay whistles		75	30
2997	20z. Stringed instruments		1·40	40
2998	25z. Cow bells		1·70	50
2999	31z. Wind instruments		2·10	65
2994/2999 Set of 6			6·25	2·00

(Des M. Piekarski. Eng P. Naszarkowski. Recess and litho)

1985 (29 June). 40th Anniv of Polish Navy. P 11½×11.
3000 **864** 5z. deep violet-blue, greenish yellow
and black..............45 30

865 Tomasz Nocznicki   **866** Hockey Players

(Des J. Konarzewski. Eng W. Zajdel (10z.), M. Kopecki (20z.). Recess)

1985 (26 July). Leaders of Peasants' Movement. T **865** and similar
horiz design. P 11×11½.
3001 10z. slate green..............45 30
3002 20z. chocolate..............1·10 80
Design:—20z. Maciej Rataj.

(Des J. Brodowski. Litho)

1985 (22 Aug). 60th Anniv (1986) of Polish Field Hockey Association.
P 11½×11.
3003 **866** 5z. multicoloured..............45 30

(Des A. Balcerzak. Photo)

1985 (1 Sept). 46th Anniv of German Invasion. Horiz designs
as T **850**. Multicoloured. P 12×11½.
3004 5z. Defence of Wizna and Capt. Wladyslaw
Raginis..............30 15
3005 10z. Battle of Mlawa and Col. Wilhelm
Liszka-Lawicz..............55 30

867 Type 20k Goods Wagon   **868** "Madonna with Child,
St. John and Angel" (Sandro
Botticelli)

(Des H. Chyliński. Litho)

1985 (18 Sept). PAFAWAG Railway Rolling Stock. T **867** and similar
horiz designs. Multicoloured. P 11½×11.
3006 5z. Type **867**..............30 15
3007 10z. Electric locomotive No. ET22-001, 1969..............45 30
3008 17z. Type OMMK wagon..............90 40
3009 20z. Type 111A passenger carriage..............1·10 50
3006/3009 Set of 4..............2·50 1·20

(Des R. Dudzicki. Photo)

1985 (25 Sept). Italia '85 International Stamp Exhibition, Rome. Sheet
81×108 mm. P 11.
MS3010 **868** 65z.+15z. multicoloured..............5·50 4·75
A limited quantity of No. **MS**3010 has the additional inscription "35 LAT
POLSKIEGO ZWIAZKU FILATELISTÓW" beneath the stamp (*price* £11.50).

869 Green-winged Teal (*Anas
crecca*)

(Des J. Desselberger. Photo)

1985 (21 Oct). Wild Ducks. T **869** and similar horiz designs.
Multicoloured. P 11×11½.
3011 5z. Type **869**..............40 15
3012 5z. Garganey (*Anas querquedula*)..............40 15
3013 10z. Tufted Duck (*Aythya fuligula*)..............75 30
3014 15z. Common Goldeneye (*Bucephala
clangula*)..............1·10 40
3015 25z. Eider (*Somateria mollissima*)..............1·50 50
3016 29z. Red-crested Pochard (*Netta rufina*)..............1·80 55
3011/3016 Set of 6..............5·25 1·80

870 UN Emblem and "Flags"

(Des H. Chyliński. Litho)

1985 (24 Oct). 40th Anniv of United Nations Organization. P 11½×11.
3017 **870** 27z. multicoloured..............1·50 65

871 Ballerina   **872** "Marysia and Burek
in Ceylon"

(Des S. Malecki. Litho)

1985 (4 Dec). Bicentenary of Polish Ballet. T **871** and similar vert
design. P 11½×11.
3018 5z. bronze green, yellow-orange and
Venetian red..............40 15
3019 15z. purplish brown, bright reddish violet
and reddish orange..............75 50
Design:—15z. Male dancer.

(Des K. Śliwka. Photo)

1985 (8 Dec). Birth Centenary of Stanislaw Ignacy Witkiewicz
(artist). T **872** and similar multicoloured designs. P 11×11½
(3021) or 11½×11 (others).
3020 5z. Type **872**..............40 15
3021 10z. "Woman with Fox" (*horiz*)..............75 30
3022 10z. "Self-portrait"..............75 30
3023 20z. "Compositions"..............1·10 40
3024 25z. "Nena Stachurska"..............1·50 50
3020/3024 Set of 5..............4·00 1·50

873 Oliwa Church Organ   **874** Human Profile
and Bach

(Des R. Dudzicki. Photo)

1985 (30 Dec). 300th Birth Anniv of Johann Sebastian Bach
(composer). Sheet 67×79 mm. P 11½×11.
MS3025 **873** 65z. multicoloured..............4·00 3·25
No. **MS**3025 also exists with additional inscription "300 rocznica
urodzin Jana Sebastian Bacha" from a limited printing (*price* £18).

(Des K. Śliwka. Litho)

1986 (16 Jan). Congress of Intellectuals for Defence of Peaceful Future
of the World, Warsaw. P 11½×11.
3026 **874** 10z. dull ultramarine, dull violet-blue
and deep cobalt..............75 40

875 Michal Kamieński and Planetary and Comet's Orbits

876 Sun

880 Paderewski (composer)

881 Footballers

(Des Z. Stasik. Litho)

1986 (7 Feb). Appearance of Halley's Comet. T **875** and similar horiz design. P 11×11½.

3027	25z. deep blue and orange-brown	1·50	50
	a. Pair. Nos. 3027/8	3·25	1·10
3028	25z. indigo, greenish blue and orange-brown	1·50	50

Design:—No. 3028, "Vega", "Planet A", "Giotto" and "Ice" space probes and comet.
Nos. 3027/8 were printed together in se-tenant pairs within the sheet.

(Des A. Heidrich. Litho)

1986 (20 Mar). Renovation of Cracow Monuments (4th series). Vert designs as T **819**. P 11½×11.

3029	5z. bistre-brown, chestnut and black	30	15
3030	10z. yellow-green, yellow-brown and black..	45	30

Designs:—5z. Collegium Maius (Jagiellonian University museum); 10z. Kazimierz Town Hall.

(Des H. Chyliński. Photo)

1986 (20 Mar). International Peace Year. P 11½×11.

3031	**876**	25z. lemon, greenish blue and blue	1·10	50

877 Grey Partridge (*Perdix perdix*)

878 Kulczyński

(Des H. Chyliński. Photo)

1986 (15 Apr). Game. T **877** and similar multicoloured designs. P 11×11½ (horiz) or 11½×11 (vert).

3032	5z. Type **877**	25	15
3033	5z. Common Rabbit (*Oryctolagus cuniculus*)	25	15
3034	10z. Common Pheasants (*Phasianus colchicus*) (horiz)	45	30
3035	10z. Fallow Deer (*Dama dama*) (horiz)	45	30
3036	20z. Hare (*Lepus europaeus*)	1·10	50
3037	40z. Argali (*Ovis ammon*)	1·80	65
3032/3037	Set of 6	3·75	1·80

(Des R. Dudzicki. Eng P. Naszarkowski. Recess and photo)

1986 (3 May). Tenth Death Anniv (1985) of Stanislaw Kulczyński (politician). P 11½×11.

3038	**878**	10z. stone and chocolate	45	30

879 "Warsaw Fire Brigade, 1871" (detail, Józef Brodowski)

(Des Z. Stasik. Eng M. Kopecki. Recess and litho)

1986 (16 May). 150th Anniv of Warsaw Fire Brigade. P 11.

3039	**879**	10z. deep brown and dull brown	45	30

(Des W. Andrzejewski. Photo)

1986 (22 May). Ameripex '86 International Stamp Exhibition, Chicago. P 11½×11.

3040	**880**	65z. deep bright blue, black and brownish grey	3·25	95

(Des R. Dudzicki. Litho)

1986 (26 May). World Cup Football Championship, Mexico. P 11½.

3041	**881**	25z. multicoloured	1·10	50

882 Wilanów

(Des J. Brodowski. Photo)

1986 (18 June). Passenger Ferries. T **882** and similar horiz designs. Multicoloured. P 11.

3042	10z. Type **882**	45	25
3043	10z. *Wawel*	45	25
3044	15z. *Pomerania*	75	40
3045	25z. *Rogalin*	1·10	50
3042/3045	Set of 4	2·50	1·30
MS3046	Two sheets, each 116×98 mm. (a) Nos. 3042/3 (*sold at* 30z.); (b) Nos. 3044/5 (*sold at* 55z.)	19·00	14·50

Nos. 3042/5 were each issued with se-tenant half stamp-size label depicting features of various harbours.
The premium on No. **MS**3046a and **MS**3046b was for the benefit of the National Association of Philatelists.

883 A. B. Dobrowolski, Map and *Kopenik* (research vessel)

(Des S. Malecki. Litho)

1986 (23 June). 25th Anniv of Antarctic Agreement. T **883** and similar horiz design. P 11½×11.

3047	5z. turquoise-green, olive-black and vermilion	45	30
3048	40z. lavender, deep violet and reddish orange	2·00	50

Design:—40z. H. Arctowski, map and *Profesor Siedlecki* (research vessel).

884 Workers and Emblem

(Des A. Szczepaniak. Photo)

1986 (29 June). Tenth Polish United Workers' Party Congress, Warsaw. P 11×11½.

3049	**884**	10z. steel blue and red	45	30

885 "Paulinite Church on Skalka in Cracow" (detail), 1627

886 PZL-106A Kruk SP-AGS (Waclaw Nyez)

(Des A. Heidrich. Photo)

1986 (15 Aug). Treasures of Jasna Góra Monastery. T **885** and similar vert designs. Multicoloured. P 11½×11.

3050	5z. Type **885**	25	15 ✓
3051	5z. "Tree of Jesse", 17th-century	25	15 ✓
3052	20z. Chalice, 18th-century	1·70	50
3053	40z. "Virgin Mary" (detail, chasuble column), 15th-century	2·30	65 ✓
3050/3053	Set of 4	4·00	1·30

(Des J. Brodowski. Litho)

1986 (21 Aug). 1985 Polish World Championship Successes. T **886** and similar horiz designs. Multicoloured. P 11×11½.

3054	5z. Type **886**	25	15 ✓
3055	10z. Windsurfing (Malgorzuta Palasz-Piasecka)	45	25 ✓
3056	10z. Glider KUBUZ-3 aerobatics (Jerzy Makula)	45	25
3057	15z. Wrestling (Bogdan Daras)	75	30
3058	20z. Individual road cycling (Lech Piasecki)	1·10	40
3059	30z. Women's modern pentathlon (Barbara Kotowska)	1·50	55
3054/3059	Set of 6	4·00	1·70

887 "Bird" in National Costume carrying Stamp

888 Schweitzer

(Des W. Freudenreich. Photo)

1986 (28 Aug). Stockholmia 86 International Stamp Exhibition. P 11×11½.

3060	**887** 65z. multicoloured	3·00	1·10 ✓
MS3061	94×80 mm. No. 3060	3·25	3·25

(Des A. Balcerzak. Photo)

1986 (1 Sept). 47th Anniv of German Invasion. Horiz design as T **850**. Multicoloured. P 12×11½.

3062	10z. Battle of Jordanów and Col. Stanislaw Maczek	45	30

(Des J. Wysocki. Eng T. Lis. Recess and photo)

1986 (26 Sept). 20th Death Anniv (1985) of Albert Schweitzer (medical missionary). P 12×11½.

3063	**888** 5z. agate, cinnamon and ultramarine	30	15 ✓

889 Airliner and Postal Messenger

890 Basilisk

(Des S. Malecki. Litho)

1986 (9 Oct). World Post Day. P 11×11½.

3064	**889** 40z. sepia, ultramarine and orange-red	1·80	80 ✓
MS3065	81×81 mm. No. 3064×2 (sold at 120z.)	30·00	19·00

(Des Elzbieta Gaudasińska. Photo)

1986 (28 Oct). Folk Tales. T **890** and similar multicoloured designs. P 11×11½ (horiz) or 11½×11 (vert).

3066	5z. Type **890**	30	25 ✓
3067	5z. Duke Popiel (vert)	30	25 ✓
3068	10z. Golden Duck	45	30 ✓
3069	10z. Boruta the Devil (vert)	45	30 ✓
3070	20z. Jánošík the Robber (vert)	90	40 ✓
3071	50z. Lajkonik (vert)	2·50	65 ✓
3066/3071	Set of 6	4·50	1·90

891 Kotarbiński

892 20th-century Windmill, Zygmuntów

(Des J. Wysocki. Litho)

1986 (19 Nov). Birth Centenary of Tadeusz Kotarbiński (philosopher). P 12×11½.

3072	**891** 10z. agate and brown	45	30

(Des M. Piekarski. Photo)

1986 (26 Nov). Wooden Architecture. T **892** and similar horiz designs. Multicoloured. P 11½×11 (3073) or 11×11½ (others).

3073	5z. Type **892**	30	15 ✓
3074	5z. 17th-century church, Bączal Dolny	30	15 ✓
3075	10z. 19th-century Oravian cottage, Zubrzyca Górna	45	30 ✓
3076	15z. 18th-century Kashubian arcade cottage, Wdzydze	75	40 ✓
3077	25z. 19th-century barn, Grzawa	1·10	50 ✓
3078	30z. 19th-century water-mill, Siolkowice Stare	1·50	80 ✓
3073/3078	Set of 6	4·00	2·10

893 Mieszko (Mieczyslaw) I

894 Star

(Des S. Malecki. Eng P. Naszarkowski (10z.), W. Zajdel (25z.). Recess and photo)

1986 (4 Dec). Polish Rulers (1st series). T **893** and similar vert design showing drawings by Jan Matejko. P 11.

3079	10z. agate and brown-olive	1·10	50 ✓
3080	25z. brownish black and reddish purple	1·80	1·10 ✓

Designs:—25z. Queen Dobrawa (wife of Mieszko I).

See also Nos. 3144/5, 3193/4, 3251/2, 3341/2, 3351/2, 3387/8, 3461/4, 3511/12, 3548/51, 3641/4, 3705/8, 3732/5, 3819/22 and 3889/92.

(Des W. Freudenreich. Photo)

1986 (12 Dec). New Year. P 11×11½.

3081	**894** 25z. multicoloured	1·10	50

895 Trip to Bielany, 1887

896 Joachim Lelewel

(Des W. Surowiecki. Litho)

1986 (19 Dec). Centenary of Warsaw Cyclists' Society. T **895** and similar designs. P 13×12½ (3082) or 12½×13 (others).

3082	5z. multicoloured		30	15
3083	5z. bistre-brown, grey-brown and black		30	15
3084	10z. multicoloured		45	30 ✓
3085	10z. multicoloured		45	30 ✓
3086	30z. multicoloured		1·50	65 ✓
3087	50z. multicoloured		2·30	80 ✓
3082/3087	Set of 6		4·75	2·10

Designs: Vert—No. 3083, Jan Stanisław Skrodzki (1895 touring record holder); 3084, Dynasy (Society's headquarters, 1892–1937); 3085, Mieczysław Barański (1896 road cycling champion); 3086, Karolina Kocięcka; 3087. Henryk Weiss (Race champion).

(Des J. Wysocki. Photo)

1986 (22 Dec). Birth Bicentenary of Joachim Lelewel (historian). P 11×12.

3088	**896**	10z. +5z. multicoloured	75	50

The premium was for the benefit of the National Committee for School Aid fund.

897 Krill (*Euphausia superba*) and *Antoni Garnuszewski* (cadet freighter)

898 "Portrait of a Woman"

(Des S. Malecki. Litho)

1987 (13 Feb). Tenth Anniv of Henryk Arctowski Antarctic Station, King George Island, South Shetlands. T **897** and similar square designs. Multicoloured. P 11½.

3089	5z. Type **897**	30	15 ✓
3090	5z. Marbled Rock Cod (*Notothenia rossi*), Antarctic Toothfish (*Dissostichus mawsoni*) and *Żuławy* (supply ship)	30	15 ✓
3091	10z. Southern Fulmar (*Fulmarus glacialoides*) and *Pogoria* (cadet brigantine)	45	25 ✓
3092	10z. Adelie Penguin (*Pigoscelis adeliae*) and *Gedania* (yacht)	45	25 ✓
3093	30z. Fur Seal (*Arctocephalus*) and *Dziunia* (research vessel)	1·10	40 ✓
3094	40z. Leopard Seal (*Hydrurga leptonyx*) and *Kapitan Ledóchowski* (research vessel)	1·50	55 ✓
3089/3094	Set of 6	3·75	1·60

(Des W. Surowiecki. Photo)

1987 (20 Mar). 50th Death Anniv (1986) of Leon Wyczółkowski (artist). T **898** and similar multicoloured designs. P 11.

3095	5z. "Cineraria Flowers" (*horiz*)	25	15
3096	10z. Type **898**	40	25
3097	10z. "Wooden Church" (*horiz*)	40	25
3098	25z. "Beetroot Lifting"	75	30
3099	30z. "Wading Fishermen" (*horiz*)	90	40
3100	40z. "Self-portrait" (*horiz*)	1·20	55
3095/3100	Set of 6	3·50	1·70

899 "Ravage" (from "War Cycle") and Grottger

900 Świerczewski

(Des W. Surowiecki. Photo)

1987 (26 Mar). 150th Birth Anniv of Artur Grottger (artist). P 11.

3101	**899**	15z. brown and stone	45	30

(Des J. Konarzewski. Eng P. Naszarkowski. Recess and photo)

1987 (27 Mar). 90th Birth Anniv of General Karol Świerczewski. P 11½×12.

3102	**900**	15z. olive-green and yellow-olive	45 ✓	30 ✓

901 Strzelecki

902 Emblem and Banner

(Des M. Piekarski. Photo)

1987 (23 Apr). 190th Birth Anniv of Pawel Edmund Strzelecki (scientist and explorer of Tasmania). P 11½×11.

3103	**901**	65z. blackish olive	1·50	80

(Des A. Szczepaniak. Litho)

1987 (8 May). Second Patriotic Movement for National Revival Congress. P 11×11½.

3104	**902**	10z. vermilion, ultramarine and drab	40	15

903 CWS "T-1" Motor Car, 1928

(Des J. Brodowski. Photo)

1987 (19 May). Polish Motor Vehicles. T **903** and similar horiz designs. Multicoloured. P 12×11½.

3105	10z. Type **903**	25	15 ✓
3106	10z. Saurer-Zawrat bus, 1936	25	15 ✓
3107	15z. Ursus-A lorry, 1928	45	25 ✓
3108	15z. Lux-Sport motor car, 1936	45	25 ✓
3109	25z. Podkowa "100" motor cycle, 1939	75	40 ✓
3110	45z. Sokół "600 RT" motor cycle, 1935	1·50	65 ✓
3105/3110	Set of 6	3·25	1·70

904 Royal Palace, Warsaw

(Des S. Malecki. Photo)

1987 (5 June). P 12×11½.

3111	**904**	50z. multicoloured	1·50	80 ✓

A miniature sheet containing No. 3111 and two labels showing Pope John Paul II and Pres. Jaruzelski exists from a limited printing (*price* £85).

905 Pope John Paul II

(Des W. Andrzejewski (50z.), J. Wysocki (others). Photo)

1987 (8 June). Third Papal Visit. T **905** and similar vert designs. Multicoloured. P 11.

3112	15z. Type **905**	45	30 ✓
	a. Pair. Nos. 3112/13	1·70	85
3113	45z. Pope and signature	1·10	55 ✓
MS3114	77×66 mm. 50z. Profile of Pope (21×27 mm). P 12×11½	1·80	1·60

Nos. 3112/13 were printed together in *se-tenant* pairs within the sheet.

906 Polish Settler at Kasubia, Ontario

(Des R. Dudzicki. Photo)

1987 (13 June). Capex '87 International Stamp Exhibition, Toronto. P 12×11½.

3115   **906**   50z. +20z. multicoloured............................ 1·80   95
The premium was for the benefit of the Polish Philatelic Union.

(Des A. Heidrich. Litho)

1987 (6 July). Renovation of Cracow Monuments (5th series). Horiz design as T **819**. P 11×11½.

3116   10z. magenta, black and yellowish green 40   15
Design:—10z. Barbican.

907 Ludwig Zamenhof (inventor) and Star

908 "Poznań Town Hall" (Stanisław Wyspiański)

(Des A. Szczepaniak. Litho)

1987 (25 July). Centenary of Esperanto (invented language). P 11×11½.

3117   **907**   45z. grey-brown, emerald and black ..... 1·50   55

(Des A. Heidrich. Litho)

1987 (8 Aug). Poznań 87 National Stamp Exhibition. P 11½×11.

3118   **908**   15z. black and salmon 45   30

909 Queen Bee

910 1984 Olympic Stamp and Laurel Wreath

(Des K. Śliwka. Photo)

1987 (20 Aug). Apimondia '87 International Bee Keeping Congress, Warsaw. T **909** and similar vert designs. Multicoloured. P 11½×11.

3119   10z. Type **909** 30   15
3120   10z. Worker bee 30   15
3121   15z. Drone 45   25
3122   15z. Hive in orchard 45   25
3123   40z. Worker bee on clover flower .... 1·20   50
3124   50z. Forest bee keeper collecting honey....... 1·70   65
3119/3124 Set of 6.. 4·00   1·80

(Des H. Chyliński. Litho German Bank Note Ptg Co, Leipzig)

1987 (28 Aug). Olymphilex '87 Olympic Stamps Exhibition, Rome. Sheet 83×57 mm. P 14.

MS3125   **910**   45z.+10z. multicoloured .... 2·00   1·90
The premium was for the benefit of the Polish Olympic Committee's fund.

(Des B. Wróblewski and A. Balcerzak. Photo)

1987 (1 Sept). 48th Anniv of German Invasion. Horiz designs as T **850**. Multicoloured. P 12×11½.

3126   10z. Battle of Mokra and Col. Julian Filipowicz   40   25
3127   10z. Fighting at Oleszyce and Brig.-Gen.
                 Józef Rudolf Kustroń 40   25

3128   15z. PZL P-7 aircraft over Warsaw and Col.
                 Stefan Pawlikowski................................... 75   40
3126/3128 Set of 3 .... 1·40   80

911 Hevelius and Sextant

(Des J. Brodowski. Litho)

1987 (15 Sept). 300th Death Anniv of Jan Hevelius (astronomer). T **911** and similar multicoloured design. P 11½×11 (15z.) or 11×11½ (40z.).

3129   15z. Type **911** 45   30 ✔
3130   40z. Hevelius and map of constellations
                 (horiz) .... 1·20   50

912 High Jump (World Acrobatics Championships, France)

913 "Stacionar 4" Telecommunications Satellite

(Des H. Chyliński. Litho German Bank Note Ptg Co, Leipzig)

1987 (24 Sept). 1986 Polish World Championship Successes. T **912** and similar horiz designs. Multicoloured. P 14.

3131   10z. Type **912** 30   15 ✔
3132   15z. Two-man canoe (World Canoeing
                 Championships, Canada) 45   25 ✔
3133   20z. Marksman (Free pistol event, World
                 Marksmanship Championships, East
                 Germany) 60   30 ✔
3134   25z. Wrestlers (World Wrestling
                 Championships, Hungary) 75   40 ✔
3131/3134 Set of 4.. 1·90   1·00

(Des Z. Stasik. Photo)

1987 (2 Oct). 30th Anniv of Launch of "Sputnik 1" (first artificial satellite). Sheet 67×82 mm. P 11½×11.

MS3135   **913**   40z. multicoloured................................. 1·80   1·60

914 Warsaw Post Office and Ignacy Przebendowski (Postmaster General)

915 The Little Mermaid

(Des S. Malecki. Litho)

1987 (9 Oct). World Post Day. P 11½×11.

3136   **914**   15z. olive-green and brown-lake............. 45   30

(Des Emilia Freudenreich. Photo)

1987 (16 Oct). Hafnia 87 International Stamp Exhibition, Copenhagen. Hans Christian Andersen's Fairy Tales. T **915** and similar horiz designs. Multicoloured. P 11×11½.

3137   10z. Type **915** 30   15 ✔
3138   10z. The Nightingale 30   15 ✔
3139   20z. The Wild Swans 60   25 ✔
3140   20z. The Little Match Girl 60   25 ✔
3141   30z. The Snow Queen 90   40 ✔
3142   40z. The Brave Tin Soldier .... 1·20   55 ✔
3137/3142 Set of 6.. 3·50   1·60

916 Col. Stanislaw Więckowski (founder)

917 Santa Claus with Christmas Trees

(Des M. Piekarski. Eng P. Naszarkowski. Recess and photo)

1987 (16 Oct). 50th Anniv of Democratic Clubs. P 12×11½.
3143 **916** 15z. black and blue 45   30

(Des S. Malecki. Eng M. Kopecki (10z.), W. Zajdel (25z.). Recess and photo)

1987 (4 Dec). Polish Rulers (2nd series). Vert designs as T **893** showing drawings by Jan Matejko. P 11.
3144   10z. blackish olive and turquoise-blue .... 1·50   80
3145   15z. deep violet-blue and ultramarine 75   50
Designs:—10z. Boleslaw I, the Brave; 15z. Mieszko (Mieczyslaw) II. No. 3144 was issued with a se-tenant inscribed label.

(Des Emilia and W. Freudenreich. Photo)

1987 (14 Dec). New Year. P 11×11½.
3146 **917** 15z. multicoloured 45   30

918 Anax imperator

919 Composition

(Des B. Wróblewski. Photo)

1988 (23 Feb). Dragonflies. T **918** and similar multicoloured designs. P 11×11½ (horiz) or 11½×11 (vert).
3147   10z. Type **918** 30   15
3148   15z. Libellula quadrimaculata (vert) 45   25
3149   15z. Agrian splendens (Calopteryx splendens) 45   25
3150   20z. Cordulegaster annulatus (vert) 60   30
3151   30z. Sympetrum pedemontanum 90   40
3152   50z. Aeshna viridis (Aeschna viridis) (vert) ...... 1·70   55
3147/3152 Set of 6 .... 4·00   1·70

(Des A. Heidrich. Litho)

1988 (8 Mar). Renovation of Cracow Monuments (6th series). Vert design as T **819**. P 11½×11.
3153   15z. greenish yellow, chestnut and black 45   30
Design:—15z. Florianska Gate.

(Des W. Freudenreich. Photo)

1988 (28 Apr). International Year of Graphic Design. P 11×11½.
3154 **919** 40z. multicoloured 90   80

920 17th-century Friesian Wall Clock with Bracket Case

921 Atlantic Salmon and Reindeer

(Des S. Zieliński. Photo)

1988 (19 May). Clocks and Watches. T **920** and similar multicoloured designs. P 11½×12 (vert) or 12×11½ (horiz).
3155   10z. Type **920** 30   15
3156   10z. 20th-century annual clock (horiz) 30   15

3157   15z. 18th-century carriage clock 40   25
3158   15z. 18th-century French rococo bracket clock 40   25
3159   20z. 19th-century pocket watch (horiz) 45   30
3160   40z. 17th-century tile-cased clock from Gdańsk by Benjamin Zoll (horiz) .... 1·10   50
3155/3160 Set of 6 .... 2·75   1·40

(Des J. Brodowski. Photo)

1988 (1 June). Finlandia 88 International Stamp Exhibition, Helsinki. P 12×11½.
3161 **921** 45z. +20z. multicoloured .... 1·50   80
The premium was for the benefit of the Polish Philatelic Union.

922 Triple Jump

923 Kukuczka

(Des J. Konarzewski. Photo)

1988 (27 June). Olympic Games, Seoul. T **922** and similar horiz designs. Multicoloured. P 11×11½.
3162   15z. Type **922** 40   15
3163   20z. Wrestling 45   15
3164   20z. Canoeing 45   15
3165   25z. Judo 55   25
3166   40z. Shooting 90   30
3167   55z. Swimming .... 1·20   50
3162/3167 Set of 6 .... 3·50   1·40

(Des J. Konarzewski. Photo)

1988 (17 Aug). Award of Special Olympic Silver Medal to Jerzy Kukuczka for Mountaineering Achievements. Sheet 84×66 mm. P 11×11½.
MS3168 **923** 70z.+10z. multicoloured .... 2·00   1·90
The premium was for the benefit of the Polish Olympic Committees fund.

924 Wheat as Graph on VDU

925 PZL P-37 Loś

(Des S. Malecki. Photo)

1988 (22 Aug). 16th European Conference of Food and Agriculture Organ Cracow. T **924** and similar vert design. P 11½×11.
3169   15z. Type **924** 45   30
3170   40z. Factory in forest 90   50

(Des A. Szczepaniak. Photo)

1988 (23 Aug). 70th Anniv of Polish Republic (1st issue). 60th Anniv of Polish State Aircraft Works. P 11×11½.
3171 **925** 45z. multicoloured .... 1·10   55
See also Nos. 3175, 3177, 3181/**MS3189** and 3190/2.

(Des B. Wróblewski and A. Balcerzak. Photo)

1988 (1 Sept). 49th Anniv of German Invasion. Horiz designs as T **850**. Multicoloured. P 12×11½.
3172   15z. Battle of Modlin and Brig.-Gen. Wiktor Thommée 60   30
3173   20z. Battle of Warsaw and Brig.-Gen. Walerian Czuma 75   50
3174   20z. Battle of Tomaszów Lubelski and Brig.-Gen. Antoni Szylling 75   50
3172/3174 Set of 3 .... 1·90   1·20

(Des A. Szczepaniak. Photo)

1988 (5 Sept). 70th Anniv of Polish Republic (2nd issue). 50th Anniv of Stalowa Wola Ironworks. Horiz design as T **925**. Multicoloured. P 11×11½.
3175   15z. View of plant 45   30

926 Postal Emblem and Tomasz Arciszewski (Postal Minister, 1918–19)

927 On the Field of Glory Medal

(Des S. Malecki. Litho)

1988 (9 Oct). World Post Day. P 11½×11.
3176 **926** 20z. multicoloured 45 30
Issued both in sheets of 30 stamps and in sheets of 15 stamps and 15 labels showing current postal emblem (*price* £1.10). Price for No. 3176 is with label.

(Des A. Szczepaniak. Photo)

1988 (12 Oct). 70th Anniv of Polish Republic (3rd issue). 60th Anniv of Military Institute for Aviation Medicine. Horiz design as T **925**. Multicoloured. P 11×11½.
3177 20z. Hanriot XIV hospital aircraft (38×28 *mm*) 45 30

(Des R. Dudzicki. Photo)

1988 (12 Oct). Polish People's Army Battle Medals (1st series). T **927** and similar vert design. Multicoloured. P 11½×11.
3178 20z. Type **927** .... 45 30 ✓
3179 20z. Battle of Lenino Cross .... 45 30 ✓
See also Nos. 3249/50.

928 "Stanislaw Malachowski" and "Kazimierz Nestor Sapieha"

929 Ignacy Daszyński (politician)

(Des A. Heidrich. Photo)

1988 (16 Oct). Bicentenary of Four Years Diet (political and social reforms). Paintings of Diet Presidents by Józef Peszko. P 11.
3180 **928** 20z. multicoloured .... 45 30 ✓

(Des M. Piekarski. Photo)

1988 (11 Nov). 70th Anniv of Polish Republic (4th issue). Personalities. T **929** and similar vert designs. P 12×11½.
3181 15z. olive-green, rosine and black 40 25
3182 15z. olive-green, rosine and black 40 25
3183 20z. brown, vermilion and black 45 30
3184 20z. brown, vermilion and black 45 30
3185 20z. brown, vermilion and black 45 30
3186 200z. slate-purple, bright scarlet and black .... 3·25 1·30
3187 200z. slate-purple, bright scarlet and black .... 3·25 1·30
3188 200z. slate-purple, bright scarlet and black .... 3·25 1·30
3181/3188 *Set of 8* .... 10·50 4·75
MS3189 102×60 mm. Nos. 3186/8 .... 41·00 40·00
Designs:—No. 3182, Wincenty Witos (politician); 3183, Julian Marchlewski (trade unionist and economist); 3184, Stanislaw Wojciechowski (politician); 3185, Wojciech Korfanty (politician); 3186, Ignacy Paderewski (musician and politician); 3187, Marshal Józef Pilsudski; 3188, Gabriel Narutowicz (President, 1922).

(Des A. Szczepaniak. Photo)

1988 (28 Nov–Dec). 70th Anniv of Polish Republic (5th issue). Horiz designs as T **925**. Multicoloured. P 11×11½.
3190 15z. Coal wharf, Gdynia Port (65th anniv) (38×28 *mm*) (12 Dec) 40 25
3191 20z. Hipolit Cegielski (founder) and steam locomotive (142nd anniv of H. Cegielski Metal Works, Poznań) (38×28 *mm*) 45 30
3192 40z. Upper Silesia Tower (main entrance) (60th anniv of International Poznań Fair) (21 Dec) 90 55
3190/3192 *Set of 3* .... 1·60 1·00

(Des S. Malecki. Eng M. Kopecki (10z.), P. Naszkowski (15z.). Recess and photo)

1988 (4 Dec). Polish Rulers (3rd series). Vert designs as T **893** showing drawings by Jan Matejko. P 11.
3193 10z. deep chocolate and lake-brown 75 50
3194 15z. deep chocolate and brown .... 1·10 80
Designs:—10z. Queen Rycheza; 15z. Kazimierz (Karol Odnowiciel) I.

930 Snowman

931 Flag

(Des W. Freudenreich. Photo)

1988 (9 Dec). New Year. P 11×11½.
3195 **930** 20z. multicoloured 45 30

(Des J. Wysocki. Photo)

1988 (15 Dec). 40th Anniv of Polish United Workers' Party. P 11½×12.
3196 **931** 20z. bright scarlet and black 45 30

932 *Blysk*

933 Ardennes

(Des M. Piekarski. Litho German Bank Note Ptg Co, Leipzig)

1988 (29 Dec). Fire Boats. T **932** and similar horiz designs. Multicoloured. P 14.
3197 10z. Type **932** 30 15
3198 15z. *Plomień* .... 40 25 ✓
3199 15z. *Żar* .... 40 25 ✓
3200 20z. *Strażak 11* .... 45 30 ✓
3201 20z. *Strażak 4* .... 45 30 ✓
3202 45z. *Strażak 25* .... 90 55 ✓
3197/3202 *Set of 6* .... 2·50 1·60

(Des H. Chyliński. Photo)

1989 (6 Mar). Horses. T **933** and similar multicoloured designs. P 11.
3203 15z. Lippizaner (*horiz*) 30 15
3204 15z. Type **933** 30 15
3205 20z. English thoroughbred (*horiz*) 45 30
3206 20z. Arab 45 30
3207 30z. Great Poland racehorse (*horiz*) 60 40
3208 70z. Polish horse .... 1·50 55
3203/3208 *Set of 6* .... 3·25 1·70

934 Wire-haired Dachshund

935 Gen. Wladyslaw Anders and Plan of Battle

(Des J. Wysocki. Photo)

1989 (3 May). Hunting Dogs. T **934** and similar vert designs. Multicoloured. P 11½×11.
3209 15z. Type **934** .... 25 15 ✓

3210	15z. Cocker Spaniel	25	15✔
3211	20z. Czech Fousek Pointer...................	30	25✔
3212	20z. Welsh Terrier..............................	30	25✔
3213	25z. English Setter	40	30✔
3214	45z. Pointer......................................	70	50✔
3209/3214 Set of 6...............................		2·00	1·40

(Des H. Chyliński. Photo)

1989 (18 May). 45th Anniv of Battle of Monte Cassino. P 11½×12.
3215   **935** 80z. multicoloured........................   90   80
  See also Nos. 3227, 3247, 3287 and 3327.

> A 50z. stamp showing Gen. Broni Grzegorz Korczyński was prepared in 1989 but not issued.

936 Marianne

937 Polonia House

(Des J. Wysocki. Litho)

1989 (3 July). Bicentenary of French Revolution. P 11½×11.
3216 **936** 100z. brownish black, bright scarlet and
           ultramarine.......................... 1·10   50
MS3217 93×118 mm. No. 3216×2 plus two labels
  (sold at 270z.)..................................... 2·40   2·40
  No. 3216 was issued with se-tenant label bearing the exhibition emblem. The premium on No. **MS**3217 was for the benefit of the Polish Philatelic Union (price £7.50).
  No. **MS**3217 without perforations on right-hand margin.

(Des A. Szczepaniak. Photo)

1989 (16 July). Opening of Polonia House (cultural centre), Pultusk. P 12×11½.
3218 **937** 100z. multicoloured..................... 1·10   50

938 Monument (Bohdan Chmielewski)

939 Xaweri Dunikowski (artist)

(Des Z. Stasik. Photo)

1989 (21 July). 45th Anniv of Civic Militia and Security Force. P 11×11½.
3219 **938** 35z. slate-blue and yellow-brown 45   30

(Des J. Wysocki. Photo)

1989 (21 July). Recipients of Order of Builders of the Republic of Poland. T **939** and similar vert designs. Multicoloured. P 11½×11.
3220	35z. Type **939**	45	30
3221	35z. Stanislaw Mazur (farmer)........................	45	30
3222	35z. Natalia Gąsiorowska (historian)...............	45	30
3223	35z. Wincenti Pstrowski (initiator of worker performance contests).............	45	30
3220/3223 Set of 4............................		1·60	1·10

940 Astronaut

941 Firemen

(Des Z. Stasik. Photo)

1989 (21 July). 20th Anniv of First Manned Landing on Moon. P 11×11½.
3224 **940** 100z. multicoloured .... 1·10   50
MS3225 85×85 mm. No. 3224 .... 6·00   4·00
  No. **MS**3225 also exists imperforate from a limited printing (price £45).

(Des W. Surowiecki. Photo)

1989 (25 July). World Fire Fighting Congress, Warsaw. P 11½×11.
3226 **941** 80z. multicoloured.....................   75   50

(Des H. Chyliński. Photo)

1989 (21 Aug). 45th Anniv of Battle of Falaise. Horiz design as T **935**. Multicoloured. P 12×11½.
3227   165z. Plan of battle and Gen. Stanislaw
          Maczek .... 1·50   80

No. 3228 is vacant.

942 Daisy

943 Museum Emblem

(Des S. Malecki. Litho (700z.) or photo (others))

1989 (25 Aug)–**91**. Plants. T **942** and similar vert design. P 14 (700z.) or 11×12 (others).
3229	**942**	40z. grey-green	45	15
3230	–	60z. deep violet	60	25
3231	**942**	150z. brown-lake (4.12.89)	75	30
3232	–	500z. deep mauve (19.12.89)	1·10	50✔
3233	–	700z. deep bluish green (26.4.91).......	45	30✔
3234	–	1000z. blue (19.12.89)	2·30	80✔
3229/3234 Set of 6............................			5·00	2·10

  Designs:—60z. Juniper; 500z. Wild rose; 700z. Lily of the valley; 1000z. Blue cornflower.
  For similar designs printed by lithography and self-adhesive, see Nos. 3297/8.

Nos. 3235/9 are vacant.

(Des L. Wróblewski (3243), B. Wróblewski and A. Balcerzak (others). Photo)

1989 (1 Sept). 50th Anniv of German Invasion. Horiz designs as T **850**. P 12×11½.
3240	25z. slate, orange and black................	60	30
3241	25z. multicoloured........................	60	30
3242	35z. multicoloured........................	90	50
3243	35z. multicoloured........................	90	50
3240/3243 Set of 4................................		2·75	1·40

  Designs:—No. 3240, Defence of Westerplatte and Captain Franciszek Dabrowski; 3241, Defence of Hel and Captain Zbigniew Przybyszewski; 3242, Battle of. Kock and Brig.-Gen. Franciszek Kleeberg; 3243, Defence of Lwów and Brig.-Gen. Wladyslaw Langner.

(Des E. Lipiński. Photo)

1989 (15 Sept). Caricature Museum. P 11½×11.
3244 **943** 40z. multicoloured..................... 45   30

944 Rafal Czerwiakowski (founder of first university Surgery Department)

(Des J. Konarzewski. Photo)

1989 (18 Sept). Polish Surgeons' Society Centenary Congress, Cracow. T **944** and similar horiz design. P 11½×12.
3245   40z. dull ultramarine and black 45   30 ✔
3246   60z. blue-green and black 60   50
  Design:—60z. Ludwik Rydygier (founder of Polish Surgeons' Society).

(Des H. Chyliński. Photo)

1989 (25 Sept). 45th Anniv of Landing at Arnhem. Vert design as T **935**. Multicoloured. P 11½×12.

3247   210z. Gen. Stanislaw Sosabowski and plan of battle.. 1·80   80

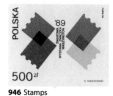

945 Emil Kaliński (Postal Minister, 1933–39)

946 Stamps

(Des S. Malecki. Photo)

1989 (9 Oct). World Post Day. P 12×11½.

3248 **945** 60z. multicoloured.. 75   65
No. 3248 was issued with a *se-tenant* label depicting Polish Mail emblem.

(Des R. Dudzicki. Photo)

1989 (12 Oct). Polish People's Army Battle Medals (2nd series). Vert designs as T **927**. Multicoloured. P 11½×11.

3249   60z. "For Participation in the Struggle for the Rule of the People" Medal.................. 45   30
3250   60z. Warsaw 1939–45 Medal........................ 45   30

(Des S. Malecki. Eng P. Naszarkowski (20z.), M. Kopecki (30z.). Recess and photo)

1989 (18 Oct). Polish Rulers (4th series). Vert designs as T **893** showing drawings by Jan Matejko. P 11.

3251   20z. slate-black and olive-grey...................... 45   30
3252   30z. sepia and yellow-brown......................... 90   50
Designs:—20z. Boleslaw II, the Bold; 30z. Wladyslaw I Herman.

(Des W. Andrzejewski. Photo)

1989 (14 Nov). World Stamp Expo '89 International Stamp Exhibition, Washington D.C. P 11×11½.

3253 **946** 500z. multicoloured............................ 2·75   1·60
No. 3253 also exists imperforate (*price* £5.50).

947 Cross and Twig

948 Ignacy Paderewski and Roman Dmowski (Polish signatories)

(Des W. Andrzejewski. Photo)

1989 (17 Nov). 70th Anniv of Polish Red Cross. P 11½×11.

3254 **947** 200z. rosine, bright green and black........ 1·10   50

(Des J. Wysocki. Photo)

1989 (21 Nov). 70th Anniv of Treaty of Versailles. P 11×11½.

3255 **948** 350z. multicoloured.......................... 1·60   80 ✓

949 Photographer and Medal depicting Maksymilian Strasz

(950)

951 Painting by Jan Ciągliński

(Des S. Malecki. Photo)

1989 (27 Nov). 150th Anniv of Photography. T **949** and similar multicoloured design. P 12×11½ (40z.) or 11½×12 (60z.).

3256   40z. Type **949**.................................... 50   30
3257   60z. Lens shutter as pupil of eye (*horiz*)........ 65   40

1989 (30 Nov). No. 2729 surch with T **950**.

3258   500z. on 4z. reddish violet............................. 2·40   1·10

(Des S. Malecki. Photo German Bank Note Ptg Co. Leipzig)

1989 (18 Dec). Flower Paintings. T **951** and similar square designs showing paintings by artists named. Multicoloured. P 13.

3259   25z. Type **951**...................................... 25   15
3260   30z. Wojciech Weiss................................. 25   15
3261   35z. Antoni Kolasiński.............................. 25   15
3262   50z. Stefan Nacht-Samborski...................... 30   25
3263   60z. Józef Pankiewicz............................... 30   25
3264   85z. Henryka Beyer................................. 50   30
3265   110z. Wladyslaw Ślewiński.......................... 65   40
3266   190z. Czeslaw Wdowiszewski....................... 95   50
3259/3266 Set of 8... 3·00   1·90

952 Christ

(Des R. Dudzicki. Photo)

1989 (21 Dec). Icons (1st series). T **952** and similar multicoloured designs. P 11.

3267   50z. Type **952**..................................... 30   15 ✓
3268   60z. Two saints with books.......................... 30   15
3269   90z. Three saints with books....................... 40   25
3270   150z. Displaying scriptures (*vert*).................. 50   30
3271   200z. Madonna and child (*vert*)................... 80   50
3272   350z. Christ with saints and angels (*vert*)....... 1·60   65
3267/3272 Set of 6... 3·50   1·80
See also Nos. 3345/50.

REPUBLIC OF POLAND

=

350 zł
(953)

1990 (31 Jan). No. 2839 surch with T **953**.

3273   350z. on 15z. lake-brown............................. 1·60   80

954 Krystyna Jamroz

955 High Jumping

(Des M. Piekarski. Photo)

1990 (9 Feb). Singers. T **954** and similar vert designs. Multicoloured. P 12×11½.

3274   100z. Type **954**.................................... 30   15
3275   150z. Wanda Wermińska............................. 50   25
3276   350z. Ada Sari....................................... 80   30
3277   500z. Jan Kiepura................................... 1·10   50
3274/3277 Set of 4... 2·40   1·10

(Des J. Brodowski. Photo)

1990 (29 Mar). Sports. T **955** and similar horiz designs. Multicoloured. P 11×11½.

3278   100z. Yachting...................................... 25   15
3279   200z. Rugby... 30   15
3280   400z. Type **955**.................................... 40   25

3281	500z. Ice skating	65	30
3282	500z. Diving	65	30
3283	1000z. Gymnastics	80	50
3278/3283 *Set of 6*		2·75	1·50

956 Kozlowski   **957** Pope John Paul II

(Des R. Dudzicki. Photo)

1990 (17 Apr). Birth Centenary (1989) of Roman Kozlowski (palaeontologist). P 11×11½.

3284	**956**	500z. olive-sepia and rosine	50	30 ✔

(Des S. Malecki. Photo)

1990 (18 May). 70th Birthday of Pope John Paul II. P 11.

3285	**957**	1000z. multicoloured	65	50

958 1860 10k. Stamp and Anniversary Stamp

(Des S. Malecki. Photo)

1990 (25 May). 130th Anniv of First Polish Postage Stamp. Sheet 65×68 mm. P 11×11½.

MS3286	**958**	1000z. red-orange and dull blue	2·40	1·60

(Des H. Chyliński. Photo)

1990 (28 May). 50th Anniv of Narvik Landings. Vert design as T **935**. Multicoloured. P 11½×12.

3287	1500z. Gen. Zygmunt Bohusz-Szyszko and plan of battle	1·10	50

959 Ball and Colosseum

(Des J. Wysocki. Photo)

1990 (8 June). World Cup Football Championship, Italy. P 11½×11.

3288	**959**	1000z. multicoloured	70	30 ✔

(960)   **961** Memorial

1990 (18 June). No. 3230 surch with T **960** in red.

3289	700z. on 60z. deep violet	55	30

(Des M. Piekarski. Photo)

1990 (28 June). 34th Anniv of 1956 Poznań Uprising. P 12×11½.

3290	**961**	1500z. multicoloured	80	50

962 People and "ZUS"   **963** *Lymnaea stagnalis* (Stagnant Pond Snail)

(Des A. Szczepaniak. Photo)

1990 (5 July). 70th Anniv of Social Insurance. P 11×11½.

3291	**962**	1500z. deep blue, cerise and pale lemon	80	50

(Des J. Brodowski. Litho)

1990 (16 July). Shells. No value expressed. T **963** and similar horiz design. P 11½×12.

3292		B (500z.) deep rose-lilac	90	50 ✔
		a. Perf 14	55	30
3293		A (700z.) deep olive	1·10	50
		a. Perf 14	90	40

Design:—B, *Viviparus viviparus* (River Snail).
Nos. 3292/3 were valid for internal postage only.

964 Cross   **965** Weather Balloon

(Des W. Freudenreich. Litho)

1990 (20 July). 50th Anniv of Katyń Massacre. P 11½×12.

3294	**964**	1500z. black and vermilion	80	50 ✔

(Des J. Konarzewski. Photo)

1990 (27 July). Polish Hydrology and Meteorology Service. T **965** and similar horiz design. Multicoloured. P 11×11½.

3295		500z. Type **965**	35	25
3296		700z. Water-height gauge	55	30

(Des S. Malecki. Litho)

1990 (13 Aug). Plants. Vert designs as T **942**. Self-adhesive. Die-cut.

3297		2000z. olive-green	1·20	65
3298		5000z. bluish violet	1·80	1·10

Designs:—2000z. Water Lily; 5000z. Iris.

Nos. 3299/3304 are vacant.

966 Women's Kayak Pairs   **967** Victory Sign

(Des R. Dudzicki. Photo)

1990 (22 Aug). 23rd World Canoeing Championships. T **966** and similar horiz design. Multicoloured. P 11×11½.

3305		700z. Type **966**	45	30
3306		1000z. Men's kayak singles	70	50

A miniature sheet containing No. 3306 and an inscribed label was sold only with the Championship programme (*price* £8.75).

(Des J. Konarzewski. Litho)

1990 (31 Aug). Tenth Anniv of Solidarity Trade Union. P 11½×11.

3307	**967**	1500z. grey, black and vermilion	80	50 ✔

968 Jacob's Ladder
(*Polemonium coeruleum*)

969 Serving Dish, 1870–87

(Des A. Balcerzak. Photo)

1990 (24 Sept). Flowers. T **968** and similar vert designs.
Multicoloured. P 11½×11.
3308	200z. Type **968**	25	15 ✓
3309	700z. Floating Heart Water Fringe (*Nymphoides peltata*)	45	25
3310	700z. Dragonhead (*Dracocephalum ruyschiana*)	45	25
3311	1000z. *Helleborus purpurascens*	55	30
3312	1500z. *Daphne cneorum*	90	40
3313	1700z. Campion (*Dianthus superbus*)	1·10	50 ✓
3308/3313	Set of 6	3·25	1·70

(Des R. Dudzicki. Photo)

1990 (31 Oct). Bicentenary of Ćmielów Porcelain Works. T **969** and similar multicoloured designs. P 11×11½ (horiz) or 11½×11 (vert).
3314	700z. Type **969**	25	15
3315	800z. Plate, 1887–90 (*vert*)	45	25
3316	1000z. Cup and saucer, 1887	65	30
3317	1000z. Figurine of dancer, 1941–44 (*vert*)	65	30
3318	1500z. Chocolate box, 1930–90 (*vert*)	90	50
3319	2000z. Vase, 1979 (*vert*)	1·30	80
3314/3319	Set of 6	3·75	2·10

970 Little Owl (*Athene noctua*)

(Des J. Desselberger. Litho)

1990 (6 Nov). Owls. T **970** and similar vert designs. Multicoloured. P 14.
3320	200z. Type **970**	35	15
3321	500z. Tawny Owl (*Strix aluco*) (value at left)	55	30
3322	500z. Tawny Owl (*different*) (value at right)	55	30
3323	1000z. Short-eared Owl (*Asio flammeus*)	90	50
3324	1500z. Long-eared Owl (*Asio otus*)	1·80	80
3325	2000z. Barn Owl (*Tyto alba*)	2·20	1·10
3320/3325	Set of 6	5·75	2·75

971 Lech Wałęsa

(Des M. Piekarski. Litho)

1990 (12 Dec). Lech Wałęsa, 1984 Nobel Peace Prize Winner and new President. P 11×11½.
3326	**971** 1700z. multicoloured	1·10	65

(Des H. Chyliński. Photo)

1990 (21 Dec). 50th Anniv of Battle of Britain. Vert designs as T **935**. Multicoloured. P 11½×12.
3327	1500z. Emblem of 303 Squadron, Polish Fighter Wing, R.A.F. and Hawker Hurricane Mk 1	1·30	80

972 Collegiate Church, Tum (12th century)

973 "King Zygmunt II August" (anon)

(Des J. Wysocki. Litho)

1990 (28 Dec). Historic Architecture. T **972** and similar vert designs. Multicoloured. P 11½×11.
3328	700z. Type **972**	65	25 ✓
3329	800z. Reszel castle (14th century)	70	30 ✓
3330	1500z. Chelmno Town Hall (16th century)	1·30	50
3331	1700z. Church of the Nuns of the Visitation, Warsaw (18th century)	1·80	80
3328/3331	Set of 4	4·00	1·70

No. 3331 was issued with *se-tenant* label bearing Polska '93 International Stamp Exhibition emblem.

(Des A. Szczepaniak. Photo)

1991 (11 Jan). Paintings. T **973** and similar vert designs. Multicoloured. P 11½.
3332	500z. Type **973**	35 ✓	15
3333	700z. "Adoration of the Magi" (*Pultusk Codex*)	55 ✓	25
3334	1000z. "St. Matthew" (*Pultusk Codex*)	65 ✓	30
3335	1500z. "Expelling of Merchants from Temple" (Mikolaj Haberschrack)	1·10 ✓	40
3336	1700z. "The Annunciation" (miniature)	1·30 ✓	50
3337	2000z. "The Three Marys" (Mikolaj Haberschrack)	1·80 ✓	80
3332/3337	Set of 6	5·25	2·20

974 Silver Fir (*Abies alba*)

975 Radziwill Palace

(Des A. Balcerzak. Photo)

1991 (22 Feb). Cones. T **974** and similar vert design. Multicoloured. P 12×11½.
3338	700z. Type **974**	55	30 ✓
3339	1500z. Weymouth Pine (*Pinus strobus*)	90	50 ✓

See also Nos. 3483/4 and 3557/8.

(Des J. Wysocki. Litho)

1991 (15 Mar). Admission of Poland into European Postal and Telecommunications Conference. P 11×12.
3340	**975** 1500z. multicoloured	1·40 ✓	50

1500 zł

(976)

977 Chmielowski

(Des S. Malecki. Eng W. Zajdel (1000z.), P. Naszarkowski (1500z.).
Recess and photo)

1991 (25 Mar). Polish Rulers (5th series). Vert designs as T **893**
showing drawings by Jan Matejko, surch as T **976** in red. P 11.
3341 1000z. on 40z. brownish black and bronze
           green .... 1·10 50
3342 1500z. on 50z. blue-black and crimson............. 1·40 95
Designs:—1000z. Boleslaw III, the Wry Mouthed; 1500z. Wladyslaw
II, the Exile.
Nos. 3341/2 were not issued unsurcharged.

(Des M. Piekarski. Litho)

1991 (29 Mar). 75th Death Anniv of Adam Chmielowski ("Brother
Albert") (founder of Albertine Sisters). P 12×11½.
3343 **977** 2000z. multicoloured..................................... 90 50 ✓

978 Battle (detail of miniature, *Schlackenwerther Codex*, 1350)

979 Title Page of Constitution

(Des F. Lüdtke. Recess and litho State Ptg Wks, Berlin)

1991 (9 Apr). 750th Anniv of Battle of Legnica. P 14.
3344 **978** 1500z. multicoloured..................................... 1·80 ✓ 80
A stamp of a similar design was issued by Germany.

(Des R. Dudzicki. Photo)

1991 (22 Apr). Icons (2nd series). Vert designs as T **952**.
Multicoloured. P 11.
3345 500z. "Madonna of Nazareth"....................... 25 ✓ 15
3346 700z. "Christ the Acheirophyte".................... 45 ✓ 25
3347 1000z. "Madonna of Vladimir"......................... 55 ✓ 30
3348 1500z. "Madonna of Kazan"............................ 1·10 ✓ 40
3349 2000z. "St. John the Baptist"......................... 1·80 ✓ 50
3350 2200z. "Christ the Pentocrator"...................... 2·00 ✓ 80
3345/3350 *Set of 6*.. 5·50 2·20

(Des S. Malecki. Eng W. Zajdel (1000z.), M. Kopecki (1500z.). Recess
and photo)

1991 (30 Apr). Polish Rulers (6th series). Vert designs as T **893**
showing drawings by Jan Matejko. P 11.
3351 1000z. blue-black and brown-red...................... 1·10 50
3352 1500z. brownish black and new blue................. 1·40 95
Designs:—1000z. Boleslaw IV, the Curly; 1500z. Mieszko (Mieczyslaw)
III, the Old.

(Des A. Heidrich. Photo (3000z.) or litho (others))

1991 (2 May). Bicentenary of 3rd May Constitution. T **979** and similar
vert designs. P 11½×11.
3353 2000z. deep brown, buff and vermilion............. 1·30 ✓ 50
3354 2500z. deep brown, stone and vermilion......... 1·40 ✓ 80
MS3355 85×85 mm. 3000z. multicoloured............ 2·20 1·90
Designs:—2500z. "Administration of Oath by Gustav Taubert" (detail,
Johann Friedrich Bolt); 3000z. "Constitution, 3 May 1791" (Jan Matejko).

980 Satellite in Earth Orbit

981 Map and Battle Scene

(Des J. Wysocki. Litho)

1991 (6 May). Europa. Europe in Space. P 12×11.
3356 **980** 1000z. multicoloured................................. 4·50 80

(Des J. Brodowski. Photo)

1991 (27 May). 50th Anniv of Participation of *Piorun* (destroyer) in
Operation against *Bismarck* (German battleship). P 12×11½.
3357 **981** 2000z. multicoloured................................. 1·30 ✓ 50

982 Arms of Cracow

983 Pope John Paul II

(Des S. Malecki. Litho)

1991 (28 May). European Security and Co-operation Conference
Cultural Heritage Symposium, Cracow. P 12×11½.
3358 **982** 2000z. deep claret and deep ultramarine 1·80 ✓ 80

(Des J. Wysocki. Litho)

1991 (1 June). Papal Visit. T **983** and similar vert design.
Multicoloured. P 11½×11.
3359 1000z. Type **983** .... 55 ✓ 30
3360 2000z. Pope in white robes .... 1·30 ✓ 50

984 Bearded Penguin

(Des S. Malecki. Litho)

1991 (21 June). 30th Anniv of Antarctic Treaty. P 12×11½.
3361 **984** 2000z. multicoloured................................. 1·30 50

985 Making Paper

986 Prisoner

(Des Z. Stasik. Litho)

1991 (8 July). 500th Anniv of Paper Making in Poland. P 11½.
3362 **985** 2500z. turquoise-blue and brown-lake...... 1·10 ✓ 50

(Des W. Freudenreich. Litho)

1991 (28 July). Commemoration of Victims of Stalin's Purges.
P 11½×12.
3363 **986** 2500z. bright scarlet and black.................... 1·10 ✓ 50

987 Pope John Paul II

988 Ball and Basket

(Des J. Wysocki. Photo)

1991 (15 Aug). Sixth World Youth Day, Czestochowa. P 11½×11.
MS3364 70×87 mm. **987** 3500z. multicoloured............. 2·20 1·90

(Des J. Konarzewski. Litho)

1991 (19 Aug). Centenary of Basketball. P 11×11½.
3365 **988** 2500z. multicoloured................................. 1·30 ✓ 50

989 "Self-portrait" (Leon Wyczólkowski)　**990** Twardowski

(Des R. Dudzicki. Photo)

1991 (7 Sept). Bydgoszcz '91 National Stamp Exhibition. P 11½×12.
3366　**989**　3000z. brown-olive and sepia........................　1·40　80
MS3367　155×92 mm. No. 3366×4..................................　6·50　5·75

(Des J. Konarzewski. Photo)

1991 (10 Oct). 125th Birth Anniv of Kazimierz Twardowski (philosopher). P 11×11½.
3368　**990**　2500z. black and brownish grey...................　1·80　80

991 Swallowtail (*Papilio machaon*)

(Des D. Opresco. Hologram and litho (**MS**3375) or litho (others))

1991 (16 Nov). Butterflies and Moths. T **991** and similar horiz designs. Multicoloured. P 12½.
3369　1000z. Type **991**..　35　25
　　a. Block of 6. Nos. 3369/7............................　4·75
3370　1000z. Dark Crimson Underwing (*Mormonia sponsa*)..　35　25
3371　1500z. Painted Lady (*Vanessa cardui*).................　55　30
3372　1500z. Scarce Swallowtail (*Iphiclides podalirius*)...　55　30
3373　2500z. Scarlet Tiger Moth (*Panaxia dominula*).　1·30　50
3374　2500z. Peacock (*Nymphalis io*)..........................　1·30　50
3369/3374　Set of 6..　4·00　1·90
MS3375　127×63 mm. 15000z. Black-veined White (*Aporia crataegi*) (46×33 mm) plus label for "Phila Nippon '91" International Stamp Exhibition......　5·50　4·75
　　Nos. 3369/74 were issued together in *se-tenant* blocks of six within the sheet.
　　No. **MS**3375 is known with the hologram printed at the bottom of the minature sheet; causing the perforations to cut through the hologram (price £450).
　　Many variaties of **MS**3375 are known; including missing or double holograms, shifted image (see above note) and imperforate sheets.

992 "The Shepherd's Bow" (Francesco Solimena)

(Des R. Dudzicki. Photo)

1991 (25 Nov). Christmas. P 11.
3376　**992**　1000z. multicoloured..................................　90　50

993 Gen. Stanislaw Kopański and Battle Map

(Des J. Brodowski. Photo)

1991 (10 Dec). 50th Anniv of Participation of Polish Troops in Battle of Tobruk. P 12×11½.
3377　**993**　2000z. multicoloured.................................　1·80　85

994 Brig.-Gen. Michal Tokarzewski Karaszewicz　**995** Lord Baden-Powell (founder)

(Des S. Malecki. Litho)

1991 (20 Dec). World War II Polish Underground Army Commanders. T **994** and similar vert designs. P 12×11½.
3378　2000z. blue-black and vermilion.........................　1·30　50
3379　2500z. crimson and violet.................................　1·80　85
3380　3000z. deep violet and bright magenta.............　2·20　1·00
3381　5000z. brown and deep olive.............................　3·00　1·70
3382　6500z. deep brown and orange-brown..............　4·00　2·00
3378/3382　Set of 5...　11·00　5·50
　　Designs:—2500z. Gen. Broni Kazimierz Sosnkowski; 3000z. Lt.-Gen. Stefan Rowecki; 5000z. Lt.-Gen. Tadeusz Komorowski; 6500z. Brig.-Gen. Leopold Okulicki.

(Des M. Piekarski. Photo)

1991 (30 Dec). 80th Anniv of Scout Movement in Poland. T **995** and similar vert designs. P 12×11½.
3383　1500z. greenish yellow and emerald.................　90　35
3384　2000z. new blue and bright lemon....................　1·10　45
3385　2500z. bright bluish violet and chrome yellow...　1·30　50
3386　3500z. bistre-brown and orange-yellow............　2·20　1·00
3383/3386　Set of 4...　5·00　2·10
　　Designs:—2000z. Andrzej Malkowski (Polish founder); 2500z. "Watch on the Vistula" (Wojciech Kossak); 3500z. Polish scout in Warsaw Uprising, 1944.

(Des S. Malecki. Eng W. Zajdel (1500z.), T. Zlotkowski (2000z.). Recess and photo)

1992 (15 Jan). Polish Rulers (7th series). Vert designs as T **893** showing drawings by Jan Matejko. P 11.
3387　1500z. sepia and brown-olive............................　1·10　50
3388　2000z. blue-black and deep turquoise-blue.....　1·40　1·00
　　Designs:—1500z. Kazimierz II, the Just; 2000z. Leszek I, the White.

996 Sébastien Bourdon　**997** Skiing

(Des M. Piekarski. Photo)

1992 (16 Jan). Self-portraits. T **996** and similar vert designs. Multicoloured. P 11.
3389　700z. Type **996**..　35　15
3390　1000z. Sir Joshua Reynolds...............................　55　25
3391　1500z. Sir Godfrey Kneller................................　90　35
3392　2000z. Bartolomé Estéban Murillo....................　1·10　45

3393 2200z. Peter Paul Rubens .... 1·30 50
3394 3000z. Diego de Silva y Velázquez .... 1·80 85
3389/3394 Set of 6... 5·50 2·30

(Des J. Konarzewski. Litho)

1992 (8 Feb). Winter Olympic Games, Albertville. T **997** and similar horiz design. Multicoloured. P 11×11½.
3395 1500z. Type **997** 90 35
3396 2500z. Ice hockey... 1·30 50

998 Manteuffel   **999** Nicolas Copernicus (astronomer)

(Des M. Jędrysik. Photo)

1992 (5 Mar). 90th Birth Anniv of Tadeusz Manteuffel (historian). P 11½×11.
3397 **998** 2500z. light brown............................... 1·30 50

(Des J. Wysocki. Photo)

1992 (3 May). Famous Poles. T **999** and similar horiz designs. Multicoloured. P 11×11½.
3398 1500z. Type **999** 55 35
3399 2000z. Frédéric Chopin (composer)................ 90 50
3400 2500z. Henryk Sienkiewicz (writer).............. 1·10 85
3401 3500z. Marie Curie (physicist)...................... 1·40 1·00
3398/3401 Set of 4... 3·50 2·40
MS3402 80×81 mm. 5000z. Kazimierz Funk (biochemist) 2·75 2·50
No. **MS**3402 commemorates Expo '92 World's Fair, Seville.

1000 Columbus and Left-hand Detail of Map

(Des J. Wysocki. Litho)

1992 (5 May). Europa. 500th Anniv of Discovery of America by Christopher Columbus. T **1000** and similar horiz design. Multicoloured. P 11×11½.
3403 1500z. Type **1000**... 55 35
    a. Horiz pair. Nos. 3403/4 .... 2·30 1·30
3404 3000z. Santa Maria and right-hand detail of Juan de la Costa map, 1500........................ 1·60 85
Nos. 3403/4 were issued together in horizontal se-tenant pairs within the sheet, each pair forming a composite design.

1001 River Czarna Wiselka   **1002** Prince Józef Poniatowski

(Des J. Brodowski. Photo)

1992 (12 June). Environmental Protection. River Cascades. T **1001** and similar vert designs. Multicoloured. P 11½×12.
3405 2000z. Type **1001**... 55 15
3406 2500z. River Swider .... 1·10 45
3407 3000z. River Tanew .... 1·40 50
3408 3500z. Mickiewicz waterfall .... 2·00 85
3405/3408 Set of 4... 4·50 1·80

(Des M. Jędrysik. Litho (**MS**3411) or photo (others))

1992 (18 June). Bicentenary of Order of Military Virtue. T **1002** and similar vert designs. Multicoloured. P 11.
3409 1500z. Type **1002**... 55 35
3410 3000z. Marshal Józef Pilsudski...................... 90 50
MS3411 108×93 mm. 20000z. "Virgin Mary of Częstochowa" (icon) (36×57 mm). Imperf................ 9·00 8·50

1003 Family and Heart

(Des J. Wysocki. Litho)

1992 (26 June). Children's Drawings. T **1003** and similar vert design. Multicoloured. P 11½×11.
3412 1500z. Type **1003**... 55 35
    a. Pair. Nos 3412/13 .... 2·00 1·30
3413 3000z. Butterfly, sun, bird and dog................ 1·30 85
Nos. 3412/13 were issued together in se-tenant pairs within the sheet.

1004 Fencing   **1005** Runners

(Des J. Konarzewski. Litho)

1992 (25 July). Olympic Games, Barcelona. T **1004** and similar horiz designs. Multicoloured. P 11×11½.
3414 1500z. Type **1004**... 35 15
3415 2000z. Boxing.. 55 35
3416 2500z. Running... 1·10 50
3417 3000z. Cycling.. 1·40 85
3414/3417 Set of 4... 3·00 1·70

(Des H. Chyliński. Photo)

1992 (29 July). Olymphilex '92 Olympic Stamps Exhibition, Barcelona. Sheet 86×81 mm. P 11×11½.
MS3418 **1005** 20000z. multicoloured............................. 9·00 8·50
No. **MS**3418 also exists imperforate from a limited issue (price £22).

1006 Statue of Korczak   **1007** Flag and "V"

(Des J. Brodowski. Photo)

1992 (5 Aug). 50th Death Anniv of Janusz Korczak (educationist). P 11×11½.
3419 **1006** 1500z. black, lake-brown and chrome yellow 90 50

(Des F. Winiarski. Photo)

1992 (14 Aug). Fifth Polish Veterans World Meeting. P 11½×11.
3420 **1007** 3000z. multicoloured...................................... 1·40 85

1008 Wyszyński

1009 National Colours encircling World Map

(Des M. Jędrysik. Litho)

1992 (15 Aug). 11th Death Anniv of Stefan Wyszyński (Primate of Poland) (3421) and First Anniv of Sixth World Youth Day (3422). T **1008** and similar vert design. Multicoloured. P 11½×11.

3421	1500z. Type **1008**	1·10	50
	a. Pair. Nos. 3421/2 plus 2 labels	2·75	1·60 ✓
3422	3000z. Pope John Paul II embracing youth	1·40	1·00

Nos. 3421/2 were issued together in blocks of two stamps and two labels showing the arms of either Wyszyński or the Pope.

(Des A. Szczepaniak. Photo)

1992 (19 Aug). World Meeting of Expatriate Poles, Cracow. P 12×11½.

3423	**1009** 3000z. multicoloured	1·60	85

1010 Polish Museum, Adampol

1011 18th-century Post Office Sign, Slonim

(Des H. Chyliński. Photo)

1992 (15 Sept). 150th Anniv of Polish Settlement at Adampol, Turkey. P 11×11½.

3424	**1010** 3500z. multicoloured	1·80	1·00

(Des Z. Stasik. Photo)

1992 (9 Oct). World Post Day. P 11½×11.

3425	**1011** 3500z. multicoloured	1·80	1·00

1012 "Dedication" (self-portrait)

1013 "Seated Girl" (Henryk Wiciński)

(Des J. Konarzewski. Litho)

1992 (26 Oct). Birth Centenary of Bruno Schulz (writer and artist). P 11×11½.

3426	**1012** 3000z. multicoloured	1·60	85 ✓

(Des H. Chyliński. Litho)

1992 (29 Oct). Polish Sculptures. T **1013** and similar square designs. Multicoloured. P 11½.

3427	2000z. Type **1013**	90	50
3428	2500z. "Portrait of Tytus Czyżewski" (Zbigniew Pronaszko)	1·10	60
3429	3000z. "Polish Nike" (Edward Wittig)	1·30	75
3430	3500z. "The Nude" (August Zamoyski)	1·40	85
3427/3430 *Set of 4*		4·25	2·40
MS3431 107×90 mm. Nos. 3427/30		4·50	4·25

No. **MS**3431 commemorates Polska '93 International Stamp Exhibition.

1014 "10th Theatrical Summer in Zamość" (Jan Mlodozeniec)

1015 Girl skipping with Snake

(Des K. Kupczyk. Litho)

1992 (30 Oct). Poster Art (1st series). T **1014** and similar multicoloured designs. P 13½.

3432	1500z. Type **1014**	55 ✓	35
3433	2000z. "Red Art" (Franciszek Starowieyski) (*horiz*)	90 ✓	50
3434	2500z. "Circus" (Waldemar Świerzy)	1·10 ✓	85
3435	3500z. "Mannequin" (Henryk Tomaszewski)	1·40 ✓	1·00
3432/3435 *Set of 4*		3·50	2·40

See also Nos. 3502/3, 3523/4, 3585/6 and 3712/15.

(Des E. Lutczyn. Photo)

1992 (16 Nov). Polska '93 International Stamp Exhibition, Poznań (1st issue). T **1015** and similar vert designs. Multicoloured. P 11.

3436	1500z. Type **1015**	55	35
3437	2000z. Boy on rocking horse with upside-down runners	90	50
3438	2500z. Boy firing bird from bow	1·10	70
3439	3500z. Girl placing ladder against clockwork giraffe	1·40	85
3436/3439 *Set of 4*		3·50	2·20

See also Nos. 3452, 3453/**MS**3457, 3466/9 and **MS**3476.

1016 Medal and Soldiers

1017 Church and Star

(Des J. Wysocki. Litho)

1992 (20 Nov). 50th Anniv of Formation of Polish Underground Army. T **1016** and similar multicoloured designs. P 13½.

3440	1500z. Type **1016**	55	35
	a. Pair. Nos. 3440/1	2·50	1·70
3441	3500z. Soldiers	1·80	1·20
MS3442 75×95 mm. 20000z.+500z. "WP AK" (26×32 *mm*) (7 contract numbers)		9·00	8·50

Nos. 3440/1 were issued together in *se-tenant* pairs within the sheet. No. **MS**3442 was also issued with five control numbers (*price £450*).

(Des J. Brodowski. Photo)

1992 (25 Nov). Christmas. P 11½×12.

3443	**1017** 1000z. multicoloured	55	15

1018 Wheat

1019 Arms of Sovereign Military Order

(Des M. Jędrysik. Photo)

1992 (5 Dec). International Nutrition Conference, Rome. T **1018** and similar vert design. Multicoloured. P 11½×11.

3444	1500z. Type **1018**	55	25
3445	3500z. Glass, bread, vegetables and jug on table	1·40	85

(Des A. Heidrich. Litho)

1992 (10 Dec). Postal Agreement with Sovereign Military Order of Malta. P 11½×11.

3446	**1019** 3000z. multicoloured	1·40	85

1020 Arms, 1295

1021 Exhibition Emblem and Stylised Stamp

(Des H. Chyliński. Photo)

1992 (14 Dec). History of the White Eagle (Poland's arms). T **1020** and similar vert designs. Each black, orange-vermilion and orange-yellow. P 11½.

3447	2000z. Type **1020**	90	35
3448	2500z. 15th-century arms	1·10	45
3449	3000z. 18th-century arms	1·30	50
3450	3500z. Arms, 1919	1·40	85
3451	5000z. Arms, 1990	2·20	1·00
3447/3451 *Set of 5*		6·25	2·75

(Des J. Wysocki. Litho)

1993 (6 Jan). Centenary of Polish Philately and Polska '93 International Stamp Exhibition, Poznań (2nd issue). P 11½.

3452	**1021** 1500z. multicoloured	70	45

1022 Amber

1023 Downhill Skier

(Des A. Jeziorkowski. Litho)

1993 (29 Jan). Polska '93 International Stamp Exhibition, Poznań (3rd issue). Amber. T **1022** and similar multicoloured designs. P 13½.

3453	1500z. Type **1022**	55	35
3454	2000z. Pinkish amber	90	50
3455	2500z. Amber in stone	1·30	85
3456	3000z. Amber containing wasp	1·80	1·20
3453/3456 *Set of 4*		4·00	2·50
MS3457	82×88 mm. 20000z. Detail of map with necklace representing amber route (44×29 *mm*) (6 control numbers)	7·25	6·75

No. **MS**3457 was also issued wiht 5 small control numbers (*price* £350) or 5 large control numbers (style as on **MS**3457) (*price* £800).

(Des H. Chyliński. Litho)

1993 (5 Feb). Winter University Games, Zakopane. P 11½×11.

3458	**1023** 3000z. multicoloured	1·30	85

1024 Flower-filled Heart

1025 Arsenal

(Des S. Malecki. Litho)

1993 (14 Feb). St. Valentine's Day. T **1024** and similar vert design. Multicoloured. P 11½×11.

3459	1500z. Type **1024**	55	25
3460	3000z. Heart in envelope	1·30	85

(Des S. Malecki. Eng W. Zajdel (1500, 3000z.), T. Zlotkowski (2000z.), M. Kopecki (2500z.). Recess and photo)

1993 (25 Mar). Polish Rulers (8th series). Vert designs as T **893** showing drawings by Jan Matejko. P 11.

3461	1500z. blackish brown and yellow-olive	90	50
3462	2000z. blue-black and deep magenta	1·30	85
3463	2500z. black and slate-green	1·80	1·00
3464	3000z. deep brown and orange-brown	2·75	1·70
3461/3464 *Set of 4*		6·00	3·75

Designs:—1500z. Wladyslaw Laskonogi; 2000z. Henryk I; 2500z. Konrad I of Masovia; 3000z. Boleslaw V, the Chaste.

No. 3464 was issued with a *se-tenant* label commemorating Polska '93 International Stamp Exhibition.

(Des A. Szczepaniak. Photo)

1993 (26 Mar). 50th Anniv of Action by Szare Szeregi (formation of Polish Scouts in the resistance forces) on Warsaw Arsenal. P 12×11½.

3465	**1025** 1500z. multicoloured	90	50

1026 Jousters with Lances

(Des F. Winiarski. Photo)

1993 (29 Mar). Polska '93 International Stamp Exhibition, Poznań (4th issue). Jousting at Golub Dobrzyn. T **1026** and similar horiz designs each showing a modern and a medieval jouster. Multicoloured. P 11×11½.

3466	1500z. Type **1026**	55	25
3467	2000z. Jousters	90	50
3468	2500z. Jousters with swords	1·10	85
3469	3500z. Officials	1·40	1·00
3466/3469 *Set of 4*		3·50	2·30

1027 Szczecin

(Des M. Jędrysik. Litho)

1993 (3 Apr). 750th Anniv of Granting of Town Charter to Szczecin. P 11½×11.

3470	**1027** 1500z. multicoloured	90	50

1028 Jew and Ruins

1029 Works by A. Szapocznikow and J. Lebenstein

(Des Ruth Avrahami. Litho)

1993 (18 Apr). 50th Anniv of Warsaw Ghetto Uprising. P 14.

3471	**1028** 4000z. black, lemon and azure	1·80	1·00

No. 3471 was issued in sheets with a row of half stamp-size inscribed labels.

A stamp of a similar design was issued by Israel.

(Des J. Wysocki. Litho)

1993 (30 Apr). Europa. Contemporary Art. T **1029** and similar horiz design. Multicoloured. P 11×11½.

3472	1500z. Type **1029**	90	50
	a. Pair. Nos. 3472/3	3·00	1·60
3473	4000z. "CXCIX" (S. Gierowski) and "Red Head" (B. Linke)	1·80	1·00

Nos. 3472/3 were issued together in *se-tenant* pairs within the sheet.

1030 "King Alexander Jagiellończyk in the Sejm" (Jan Laski, 1505)

(Des A. Jeziorkowski. Photo)

1993 (2 May). 500th Anniv of Parliament. P 11.
3474 **1030** 2000z. multicoloured 90 50

1031 Nullo

(Des R. Dudzicki. Photo)

1993 (5 May). 130th Death Anniv of Francesco Nullo (Italian volunteer in January 1863 Rising). P 11×11½.
3475 **1031** 2500z. multicoloured .... 1·30 85

1032 Lech's Encounter with the White Eagle after Battle of Gniezno

1033 Cap

(Des A. Jeziorkowski. Eng C. Slania. Recess)

1993 (7 May). Polska '93 International Stamp Exhibition, Poznań (5th issue). Sheet 103×86 mm. P 13½.
MS3476 **1032** 50000z. deep brown .... 16·00 15·00
No. **MS**3476 also exists imperforate from a limited issue (*price* £31).

(Des J. Wysocki. Litho)

1993 (21 May). Third World Congress of Cadets of the Second Republic. P 11×11½.
3477 **1033** 2000z. multicoloured .... 1·10 ✔ 50

1034 Copernicus and Solar System

1035 *Fiki Miki* and Lion

(Des J. Konarzewski. Litho)

1993 (24 May). 450th Death Anniv of Nicolas Copernicus (astronomer). P 11×11½.
3478 **1034** 2000z. multicoloured .... 1·30 85

(Des H. Chyliński. Litho)

1993 (1 June). 40th Death Anniv of Kornel Makuszyński (writer of children's books). T **1035** and similar horiz designs. Multicoloured. P 11×11½.
3479 1500z. Type **1035** 55 35
3480 2000z. Billy goat 90 50
3481 3000z. *Fiki Miki* .... 1·40 85
3482 5000z. Billy goat riding ostrich..................... 2·20 1·20
3479/3482 *Set of 4*... 4·50 2·50

(Des A. Balcerzak. Photo)

1993 (30 June). Cones. Vert designs as T **974**. Multicoloured. P 12×11½.
3483 10000z. Arolla Pine (*Pinus cembra*)...................... 4·00 2·50
3484 20000z. Scots Pine (*Pinus sylvestris*) .... 7·50 4·25

1036 Eurasian Tree Sparrow (*Passer montanus*)

1037 Soldiers Marching

(Des K. Rogaczewska. Litho)

1993 (15 July). Birds. T **1036** and similar vert designs. Multicoloured. P 11½×11.
3485 1500z. Type **1036**.............................. 55 35
3486 2000z. Pied Wagtail (*Motacilla alba*)................... 1·10 50
3487 3000z. Syrian Woodpecker (*Dendrocopos syriacus*)... 1·40 85
3488 4000z. Eurasian Goldfinch (*Carduelis carduelis*) 2·20 1·20
3489 5000z. Common Starling (*Sturnus vulgaris*)...... 2·30 1·70
3490 6000z. Northern Bullfinch (*Pyrrhula pyrrhula*) .. 3·00 2·00
3485/3490 *Set of 6*.. 9·50 6·00

(Des M. Jędrysik. Photo)

1993 (20 July). Bicentenary of Dąbrowski's Mazurka (national anthem) (1st issue). P 11×11½.
3491 **1037** 1500z. multicoloured 90 50
See also Nos. 3526, 3575, 3639 and 3700/**MS**3701.

1038 "Madonna and Child" (St. Mary's Basilica, Lesna Podlaska)

1039 Handley Page H.P.61 Halifax A.IX

(Des J. Wysocki. Litho)

1993 (15 Aug). Sanctuaries to St. Mary. T **1038** and similar vert design. Multicoloured. P 11×11½ (with one elliptical hole on each vert side).
3492 1500z. Type **1038**............................... 55 35
3493 2000z. "Madonna and Child" (St. Mary's Church, Swieta Lipka) .... 1·10 70
Each issued in sheets of nine stamps.

(Des M. Jędrysik. Litho)

1993 (15 Sept). The Polish Rangers (Second World War air troop). P 11×11½ (with one elliptical hole on each horiz side).
3494 **1039** 1500z. multicoloured 90 50

1040 Trumpet Player

1041 Postman

(Des J. Konarzewski. Litho)

1993 (27 Sept). Jazz Jamboree '93 International Jazz Festival, Warsaw. P 11½ (with one elliptical hole on each horiz side).

3495	**1040**	2000z. multicoloured	1·10	50

(Des S. Malecki. Eng T. Zlotkowski. Recess and photo)

1993 (9 Oct). World Post Day. P 11½×11.

3496	**1041**	2500z. agate, lavender-grey and blue....	1·30	85

1042 St. Jadwiga (miniature, *Schlackenwerther Codex*)   **1043** Pope John Paul II

(Des A. Heidrich. Litho State Ptg Wks, Berlin)

1993 (14 Oct). 750th Death Anniv of St. Jadwiga of Silesia. P 14.

3497	**1042**	2500z. multicoloured	1·30	85

A stamp of a similar design was issued by Germany.

(Des J. Wysocki. Litho)

1993 (16 Oct). 15th Anniv of Election of Pope John Paul II. Sheet 70×92 mm. P 11½×11 (with one elliptical hole on each vert side).

MS3498	**1043**	20000z. multicoloured	9·00	8·50

1044 Eagle and Crown   **1045** St. Nicholas

(Des J. Wysocki. Litho)

1993 (11 Nov). 75th Anniv of Republic. T **1044** and similar vert design. Multicoloured. P 11½×11 (with one elliptical hole on each vert side).

3499		4000z. Type **1044**	2·20	1·20
MS3500		66×89 mm. 20000z. Silhouette and shadow of flying eagle (31×38 mm)	11·00	10·50

On No. **MS3500** the perforations on each vertical side, as well as containing an elliptical hole, are interrupted along that part of the design showing the eagle.

(Des A. Gosik. Litho)

1993 (25 Nov). Christmas. P 12×11½ (with one elliptical hole on each vert side).

3501	**1045**	1500z. multicoloured	90	50

(Des Krystyna Hoffman-Pagowska. Litho)

1993 (10 Dec). Poster Art (2nd series). Vert designs as T **1014**. Multicoloured. P 11×11½ (with one elliptical hole on each vert side).

3502		2000z. "Come and see Polish mountains" (M. Urbaniec)	1·30	85
3503		5000z. Production of Alban Berg's *Wozzeck* (J. Lenica)	2·20	1·20

1046 Daisy shedding Petals

1047 Cross-country Skiing

(Des A. Gosik. Litho)

1994 (14 Jan). Greetings Stamp. P 11½×11 (with one elliptical hole on each vert side).

3504	**1046**	1500z. multicoloured	90	50

(Des M. Urbaniec. Photo)

1994 (12 Feb). Winter Olympic Games, Lillehammer, Norway. T **1047** and similar vert designs. Multicoloured. P 11½×11.

3505		2500z. Type **1047**	1·30	85
3506		5000z. Ski jumping	2·20	1·20
MS3507		81×80 mm. 10000z. Downhill skiing	4·50	4·25

The miniature sheet also commemorates the centenary of the International Olympic Committee.

1048 Bem and Cannon

(Des J. Wysocki. Litho)

1994 (14 Mar). Birth Bicentenary of General Józef Bem. P 11½ (with one elliptical hole on each horiz side).

3508	**1048**	5000z. multicoloured	2·20	1·20

1049 Jan Zamojski (founder)   **1050** Cracow Battalion Flag and Scythes

(Des Y. Erol. Litho)

1994 (15 Mar). 400th Anniv of Zamojski Academy, Zamość. P 11½×11 (with one elliptical hole on each vert side).

3509	**1049**	5000z. violet-grey, black and light brown	2·20	1·20

(Des M. Jędrysik. Litho)

1994 (24 Mar). Bicentenary of Tadeusz Kosciuszko's Insurrection. P 11½×11 (with one elliptical hole on each vert side).

3510	**1050**	2000z. multicoloured	1·10	50

(Des S. Malecki. Eng T. Zlotkowski (2500z.), W. Zajdel (5000z.). Recess and photo)

1994 (15 Apr). Polish Rulers (9th series). Vert designs as T **893** showing drawings by Jan Matejko. P 11.

3511		2500z. black and new blue	1·30	85
3512		5000z. blue-black, dull violet and reddish violet	3·00	1·70

Designs:—2500z. Leszek II, the Black; 5000z. Przemysl II.

1051 Oil Lamp, Open Book and Spectacles   **1052** "Madonna and Child"

(Des T. Boguslawski. Litho)

1994 (30 Apr). Europa. Inventions and Discoveries. T **1051** and similar vert design. Multicoloured. P 11½×11 (with one elliptical hole on each vert side).

3513		2500z. Type **1051** (invention of modern oil lamp by Ignacy Lukasiewicz)	1·10	85
3514		6000z. Illuminated filament forming "man in the moon" (astronomy)	2·50	1·70

(Des Z. Stasik. Litho)

1994 (16 May). St. Mary's Sanctuary, Kalwaria Zebrzydowska. P 11½×11 (with one elliptical hole on each vert side).

3515 **1052** 4000z. multicoloured .... 1·80   1·00

1053 Abbey Ruins and Poppies   **1054** Mazurka

(Des A. Heidrich. Litho)

1994 (18 May). 50th Anniv of Battle of Monte Cassino. P 11×11½ (with one elliptical hole on each horiz side).

3516 **1053** 6000z. multicoloured .... 2·20   1·20

(Des A. Heidrich. Litho)

1994 (25 May). Traditional Dances. T **1054** and similar vert designs showing paintings by Zofia Stryjeńska. Multicoloured. P 11½ (with one elliptical hole on each vert side).

3517	3000z. Type **1054**	55	35
3518	4000z. Coralski	1·10	60
3519	9000z. Krakowiak	2·75	1·40
3517/3519 *Set of 3*		4·00	2·10

1055 Cogwheels   **1056** Optic Fibre Cable

(Des H. Chyliński. Litho)

1994 (7 June). 75th Anniv of International Labour Organization. P 11½ (with one elliptical hole on each horiz side).

3520 **1055** 6000z. greenish blue, bright new blue and black .... 1·80   1·00

(Des J. Górski. Litho)

1994 (10 June). 75th Anniv of Polish Electricians Association. P 11×11½ (with one elliptical hole on each horiz side).

3521 **1056** 4000z. multicoloured .... 1·40   85

1057 Map of Americas on Football   **1058** Znaniecki

(Des M. Nadolski. Litho)

1994 (17 June). World Cup Football Championship, USA. P 11½×11 (with one elliptical hole on each horiz side).

3522 **1057** 6000z. multicoloured .... 2·20   1·20

1994 (4 July). Poster Art (3rd series). Multicoloured designs as T **1014**. Litho. P 11×11½ (4000z.) or 11½×11 (6000z.) (each with one elliptical hole on one side).

3523 4000z. "Monsieur Fabre" (Wiktor Górka) .... 1·30   85
3524 6000z. "8th OISTAT Congress" (Hubert Hilscher) (*horiz*) .... 2·20   1·20

(Des A. Gosik. Litho)

1994 (15 July). 36th Death Anniv of Professor Florian Znaniecki. P 11½ (with one elliptical hole on each vert side).

3525 **1058** 9000z. deep olive, bistre and yellow ...... 3·50   2·00

(Des M. Jędrysik. Litho)

1994 (20 July). Bicentenary of Dąbrowski's Mazurka (2nd issue). Horiz designs as T **1037**. Multicoloured. P 11×11½.

3526 2500z. Troops preparing to charge .... 1·30   85

1059 Polish Eagle and Ribbon   **1060** "Stamp" protruding from Pocket

(Des Y. Erol. Litho)

1994 (1 Aug). 50th Anniv of Warsaw Uprising. P 11½×11 (with one elliptical hole on each vert side).

3527 **1059** 2500z. multicoloured .... 1·30   85

(Des T. Boguslawski. Litho)

1994 (16 Aug). Philakorea 1994 International Stamp Exhibition, Seoul. P 11½×11 (with one elliptical hole on each vert side).

3528 **1060** 4000z. multicoloured .... 1·40   1·00

1061 Basilica of St. Brigida, Gdańsk   **1062** "Nike" (goddess of Victory)

(Des J. Wysocki. Litho)

1994 (28 Aug). Sanctuaries. P 11½×11 (with one elliptical hole on each vert side).

3529 **1061** 4000z. multicoloured .... 1·40   1·00

(Des M. Buszewicz. Litho)

1994 (5 Sept). Centenary of International Olympic Committee. P 11×11½ (with one elliptical hole on each horiz side).

3530 **1062** 4000z. multicoloured .... 1·40   1·00

1063 Komeda and Piano Keys   **1064** Long-finned Bristle-mouthed Catfish (*Ancistrus dolichopterus*)

(Des A. Pągowski. Litho)

1994 (22 Sept). 25th Death Anniv of Krzysztof Komeda (jazz musician). P 11½ (with one elliptical hole on each horiz side).

3531 **1063** 6000z. multicoloured .... 1·80   1·00

(Des J. Brodowski. Litho)

1994 (28 Sept). Fish. T **1064** and similar vert designs. Multicoloured. P 11½×11 (with one elliptical hole on each vert side).

3532	4000z. Type **1064**	1·60	1·00
	a. Horiz strip of 4. Nos. 3532/5	6·75	
3533	4000z. Freshwater Angelfish (*Pterophyllum scalare*)	1·60	1·00
3534	4000z. Red Swordtail (*Xiphophorus helleri*), Neon Tetra (*Paracheirodon innesi*) and Berlin Platy	1·60	1·00
3535	4000z. Neon Tetra and Guppies (*Poecilia reticulata*)	1·60	1·00
3532/3535 *Set of 4*		5·75	3·50

Nos. 3532/5 were issued together in horizontal *se-tenant* strips of four stamps within the sheet, each strip forming a composite design.

1065 Arms of Polish
Post, 1858

1066 Kolbe

(Des B. Orliński. Litho)

1994 (9 Oct). World Post Day. P 11½×11 (with one elliptical hole on
each vert side).
3536　**1065**　4000z. multicoloured .... 1·30　　85

(Des M. Jędrysik. Photo)

1994 (24 Oct). Maksymilian Maria Kolbe (concentration camp victim)
Year. P 11×11½.
3537　**1066**　2500z. multicoloured .... 1·10　　85

1067 Pigeon

(Des Krystyna Rogaczewska. Litho)

1994 (28 Oct). Pigeons. T **1067** and similar horiz designs.
Multicoloured. P 11×11½ (with one elliptical hole on each horiz
side).
3538　4000z. Type **1067** .... 1·10　　50
　　　　a. Block of 4. Nos. 3538/41 .... 5·25
3539　4000z. Friar Pigeon .... 1·10　　50
3540　6000z. Silver Magpie Pigeon .... 1·40　1·00
3541　6000z. Danzig Pigeon (black) .... 1·40　1·00
3538/3541 Set of 4 .... 4·50　2·75
MS3542 79×94 mm. 10000z. Short-tail Pigeon .... 3·50　3·25
Nos. 3538/41 were issued together in *se-tenant* blocks of four within
the sheet.

1068 Musicians playing
Carols

(Des Jadwiga and Z. Okrassa. Litho)

1994 (25 Nov). Christmas. P 11×11½ (with one elliptical hole on each
horiz side).
3543　**1068**　2500z. multicoloured .... 1·10　　50

1069 Landscape and EU Flag

1070 "I Love You" on
Pierced Heart

(Des W. Freudenreich. Litho)

1994 (15 Dec). Application by Poland for Membership of European
Union. P 11×11½ (with one elliptical hole on each horiz side).
3544　**1069**　6000z. multicoloured .... 2·75　1·70

Currency Reform
10000 Old Zlotys = 1 New Zloty

(Des A. Pągowski. Litho)

1995 (31 Jan). Greetings Stamp. P 11½×11 (with one elliptical hole on
each vert side).
3545　**1070**　35g. bright crimson and ultramarine .. 1·10　　55

1071 Rain, Sun and Water

(Des H. Chyliński. Litho)

1995 (31 Jan). 75th Anniv of Hydrological-Meteorological Service.
P 11×11½ (with one elliptical hole on each horiz side).
3546　**1071**　60g. multicoloured .... 1·30　　90

1072 Flag and Sea

(Des T. Boguslawski. Litho)

1995 (10 Feb). 75th Anniv of Poland's "Marriage to the Sea" (symbolic
ceremony commemorating renewal of access to sea). P 11×11½
(with one elliptical hole on each horiz side).
3547　**1072**　45g. multicoloured .... 1·10　　55

(Des S. Malecki. Eng W. Zajdel (35, 80g.), M. Kopecki (45, 60g.).
Recess and photo)

1995 (28 Feb). Polish Rulers (10th series). Vert designs as T **893**
showing drawings by Jan Matejko. P 11.
3548　35g. blackish brown, brown and pale
　　　　　yellow-brown .... 55　　35
3549　45g. blackish olive, deep dull green and
　　　　　sage green .... 90　　55
3550　60g. sepia and ochre .... 1·30　　90
3551　80g. blue-black and blue .... 1·40　1·10
3548/3551 Set of 4 .... 3·75　2·50
　Designs:—35g. Waclaw II; 45g. Wladyslaw I; 60g. Kazimierz III, the
Great; 80g. Ludwik Węgierski.

1073 St. John

1074 Eggs

(Des Z. Okrassa. Litho)

1995 (8 Mar). 500th Birth Anniv of St. John of God (founder of Order
of Hospitallers). P 12×11½ (with one elliptical hole on each vert
side).
3552　**1073**　60g. multicoloured .... 1·30　　90

(Des M. Wasilewski. Litho)

1995 (16 Mar). Easter. T **1074** and similar horiz designs, showing
decorated Easter eggs. Multicoloured (background colours given).
P 11½ (with one elliptical hole on each horiz side).
3553　35g. red .... 55　　35
3554　35g. deep lavender .... 55　　35
3555　45g. bright greenish blue .... 90　　55
3556　45g. blue-green .... 90　　55
3553/3556 Set of 4 .... 2·50　1·60

(Des A. Balcerzak. Photo)

1995 (27 Mar). Cones. Vert designs as T **974**. Multicoloured.
P 12×11½.
3557　45g. European Larch (*Larix decidua*) .... 90　　55
3558　80g. Mountain Pine (*Pinus mugo*) .... 1·40　　90

1075 Polish Officer's Button and Leaf

1076 Rose and Barbed Wire

(Des. M. Buszewicz. Litho)

1995 (13 Apr). Katyń Commemoration Year. P 11×11½ (with one elliptical hole on each horiz side).
3559   **1075**   80g. multicoloured .... 1·80   1·10

(Des T. Boguslawski. Litho)

1995 (28 Apr). Europa. Peace and Freedom. T **1076** and similar horiz design. Multicoloured. P 11×11½ (with one elliptical hole on each horiz side).
3560   35g. Type **1076** (liberation of concentration
      camps).. 90   55
3561   80g. Flowers in helmet........................... 1·80   1·30

1077 Storks

1078 Pope and Wadowice Church Font

(Des J. Wysocki. Litho)

1995 (6 May). 50th Anniv of Return of Western Territories. P 11½ (with one elliptical hole on each horiz side).
3562   **1077**   45g. multicoloured .... 1·10   55

(Des A. Gosik. Litho)

1995 (18 May). 75th Birthday of Pope John Paul II. P 11½ (with one elliptical hole on each vert side).
3563   **1078**   80g. multicoloured .... 1·80   1·10

1079 Puppets under Spotlight ("Mirómagia")

1080 Cockerill Steam Locomotive and Train, Warsaw–Vienna, 1845

(Des H. Chyliński. Litho)

1995 (25 May). 50th Anniv of Groteska Fairy Tale Theatre. T **1079** and similar multicoloured designs. P 11×11½ (horiz) or 11½×11 (vert) (each with one elliptical hole on two opposite sides).
3564   35g. Type **1079**............................. 70   55
    a. Pair. Nos. 3564/5......................... 1·50   1·20
3565   35g. Puppets in scene from play 70   55
3566   45g. Puppet leaning on barrel ("Thomas
      Fingerchen") (*vert*) .... 1·10   70
    a. Pair. Nos. 3566/7......................... 2·30   1·50
3567   45g. Clown ("Bumstara Circus") .... 1·10   70
3564/3567 *Set of 4*.. 3·25   2·30
Stamps of the same value were issued together in *se-tenant* pairs within their sheets.

(Des M. Jędrysik. Litho)

1995 (9 June). 150th Anniv of Polish Railways. T **1080** and similar horiz designs. Multicoloured. P 11½ (with one elliptical hole on each horiz side).
3568   35g. Type **1080**............................... 70   55
    a. Pair. Nos. 3568/9......................... 2·10   1·60
3569   60g. Lux-Torpedo diesel railcar, 1927 .... 1·30   90
3570   80g. Electric freight train, 1936............. 1·60   1·10
    a. Pair. Nos. 3570/1......................... 4·00   2·75
3571   1z. Euro City "Sobieski" express, Warsaw–
      Vienna line, 1992 .... 2·20   1·40
3568/3571 *Set of 4*.. 5·25   3·50

Nos. 3568/9 and 3570/1 respectively were issued together in *se-tenant* pairs within their sheets.

1081 Symbols of Nations

(Des J. Konarzewski. Litho)

1995 (26 June). 50th Anniv of United Nations Organization. P 11½ (with one elliptical hole on each horiz side).
3572   **1081**   80g. multicoloured .... 1·80   1·10

1082 Bank

(Des M. Piekarski. Litho)

1995 (30 June). 125th Anniv of Warsaw Commercial Bank. P 11½ (with one elliptical hole on each horiz side).
3573   **1082**   45g. multicoloured .... 1·10   55

1083 Loaf and Four-leaved Clover

1084 Rowan Berries (*Sorbus aucuparia*)

(Des J. Konarzewski. Litho)

1995 (13 July). Centenary of Peasant Movement. P 11×11½ (with one elliptical hole on each horiz side).
3574   **1083**   45g. multicoloured .... 1·10   55

(Des M. Jędrysik. Photo)

1995 (20 July). Bicentenary of Dąbrowski's Mazurka (3rd issue). Horiz designs as T **1037**. Multicoloured. P 11×11½.
3575   35g. Mounted troops .... 1·10   55

(Des A. Balcerzak. Photo)

1995 (31 July). Fruits of Trees. No value expressed. T **1084** and similar vert design. Multicoloured. P 12×11½.
3576   B (35g.) Acorns and Sessile Oak leaves
      (*Quercus petraea*)........................ 70   35
    a. Phosphorescent paper................... 1·10   55
3577   A (45g.) Type **1084**......................... 1·10   55
    a. Phosphorescent paper................... 1·30   90

1085 Madonna and Child

1086 Marshal Jósef Pilsudski

(Des Z. Stasik. Litho)

1995 (2 Aug). Basilica of the Holy Trinity, Leżajsk. P 11½×11 (with one elliptical hole on each vert side).
3578   **1085**   45g. multicoloured .... 1·10   55

(Des A. Heidrich. Litho)

1995 (14 Aug). 75th Anniv of Defence of Warsaw and of Riga Peace Conference. P 11×11½ (with one elliptical hole on each horiz side).
3579   **1086**   45g. multicoloured .... 1·10   55

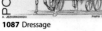

1087 Dressage

1088 Warsaw Technical University

(Des A. Jeziorkowski. Litho)

1995 (23 Aug). World Carriage Driving Championships, Poznań. T **1087** and similar horiz design. Multicoloured. P 11½ (with one elliptical hole on each horiz side).

3580	60g. Type **1087**	1·30	90
	a. Pair. Nos. 3580/1	3·25	2·30
3581	80g. Cross-country event	1·80	1·30

Nos. 3580/1 were issued together in se-tenant pairs within the sheet.

(Des J. Wysocki. Litho)

1995 (30 Aug). Warsaw '95 National Stamp Exhibition. T **1088** and similar multicoloured design. P 11½×11 (with one elliptical hole on two opposite sides).

3582	35g. Type **1088**	90	55
MS3583	94×71 mm. 1z. Castle Place, Warsaw (horiz). P 11×11½	2·20	2·00

1089 Russian Space Station and US Spacecraft

1090 Bar from *Polonaise* (Frédéric Chopin)

(Des Z. Stasik. Litho)

1995 (10 Sept). 11th World Cosmonauts Congress, Warsaw. P 11½×11 (with one elliptical hole on each vert side).

3584	**1089** 80g. multicoloured	1·80	1·10

(Des Krystyna Hoffman-Pagowska. Litho)

1995 (27 Sept). Poster Art (4th series). Vert designs as T **1014**. Multicoloured. P 11×11½ (with one elliptical hole on each vert side).

3585	35g. "The Crazy Locomotive" (Jan Sawka)	90	55
3586	45g. "The Wedding" (Eugeniusz Get Stankiewicz)	1·10	70

(Des T. Boguslawski. Litho)

1995 (1 Oct). 13th International Chopin Piano Competition. P 11×11½ (with one elliptical hole on each horiz side).

3587	**1090** 80g. multicoloured	2·00	1·10

1091 Postman

1092 Acrobatic Pyramid

(Des M. Jędrysik. Litho)

1995 (9 Oct). World Post Day. T **1091** and similar vert design. Multicoloured. P 11½ (with one elliptical hole on each vert side).

3588	45g. Type **1091**	90	55
3589	80g. Feather fixed to envelope by seal	1·60	1·10

(Des J. Brodowski. Litho)

1995 (26 Oct). World Acrobatic Sports Championships, Wroclaw. P 11½×11 (with one elliptical hole on each vert side).

3590	**1092** 45g. multicoloured	1·10	55

1093 Groszkowski and Formula

1094 Crib

(Des A. Pągowski. Litho)

1995 (10 Nov). 11th Death Anniv of Professor Janusz Groszkowski (radio-electronic scientist). P 11½ (with one elliptical hole on each horiz side).

3591	**1093** 45g. multicoloured	1·10	55

(Des H. Chyliński. Litho)

1995 (27 Nov). Christmas. T **1094** and similar vert design. Multicoloured. P 12½×11½ (with one elliptical hole on each vert side).

3592	35g. Type **1094**	90	55
	a. Horiz pair. Nos. 3592/3	2·30	1·40
3593	45g. Wise men, Christmas tree and star of Bethlehem	1·30	70

Nos. 3592/3 were issued together in horizontal se-tenant pairs within the sheet, each pair forming a composite design.

1095 Blue Tit (*Parus caeruleus*)

1096 Extract from Poem and Bow

(Des J. Desselberger. Litho)

1995 (15 Dec). Song Birds. T **1095** and similar square designs. Multicoloured. P 11½ (with one elliptical hole on each vert side).

3594	35g. Type **1095**	70	45
	a. Block of 4. Nos. 3594/7	4·75	
3595	45g. Long-tailed Tit (*Aegithalos caudatus*)	90	55
3596	60g. Great Grey Shrike (*Lanius excubitor*)	1·30	90
3597	80g. Hawfinch (*Coccothraustes coccothraustes*)	1·60	1·10
3594/3597	Set of 4	4·00	2·75

Nos. 3594/7 were issued together in se-tenant blocks of four stamps within the sheet.

(Des M. Buszewicz. Litho)

1995 (22 Jan). 75th Birth Anniv of Krzysztof Karnil Baczyński (poet). P 11×11½ (with one elliptical hole on each horiz side).

3598	**1096** 35g. multicoloured	90	55
	a. Tête-bêche (pair)	1·90	1·20

1097 Cherries and "I love you"

1098 Romanesque-style Inowłódz Church

(Des T. Boguslawski. Litho)

1996 (31 Jan). Greetings Stamp. P 11½×11 (with one elliptical hole on each vert side).

3599	**1097** 40g. multicoloured	90	55

(Des A. Gosik. Litho)

1996 (27 Feb). Architectural Styles. T **1098** and similar vert designs. Multicoloured. P 11½ (with one elliptical hole on each vert side).

3600	40g. Type **1098**	90	70
3601	55g. Gothic-style St. Mary the Virgin's Church, Cracow	1·30	90
3602	70g. Renaissance-style St. Sigismund's Chapel, Wawel Castle	1·60	1·10

3603	1z. Baroque-style Church of the Order of the Holy Sacrament, Warsaw	2·30	1·60
3600/3603	*Set of 4*	5·50	3·75

1099 *Oceania* (experimental sailing ship)   **1100** 16th-century Warsaw

(Des M. Piekarski. Litho)

1996 (11 Mar). Sailing Ships. T **1099** and similar horiz designs. Multicoloured. P 11×11½ (with one elliptical hole on each horiz side).

3604	40g. Type **1099**	90	70
	a. Strip of 4. Nos. 3604/7	5·75	
3605	55g. *Zawisza Czarny* (cadet schooner)	1·30	90
3606	70g. *General Zaruski* (cadet ketch)	1·60	1·30
3607	75g. *Fryderyk Chopin* (cadet brig)	1·80	1·40
3604/3607	*Set of 4*	5·00	3·75

Nos. 3604/7 were issued together in *se-tenant* strips of four stamps within the sheet.

(Des A. Heidrich. Litho)

1996 (18 Mar). 400th Anniv of Warsaw. P 11½.

3608	**1100**	55g. multicoloured	1·30	90

1101 Bull (Taurus)   **1102** Hanka Ordonówna (singer)

(Des M. Jędrysik. Photo)

1996 (21 Mar–31 July). Signs of the Zodiac. T **1101** and similar vert designs. Multicoloured. P 12×11½.

3609	5g. Workman in water (Aquarius) (19 July).	20	10
	a. Phosphorescent paper	25	10
3610	10g. "Fish-person" holding fish (Pisces) (31 July)	20	10
	a. Phosphorescent paper	25	10
3611	20g. Type **1101** (21 Apr)	25	10
	a. Phosphorescent paper	35	20
3612	25g. Twins looking through keyhole (Gemini) (10 May)	35	20
	a. Phosphorescent paper	45	25
3613	30g. Crab smoking pipe (Cancer) (20 June)	45	20
	a. Phosphorescent paper	55	25
3614	40g. Maid and cogwheels (Virgo) (31 May)	55	35
	a. Phosphorescent paper	70	35
3615	50g. Lion in military uniform (Leo) (31 May)	70	35
	a. Phosphorescent paper	1·10	45
3616	55g. Couple with head and shoulders as scales (Libra) (10 June)	80	45
3617	70g. Ram with ram-head (Aries)	90	55
	a. Phosphorescent paper	1·10	70
3618	1z. Woman with scorpion's tail hat (Scorpio) (20 June)	1·40	90
	a. Phosphorescent paper	1·80	1·30
3619	2z. Archer on motor cycle (Sagittarius) (28 June)	3·00	2·00
	a. Phosphorescent paper	3·50	2·50
3620	5z. Office worker shielding face with paper mask (Capricorn) (10 July)	7·25	4·75
	a. Phosphorescent paper	8·00	5·50
3609/3620	*Set of 12*	14·50	9·00

(Des A. Gosik. Litho)

1996 (30 Apr). Europa. Famous Women. T **1102** and similar vert design. Multicoloured. P 11½×11 (with one elliptical hole on each vert side).

3621	40g. Type **1102**	90	70
3622	1z. Pola Negri (actress)	1·80	1·60

1103 Flag of Osiek and Old Photographs forming "1921"   **1104** On Bergamuty Islands

(Des J. Wysocki. Litho)

1996 (2 May). 75th Anniv of Silesian Uprising. P 11×11½ (with one elliptical hole on each horiz side).

3623	**1103**	55g. bright scarlet, bronze green and black	1·30	90

(Des M. Jędrysik. Litho)

1996 (31 May). 50th Anniv of United Nations Children's Fund. Scenes from fairy tales by Jan Brzechwa. T **1104** and similar vert designs. Multicoloured. P 11½×11 (with one elliptical hole on each vert side).

3624	40g. Type **1104**	70	55
3625	40g. Waiters carrying trays of apples (nursery rhyme)	70	55
3626	55g. Vegetable characters (At the Market Stall)	1·10	70
3627	55g. Chef holding duck (Wacky Duck)	1·10	70
3628	70g. Woman and birdchild (The Fibber)	1·40	90
3629	70g. Red fox (The Impishness of Witalis Fox)	1·40	90
3624/3629	*Set of 6*	5·75	3·75

1105 "City Walls and Building"   **1106** Discus on Ribbon

(Des A. Balcerzak. Litho)

1996 (21 June). Paintings by Stanislaw Noakowski. T **1105** and similar vert designs. Multicoloured. P 11½×11 (with one elliptical hole on each vert side).

3630	40g. Type **1105**	90	55
3631	55g. "Renaissance Bedroom"	1·10	70
3632	70g. "Rural Gothic Church"	1·40	1·10
3633	1z. "Renaissance Library"	2·20	1·40
3630/3633	*Set of 4*	5·00	3·50

(Des T. Boguslawski. Litho)

1996 (5 July). Olympic Games, Atlanta, and Centenary of Modern Olympic Games. T **1106** and similar multicoloured designs. P 11½×11 (vert) or 11×11½ (horiz) (with one elliptical hole on two opposite sides).

3634	40g. Type **1106** (gold medal, Halina Konopacka, 1928)	90	55
3635	55g. Tennis ball (*horiz*)	1·30	70
3636	70g. Polish Olympic Committee emblem (*horiz*)	1·80	1·10
3637	1z. Bicycle wheel	2·30	1·40
3634/3637	*Set of 4*	5·75	3·50

1107 Tweezers holding Stamp showing Emblem   **1108** St. Mary of Przeczyca

(Des T. Boguslawski. Litho)

1996 (5 July). Olymphilex '96 International Sports Stamp Exhibition, Atlanta. P 11×11½ (with one elliptical hole on each horiz side).
3638 **1107** 1z. multicoloured .... 2·20 1·30

(Des M. Jędrysik. Photo)

1996 (20 July). Bicentenary of Dąbrowski's Mazurka (4th issue). Horiz design as T **1037**. Multicoloured. P 11×11½.
3639 40g. Charge of Polish cavalry at Somosierra. 1·10 55

(Des Z. Stasik. Litho)

1996 (2 Aug). St. Mary's Church, Przeczycka. P 11½.
3640 **1108** 40g. multicoloured .... 1·10 55

(Des S. Malecki. Eng W. Zajdel (40g.), M. Kopecki (55g.) P. Krajewski (others). Recess and photo)

1996 (29 Aug). Polish Rulers (11th series). Vert designs as T **893**. P 11.
3641 40g. agate and bistre 90 55
3642 55g. deep reddish lilac and deep mauve....... 1·30 70
3643 70g. violet-grey and brownish grey............. 1·80 90
3644 1z. blackish green, grey-green and olive-yellow .... 2·30 1·30
3641/3644 Set of 4 .... 5·75 3·00
Designs:—40g. Queen Jadwiga (wife of Wladyslaw II); 55g. Wladyslaw II Jagiello; 70g. Wladyslaw III Warneńczyk; 1z. Kazimierz IV Jagiellończyk.

1109 Mt. Giewont and Edelweiss   **1110** Seifert

(Des J. Brodowski. Litho)

1996 (5 Sept). The Tatra Mountains. T **1109** and similar horiz designs. Multicoloured. P 11½ (with one elliptical hole on each horiz side).
3645 40g. Type **1109** 70 55
3646 40g. Mt. Krzesanica and Spring Gentian....... 70 55
3647 55g. Mt. Kościelec and Leopard's Bane .... 1·10 70
3648 55g. Mt. Świnica and Clusius Gentian............. 1·10 70
3649 70g. Mt. Rysy and Ragwort....................... 1·40 90
3650 70g. Mieguszowieckie peaks and Pine Trees ... 1·40 90
3645/3650 Set of 6 .... 5·75 3·75

(Des W. Świerzy. Litho)

1996 (25 Sept). 50th Birth Anniv of Zbigniew Seifert (jazz musician). P 11½ (with one elliptical hole on each vert side).
3651 **1110** 70g. multicoloured .... 1·80 1·10

1111 "Changing of Horses at Post Station" (detail, Mieczyslaw Watorski)

(Des S. Malecki. Photo)

1996 (9 Oct). World Post Day. 75th Anniv of Post and Telecommunications Museum, Wroclaw. T **1111** and similar horiz design showing paintings. Multicoloured. P 12×11½.
3652 40g. Type **1111** .... 1·10 55
MS3653 102×81 mm. 1z.+20g. "Mail Coach at Jagniątków with View over Karkonosze" (Professor Täger) (42×30 mm). P 11×11½ .... 2·75 2·50

1112 Father Christmas on Horse-drawn Sleigh

(Des J. Brodowski. Litho)

1996 (27 Nov). Christmas. T **1112** and similar horiz designs. Multicoloured. P 11½×12 (with one elliptical hole on each horiz side).
3654 40g. Type **1112**............................. 70 35
3655 55g. Carol singers with star lantern................. 1·10 55

1113 Head of Male   **1114** Wislawa Szymborska

(Des J. Wysocki. Litho)

1996 (4 Dec). The European Bison (*Bison bonasus*). T **1113** and similar vert designs. Multicoloured. P 11½ (with one elliptical hole on each vert side).
3656 55g. Type **1113**............................. 1·10 70
a. Strip of 4. Nos. 3656/9............................. 4·75
3657 55g. Head of female .... 1·10 70
3658 55g. Pair of bison............................. 1·10 70
3659 55g. Male............................. 1·10 70
3656/3659 Set of 4 .... 4·00 2·50
Nos. 3656/9 were issued together in se-tenant strips of four stamps within the sheet.

(Des J. Wysocki. Litho)

1996 (10 Dec). Award of Nobel Prize for Literature to Wislawa Szymborska (poet). P 11½ (with one elliptical hole on each vert side).
3660 **1114** 1z. multicoloured .... 2·20 1·30

1115 "I Love You" on King of Hearts Playing Card   **1116** Blessing the Palms

(Des J. Konarzewski. Litho)

1997 (14 Jan). Greetings Stamps. T **1115** and similar horiz design. Multicoloured. Phosphorescent paper. P 11×11½ (with one elliptical hole on each horiz side).
3661 B (40g.) Type **1115**............................. 70 35
a. Vert pair. Nos. 3661/2............................. 1·90 95
3662 A (55g.) Queen of hearts playing card....... 1·10 55
Nos. 3661/2 were issued together in vertical se-tenant pairs. each pair forming a composite design.
No. 3661 was sold as the rate for postcards and No. 3662 for letters up to 20 grams.

(Des Maria Dziekańska. Litho)

1997 (14 Mar). Easter. Traditional Customs. T **1116** and similar horiz designs. Multicoloured. Phosphorescent paper. P 11×11½ (with one elliptical hole on each horiz side).
3663 50g. Type **1116**............................. 70 45
3664 60g. Woman and child painting easter eggs ... 90 55
3665 80g. Priest blessing the food............................. 1·30 90
3666 1z.10 Man throwing water over woman's skirts on Easter Monday .... 1·80 1·10
3663/3666 Set of 4 .... 4·25 2·75

1117 Long Market and Town Hall (after Mateusz Deisch)   **1118** St. Adalbert and Monks addressing Pagans

(Des T. Boguslawski. Photo and recess)

1997 (18 Apr). Millenary of Gdańsk. T **1117** and similar design. Each brown, pale cinnamon and carmine-red. P 11½×11.

| 3667 | 50g. Type **1117** | 90 | 55 |

MS3668 94×71 mm. 1z.10 St Mary's Church and Hall of the Main Town (after Mateusz Merian) (*horiz*).
P 11×11½ .... 2·75 2·50

No. **MS**3668 also exists imperforate (*price £22*).

(Des A. Heidrich (50, 60g.), V. Suchanek (1z.10).
Eng C. Slania. Recess)

1997 (19–23 Apr). Death Millenary of St. Adalbert (Bishop of Prague). T **1118** and similar designs. P 11×11½ (50g.) or 11½×11 (others).

3669	50g. sepia	70	35
3670	60g. blackish green	90	55
3671	1z.10 deep lilac (23.4)	1·80	1·10
3669/3671	*Set of 3*	3·00	1·80

Designs: Vert—60g. St. Adalbert and anniversary emblem; 1z.10 St. Adalbert.

Stamps of a similar design were also issued by Czech Republic, Germany, Hungary and Vatican City.

1119 Mansion House, Lopuszna

1120 The Crock of Gold

(Des A. Gosik. Photo)

1997 (30 Apr)–**2001**. Polish Manor Houses. T **1119** and similar horiz designs. Multicoloured. Phosphorescent paper. P 11½×12.

3672	10g. Lipkowie, Warsaw (20.6.01)	20	10
3672a	50g. Type **1119**	70	35
3673	55g. Henryk Sienkiewicz Museum, Oblęgorek (3.3.98)	80	45
3674	60g. Żyrzyn	90	55
3675	65g. Stanisław Wyspiański Museum, Bronowice, near Cracow (3.3.98)	1·00	65
3675a	70g. Modlnica (15.6.99)	1·10	70
3675b	80g. Grabonóg Gostyń (14.4.00)	1·30	80
3676	90g. Oborg, near Warsaw (3.3.98)	1·40	90
3676a	1z. Krzeslawice (15.6.99)	1·50	1·00
3677	1z.10 Ożarów (23.5.97)	1·60	1·10
3678	1z.20 Józef Krasnewski Museum, Biala Podlaska (3.3.98)	1·80	1·20
3678a	1z.40 Winna Góra (15.6.99)	2·00	1·30
3678b	1z.50 Sulejowku, Warsaw (20.6.01)	2·20	1·40
3678c	1z.55 Żelazowa Wola (14.4.00)	2·30	1·40
3678d	1z.60 Potok Zloty (15.6.99)	2·50	1·50
3678e	1z.65 Sucha, Wegrów (14.4.00)	2·75	1·60
3679	1z.70 Tulowice (23.5.97)	3·00	1·70
3679a	1z.85 Kaśna Dolna (15.6.99)	3·00	1·80
3679b	1z.90 Petrykozach, Mszczonowa (28.2.01)	3·25	2·00
3680	2z.20 Kuznocin (23.5.97)	3·50	2·30
3681	2z.65 Liwia, Wegrów (14.4.00)	4·00	2·50
3682	3z. Janowcu, Pulaw (28.2.01)	4·50	2·75
3683	10z. Koszuty (23.5.97)	14·50	11·00
3672/3683	*Set of 23*	55·00	35·00

No. 3684 is vacant.

(Des M. Wasilewski. Litho)

1997 (5 May). Europa. Tales and Legends. T **1120** and similar horiz design. Phosphorescent paper. P 11½×12 (with one elliptical hole on each horiz side).

| 3685 | 50g. Type **1120** | 90 | 55 |
| 3686 | 1z.10 Wars, Sawa and mermaid-siren | 2·75 | 1·80 |

1121 World Map and Emblem

(Des J. Wysocki. Litho)

1997 (6 May). 46th International Eucharistic Congress, Wroclaw. Phosphorescent paper. P 11½ (with one elliptical hole on each horiz side).

| 3687 | **1121** | 50g. multicoloured | 90 | 55 |

1122 Golden Gate Bridge

(Des M. Buszewicz. Photo)

1997 (20 May). Pacific 97 International Stamp Exhibition, San Francisco. Phosphorescent paper. P 11½×11 (with one elliptical hole on each horiz side).

| 3688 | **1122** | 1z.30 multicoloured | 2·20 | 1·30 |

1123 Pope John Paul II

(Des J. Wysocki. Litho)

1997 (28 May). Fifth Papal Visit. Sheet 76×90 mm. Phosphorescent paper. P 11×11½ (with one elliptical hole on each vert side).

| **MS**3689 | **1123** | 1z.10 multicoloured | 2·30 | 2·20 |

1124 European Long-eared Bat (*Plecotus auritus*)

(Des J. Brodowski. Litho)

1997 (30 May). Bats. T **1124** and similar horiz designs. Multicoloured. Phosphorescent paper. P 11×11½ (with one elliptical hole on each horiz side).

3690	50g. Type **1124**	70	55
3691	60g. Common Noctule (*Nyctalus noctula*)	90	70
3692	80g. Brown Bat (*Myotis myotis*)	1·10	90
3693	1z.30 Red Bat (*Vespertilio murinus*)	2·00	1·30
3690/3693	*Set of 4*	4·25	3·00

1125 "Founding of the Main School" (Jan Matejko)

1126 Map highlighting Settled Area

(Des J. Wysocki. Photo)

1997 (6 June). 600th Anniv of Faculty of Theology, Jagiellonian University, Cracow. Phosphorescent paper. P 11.

| 3694 | **1125** | 80g. multicoloured | 1·10 | 70 |

(Des A. Radziejowski. Litho)

1997 (6 June). Centenary of Polish Migration to Argentina. Phosphorescent paper. P 11½ (with one elliptical hole on each vert side).
3695 **1126** 1z.40 multicoloured .... 2·20 1·40

1127 "Return from War to the Village"

(Des A. Balcerzak. Photo)

1997 (4 July). Paintings by Juliúsz Kossak. T **1127** and similar horiz designs. Multicoloured. Phosphorescent paper. P 11.
3696	50g. Type **1127**	90	55
3697	60g. "Cracowian Wedding"	1·10	70
3698	80g. "In the Stable"	1·40	90
3699	1z.10 "Stablehand with Pair of Horses"	2·00	1·30
3696/3699 *Set of 4*		4·75	3·00

(Des M. Jędrysik. Photo)

1997 (18 July). Bicentenary of Dąbrowski's Mazurka (5th issue). Horiz designs as T **1037**. Phosphorescent paper. P 11×11½.
3700 50g. Dabrowski and Wybicki's arrival in Poznál, 1806 .... 90 55
MS3701 85×77 mm. 1z.10 Manuscript of lyrics and Józef Wybicki (composer) .... 2·30 2·20

1128 Strzelecki and Route Map around Australia

1129 Flooded Houses

(Des A. Jeziorkowski. Litho)

1997 (20 July). Birth Bicentenary of Pawel Strzelecki (explorer). Phosphorescent paper. P 11½ (with one elliptical hole on each horiz side).
3702 **1128** 1z.50 multicoloured .... 2·75 1·80

(Des M. Jędrysik. Photo)

1997 (18 Aug). Flood Relief Fund. Phosphorescent paper. P 11½×12.
3703 **1129** 60g. +30g. multicoloured .... 1·80 1·30

1130 "Holy Mother of Consolation" (icon)

1131 Kosz

(Des Z. Stasik. Litho)

1997 (28 Aug). Church of the Holy Mother of Consolation and St. Michael the Archangel, Górká Duchowa. Phosphorescent paper. P 11½×11 (with one elliptical hole on each vert side).
3704 **1130** 50g. multicoloured 90 55

(Des S. Malecki. Eng P. Krajewski (60g.), W. Zajdel (others). Recess and photo)

1997 (22 Sept). Polish Rulers (12th series). Vert designs as T **893**. P 11.
3705	50g. agate, red-brown and olive-bistre	1·10	55
3706	60g. deep dull purple and grey-blue	1·30	70
3707	80g. slate-green, deep dull green and grey-olive	1·80	1·10
3708	1z.10 blackish purple and reddish lilac	2·30	1·40
3705/3708 *Set of 4*		5·75	3·50

Designs:—50g. Jan I Olbracht; 60g. Aleksander Jagiellończyk; 80g. Zygmunt I, the Old; 1z.10 Zygmunt II August.

(Des J. Stanny. Litho)

1997 (3 Oct). 24th Death Anniv of Mieczyslaw Kosz (jazz musician). Phosphorescent paper. P 12×11½ (with one elliptical hole on each vert side).
3709 **1131** 80g. multicoloured .... 1·30 90

1132 Globe and Posthorn

(Des W. Walkuski. Litho)

1997 (9 Oct). World Post Day. Phosphorescent paper. P 11½×12 (with one elliptical hole on each horiz side).
3710 **1132** 50g. multicoloured 90 55

1133 St. Basil's Cathedral, Moscow

1134 Nativity

(Des J. Konarzewski. Litho)

1997 (13 Oct). Moskva 97 International Stamp Exhibition, Moscow. Phosphorescent paper. P 11×11½ (with one elliptical hole on each horiz side).
3711 **1133** 80g. multicoloured .... 1·30 1·10

(Des A. Pągowski. Litho)

1997 (14 Nov). Poster Art (5th series). Designs as T **1014**. Phosphorescent paper. P 11½×11 (3712) or 11×11½ (others) (each with one elliptical hole on two opposite sides).
3712	50g. multicoloured	70	45
3713	50g. black	70	45
3714	60g. multicoloured	90	55
3715	60g. black	90	55
3712/3715 *Set of 4*		3·00	1·80

Posters: Horiz—No. 3712, Advertisement for Radion washing powder (Tadeusz Gronowski). Vert—No. 3713, Production of Stanislaw Witkiewicz's play *Shoemakers* (Roman Cieślewicz); 3714, Production of Aleksander Fredro's play *A Husband and a Wife* (Andrzej Pągowski); 3715, Production of ballet *Goya* (Wiktor Sadowski).

(Des Krystyna Pagowska. Litho)

1997 (27 Nov). Christmas. T **1134** and similar multicoloured designs. Phosphorescent paper. P 11½×11 (50g., 1z.10) or 11×11½ (60, 80g.) (each with one elliptical hole on two opposite sides).
3716	50g. Type **1134**	70	55
3717	60g. Christmas Eve feast (*horiz*)	90	65
3718	80g. Family going to church for Midnight Mass (*horiz*)	1·30	90
3719	1z.10 Waits (carol singers representing animals)	1·80	1·30
3716/3719 *Set of 4*		4·25	3·00

1135 Common Shelducks (*Tadorna tadorna*)

1136 Ski Jumping

(Des J. Desselberger. Litho)

1997 (4 Dec). Precocial Chicks. T **1135** and similar square designs. Multicoloured. Phosphorescent paper. P 11½ (with one elliptical hole on each vert side).
3720 50g. Type **1135** 90 70
a. Block of 4. Nos. 3720/3 .... 3·75

3721	50g. Goosanders (*Mergus merganser*)	90	70
3722	50g. Common Snipes (*Gallinago gallinago*)	90	70
3723	50g. Moorhens (*Gallinula chloropus*)	90	70
3720/3723	*Set of 4*	3·25	2·50

Nos. 3720/3 were issued together in *se-tenant* blocks of four stamps within the sheet.

(Des W. Walkuski. Litho)

1998 (5 Jan). Winter Olympic Games, Nagano, Japan. Phosphorescent paper. P 11½ (with one elliptical hole on each vert side).

3724	**1136**	1z.40 multicoloured	2·20	1·40

1137 Dog wearing Cat T-shirt inscr "I Love You"

1138 Paschal Lamb

(Des Malgorzata Osa. Litho)

1998 (14 Jan). Greetings Stamps. No value expressed. T **1137** and similar vert design. Multicoloured. Phosphorescent paper. P 11½ (with one elliptical hole on each vert side).

3725	B (55g.) Type **1137**	70	55
3726	A (65g.) Cat wearing dog T-shirt	90	70

No. 3725 was sold as the rate for postcards and No. 3726 for letters up to 20 grams.

(Des A. Gosik. Photo)

1998 (15 Jan). Polish Manor Houses. No value expressed. Horiz designs as T **1119**. Multicoloured. Phosphorescent paper. P 11½.

3727	B (55g.) Gluchy	70	55
3728	A (65g.) Jan Kochanowski Museum, Czarnolas	90	70

No. 3727 was sold as the rate for postcards and No. 3728 for letters up to 20 grams.

(Des A. Pągowski. Litho)

1998 (12 Mar). Easter. T **1138** and similar vert design. Multicoloured. Phosphorescent paper. P 11½ (with one elliptical hole on each vert side).

3729	55g. Type **1138**	70	55
3730	65g. The Resurrected Christ	1·10	70

1139 Polish National Guard and Civilians at Lviv Barricades

1140 Grey Seal (*Halichoerus grypus*)

(Des M. Jędrysik. Eng W. Zajdel. Recess)

1998 (20 Mar). 150th Anniv of 1848 Revolutions. Phosphorescent paper. P 11×11½.

3731	**1139**	55g. blackish brown	90	55

(Des S. Malecki. Eng W. Zajdel (55g.), M. Kopecki (80g.), P. Krajewski (others). Recess and photo)

1998 (31 Mar). Polish Rulers (13th series). Vert designs as T **893**. P 11.

3732	55g. reddish brown and yellow-brown	70	55
3733	65g. slate-purple, deep purple and magenta	90	70
3734	80g. bottle green and dull yellowish green	1·30	90
3735	90g. blackish lilac, deep purple and magenta	1·40	1·00
3732/3735	*Set of 4*	3·75	2·75

Designs:—55g. Henryk Walezy; 65g. Queen Anne Jagiellońka (wife of Stefan I); 80g. Stefan I Batory; 90g. Zygmunt III Wasa.

(Des J. Brodowski. Litho)

1998 (28 Apr). Protection of Baltic Sea. Marine Life. T **1140** and similar vert designs. Multicoloured. Phosphorescent paper. P 11½×11 (with one elliptical hole on each vert side).

3736	65g. Type **1140**	90	80
	a. Horiz strip of 6. Nos. 3736/41	5·75	
3737	65g. *Pomatoschistus microps* (fish), jellyfish and shells	90	80
3738	65g. Twaite Shad (*Alosa fallax*) and Pipefish (*Syngnathus typhle*)	90	80
3739	65g. Common Sturgeon (*Acipenser sturio*)	90	80
3740	65g. Atlantic Salmon (*Salmo salar*)	90	80
3741	65g. Common Porpoise (*Phocoena phocoena*)	90	80
3736/3741	*Set of 6*	4·75	4·25
MS3742	76×70 mm. 1z.20 Grey Seal	2·30	2·20

Nos. 3736/41 were issued together in horizontal *se-tenant* strips of six stamps within the sheet, each strip forming a composite design.

1141 Exhibition Emblem and 1948 Israeli 500m. Stamp

(Des M. Buszewicz. Litho)

1998 (30 Apr). Israel '98 International Stamp Exhibition, Tel Aviv. Phosphorescent paper. P 11½ (with one elliptical hole on each horiz side).

3743	**1141**	90g. multicoloured	1·60	1·40

1142 Festival Emblem

(Des W. Freudenreich. Litho)

1998 (5 May). Europa. National Festivals. T **1142** and similar horiz design. Phosphorescent paper. P 11½ (with one elliptical hole on each horiz side).

3744	55g. multicoloured	90	70
	a. Pair. Nos. 3744/45	3·25	3·00
3745	1z.20 black, bright scarlet and ultramarine	2·20	2·00

Designs:—55g. Type **1142** ("Warsaw Autumn" International Festival of Music); 1z.20 State flag and opening bars of Welcome the May Dawn (3rd of May Constitution Day).

Nos. 3744/5 were issued together in *se-tenant* pairs within the sheet.

D 1143

1144 "Longing Holy Mother"

1998 (18 June). POSTAGE DUE. Type D **1143** and similar horiz designs. Litho. P 14.

D3746	5g. deep violet-blue, bright reddish violet and lemon	25	20
D3747	10g. deep violet-blue, turquoise-blue and lemon	35	25
D3748	20g. indigo, bright green and lemon	55	45
D3749	50g. blue-black and lemon	90	70
D3750	80g. deep violet-blue, orange and lemon	1·60	1·30
D3751	1z. deep violet-blue, bright crimson and lemon	2·20	1·60
D3746/3751	*Set of 6*	5·25	4·00

(Des J. Konarzewski. Litho)

1998 (28 June). Coronation of "Longing Holy Mother" (icon in Powsin church). Phosphorescent paper. P 11½ (with one elliptical hole on each vert side).
3752 **1144** 55g. multicoloured............................ 95 90

1145 "Triple Self-portrait"   **1146** Anniversary Inscription

(Des W. Freudenreich. Litho)

1998 (10 July). 30th Death Anniv of Nikifor (Epifan Drowniak) (artist) T **1145** and similar vert designs. Multicoloured. Phosphorescent paper. P 11½ (with one elliptical hole on each vert side).
3753 55g. Type **1145**............................ 1·00 90
3754 65g. "Cracow Office"............................ 1·20 1·10
3755 1z.20 "Orthodox Church"............................ 2·10 2·00
3756 2z.35 "Ugrybów Station"............................ 4·25 4·00
3753/3756 Set of 4............................ 7·75 7·25

(Des W. Freudenreich. Litho)

1998 (13 July). 80th Anniv of Main Board of Statistics. Phosphorescent paper. P 11×11½ (with one elliptical hole on each horiz side).
3757 **1146** 55g. multicoloured............................ 1·00 90

1147 "Madonna and Child"   **1148** Jesus (stained glass window)

(Des Z. Stasik. Litho)

1998 (14 Aug). Basilica of the Visitation of St. Mary the Virgin, Sejny. Phosphorescent paper. P 11½×11 (with one elliptical hole on each vert side).
3758 **1147** 55g. multicoloured............................ 1·00 90

(Des J. Konarzewski. Litho)

1998 (28 Aug). Bicentenary of Diocese of Warsaw. Phosphorescent paper. P 11½ (with one elliptical hole on each horiz side).
3759 **1148** 65g. multicoloured............................ 1·00 90

1149 Szczecin   **1150** Pierre and Marie Curie (physicists)

(Des A. Heidrich. Eng C. Slania. Recess and photo)

1998 (18 Sept). 17th Congress of Polish Union of Stamp Collectors. Sheet 114×77 mm containing T **1149** and similar horiz design. Each indigo and cream. Phosphorescent paper. P 11×11½.
MS3760 65g.×2 Composite design showing 17th-century engraving of Szczecin from *Descriptio Urbis Stettinensis* by Paul Feideborn............................ 2·50 2·30
No. **MS**3760 also exists imperforate (*price £39*).

(Des T. Boguslawski. Litho)

1998 (18 Sept). Centenary of Discovery of Polonium and Radium. Phosphorescent paper. P 11×11½ (with one elliptical hole on each horiz side).
3761 **1150** 1z.20 multicoloured............................ 2·00 1·80

1151 Mazowsze Dancers

(Des M. Buszewicz. Litho)

1998 (22 Sept). 50th Anniv of Mazowsze Song and Dance Group. T **1151** and similar vert design. Multicoloured. Phosphorescent paper. P 11½×11 (with one elliptical hole on each vert side).
3762 65g. Type **1151**............................ 1·10 90
   a. Horiz pair. Nos. 3762/3............................ 2·30 1·90
3763 65g. Dancers (*different*)............................ 1·10 90
Nos. 3762/3 were issued together in horizontal *se-tenant* pairs throughout the sheet, each pair forming a composite design.

1152 Mniszchów Palace

(Des A. Heidrich. Eng G. Broux. Recess and photo)

1998 (28 Sept). Belgium Embassy, Warsaw. Phosphorescent paper. P 11½.
3764 **1152** 1z.20 multicoloured............................ 2·10 1·80
A stamp of a similar design was issued by Belgium.

1153 "King Sigismund" (Studio of Rubens)   **1154** Coloured Envelopes

(Des A. Heidrich. Eng C. Slania. Recess)

1998 (3 Oct). 400th Anniv of Battle of Stångebro. Phosphorescent paper. P 11½×11.
3765 **1153** 1z.20 purple-brown............................ 2·10 1·80
A stamp of a similar design was issued by Sweden.

(Des M. Wasilewski. Litho)

1998 (9 Oct). World Post Day. Phosphorescent paper. P 11½×11 (with one elliptical hole on each vert side).
3766 **1154** 65g. multicoloured............................ 1·10 90

1155 Pope John Paul II and People of Different Races   **1156** State Flags and 1919 Seal

(Des W. Walkuski. Litho)

1998 (16 Oct). 20th Anniv of Selection of Karol Wojtyla to Papacy. Phosphorescent paper. P 11½ (with one elliptical hole on each vert side).
3767 **1155** 65g. multicoloured............................ 1·10 90

(Des A. Heidrich. Litho)

1998 (11 Nov). 80th Anniv of Independence. Phosphorescent paper.
P 11½ (with one elliptical hole on each horiz side).
3768　**1156**　65g. black, vermilion and gold .... 1·10　90

1157 "Nativity"　　**1158** Anniversary Emblem

(Des J. Wysocki. Photo)

1998 (27 Nov). Christmas, *Grudziądz Polyptych*. T **1157** and similar
vert design. Phosphorescent paper. P 11½×11.
3769　55g. Type **1157**....................... 85　70
3770　65g. "Adoration of the Wise Men"..................... 1·10　90

(Des W. Freudenreich. Litho)

1998 (10 Dec). 50th Anniv of Universal Declaration of Human Rights.
Phosphorescent paper. P 11×11½ (with one elliptical hole on
each horiz side).
3771　**1158**　1z.20 new blue and deep ultramarine . 2·10　1·80

1159 Maryla Wereszczakówna　**1160** *Piorun* (destroyer),
and Moonlit Night　　1942–46

(Des J. Wysocki. Litho)

1998 (24 Dec). Birth Bicentenary of Adam Mickiewicz (poet). T **1159**
and similar multicoloured designs. Phosphorescent paper. P 11½
(with one elliptical hole on each horiz side).
3772　55g. Type **1159**........................ 85　70
3773　65g. Cranes flying over tomb of Maria
　　　Potocka .... 1·10　90
3774　90g. Burning candles and cross............. 1·50　1·30
3775　1z.20 House, field of flowers and Uhlan's
　　　shako............................. 1·90　1·60
3772/3775 *Set of 4*............................. 4·75　4·00
MS3776 61×76 mm. 2z.45 Mickiewicz (bust by Jean
David d'Angers) (30×38 *mm*). P 11½×11 (with one
elliptical hole on each side)............... 5·25　5·00

(Des T. Boguslawski. Litho)

1999 (4 Jan). 80th Anniv (1998) of Polish Navy T **1160** and similar
horiz design. Multicoloured. Phosphorescent paper. P 11×11½
(with one elliptical hole on each horiz side).
3777　55g. Type **1160**..................... 85　70
　　a. Pair. Nos. 3777/8................. 1·80　1·50
3778　55g. *Piorun* (missile corvette), 1994.................. 85　70
Nos. 3777/8 were issued together in *se-tenant* pairs within the sheet.

1161 Dominoes

(Des J. Konarzewski. Litho)

1999 (5 Feb). Greetings stamps. Value expressed by letter. T **1161**
and similar square design. Multicoloured. Phosphorescent paper.
P 11½ (with one elliptical hole on each vert side).
3779　B (60g.) Type **1161**.................... 85　70
3780　A (65g.) Dominoes (*different*) .... 1·10　90
No. 3779 was sold as the rate for postcards and No. 3780 for letters
up to 20 grams.

1162 Ernest Malinowski and
Railway Bridge over Verrugas
Canyon

(Des J. Konarzewski. Litho)

1999 (12 Feb). Polish Engineers. T **1162** and similar horiz design.
Multicoloured. Phosphorescent paper. P 11½ (with one elliptical
hole on each horiz side).
3781　1z. Type **1162** (death centenary)............. 1·50　1·30
3782　1z.60 Rudolf Modrzejewski and Benjamin
　　　Franklin Bridge over Delaware River,
　　　Philadelphia........................ 2·50　2·20

1163 "Prayer in Ogrójec"　**1164** Chinese Ideograms

(Des J. Wysocki. Photo)

1999 (5 Mar). Easter. T **1163** and similar vert designs. Multicoloured.
Phosphorescent paper. P 11½×11.
3783　60g. Type **1163**................... 85　70
3784　65g. "Carrying the Cross"................. 95　80
3785　1z. "Pietà"........................ 1·50　1·30
3786　1z.40 "Resurrection"................. 2·10　1·80
3783/3786 *Set of 4*................. 4·75　4·25
Nos. 3783/4 and 3786 show details of the *Grudziądz polyptych*.

(Des Malgorzata Osa. Litho)

1999 (31 Mar). China '99 International Stamp Exhibition, Peking. Sheet
80×96 mm. Phosphorescent paper. P 11½×11 (with one elliptical
hole on each vert side).
MS3787 **1164**　1z.70 multicoloured............... 3·25　3·00

1165 "Victorious　　**1166** Jan Skrzetuski passing Zbara
St. Mary of Kozielsk"　Fortress (*With Fire and Sword*)
(sculpture)

(Des J. Wysocki. Litho)

1999 (2 Apr). Images of Virgin Mary made by Polish Prisoners
of War. T **1165** and similar vert design. Multicoloured.
Phosphorescent paper. P 11½ (with one elliptical hole on each
vert side).
3788　60g. Type **1165**..................... 85　70
3789　70g. "St. Mary of Katyń" (bas-relief,
　　　Stanislaw Balos)................. 1·10　90

(Des A. Gosik. Photo)

1999 (6 Apr). Heroes of *The Trilogy* (novels) by Henryk
Sienkiewicz. T **1166** and similar horiz designs. Multicoloured.
Phosphorescent paper. P 11½ (with one elliptical hole on each
horiz side).
3790　70g. Type **1166**..................... 1·10　90
　　a. Block of 6. Nos. 3790/5 .... 6·75
3791　70g. Onufry Zagloba and 17th-century map
　　　of Poland (at three parts)............. 1·10　90
3792　70g. Longinus Podbipięta defending Zbara
　　　and three Tartars (*With Fire and Sword*). 1·10　90
3793　70g. Bohun with Helena Kuncewiczówna on
　　　way to Czarci Jar (*With Fire and Sword*). 1·10　90

3794   70g. Andrzej Kmicic and cannon at Jasna
        Góra Monastery (*The Deluge*)..................... 1·10   90
3795   70g. Michel Jerzy Wolodyjowski and Basia
        Jeziorkowska fencing (*Pan Michael*)........ 1·10   90
3790/3795 *Set of 6*... 6·00   4·75
    Nos. 3790/5 were issued together in *se-tenant* blocks of six stamps
within sheets of 12.

1167 Polish Flag and N.A.T.O. Emblem

1168 Anniversary Emblem and Headquarters, Strasbourg

(Des J. Kornarzewski. Litho)

1999 (22 Apr). Accession of Poland into and 50th Anniv of North Atlantic Treaty Organization. Phosphorescent paper. P 11½ (with one elliptical hole on each horiz side).
3796   **1167**   70g. multicoloured....................................... 1·30   1·10

(Des M. Jędrysik. Litho)

1999 (5 May). 50th Anniv of Council of Europe. Phosphorescent paper. P 11½×11 (with one elliptical hole on each vert side).
3797   **1168**   1z. multicoloured....................................... 2·10   1·80

1169 Three-toed Woodpecker

1170 Mountain Biking

(Des J. Desselberger. Litho)

1999 (5 May). Europa. Parks and Gardens. Bialowieski National Park. Phosphorescent paper. P 11½ (with one elliptical hole on each vert side).
3798   **1169**   1z.40 multicoloured.............................. 3·25   2·75

(Des J. Kornarzewski. Litho)

1999 (1 June). Youth Sports. T **1170** and similar horiz designs. Multicoloured. Phosphorescent paper. P 11½ (with one elliptical hole on each horiz side).
3799   60g. Type **1170**.. 85   70
3800   70g. Snowboarding.................................. 1·10   90
3801   1z. Skateboarding.................................... 1·70   1·40
3802   1z.40 Rollerblading.................................. 2·30   2·00
3799/3802 *Set of 4*.. 5·25   4·50

1171 St. Mary's Church, Cracow, Pope John Paul II and Crowd

(Des J. Wysocki. Litho)

1999 (5 June). Sixth Papal Visit to Poland. T **1171** and similar horiz designs. Multicoloured. Phosphorescent paper. P 12×11½ (with one elliptical hole on each vert side).
3803   60g. Type **1171**....................................... 85   70
        a. Strip of 4. Nos. 3803/6......................
3804   70g. Pope and crowd with crosses .... 1·10   90
3805   1z. Pope and cheering teenagers................. 1·70   1·40

3806   1z.40 Eiffel Tower (Paris), "Christ the Saviour"
        (statue, Rio de Janeiro), Pope and
        church at Fatima, Portugal .... 2·30   2·00
3803/3806 *Set of 4*... 5·25   4·50

1172 Ignacy Paderewski and Roman Dmowski (signatories)

1173 "St. Mary Carefully Listening" (icon)

(Des M. Jédrysic. Litho)

1999 (28 June). 80th Anniv of Treaty of Versailles. Phosphorescent paper. P 11×11½ (with one elliptical hole on each horiz side).
3807   **1172**   1z.40 multicoloured........................... 2·30   2·00

(Des Z. Stasik. Photo)

1999 (9 July). St. Mary's Sanctuaries. T **1173** and similar vert design. Multicoloured. Phosphorescent paper. P 11½×11 (with one elliptical hole on each vert side).
3808   60g. Type **1173** (church of St. Mary Queen
        of Poland, Rokitno) 85   70
3809   70g. "Mary" (statue, Ms. Jazlowiecka),
        Convent of Order of the Immaculate
        Conception, Szymanów............................. 1·10   90

1174 Great Diving Beetle (*Dytiscus marginalis*)

(Des J. Brodowski. Litho)

1999 (16 July). Water Insects. T **1174** and similar horiz designs. Multicoloured. Phosphorescent paper. P 11½×12 (with one elliptical hole on each horiz side).
3810   60g. Type **1174**....................................... 85   70
3811   60g. *Corixa punctata*................................ 85   70
3812   70g. *Limnophilus*..................................... 1·10   90
3813   70g. *Perla marginata*................................ 1·10   90
3814   1z.40 Emperor Dragonfly (*Anax imperator*)...... 2·30   2·00
3815   1z.40 *Ephemera vulgata*.............................. 2·30   2·00
3810/3815 *Set of 6*... 7·75   6·50

1175 Książ Castle

(Des A. Heidrich. Eng C. Slania. Recess and photo)

1999 (14 Aug). Walbrzych '99 18th National Stamp Exhibition. Sheet 74×105 mm. Phosphorescent paper. P 11.
MS3816   **1175**   1z. deep violet-blue................................. 3·00   2·75
    No. **MS**3816 also exists imperforate (*price £25*).

1176 Red Deer (*Cervus elaphus*)

1177 Emblem

(Des O. Koszel (3817), J. Brodowski
(3818). Litho)

1999 (22 Sept). Eastern Carpathian Mountains International
Biosphere Reserve (covering Polish, Ukrainian and Slovakian
National Parks). T **1176** and similar horiz design. Multicoloured.
Phosphorescent paper. P 11×11½ (with one elliptical hole on
each horiz side).

3817	1z.40 Type **1176**	2·10	1·80
	a. Pair. Nos. 3817/18	4·50	3·75
3818	1z.40 Wild Cat (*Felis silvestris*)	2·10	1·80

Stamps of a similar design were issued by Ukraine.

(Des S. Malecki. Eng W. Zajdel. 60g., 70g.) or P. Krajewski (others).
Recess and photo)

1999 (25 Sept). Polish Rulers (14th series). Vert designs as T **893**.
Phosphorescent paper. P 11.

3819	60g. olive-black, grey-olive and brown-olive	1·10	90
3820	70g. reddish brown and orange-brown	1·30	1·10
3821	1z. blue-black and dull ultramarine	1·70	1·40
3822	1z.40 deep dull purple and purple	2·50	2·20
3819/3822 *Set of 4*		6·00	5·00

Designs:—60g. Wladyslaw IV Waza; 70g. Jan II Kazimierz; 1z. Michal
Korybut Wiśniowiecki; 1z.40 Jan III Sobieski.

(Des Agnieszka Sobczyńska. Litho)

1999 (9 Oct). 125th Anniv of Universal Postal Union. World Post Day.
Phosphorescent paper. P 11½ (with one elliptical hole on each
horiz side).

3823	**1177** 1z.40 multicoloured	2·30	2·00

1178 Chopin and Academy of
Fine Arts, Warsaw

1179 Popieluszko

(Des A. Heidrich. Eng C. Slania. Recess)

1999 (17 Oct). 150th Death Anniv of Frédéric Chopin (composer).
Phosphorescent paper. P 11×11½.

3824	**1178** 1z.40 blackish green	2·30	2·00

A stamp of a similar design was issued by France.

(Des M. Jędrysik. Litho)

1999 (19 Oct). 15th Death Anniv of Father Jerzy Popieluszko.
Phosphorescent paper. P 11½×11 (with one elliptical hole on
each vert side).

3825	**1179** 70g. multicoloured	1·10	90

1180 Barbed Wire

(Des T. Boguslawski. Litho)

1999 (21 Oct). Homage to 20th-century Heroes of Poland. Sheet
93×70 mm. Phosphorescent paper. P 11½×11 (with one elliptical
hole on each vert side).

MS3826 **1180** 1z. multicoloured		2·10	2·00

1181 Angel (Silent Night)

(Des Agnieszka Sobczyńska. Litho)

1999 (26 Nov). Christmas. T **1181** and similar horiz designs inscr
in Polish with the opening lines of carols. Multicoloured.
Phosphorescent paper. P 11½ (with one elliptical hole on each
horiz side).

3827	60g. Type **1181**	1·10	90
3828	70g. Angel (Sleep, Jesus Baby)	1·30	1·10
3829	1z. Angel (Let's Go Everybody to the Stable)	1·70	1·40
3830	1z.40 Angel (The God is Born)	2·50	2·20
3827/3830 *Set of 4*		6·00	5·00

1182 Polish Museum,
Rapperswil Castle,
Switzerland

1183 "Proportions of Man"
(Da Vinci)

(Des J. Wysocki. Litho)

1999 (6 Dec). Polish Overseas Cultural Buildings. T **1182** and similar
vert designs. Multicoloured. Phosphorescent paper. P 11½ (with
one elliptical hole on each vert side).

3831	1z. Type **1182**	1·70	1·40
3832	1z.40 Marian Priests' Museum, Fawley Court, England	2·50	2·20
3833	1z.60 Polish Library, Paris, France	2·75	2·30
3834	1z.80 Polish Institute and Gen. Sikorski Museum, London, England	3·25	2·75
3831/3834 *Set of 4*		9·25	7·75

(Des J. Konarzewski. Litho)

2000 (2 Jan). New Year 2000. Phosphorescent paper. P 11½ (with one
elliptical hole on each vert side).

3835	**1183** A (70g.) multicoloured	1·30	1·10

1184 Bronislaw Malinowski
(sociologist)

1185 Otto III granting
Crown to Boleslaw I

(Des W. Walkuski. Litho)

2000 (22 Feb). Polish Personalities. T **1184** and similar square design.
Multicoloured. Phosphorescent paper. P 11½ (with one elliptical
hole on each vert side).

3836	1z.55 Type **1184**	2·75	2·30
3837	1z.95 Józef Zwierzycki (geologist)	3·25	3·00

(Des M. Jędrysik. Photo)

2000 (12 Mar). 1000th Anniv of the Gniezno Summit and the Catholic
Church in Poland. T **1185** and similar multicoloured designs.
Phosphorescent paper. P 11½×11.

3838	70g. Type **1185**	1·10	90
3839	80g. Archbishop of Gnesna, and Bishops of Cracovia, Wratislavia and Colberga	1·30	1·10
MS3840 77×65 mm. 1z.55 Provincial representatives presenting gifts to Otto III as Roman Emperor (*horiz*). P 11×11½		2·75	2·50

1186 Jesus in Tomb

(Des Agnieszka Sobczyńska. Litho)

2000 (24 Mar). Easter. T **1186** and similar horiz design. Multicoloured. Phosphorescent paper. P 11×11½ (with one elliptical hole on each horiz side).

3841	70g. Type **1186**	1·10	90
3842	80g. Resurrected Christ	1·30	1·10

1187 Saurolophus

(Des J. Brodowski. Litho)

2000 (24 Mar). Prehistoric Animals. T **1187** and similar horiz designs. Multicoloured. Phosphorescent paper. P 12×11½ (with one elliptical hole on each vert side).

3843	70g. Type **1187**	1·10	90
3844	70g. Gallimimus	1·10	90
3845	80g. Saichania	1·30	1·10
3846	80g. Protoceratops	1·30	1·10
3847	1z.55 Prenocephale	2·50	2·20
3848	1z.55 Velociraptor	2·50	2·20
3843/3848	Set of 6	8·75	7·50
MS3848a	150×145 mm. Nos. 3843/8	12·50	12·00

1188 Wajda

1189 Pope John Paul kneeling, St. Peter's Basilica, Rome

(Des M. Buszewicz. Litho)

2000 (26 Mar). Presentation of American Film Academy Award to Andrzej Wajda (film director). Phosphorescent paper. P 11½ (with one elliptical hole on each horiz side).

3849	**1188** 1z.10 black	1·90	1·60
	a. *Tête-bêche* (pair)	4·00	3·50

No. 3849 was issued in *tête-bêche* pairs throughout the sheet.

(Des J. Wysocki. Litho)

2000 (7 Apr). Holy Year 2000. Opening of Holy Door, St. Peter's Basilica, Rome. Phosphorescent paper. P 11½×11 (with one elliptical hole on each vert side).

3850	**1189** 80g. multicoloured	1·30	1·10

1190 Artist and Model, Poster for *Wesele* (play), and Building

1191 Dying Rose

(Des M. Jędrysik (3851/2), A. Heidrich (**MS**3853). Eng C. Slania (**MS**3853). Litho (3851/2) or recess (**MS**3853))

2000 (26 Apr). Crakow, European City of Culture. T **1190** and similar horiz designs. Phosphorescent paper. P 11½×11 (with one elliptical hole on each vert side).

3851	70g. multicoloured	1·10	90
3852	1z.55 multicoloured	3·25	2·75
MS3853	110×77 mm. 1z.75 blue (39×30 *mm*).		
	P 11×11½	4·25	4·00

Designs: As Type **1190**—No. 3852, Jagiellonian University, Pope John Paul II, Queen Jadwiga and Krzysztof Penderecki (composer). 38×30 mm—**MS**3853, View of Crackow (wood carving), 1489. No. **MS**3853 also exists imperforate (*price* £32).

(Des W. Walkuski. Litho)

2000 (28 Apr). "Stop Drug Addiction" Campaign. Phosphorescent paper. P 11×11½ (with one elliptical hole on each vert side).

3854	**1191** 70g. multicoloured	1·10	90

1192 "Building Europe"

1193 Pope John Paul II

(Des J.-P. Cousin. Litho)

2000 (9 May). Europa. Phosphorescent paper. P 11½ (with one elliptical hole on each vert side).

3855	**1192** 1z.55 multicoloured	4·25	4·00

(Des and eng C. Slania. Recess and litho (3857) or recess (others))

2000 (9 May). 80th Birthday of Pope John Paul II. T **1193** and similar vert designs. Phosphorescent paper. P 13.

3856	80g. deep reddish violet	1·50	1·30
3857	1z.10 multicoloured	1·90	1·60
3858	1z.55 deep bluish green	2·75	2·30
3856/3858	Set of 3	5·50	4·75

Designs:—No. 3857, Holy Mother, Częstochowa; 3858, Pastoral Staff. Stamps of a similar design were issued by Vatican City.

1194 Woman's Face and Fan

1195 Family

(Des J. Konarzewski. Litho)

2000 (26 May). España 2000 International Stamp Exhibition, Madrid. Phosphorescent paper. P 11½×11 (with one elliptical hole on each vert side).

3859	**1194** 1z.55 multicoloured	2·75	2·30

(Des D. Litwiniec. Litho)

2000 (31 May). Parenthood. Phosphorescent paper. P 11½×11 (with one elliptical hole on each vert side).

3860	**1195** 70g. multicoloured	1·10	90

1196 Cathedral Façade

1197 Karol Marcinkowski

(Des A. Gosik. Litho)

2000 (15 June). Millenary of Wroclaw. Sheet 70×90 mm. Phosphorescent paper. P 11×11½ (with one elliptical hole on each vert side).

MS3861	**1196** 1z.55 multicoloured	3·25	3·00

(Des M. Jędrysik. Litho)

2000 (23 June). Personalities. T **1197** and similar horiz design. Multicoloured. Phosphorescent paper. P 11×11½ (with one elliptical hole on each horiz side).

3862	70g.	Type **1197** (founder of Scientific Assistance Association)	1·10	90
3863	80g.	Josemaría Escrivá de Balaguer (founder of Priests' Association of St. Cross, 1943)	1·30	1·10

1198 Gerwazy and the Count

1199 Pope John Paul II and St. Peter's Basilica, Rome

(Des A. Heidrich. Eng I. Zlotkowski (3864/5), P. Krajewski (3866/7), W. Zajalel (3868/9). Recess)

2000 (30 June). *Pan Tadeusz* (poem by Adam Mickiewicz). T **1198** and similar vert designs showing illustrations by Michal Elwiro Andriolli from the 1882 edition. Phosphorescent paper. P 11.

3864	70g.	bistre-brown	1·10	90
3865	70g.	bistre-brown	1·10	90
3866	80g.	slate-green	1·30	1·10
3867			1·30	1·10
			1·90	1·60
			1·90	1·60
			7·75	6·50

...and the Judge; 3866; Father ...ing in forest; 3868, Jankiel ...d Tadeusz.

...ho)

...e. T **1199** and similar vert ...t paper. P 11½ (with one

		1·30	1·10
		2·75	2·30

...Mary and Jesus ...ng), Różanystok

...)

2000 (2 July). Birth Bicentenary of Piotr Michalowski (artist). T **1200** and similar multicoloured designs. Phosphorescent paper. P 11½×11 (70, 80g.) or 11½ (others) (with one elliptical hole on each horiz side).

3872	70g.	Type **1200**	1·10	90
3873	80g.	"Portrait of a Boy in a Hat"	1·30	1·10
3874	1z.10	"Stable-boy Bridling Percherons" (*horiz*)	1·90	1·60
3875	1z.55	"Horses with Cart" (*horiz*)	2·75	2·30
3872/3875	*Set of 4*		6·25	5·25

(Des Z. Stasik (No. 3876) and M. Jędrysik (No. 3877). Litho)

2000 (14 Aug). St. Mary's Sanctuaries. T **1201** and similar vert design. Multicoloured. Phosphorescent paper. P 11½×11 (with one elliptical hole on each vert side).

3876	70g.	Type **1201**	1·10	90
3877	1z.55	Mary with crown supported by angels, Licheń	2·75	2·30

1202 John Bosco (founder of movement)

1203 Victory Sign

(Des J. Wysocki. Litho)

2000 (25 Aug). Salesian Society (religious educational institution) in Poland. Phosphorescent paper. P 11×11½ (with one elliptical hole on each horiz side).

3878	**1202**	80g. multicoloured	1·30	1·10

(Des T. Boguslaski. Litho)

2000 (31 Aug). 20th Anniv of Solidarity Trade Union. Sheet 60×78 mm. Phosphorescent paper. P 11½ (with one elliptical hole on each vert side).

MS3879	**1203**	1z.65 multicoloured	4·25	4·00

1204 Running

1205 Postman (Tomasz Wistuba)

(Des J. Wysocki. Litho)

2000 (1 Sept). Olympic Games, Sydney. T **1204** and similar horiz designs. Multicoloured. Phosphorescent paper. P 11½ (with one elliptical hole on each horiz side).

3880	70g.	Type **1204**	1·10	90
3881	80g.	Diving, windsurfing, sailing and kayaking	1·30	1·10
3882	1z.10	Weight lifting, high jumping and fencing	1·90	1·60
3883	1z.55	Athletics, basketball and judo	2·50	2·20
3880/3883	*Set of 4*		6·00	5·25

(Des J. Konarzewski. Litho)

2000 (9 Oct). World Post Day. Winning Entries in Children's Painting Competition. T **1205** and similar multicoloured designs. Phosphorescent paper. P 11½×11 (70g.) or 11×11½ (others) (with one elliptical hole on two opposite sides).

3884	70g.	Type **1205**	1·10	90
3885	80g.	Customers and flying stork in Post Office (Katarzyna Chrzanowska) (*horiz*).	1·30	1·10
3886	1z.10	Post Office on "stamp" (Joanna Żbik) (*horiz*)	1·90	1·60
3887	1z.55	Woman at Post Office counter (Katarzyna Lonak) (*horiz*)	2·50	2·20
3884/3887	*Set of 4*		6·00	5·25

1206 Man with Postage Stamp Wings

1207 Priest and Cross

(Des R. Konrad. Litho)

2000 (12 Oct). 50th Anniv of Polish Philatelic Union. Sheet 75×60 mm. Phosphorescent paper. P 11×11½ (with one elliptical hole on each horiz side).

MS3888	**1206**	1z.55 multicoloured	3·25	3·00

(Des S. Malecki. Eng T. Zlotkowski (70g.), P. Krajewski (1z.55), W. Zajdei (others). Recess and photo)

2000 (23 Oct). Polish Rulers (15th series). Vert designs as T **893**. P 11.
3889	70g. slate-black, brown-olive and light yellow-olive	1·10	90
3890	80g. black and dull purple	1·30	1·10
3891	1z.10 blue-black, deep blue and cobalt	1·90	1·60
3892	1z.55 black and purple-brown	2·50	2·20
3889/3892	Set of 4	6·00	5·25

Designs:—70g. August II; 80g. Stanislaw Leszczyński; 1z.10 August III; 1z.55 Stanislaw August Poniatowski.

(Des J. Wysocki. Litho)

2000 (15 Nov). 60th Anniv of Katyń Massacre. T **1207** and similar vert design. Multicoloured. Phosphorescent paper. P 11½ (with one elliptical hole on each vert side).
3893	70g. Type **1207**	1·10	90
3894	80g. Pope John Paul II kneeling at monument, Muranów	1·30	1·10

1208 Nativity   **1209** Building Façade

(Des M. Jędrysik. Litho)

2000 (27 Nov). Christmas. T **1208** and similar vert designs. Multicoloured. Phosphorescent paper. P 11½ (with one elliptical hole on each vert side).
3895	70g. Type **1208**	1·10	90
3896	80g. Wedding at Cana	1·30	1·10
3897	1z.10 The Last Supper	1·90	1·60
3898	1z.55 The Ascension	2·50	2·20
3895/3898	Set of 4	6·00	5·25

(Des A. Gosik. Litho)

2000 (4 Dec). Centenary of Warsaw Art Gallery. Phosphorescent paper. P 11½×11 (with one elliptical hole on each vert side).
3899	**1209** 70g. multicoloured	1·10	90

1210 Privately Issued Stamp   **1211** Pope John Paul II, Emblem and Crowd

(Des M. Buszewicz. Litho)

2000 (13 Dec). Underground Post during Martial Law, 1982–89. Phosphorescent paper. P 11½×11 (with one elliptical hole on each vert side).
3900	**1210** 80g. multicoloured	1·50	1·30
	a. Tête-bêche (pair)	3·25	2·75

No. 3900 was issued with a se-tenant label forming a composite design of the stamp.

(Des J. Wysocki. Litho)

2001 (6 Jan). End of Holy Year 2000. Value expressed by letter. Phosphorescent paper. P 12×11½ (with one elliptical hole on each vert side).
3901	**1211** A (1z.) multicoloured	1·70	1·40

1212 Mountains reflected in Ski Goggles   **1213** Computer Mouse

(Des J. Konarzewski. Litho)

2001 (7 Feb). 20th University Games, Zakopane. Phosphorescent paper. P 11×11½ (with one elliptical hole on each horiz side).
3902	**1212**	1z. multicoloured	1·70	1·40

(Des Agnieszka Sobczyńska. Litho)

2001 (22 Feb). The Internet. Phosphorescent paper. P 11×11½ (with one elliptical hole on each horiz side).
3903	**1213**	1z. multicoloured	1·70	1·40

1214 Adam Malysz (ski jumper)   **1215** Tomb of the Resurrected Christ

(Des J. Wysocki. Litho)

2001 (23 Feb). World Classic Seniors Championships, Lahti. T **1214** and similar horiz designs. Multicoloured. Phosphorescent paper. P 11½ (with one elliptical hole on each horiz side).
3904	1z. Type **1214**	2·10	1·80
3905	1z. As Type **1214** but additionally inscribed "Adam Malysz"	1·70	1·40
3906	1z. As No. 3905 but additionally inscribed "Mistrzem Świata"	1·70	1·40
3904/3906	Set of 3	5·00	4·25

(Des M. Jędrysik. Litho)

2001 (16 Mar). Easter. T **1215** and similar square design. Multicoloured. Phosphorescent paper. P 11½ (with one elliptical hole on each vert side).
3907	1z. Type **1215**	1·70	1·60
3908	1z.90 Resurrected Christ and Apostles	3·25	3·00

1216 Emblem and Basketball Players

(Des D. Litwiniec. Litho)

2001 (28 Apr). 12th Salesian Youth World Championships, Warsaw. Phosphorescent paper. P 12×11½ (with one elliptical hole on each vert side).
3909	**1216**	1z. multicoloured	1·70	1·60

1217 Water Droplet   **1218** Man and Mermaid on Beach ("Holiday Greetings")

(Des J. Wysocki. Litho)

2001 (5 May). Europa. Water Resources. Phosphorescent paper. P 11½×11 (with one elliptical hole on each vert side).
3910	**1217** 1z.90 multicoloured	3·25	3·00

(Des W. Terechowicz. Litho)

2001 (10 May). Greetings Stamps. T **1218** and similar vert design. Multicoloured. Phosphorescent paper. P 11½×12 (with one elliptical hole on each vert side).
3911	1z. Type **1218**	1·70	1·60
3912	1z. Man presenting bouquet to woman ("Best Wishes")	1·70	1·60

1219 "Christ blessing Children of Września" (Marian Turwid) (stained-glass window), Parish Church, Września

1220 Polish Scientific Institute and Wanda Stachiewicz Library, Montreal, Canada

(Des Agnieszka Sobczyńska. Litho)

2001 (20 May). Centenary of Support of Września Schoolchildren for the Polish Language. Phosphorescent paper. P 11½ (with one elliptical hole on each vert side).
3913   **1219**   1z. multicoloured .... 1·70   1·60

(Des M. Buszewicz. Litho)

2001 (29 June). Polish Institutions Abroad. T **1220** and similar horiz designs. Multicoloured. Phosphorescent paper. P 11½ (with one elliptical hole on each horiz side).
3914   1z. Type **1220**... 1·90   1·80
    a. Tête-bêche (pair).. 4·00   3·75
3915   1z.90 Bust of Jósef Pilsudski, Jósef Pilsudski
    Institute, New York....................................... 3·50   3·25
    a. Tête-bêche (pair).. 7·25   6·75
3916   2z.10 Polonia Museum, Archives and Library,
    Orchard Lake, Michigan .... 4·00   3·75
    a. Tête-bêche (pair).. 8·25   7·75
3917   2z.20 Polish Museum, Chicago .... 4·25   4·00
    a. Tête-bêche (pair).. 8·75   8·25
3914/3917 Set of 4.. 12·50   11·50
Nos. 3914/17 were each issued in sheets of 20 the lower four rows printed tête-bêche with the top row upright thus giving eight tête-bêche pairs.

1221 Snowdrop (Galanthus nivalis) and European Lynx (Lynx lynx)

(Des A. Balcerzak. Litho)

2001 (10 July). Convention on International Trade of Wild Animals and Plants Threatened with Extinction (CITES). T **1221** and similar horiz designs. Multicoloured. Phosphorescent paper. P 11½ (with one elliptical hole on each horiz side).
3918   1z. Type **1221**.. 1·90   1·80
3919   1z. Apollo Butterfly (Parnassius apollo) and
    Orchid (Orchis sambucina)....................... 1·90   1·80
3920   1z. Eagle Owl (Bubo bubo) and Adonis
    vernalis (plant)... 1·90   1·80
3921   1z.90 Lady's Slipper Orchid (Cypripedium
    calceolus) and Brown Bear (Ursus
    arctos) .... 3·50   3·25
3922   1z.90 Peregrine Falcon (Falco peregrinus) and
    Orchis pallens .... 3·50   3·25
3923   1z.90 Wide Leaf Orchid (Orchis latifolia) and
    European Otter (Lutra lutra) .... 3·50   3·25
3918/3923 Set of 6.. 14·50   13·50
MS3924 90×70 mm. 2z. World map and emblem
(35×28 mm)... 4·50   4·25

1222 Cardinal Wyszyński and Text

(Des J. Konarzewski. Litho)

2001 (3 Aug). Birth Centenary of Cardinal Stefan Wyszyński. (Primate of Poland 1948–1981). Phosphorescent paper. P 11½ (with one elliptical hole on each horiz side).
3925   **1222**   1z. multicoloured.................................... 2·00   1·80

1223 Kolbe and Handwriting

1224 "St. Mary of the Beautiful Love" (icon)

(Des M. Jędrysik. Litho)

2001 (14 Aug). 60th Death Anniv of Maksymilian Maria Kolbe (founder of Knighthood of the Immaculate, and concentration camp victim). Phosphorescent paper. P 11½ (with one elliptical hole on each horiz side).
3926   **1223**   1z. multicoloured.................................... 2·00   1·20

(Des M. Jędrysik (No. 3928) and Z. Stasik (others). Litho)

2001 (14 Aug). St. Mary's Sanctuaries. T **1224** and similar vert designs. Multicoloured. Phosphorescent paper. P 11½×11 (with one elliptical hole on each vert side).
3927   1z. Type **1224** (Cathedral of St. Martin
    and St. Nicolas, Bydgoszcz) .... 2·00   1·80
3928   1z. St. Mary of Ludźmierz, Basilica of the
    Assumption of St. Mary, Ludźmierz........ 2·00   1·80
3929   1z.90 St. Mary the Winner, Church of
    St. Mary in Piasek, Wroclaw...................... 3·75   3·25
3927/3929 Set of 3.. 7·00   6·25

1225 Model of Sanctuary

1226 Ligia, Vinius and Petrinius

(Des M. Osa. Litho)

2001 (31 Aug). Completion of Section of God's Mercy Sanctuary at Cracow-Lagiewniki. Phosphorescent paper. P 11½×11 (with one elliptical hole on each vert side).
3930   **1225**   1z. multicoloured.................................... 2·20   2·00

(Des J. Wysocki. Litho)

2001 (1 Sept). Quo Vadis (film directed by Jerzy Kawalerowicz). T **1226** and similar horiz designs depicting scenes from the film. Multicoloured. Phosphorescent paper. P 11½ (with one elliptical hole on each horiz side).
3931   1z. Type **1226**.. 2·20   2·00
    a. Sheetlet of 6. Nos. 3931/6 .... 13·50
3932   1z. Nero singing at feast............................... 2·20   2·00
3933   1z. St. Peter in the catacombs and the
    baptism of Chilon Chilonides.................... 2·20   2·00
3934   1z. Chilon Chilonides and crowd fleeing fire 2·20   2·00
3935   1z. Liga tied to the back of a bull and in
    the arms of Ursus.. 2·20   2·00
3936   1z. St. Peter blessing Vincius and Liga.......... 2·20   2·00
3931/3936 Set of 6.. 12·00   11·00
Nos. 3931/6 were issued together in se-tenant sheetlets of six stamps.

1227 Copper Furnace

(Des and eng M. Jędrysik. Litho (No. **MS**3940) or recess and litho (others))

2001 (1 Sept). Euro Cuprum 2001 European Stamp Exhibition, Lubin. T **1227** and similar horiz designs. Multicoloured. Phosphorescent paper. P 11½ (with one elliptical hole on each horiz side).

3937	1z. Type **1227**		2·20	2·00
3938	1z.90 Engraver at work and men dressing copper sheets		3·75	3·25
3939	2z. Inking plates and engraving press		4·25	3·75
3937/3939 Set of 3			9·25	8·00
MS3940	88×76 mm. 3z. 18th-century engraving of Lubin and burin (50×39 mm)		6·50	6·25

No. **MS**3940 also exists imperforate (price £22).

1228 "Battle of Chocim" (detail, Stanislaw Batowski-Kaczor) and Breast-plate of Stanislaw Skórkowski's Armour

(Des A. Gosik. Litho)

2001 (10 Sept). "One Century Passes it Over to Another Century" Exhibition, Polish Military Museum, Warsaw. Phosphorescent paper. P 11½ (with one elliptical hole on each horiz side).

3941	**1228**	1z. multicoloured	2·20	2·00

1229 Steam and Electric Locomotives

(Des A. Gosik. Litho)

2001 (24 Sept). 75th Anniv of Polish State Railways. Phosphorescent paper. P 12×11½ (with one elliptical hole on each vert side).

3942	**1229**	1z. multicoloured	2·20	2·00

1230 Street Scene (Marcin Kuroń)

(Des J. Konarzewski. Litho)

2001 (28 Sept). Winners of "Poland in 21st Century" (children's painting competition). T **1230** and similar square designs. Multicoloured. Phosphorescent paper. P 11½ (with one elliptical hole on each vert side).

3943	1z. Type **1230**		2·20	2·00
3944	1z.90 Rockets behind girl and boy (Agata Grzyb)		3·75	3·25
3945	2z. Futuristic car and house on wheels (Joanna Sadrakula)		4·00	3·50
3943/3945 Set of 3			9·00	8·00

1231 Football and Players

1232 Children encircling Globe

(Des J. Konarzewski. Litho)

2001 (6 Oct). Qualification of Poland for World Cup Football Championship, Japan and South Korea. Phosphorescent paper. P 11½×12 (with one elliptical hole on each horiz side).

3946	**1231**	1z. multicoloured	2·20	2·00

(Des Urska Golob. Litho)

2001 (9 Oct). World Post Day. United Nations Year of Dialogue among Civilizations. Phosphorescent paper. P 11½ (with one elliptical hole on each vert side).

3947	**1232**	1z.90 multicoloured	3·75	3·25
		a. Tête-bêche (pair)		6·75

1233 "100 Years Ago" (detail, Wlodzimierz Kugler)

1234 Violin Peg Box and Scroll

(Des Agnieszka Sobczyńska. Photo)

2001 (9 Oct). 80th Anniv of Post and Telecommunication Museum, Wroclaw. Sheet 87×70 mm. Phosphorescent paper. P 11×11½.

MS3948	**1233**	3z.+75g. multicoloured	8·75	8·50

(Des M. Buszewicz. Litho)

2001 (13 Oct). 12th Henryk Wieniawski International Violin Competition, Poznań. Phosphorescent paper. P 11½ (with one elliptical hole on each horiz side).

3949	**1234**	1z. multicoloured	2·20	2·00

1235 Pope John Paul II

1236 Building Façade

(Des J. Wysocki. Litho)

2001 (14 Oct). Papal Day. Phosphorescent paper. P 11½ (with one elliptical hole on each vert side).

3950	**1235**	1z. multicoloured	2·20	2·00

(Des M. Buszewicz and W. Żagan. Litho)

2001 (5 Nov). Centenary of National Philharmonic Orchestra. Phosphorescent paper. P 11½ (with one elliptical hole on each vert side).

3951	**1236**	1z. multicoloured	2·20	2·00
		a. Tête-bêche (pair)	4·75	4·25

1237 Pope John Paul II

1238 Lower Silesian Crib

(Des T. Boguslawski. Litho)

2001 (11 Nov). New Millennium. T **1237** and similar horiz designs. Multicoloured. Phosphorescent paper. P 11½ (with one elliptical hole on each horiz side).

3952	1z. Type **1237**		2·20	2·00
	a. Sheetlet of 16. Nos. 3952/67		36·00	
3953	1z. President Lech Wałęsa and cover of 1791 constitution		2·20	2·00
3954	1z. Covers of Glos Wolny Wolność Ubespieczaiacy, Kultura, Zniewolony umysl and O skutecznym rad sposobie (magazines)		2·20	2·00

3955	1z. Wojciech Boguslawski (actor and dramatist) and Jerzy Grotowski (director)	2·20	2·00
3956	1z. General Józef Pilsudski (soldier and President 1918–22) and posters (1989).	2·20	2·00
3957	1z. N.A.T.O. emblem and General Kazimierz Pulaski (soldier)	2·20	2·00
3958	1z. Nicolaus Copernicus and Aleksander Wolszczan (astronomers)	2·20	2·00
3959	1z. Jan of Glogów (wood engraving) (mathematician and astronomer) and Tadeusz Kotarbiński (physicist)	2·20	2·00
3960	1z. "Do Broni" (poster, 1920) and "Bitwa pod Grunwaldem" (detail) (painting, Jan Matejko)	2·20	2·00
3961	1z. Leaders of November Uprising, 1830.	2·20	2·00
3962	1z. Head of John the Apostle (detail) (wooden altarpiece, Wit Stwosz) and sculpture by Magdalena Abakanowicz.	2·20	2·00
3963	1z. Frédérik Chopin, Krzysztof Penderecki (composers) and score of Mazurka No. 10 by Karol Szymanowski	2·20	2·00
3964	1z. Royal Castle, Warsaw and view of Cracow (wood engraving)	2·20	2·00
3965	1z. Jan III Sobieski (painting) and emblem of European Union	2·20	2·00
3966	1z. Wislawa Szymborska (Nobel Prizewinner for Literature) and Mikolaj Rej (poet)	2·20	2·00
3967	1z. Janusz Kusociński and Robert Korzeniowski (athletes)	2·20	2·00
3952/3967 Set of 16		32·00	29·00

Nos. 3952/67 were issued together in *se-tenant* sheetlets containing two blocks of eight stamps separated by a central gutter.

(Des J. Wysocki. Litho)

2001 (27 Nov). Christmas. T **1238** and similar square design. Multicoloured. Phosphorescent paper. P 11½ (with one elliptical hole on each vert side).

3968	1z. Type **1238**	2·00	1·80
3969	1z.90 Lower Silesian Crib (*different*)	3·75	3·25

 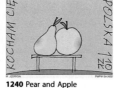

1239 Radio Station Building and Virgin Mary (statue)   **1240** Pear and Apple

(Des J. Brodowski. Litho)

2001 (7 Dec). Tenth Anniv of "Radio Maryja" (religious broadcasting station). T **1239** and similar horiz designs. Multicoloured. Phosphorescent paper. P 11×11½ (with one elliptical hole on each horiz side).

3970	1z. Type **1239**	2·20	2·00
MS3971	176×78 mm. 1z. Virgin Mary (statue) and crowd; 1z. Type **1239**; 1z. Crowd and crowned Virgin Mary (statue)	6·25	6·00

(Des M. Jędrysik. Litho)

2002 (4 Feb). Valentine's Day. Phosphorescent paper. P 11½ (with one elliptical hole on each horiz side).

3972	**1240** 1z.10 multicoloured	2·20	2·00

1241 Downhill, Biathlon, Ice-skating and Ski Jumping

(Des J. Konarzewski. Litho)

2002 (8 Feb). Winter Olympic Games, Salt Lake City, USA. Phosphorescent paper. P 11½×11 (with one elliptical hole on each horiz side).

3973	**1241** 1z.10 multicoloured	2·75	2·30

No. 3973 was issued with a *se-tenant* stamp-size label in sheets of 18 stamps and 18 labels.

1242 Jan Czerski   **1243** Gniezno

(Des M. Jędrysik. Litho)

2002 (22 Feb). Explorers. T **1242** and similar horiz designs. Multicoloured. Phosphorescent paper. P 11½ (with one elliptical hole on each horiz side).

3974	2z. Type **1242**	4·00	3·50
3975	2z. Bronislaw Pilsudski	4·00	3·50

2002 (1 Mar)–**08**. Polish Cities. T **1243** and similar multicoloured designs. Phosphorescent paper. P 11½.

3975a	5g. Sandomierz (*horiz*) (1.1.04)	35	20
3975b	20g. Sieradz (29.7.05)	45	30
3975c	30g. Katowice (*horiz*) (5.10.05)	55	40
3975d	1z.20 Torun (31.1.03)	1·80	1·20
3975e	1z.25 Gdańsk (9.1.04)	1·90	1·30
3975ea	1z.30 Poznań (*horiz*) (3.1.05)	2·00	1·40
3975eb	1z.35 Gorzów Wielkopolski (19.1.07)	2·20	1·60
3975ec	1z.45 Racibórz (1.7.08)	3·25	2·30
3975h	1z.80 Kalisz (1.7.02)	2·75	2·00
3975i	1z.90 Łódź (*horiz*) (14.5.04)	3·00	2·10
3976	2z. Type **1243**	3·25	2·30
3977	2z.10 Kraków	3·50	2·50
3977a	2z.20 Sopot (29.7.05)	3·75	2·75
3977b	2z.40 Częstochowa (*horiz*) (24.4.06)	4·00	3·00
3977c	2z.60 Plock (*horiz*) (1.7.02)	4·25	3·00
3977d	2z.80 Szczecin (*horiz*) (30.5.05)	4·50	3·25
3978	3z.20 Warsaw	4·50	3·50
3978a	3z.40 Kazimierz Dolny (10.4.03)	4·75	3·75
3978b	3z.45 Lublin (*horiz*) (23.2.04)	5·00	4·00
3978ba	3z.50 Przemyśl (bright green and deep green) (30.4.05)	5·25	4·00
3978bc	3z.55 Chorzów (15.6.07)	5·50	4·25
3978bd	3z.65 Jelenia Góra (1.8.08)	5·75	4·75
3975a/3978bd Set of 22		65·00	48·00

No. 3975i was issued with a *se-tenant* "Priority" label.

1244 Flowers

(Des A. Gosik. Litho)

2002 (8 Mar). Easter. T **1244** and similar vert design. Multicoloured. Phosphorescent paper. P 11½×12 (with one elliptical hole on each horiz side).

3979	1z.10 Type **1244**	2·20	1·20
3980	2z. Chicks	3·75	2·00

1245 Labrador Retriever and Puppies

(Des J. Wysocki. Litho)

2002 (25 Mar). Domestic and Wild Animals. T **1245** and similar horiz designs. Multicoloured. Phosphorescent paper. P 12×11½ (with one elliptical hole on each vert side).

3981	1z.10 Type **1245**	2·20	1·20
	a. Horiz strip of 4. Nos. 3981/4	9·00	
3982	1z.10 Cat and kittens	2·20	1·20
3983	1z.10 Wolf and cubs	2·20	1·20

3984   1z.10 Lynx and kittens...................................... 2·20   1·20
3981/3984 *Set of 4*... 8·00   4·25
Nos. 3981/4 were issued together in horizontal *se-tenant* strips of four stamps within the sheet.

1246 Soldiers marching

1247 Trees (Amanda Żejmis)

(Des M. Osa. Litho)

2002 (26 Mar). 60th Anniv of Evacuation of General Wladislaw Ander's Army from USSR. Phosphorescent paper. P 11½ (with one elliptical hole on each vert side).
3985   **1246**   1z.10 multicoloured....................... 2·20   1·20

(Des M. Buszewicz. Litho)

2002 (17 Apr). Paintings. T **1247** and similar multicoloured designs. Phosphorescent paper. P 11½×11 (Nos. 3986/7) or 11×11½ (others) (with one elliptical hole on each vert (Nos. 3986/7) or horiz (others) side).
3986   1z.10 Type **1247**................................ 2·20   1·20
3987   1z.10 Vase and ornaments (Henryk
         Paraszczuk).................................... 2·20   1·20
3988   2z. Landscape (Lucjan Matula) (*horiz*).......... 4·50   2·00
3989   3z.20 Basket of flowers (Józefa Laciak) (*horiz*)   6·50   3·50
3986/3989 *Set of 4*... 14·00   7·00

1248 Stylized Figures

1249 Radio Microphone

(Des J. Wysocki. Litho)

2002 (30 Apr). National Census. Phosphorescent paper. P 11×11½ (with one elliptical hole on each horiz side).
3990   **1248**   1z.10 multicoloured....................... 2·20   1·20

(Des J. Wysocki. Litho)

2002 (2 May). 50th Anniv of "Radio Free Europe". Phosphorescent paper. P 12×11½ (with one elliptical hole on each vert side).
3991   **1249**   2z. multicoloured.......................... 4·00   2·00

1250 Fireman

1251 Circus Artist

(Des Agnieszka Sobczyńska. Litho)

2002 (4 May). Tenth Anniv of State Fire Brigade. Phosphorescent paper. P 11×11½ (with one elliptical hole on each horiz side).
3992   **1250**   1z.10 multicoloured....................... 2·20   1·20

(Des A. Pągowski. Litho)

2002 (5 May). Europa. Circus. Phosphorescent paper. P 11×11½ (with one elliptical hole on each vert side).
3993   **1251**   2z. multicoloured.......................... 4·50   3·00

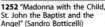

1252 "Madonna with the Child, St. John the Baptist and the Angel" (Sandro Botticelli)

1253 Maria Konopnicka

(Des M. Buszewicz. Litho)

2002 (18 May). 140th Anniv of the National Gallery, Warsaw. Phosphorescent paper. P 11½ (with one elliptical hole on each vert side).
3994   **1252**   1z.10 multicoloured....................... 2·20   1·20

(Des A. Heidrich. Eng C. Slania. Recess and photo)

2002 (23 May). 160th Birth Anniv of Maria Konopnicka (poet and writer). Phosphorescent paper. P 11½×11.
3995   **1253**   1z.10 brown, ochre and turquoise-
         green.. 2·20   1·20

1254 Scooter

1255 Football and Globe

(Des P. Pyzik. Litho)

2002 (31 May). Children's Games. T **1254** and similar vert designs. Multicoloured Phosphorescent paper. P 11½ (with one elliptical hole on each vert side).
3996   1z.10 Type **1254**................................ 2·20   1·20
         a. Horiz strip of 3. Nos. 3996/8.............. 6·75
3997   1z.10 Flying kite............................... 2·20   1·20
3998   1z.10 Badminton................................. 2·20   1·20
3996/3998 *Set of 3*.. 6·00   3·25
Nos. 3996/8 were issued together in horizontal *se-tenant* strips of three stamps within sheets of six, the bottom row inverted, giving three vertical *tête-bêche* pairs (*price per sheet* £14).

(Des J. Konerzewski. Litho)

2002 (1 June). World Cup Football Championship, Japan and South Korea. T **1255** and similar vert design. Multicoloured. Phosphorescent paper. P 11½×11 (with one elliptical hole on each vert side).
3999   1z.10 Type **1255**................................ 2·20   1·20
         a. Horiz pair, Nos. 3999/4000.................. 6·50   3·50
4000   2z. Player chasing ball......................... 4·00   2·00
Nos. 3999/4000 were issued together in horizontal *se-tenant* pairs in sheetlets of four (*price per sheetlet* £13.50).

Nos. 4001/14 are vacant.

1256 Domeyko and Santiago University, Chile

(Des M. Jędrysik. Litho)

2002 (3 July). Birth Bicentenary of Ignacego Domeyki (scientist). Fluorescent paper. P 11½ (with one elliptical hole on each horiz side).
4015   **1256**   2z.60 multicoloured....................... 5·50   3·25
A stamp of a similar design was issued by Chile.

1257 Hibiscus and Tulips

(Des J. Wysocki. Litho)

2002 (12 July). Philakorea 2002 International Philatelic Exhibition, Seoul and Amphile—2002 International Philatelic Exhibition, Amsterdam. Fluorescent paper. P 11½ (with one elliptical hole on each horiz side).

4016	**1257**	2z. multicoloured	4·00	2·30

1258 Pope John Paul II and Basilica of Virgin Mary of the Angel, Kalwaria Zebrzydowska

1259 "Holy Lady of Assistance"

(Des J. Wysocki. Litho)

2002 (5 Aug). Seventh Papal Visit To Poland (1st issue). T **1258** and similar horiz design. Multicoloured. Phosphorescent paper. P 11½ (with one elliptical hole on each horiz side).

4017		1z.10 Type **1258**	2·20	1·30
4018		1z.80 Pope John Paul II and Sanctuary of God's Mercy, Sisters of Virgin Mary's Convent, Lagiewniki	3·75	2·20

See also No. **MS**4022.

(Des Z. Stasik. Litho)

2002 (14 Aug). St. Mary's Sanctuaries. T **1259** and similar vert designs. Multicoloured. Phosphorescent paper. P 11½×11 (with one elliptical hole on each vert side).

4019		1z.10 Type **1259** (Church of the Holy Lady of Assistance, Jaworzno)	2·20	1·30
4020		1z.10 "Holy Virgin of Opole" (Cathedral of Holy Cross, Opole)	2·20	1·30
4021		2z. "Holy Virgin of Trąbki" (Church of the Assumption of the Holy Lady, Trąbki Wielkie)	4·50	2·50
4019/4021		Set of 3	8·00	4·50

1260 Pope John Paul II and Wawel Castle, Cracow

1262 Cześnik Raptusiewicz and Dyndalski

1261 Spa Building, Ciechocinku

(Des M. Jędrysik. Eng C. Slania. Recess)

2002 (16 Aug). Seventh Papal Visit To Poland (2nd issue). Sheet 73×57 mm. Phosphorescent paper. P 11×11½.

MS4022	**1260**	3z.20 blue-black	6·50	6·25

(Des A. Heidrich. Eng C. Slania. Recess)

2002 (1 Sept). 18th Polish Philatelic Association Convention, Ciechocinku. Sheet 74×105 mm. Phosphorescent paper. P 11.

MS4023	**1261**	3z.20 chocolate	6·50	6·25

No. **MS**4023 also exists imperforate (price £22).

(Des M. Buszewicz. Litho)

2002 (12 Sept). *Zemsta* (Revenge) (film directed by Andrzej Wajda). Sheet 177×137 mm containing T **1262** and similar horiz designs showing scenes from the film. Multicoloured. Phosphorescent paper. P 11½ (with one elliptical hole on each horiz side).

MS4024	1z.10 Type **1262**; 1z.10 Klara and Waclaw; 1z.10 Papkin; 1z.10 Regent Milczek and Papkin; 1z.10 Regent Milczek and Cześnik Raptusiewicz; 1z.10 Podstolina and Klara	14·50	13·50

1263 Schwarzkopf Okl-359

(Des J. Brodowski. Litho)

2002 (21 Sept). Steam Locomotives. T **1263** and similar horiz designs showing locomotives from Wolsztyn Railway Museum. Multicoloured. Phosphorescent paper. P 12×11½ (with one elliptical hole on each vert side).

4025		1z.10 Type **1263**	2·20	1·30
		a. Horiz strip of 4. Nos. 4025/8	13·00	
4026		1z.10 Fablok 0149-7	2·20	1·30
4027		2z. Krolewiec Tki3-87	4·00	2·30
4028		2z. Express locomotive Pm 36-2	4·00	2·30
4025/4028		Set of 4	11·00	6·50

Nos. 4025/8 were issued both separately in sheets of 20 stamps or together in horizontal *se-tenant* strips of four stamps within sheets of 12.

Stamps from the *se-tenant* sheetlets have elliptical holes towards the top of the vertical perforations whereas stamps from the individual sheets have the elliptical hole at the foot.

1264 Hands holding Pens

1265 Emblem

(Des M. Buszewicz. Litho)

2002 (9 Oct). World Post Day. Phosphorescent paper. P 11×11½ (with one elliptical hole on each horiz side).

4029	**1264**	2z. multicoloured	4·00	2·30

(Des A. Pągowski. Litho)

2002 (25 Oct). Anti-Cancer Campaign. Phosphorescent paper. P 11½ (with one elliptical hole on each horiz side).

4030	**1265**	1z.10 multicoloured	2·20	1·30

1266 Emblem

1267 St. Stanislaw

(Des J. Wysocki. Litho)

2002 (25 Oct). 50th Anniv of Polish Television. Sheet 185×115 mm containing T **1266** and similar horiz designs showing emblems of television programmes. Multicoloured. Phosphorescent paper. P 11×11½ (with one elliptical hole on each horiz side).

MS4031	1z.10 Type **1266** (TV News); 1z.10 TV Theatre; 1z.10 "Pegaz" (cultural programme); 1z.10 "Teleranek" (children's programme)	8·75	8·50

(Des W. Terechowicz. Litho)

2002 (8 Nov). Saints. Sheet 136×165 mm containing T **1267** and similar vert designs. Multicoloured. Fluorescent paper. P 11½×11 (with one elliptical hole on each vert side).

MS4032 1z.10 Type **1267**; 1z.10 St. Kazimierz; 1z.10 St. Faustyna Kowalska; 1z.10 St. Benedict; 1z.10 St. Cyril and St. Methody; 1z.10 St. Catherine of Siena ...... 13·00   12·50

1268 Christmas Tree Baubles

(Des M. Kamler. Litho)

2002 (27 Nov). Christmas. T **1268** and similar horiz design. Multicoloured. Fluorescent paper. P 11×11½ (with one elliptical hole on each horiz side).

4033	1z.10 Type **1268**.	2·20	1·30
4034	2z. Small purple and large yellow baubles.	3·75	2·20

1269 "POLSKA" superimposed on "EUROPA"

(Des M. Buszewicz. Photo)

2003 (18 Feb). Poland's Accession to European Union (1st issue). Negotiations. P 11×11½.

4035	**1269**	1z.20 multicoloured.	2·75	1·60

See also No. 4067, 4069 and 4120.

1270 Pope John Paul II on Balcony of St. Peter's Basilica, 1978

1271 Pope John Paul II

(Des O. Mauro and G. Fabrizio. Litho)

2003 (20 Mar). 25th Anniv of the Pontificate of Pope John Paul II (1st issue). T **1270** and similar horiz designs. Multicoloured. P 14×13½.

4036	1z.20 Type **1270**.	2·20	1·30
	a. Sheet. Nos. 4036/60	60·00	
4037	1z.20 Celebrating mass, Victory Square, Warsaw, 1979.	2·20	1·30
4038	1z.20 Addressing young people, Parc des Princes Stadium, Paris, 1980	2·20	1·30
4039	1z.20 Assassination attempt, St. Peter Square, 1981	2·20	1·30
4040	1z.20 Giving homily surrounded by flowers, Portugal, 1982.	2·20	1·30
4041	1z.20 Kneeling in front of Holy Doors, start of Holy Year of Redemption, 1983	2·20	1·30
4042	1z.20 Meeting Sandro Pertini, Pres. of Italy, 1984.	2·20	1·30
4043	1z.20 International Youth Day, Rome, 1985.	2·20	1·30
4044	1z.20 First visit of Pope to Synagogue, 1986.	2·20	1·30
4045	1z.20 Inaugurating Year of Mary, 1987	2·20	1·30
4046	1z.20 Visiting European Parliament, Strasbourg, 1988.	2·20	1·30
4047	1z.20 Meeting Mikhail Gorbachev, pres. Soviet Union, 1989.	2·20	1·30
4048	1z.20 Visiting lepers in Guinea-Bissau, 1990	2·20	1·30
4049	1z.20 Addressing Bishop's Synod, 1991.	2·20	1·30
4050	1z.20 Pronouncing the Catechism, 1992	2·20	1·30
4051	1z.20 Enthroned, Assisi, 1993	2·20	1·30
4052	1z.20 Celebrating Mass in the Sistine Chapel, 1994.	2·20	1·30
4053	1z.20 Addressing the United Nations, 1995.	2·20	1·30

4054	1z.20 Walking through the Brandenburg Gate with Chancellor Helmut Kohl, 1996.	2·20	1·30
4055	1z.20 Celebrating Mass in Sarajevo, 1997	2·20	1·30
4056	1z.20 With Fidel Castro, Cuba, 1998	2·20	1·30
4057	1z.20 Opening door, Christmas, 1999.	2·20	1·30
4058	1z.20 With young people, World Youth Day, Rome, 2000	2·20	1·30
4059	1z.20 Closing door of St. Peter's Basilica, 2001	2·20	1·30
4060	1z.20 Visiting the Italian Parliament, 2002.	2·20	1·30
4036/4060	*Set of 25*	50·00	29·00

Nos. 4036/60 were issued in *se-tenant* sheets of 25 stamps. Stamps of a similar design were issued by Vatican City.

(Des O. Mauro and G. Fabrizio. Silk screen printed)

2003 (20 Mar). 25th Anniv of the Pontificate of Pope John Paul II (2nd issue). Die-cut perf 12½×13.

4061	**1271**	10z. silver.	22·00	26·00

No. 4061 was silk screen printed on silver foil with self-adhesive pad covered by a peel-off protector on the back.

A stamp of a similar design was issued by Vatican City.

1272 Andrzej Modrzewski   **1273** "Christ Anxious"

(Des M. Jędrysik. Eng W. Zajdel. Recess)

2003 (28 Mar). 500th Birth Anniv of Andrzej Frycz Modrzewski (writer). P 11½×11.

4062	**1272**	1z.20 grey-black.	2·40	1·40

(Des M. Osa. Photo)

2003 (28 Mar). Easter. Folk Sculpture. T **1273** and similar vert design. Multicoloured. P 11½×11.

4063	1z.20 Type **1273**.	2·40	1·40
4064	2z.10 "Christ Vanquisher".	4·00	2·30

1274 Poznań Ancient and Modern

(Des A. Jeziorkowski. Eng P. Krajewski (**MS**4066). Photo (4065) or Recess (**MS**4066))

2003 (15 Apr). 750th Anniv of Poznań. T **1274** and similar horiz design. P 11½.

4065	1z.20 multicoloured	2·40	1·40
MS4066	95×72 mm 3z.40 cinnamon and brownish black (40×31 *mm*). P 11×11½.	6·25	5·75

Designs:—3z.40 Ancient view of city and city arms.

1275 Portico and Clouds   **1276** Poster for "Vanitas" Exhibition (Wieslaw Walkuski)

(Des M. Buszewicz. Photo)

2003 (16 Apr). Poland's Accession to European Union (2nd issue). P 11×11½.

4067	**1275**	1z.20 multicoloured	2·75	1·60

2003 (5 May). Europa. Poster Art. Photo. P 11.
4068 **1276** 2z.10 multicoloured .... 4·50 2·50

1277 "POLSKA" superimposed on "EUROPA" **1278** Island Palace (south view)

(Des M. Buszewicz. Photo)

2003 (26 May). Poland's Accession to European Union (3rd issue). Referendum. P 11×11½.
4069 **1277** 1z.20 multicoloured .... 2·75 1·60

(Des S. Wieczorek. Photo)

2003 (30 May). Royal Baths, Lazienki Park, Warsaw. T **1278** and similar horiz designs. Multicoloured. P 11×11½.
4070 1z.20 Type **1278**... 2·40 1·40
4071 1z.80 Island Palace (north view).......................... 3·50 2·10
4072 2z.10 Myślewicki Palace .... 4·25 2·50
4073 2z.60 Amphitheatre .... 5·25 3·00
4070/4073 Set of 4... 14·00 8·00

1279 Pyramids and Camel (Anna Golębiewska)

2003 (20 June). Children's Paintings. Stamp Design Competition Winners. T **1279** and similar multicoloured designs on theme "My Dream Vacation". Photo. P 11.
4074 1z.20 Type **1279**.. 2·40 1·40
4075 1z.80 Girl windsurfing (Marlena Krejpcio) (vert) .... 3·50 2·10
4076 2z.10 Wind-surfer and fish (Michal Korzeń)..... 4·25 2·50
4077 2z.60 Girl and hens (Ewa Zajdler)...................... 5·25 3·00
4074/4077 Set of 4... 14·00 8·00

 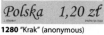 

1280 "Krak" (anonymous) **1281** Katowice Cathedral

(Des J. Stanny. Photo)

2003 (30 June). Fairy Tales. T **1280** and similar vert designs. Multicoloured. P 11.
4078 1z.20 Type **1280**.. 2·40 1·40
4079 1z.80 "Stupid Mateo" (Jósef Kraszewski) .... 3·50 2·10
4080 2z.10 "Frog Princess" (Antoni Gliński)............... 4·25 2·50
4081 2z.60 "Crock of Gold" (Jósef Kraszewski).......... 5·25 3·00
4078/4081 Set of 4... 14·00 8·00

(Des Magdalena Jonczyk Eng W. Zajdel. Recess and photo)

2003 (18 Aug). Katowice 2003 National Stamp Exhibition. Sheet 94×71 mm. P 11½×11.
MS4082 **1281** 3z.40 brownish black, orange-brown and yellow-ochre .... 7·75 7·50
No. **MS**4082 also exists imperforate (price £22).

1282 "Self Portrait" **1283** Post Horn

(Des J. Wysocki. Photo)

2003 (30 Sept). Birth Centenary of Julian Falat (artist). T **1282** and similar multicoloured designs. P 11½×11 (vert) or 11×11½ (horiz).
4083 1z.20 Type **1282**.. 2·40 1·40
4084 1z.80 "Spear Men" .... 3·50 2·10
4085 2z.10 "Winter Landscape with River and Bird" (horiz) .... 4·25 2·50
4086 2z.60 "Aboard Ship-Merchants of Ceylon" (horiz) .... 5·25 3·00
4083/4086 Set of 4... 14·00 8·00

(Des A. Gosik. Photo)

2003 (9 Oct). World Post Day. P 11½×11.
4087 **1283** 2z.10 multicoloured .... 4·00 2·30

1284 "Holy Virgin of Częstochowa" **1285** Motor Cycle (1903)

(Des Z. Stasik. Litho)

2003 (14 Oct). St. Mary's Sanctuaries. T **1284** and similar vert designs. Multicoloured. Phosphorescent paper. P 11½×11.
4088 1z.20 Type **1284** (Church of the Holy Redeemer, Warsaw).. 2·20 1·30
4089 1z.80 "Holy Mother Benevolent" (Basilica of Assumption of Holy Virgin, Krzeszowice)........ 3·25 2·00
4090 2z.10 "Holy Virgin" (Church of the Holy Virgin, Zieleniec)... 4·50 2·50
4088/4090 Set of 3... 9·00 5·25

(Des J. Konarzewski. Photo)

2003 (20 Oct). Centenary of Motor Cycle Racing in Poland. T **1285** and similar horiz designs. Multicoloured. P 11×11½.
4091 1z.20 Type **1285**.. 2·20 1·40
a. Strip of 3. Nos. 4091/3........................... 6·75
4092 1z.20 Rudge (c. 1930)...................................... 2·20 1·40
4093 1z.20 NSU (c. 1940).. 2·20 1·40
4091/4093 Set of 3... 6·00 3·75
Nos. 4091/3 were issued in horizontal se-tenant strips of three within sheets of 12 stamps.

1286 Dancers wearing Traditional Costume **1287** Perching Adult holding Fish

(Des J. Konarzewski. Photo)

2003 (29 Oct). 50th Anniv of Folk Dance Troup "Śląsk". T **1286** and similar vert design. Multicoloured. P 11½×11.
4094 1z.20 Type **1286**.. 2·20 1·40
a. Pair. Nos. 4094/5................................... 4·75 3·00

4095   1z.20 Dancers (*different*)...................................... 2·20   1·40

Nos. 4094/5 were issued in horizontal *se-tenant* pairs within sheets of four stamps, each pair forming a composite design (*price for sheet £10*).

(Des J. Brodowski. Photo)

2003 (31 Oct). Endangered Species. Osprey (*Pandion haliaetus*). T **1287** and similar vert designs. Multicoloured. P 11½×11.

4096		1z.20 Type **1287**...............................	2·20	1·40
	a.	Strip of 4. Nos. 4096/9...........	9·00	
	b.	Sheet of 8. Nos. 4096/9, each×2.............	19·00	
4097		1z.20 Adult and chicks on nest	2·20	1·40
4098		1z.20 Adult catching fish (one wing visible)...	2·20	1·40
4099		1z.20 Adult carrying fish (both wings visible)	2·20	1·40
4096/4099		*Set of 4*...	8·00	5·00

Nos. 4096/9 were issued in horizontal *se-tenant* strips of four within sheets of eight stamps, each strip forming a composite design.

1288 Two White Storks

(Des J. Wysocki. Photo)

2003 (31 Oct). www.poland.gov.pl (Poland on the internet). P 11×11½.

4100   **1288** 2z.10 multicoloured.................................. 4·00   2·50

1289 The Nativity

(Des A. Gosik. Photo)

2003 (27 Nov). Christmas. T **1289** and similar multicoloured designs. P 11½ (with one elliptical hole on each horiz (4101/2) or vert (4103/4) side).

4101	1z.20 Type **1289**....................................	2·40	1·50
4102	1z.80 Three Kings...................................	3·50	2·20
4103	2z.10 Angel appearing to Mary (*vert*)...............	4·25	2·75
4104	2z.60 Holy Family (*vert*).............................	5·25	3·25
4101/4104	*Set of 4*...	14·00	8·75

1290 Wislawa Szymborska

1291 Heart

(Des M. Jędrysik. Litho)

2003 (12 Dec). Polish Influence Abroad (1st series). T **1290** and similar designs showing designs from other countries' stamps. P 11½ (with one elliptical hole on each vert (4106, 4108) or horiz (4105, 4108) side).

4105	1z.20 brown-purple, slate-green and black.....	2·40	1·50
4106	1z.80 ultramarine, bright blue and black		
	(*horiz*)..	3·50	2·20
4107	2z.10 deep purple, pale azure and black........	4·25	2·75
4108	2z.60 slate and black (*horiz*)......................	5·25	3·25
4105/4108	*Set of 4*...	14·00	8·75

Designs:—1z.20 Wislawa Szymborska (writer) (as Sweden No. 2120); 1z.80 Marie Sklodowska-Curie (physicist) (as France No. 1765); 2z.10 Czeslaw Milosz (writer) (as Sweden No. 1299); 2z.60 "Holy Virgin of Częstochowa" (as Vatican City No. 481).

See also Nos. 4112/13

(Des Y. Paszkiewicz. Photo)

2004 (5 Jan). Orchestra of Holy Day Assistance (fund raising charity). P 11×11½.

4109   **1291** 1z.25 multicoloured.................................. 2·20   1·40

1292 Airliner   **1293** Boy and Girl with Heart-shaped Balloon

(Des J. Brodowski. Photo)

2004 (21 Jan). 75th Anniv of LOT (Polish airlines). P 11×11½.

4110   **1292** 1z.25 multicoloured.................................. 2·20   1·40

(Des E. Luczyn. Photo)

2003 (2 Feb). St. Valentine. P 11×11½.

4111   **1293** 1z.25 multicoloured.................................. 2·20   1·40

1294 Helena Paderewska   **1295** Chocolate Rabbit

(Des M. Jędrysik. Litho)

2004 (27 Feb). Polish Influence Abroad (2nd series). T **1294** and similar horiz design. Multicoloured. P 11.

4112	2z.10 Type **1294** (co-founder of USA Polish White Cross (humanitarian organization)............................	4·00	2·50
4113	2z.10 Lucjan Bojnowski (New Britain, USA church pioneer)............................	4·00	2·50

(Des T. Boguslawski. Photo)

2004 (12 Mar). Easter. T **1295** and similar horiz design. Multicoloured. P 11×11½.

4114	1z.25 Type **1295**....................................	2·20	1·40
4115	2z.10 Ceramic lamb................................	4·00	2·50

1296 Beaver and Frog   **1297** Map of Europe and New Members' Flags

(Des J. Brodowski. Litho)

2004 (31 Mar). Fauna. T **1296** and similar horiz designs. Multicoloured. P 11½ (with one elliptical hole on each horiz side).

4116	1z.25 Type **1296**....................................	2·20	1·40
	a. Strip of 4. Nos. 4116/19	9·00	
4117	1z.25 Kingfisher, Crayfish, Roach and Water Beetle..............................	2·20	1·40
4118	1z.25 Grayling, Leech and Water Snail..............	2·20	1·40
4119	1z.25 Pike, Grebe and Roach	2·20	1·40
4116/4119	*Set of 4*...	8·00	5·00

Nos. 4116/19 were issued in horizontal *se-tenant* strips of four within sheets of 20 stamps, each strip forming a composite design.

The strips were laid *tête-bêche* giving three strips upright and two upside down.

(Des J. Golik. Litho)

2004 (1 May). Poland's Accession to European Union (4th issue). P 11½ (with one elliptical hole on each vert side).

4120   **1297** 2z.10 multicoloured.................................. 4·50   2·75

No. 4120 was issued with a *se-tenant* stamp-size label showing arms.

1298 Rucksack as Landscape

1299 Figure (sculpture, St. Mariacki Square, Kraków)

(Des J. Konarzewski. Litho)

2004 (5 May). Europa. Holidays. P 11½ (with one elliptical hole on each vert side).
4121 **1298** 2z.10 multicoloured.................................. 4·00 2·50

(Des M. Kopecki. Recess and photo)

2004 (7 May). Tenth Government Postage Stamp Printers' Conference, Krakow. P 11×12.
4122 **1299** 3z.45 multicoloured.................................. 6·50 4·25
No. 4122 was issued with a half stamp-size label attached at foot.

1300 Pope John Paul II

1301 Crimson Rosella (*Platycercus elegans*)

(Des M. Olivieri and F. Guarniera. Litho Cartor)

2004 (2 June). Pope John Paul II visits to Poland, 1979–2002. Two sheets, each 115×185 mm containing T **1300** and similar vert designs. Multicoloured. Two phosphor bands. P 13½×13.
MS4123 (a) 1z.25×4, Type **1300** (1979); At prayer (1983); Holding reliquary (1987); Resting head against staff (1991). (b) 1z.25×4, Holding staff (1991); With raised hand (1997); Seated facing right (1999); Seated facing left (2002) .... 18·00 17·00
The stamps of **MS**4123a/b were arranged in strips of three, each stamp with a *se-tenant* label at left and right.
The labels were inscribed with the either the Papal Arms or the Polish Arms and the year of the visit.
Stamps of the same design were issued by Vatican City.

(Des A. Balcerzak Litho)

2004 (30 June). Birds. T **1301** and similar vert designs. Multicoloured. P 11½ (with one elliptical hole on each vert side).
4124 1z.25 Type **1301**.................................. 2·20 1·40
a. Block of 4. Nos. 4124/7 .... 9·00
4125 1z.25 Cockatiel (*Nymphicus hollandicus*) .... 2·20 1·40
4126 1z.25 Budgerigar (*Melopsittacus undulates*) ..... 2·20 1·40
4127 1z.25 Spotted-side Finch (*Poephila guttata*), Gouldian Finch (*Chloebia gouldiae*) and Java Sparrow (*Padda oryzivora*) .... 2·20 1·40
4124/4127 Set of 4.................................. 8·00 5·00
Nos. 4124/7 were issued in *se-tenant* blocks of four within sheets of eight stamps.

1302 "Self-portrait wearing White"

1303 Sun Wu-Kung (monkey king)

(Des J. Wysoki. Photo)

2004 (15 July). 150th Birth Anniv of Jacek Malczewski (artist). T **1302** and similar multicoloured designs. P 11½×11 (vert) or 11×11½ (horiz).
4128 1z.25 Type **1302**.................................. 2·20 1·40
4129 1z.90 "Ellenai".................................. 3·50 2·20
4130 2z.10 "Tobias with Harpy" (*horiz*) .... 4·00 2·50
4131 2z.60 "The Unknown Note" (*horiz*) .... 4·75 3·00
4128/4131 Set of 4.................................. 13·00 8·25

(Des E. Libera. Litho)

2004 (30 July). Singapore International Stamp Exhibition. Sheet 90×70 mm. P 11½ (with one elliptical hole on each horiz side).
MS4132 **1303** 3z.45 multicoloured................................. 6·50 6·25
No. **MS**4132 also exists imperforate (*price £26*).

1304 Boxer

1305 Witold Gombrowicz

(Des J. Wysocki. Litho)

2004 (2 Aug). Olympic Games, Athens. Sheet 198×117 mm containing T **1304** and similar horiz designs. Multicoloured. P 11½ (with one elliptical hole on each horiz side).
MS4133 1z.25×4, Type **1304**; Hurdler; Show jumper; Wrestler .... 8·75 8·50
The stamps and margin of **MS**4133 form a composite design.

(Des B. Paczowski. Litho)

2004 (4 Aug). Birth Centenary of Witold Gombrowicz (writer). P 11½. (with one elliptical hole on each vert side).
4134 **1305** 1z.25 ultramarine.................................. 2·20 1·40
a. Tête-bêche (pair).................................. 4·75 3·00

1306 "Holy Mother of Miedzna"

1307 Czeslaw Niemen

(Des J. Pietras (4135, 4137, 4143 and 4149), E. Libera (4136, 4139, 4142 and 4146), M. Osa (4138 and 4141), M. Jędrysik (4140, 4145, 4147/8 and 4150) or W. Terechowicz (4144 and 4151). Litho)

2004 (14 Aug). St. Mary's Sanctuaries. T **1306** and similar vert designs. Multicoloured. P 11½×11 (with one elliptical hole on each vert side).
4135 1z.25 Type **1306** (Church of the Annunciation of Our Lady of Miedzna). 2·20 1·40
4136 1z.25 "Holy Mary and Family" (John the Baptist Basilica, Studzianna). 2·20 1·40
4137 1z.25 "Holy Virgin of Sianow" (Church of the Nativity of Our Lady of Sianów). 2·20 1·40
4138 1z.25 "Holy Mary of Rywald" (St. Sebastian and Nativity of Our Lady, Rywald). 2·20 1·40
4139 1z.25 "Holy Mary of Piekary" (Name of Our Lady and St. Bartholome Basilica, Piekary Śląskie). 2·20 1·40
4140 1z.25 "Holy Mary of Ruda" (Assumption of Our Lady Church, Ruda). 2·20 1·40
4141 1z.25 "Holy Mary of Lomża" (Archangel St. Michael Cathedral, Lomża). 2·20 1·40
4142 1z.25 "Holy Mary of Perpetual Assistance" (Barefoot Carmelite Convent, Niedzwiady). 2·20 1·40
4143 1z.25 "Holy Mary of Rychwald" (St. Nicholas and Our Lady of Scapular, Rychwald). 2·20 1·40
4144 1z.25 "Crying Holy Mary" (St. John the Baptist and Evangelist, Lublin). 2·20 1·40
4145 1z.25 "Holy Mary of Dzików" (Assumption of Our Lady Convent, Tarnobrzeg). 2·20 1·40
4146 1z.25 "Holy Mary of Rzeszów" (Assumption of Our Lady Church, Rzeszów). 2·20 1·40

4147   1z.25 "Gracious Holy Mary" (St. Stanislaw,
St. Peter and St. Paul, Lubaczów)............   2·20   1·40
4148   1z.25 "Holy Mother of Fatima" (Immaculate
Heart of Our Lady of Fatima, Szczecin).   2·20   1·40
4149   1z.25 "Pieta of Skrzatusz" (Assumption of
Our lady Church, Skrzatusz) ....   2·20   1·40
4150   1z.25 "Pieta of Obory" (Visitation of Our
Lady Church, Obory) ....   2·20   1·40
4151   1z.25 "Holy Mary of Jasna Góra" (Queen of
Poland Sanctuary, Jasnagora)....................   2·20   1·40
4135/4151 *Set of 17* ....   34·00   21·00

(Des J. Konarzewski. Litho)

2004 (30 Aug). Czeslaw Wydrzycki (Niemen) (musician) Commemoration.
P 11½ (with one elliptical hole on each horiz side).
4152   **1307**   1z.25 black................   2·20   1·40

1308 Raft on River Dunajec

(Des J. Brodowski. Litho)

2004 (3 Sept). Raft Men working on River Dunajec (bordering Slovakia
and Poland). P 11½ (with one elliptical hole on each horiz side).
4153   **1308**   2z.10 multicoloured ....   4·00   2·50
A stamp of the same design was issued by Slovakia.

1309 Motor Cyclists

(Des J. Konarzewski. Litho)

2004 (11 Sept). Motor Sports. T **1309** and similar horiz designs.
Multicoloured. P 11×11½ (with one elliptical hole on each horiz side).
4154   1z.25 Type **1309**................   2·20   1·40
     a. Strip of 4. Nos. 4154/7............   9·00
4155   1z.25 Race car............   2·20   1·40
4156   1z.25 Kart racing ....   2·20   1·40
4157   1z.25 Motor cyclist (2004 International Six
Day's Enduro)............   2·20   1·40
4154/4157 *Set of 4*............   8·00   5·00
Nos. 4154/7 were issued in *se-tenant* strips of four stamps within
the sheet, each strip forming a composite design.

1310 Binary Codes forming
Postman

1311 Holy Mary Church,
Kraków

(Des M. Jędrysik. Litho)

2004 (9 Oct). World Post Day. P 11½ (with one elliptical hole on each
horiz side).
4158   **1310**   2z.10 multicoloured ....   4·00   2·50

(Des A. Gosik. Litho)

2004 (20 Oct). World Heritage Sites. T **1311** and similar multicoloured
designs. P 11½ (with one elliptical hole on each vert (4159/61) or
horiz side (4162/3)).
4159   1z.25 Type **1311**...   2·20   1·40
4160   1z.25 Tower, St. John the Baptist and
Evangelist Cathedral, Toruń......................   2·20   1·40
4161   1z.25 Town Hall, Zamość.............................   2·20   1·40
4162   1z.25 Riverside, Warsaw (*horiz*) ....   2·20   1·40
4163   1z.25 Castle, Malbork (*horiz*) ....   2·20   1·40
4159/4163 *Set of 5*...   10·00   6·25

1312 People entering   **1313** Protoplanet circling Sun
Church

(Des J. Brodowski. Photo)

2004 (5 Nov). Christmas. T **1312** and similar multicoloured design. P 11½.
4164   1z.25 Type **1312**...   2·20   1·40
4165   1z.25 Decorated window (*horiz*)........................   4·00   2·50

(Des J. Pietras. Litho)

2004 (3 Dec). History of Earth. T **1313** and similar horiz designs.
Multicoloured. P 11½ (with one elliptical hole on each horiz side).
4166   1z.25 Type **1313**...   2·20   1·40
     a. Block of 4. Nos. 4166/9.........................   9·00
4167   1z.25 Asteroids bombarding earth......................   2·20   1·40
4168   1z.25 Dinosaurs..   2·20   1·40
4169   1z.25 International space station in orbit ....   2·20   1·40
4166/4169 *Set of 4*...   8·00   5·00
Nos. 4166/9 were issued in *se-tenant* blocks of four within sheets of
eight stamps.

 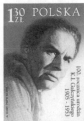

1314 "13"   **1315** Konstanty
Galczyński

(Des I. Tratkowski and J. Owsiak. Photo)

2005 (6 Jan). Orchestra of Holy Day Assistance (fund raising charity).
P 11×11½.
4170   **1314**   1z.30 multicoloured.....................................   2·40   1·50

(Des A. Gosik. Photo)

2005 (14 Jan). Birth Centenary of Konstanty Ildefons Galczyński
(writer). P 11½×11.
4171   **1315**   1z.30 multicoloured.....................................   2·40   1·50
     a. *Tête-bêche* (pair).....................................   5·00   3·25

1316 Mikolaj Rej   **1317** Masked Swordsman and
Carved Heart on Tree

(Des M. Buszewicz. Photo)

2005 (26 Jan). 500th Birth Anniv of Mikolaj Rej (writer). P 11½.
4172   **1316**   1z.30 black and scarlet-vermilion ....   2·40   1·50

(Des A. Niemierko. Photo)

2005 (1 Feb). Greetings Stamp. P 11½.
4173   **1317**   1z.30 multicoloured.....................................   2·40   1·50
No. 4173 was also available in sheets of 20 stamps and 20 labels which
could be personalised by the addition of a photograph, text or image.

1318 Rabbit

(Des Agnieszka Sobczyńska. Photo)

2005 (1 Mar). Easter. T **1318** and similar vert design. Multicoloured. P 12.

4174	1z.30 Type **1318**	2·40	1·50
4175	2z.20 Chick	4·25	2·75

1319 "The Little Mermaid"   **1320** Pope John Paul II

(Des Agnieszka Sobczyńska. Litho)

2005 (15 Mar). Birth Bicentenary of Hans Christian Andersen (writer). T **1319** and similar vert design. Multicoloured. P 11½ (with one elliptical hole on each vert side).

4176	1z.30 Type **1319**	2·40	1·50
4177	1z.30 "The Snow Queen"	2·40	1·50

(Des A. Pągowski. Litho)

2005 (8 Apr). Pope John Paul II Commemoration (1st issue). P 11½×12 (with one elliptical hole on each vert side).

4178	**1320** 1z.30 multicoloured	2·40	1·50

See also No. **MS**4184

1321 Sky Diving   **1322** Shell

(Des Magdalena Blażków. Litho)

2005 (15 Apr). Extreme Sports. T **1321** and similar vert designs. Multicoloured. P 11½ (with one elliptical hole on each horiz side).

4179	1z.30 Type **1321**	2·40	1·50
	a. Block of 4. Nos. 4179/82	9·75	
4180	1z.30 Bungee jumping	2·40	1·50
4181	1z.30 Rock climbing	2·40	1·50
4182	1z.30 White water rafting	2·40	1·50
4179/4182 Set of 4		8·75	5·50

Nos. 4179/82 were issued in *se-tenant* blocks of four stamps within the sheet.

(Des J. Wysocki. Litho)

2005 (21 Apr). Pacific Explorer International Stamp Exhibition, Sydney. Sheet 90×70 mm. P 11½ (with one elliptical hole on each horiz side).

MS4183	**1322** 3z.50 multicoloured	6·50	6·25

No. **MS**4183 was also available imperforate (*price* £33).

1323 Pope John Paul II   **1324** Bread

(Des W. Terechowicz. Litho)

2005 (22 Apr). Pope John Paul II Commemoration (2nd issue). Sheet 70×83 mm. P 11½ (with one elliptical hole on each vert side).

MS4184	**1323** 3z.50 multicoloured	6·50	6·25

(Des M. Blażków and C. Hladki. Litho and embossed)

2005 (5 May). Europa. Gastronomy. P 11½ (with one elliptical hole on each horiz side).

4185	**1324** 2z.20 multicoloured	4·50	2·75

1325 Rubble

(Des M. Buszewicz. Litho)

2005 (6 May). 60th Anniv of End of World War II. P 12×11½ (with one elliptical hole on each vert side).

4186	**1325** 1z.30 black and vermilion	2·40	1·50

1326 "The Hour of the Crimson Rose" (M. Krüger)

(Des Agnieszka Sobczyńska. Litho)

2005 (1 June). Stories. Sheet 124×124 mm containing T **1326** and similar square designs. Multicoloured. P 12×11½ (with one elliptical hole on each vert side).

MS4187	1z.30 Type **1326**; 2z. "The Little Prince" (Antoine de Saint-Exupéry); 2z.20 "2000 Leagues under the Sea" (Jules Verne); 2z.80 "In the Desert and the Forest" (H. Sienkiewicz)	15·00	14·00

1327 "Stanislaw Kostka Potocki" (Jacques-Louis David)

(Des J. Wysocki. Litho)

2005 (21 June). Bicentenary of National Museum, Wilanów. Sheet 95×130 mm containing T **1327** and similar vert designs. Multicoloured. P 12.

MS4188	1z.30 Type **1327**; 2z.17th-century Nautilus wine cup; 2z.20 Flower girl (18th-century porcelain); 2z.80 19th-century clock	15·00	14·00

No. **MS**4188 was issued *se-tenant* with four half stamp-size labels.

1328 Embroidered Rose (Podhale)   **1329** Hurdling

(Des E. Skrzypek and M. Malczyńska. Litho)

2005 (15 July). Embroidery. T **1328** and similar vert designs showing embroidered roses. P 11½ (with one elliptical hole on each vert side).

4189	1z.30 Type **1328**	2·40	1·50
4190	2z. Rose (Lowicz)	3·75	2·40
4191	2z.20 Rose (Lowicz) (*different*)	4·25	2·75
4192	2z.80 Rose (Lowicz) (*different*)	5·25	3·25
4189/4192 Set of 4		14·00	9·00

(Des Magdalena Blażków. Litho)

2005 (8 Aug). International Athletics Championship, Helsinki. Sheet 200×115 mm containing T **1329** and similar horiz designs. Multicoloured. P 11½ (with one elliptical hole on each horiz side).
MS4193 1z.30 Type **1329**; 1z.30 Shot put; 2z. Triple
jump; 2z. Pole vault .... 12·00 11·00

1330 Józef Pilsudski **1331** Lech Walęsa
(Commander in Chief) (founder)

(Des Maria Dziekańska. Litho)

2005 (12 Aug). 85th Anniv of Battle of Warsaw ("Miracle on the Vistula"). Sheet 70×90 mm. P 11½.
MS4194 **1330** 3z.50 multicoloured...................... 6·50 6·25

(Des Maria Dziekańska. Litho)

2005 (17 Aug). 25th Anniv of Solidarity (trade union). P 11½ (with one elliptical hole on each vert side).
4195 **1331** 2z.20 scarlet vermilion, dark grey and
black.. 4·25 2·75

1332 "80" **1333** Music Score and Frederick
Chopin

(Des Maria Dziekańska. Litho)

2005 (1 Sept). 80th Anniv of Radio. P 11½ (with elliptical hole on each vert side).
4196 **1332** 1z.30 rosine and black..................... 2·40 ✓ 1·50

(Des Maria Dziekańska. Litho)

2005 (16 Sept). Frederick Chopin International Piano Competition. P 11½ (with one elliptical hole on each horiz side).
4197 **1333** 2z.20 green, scarlet vermilion and
black.. 4·25 2·75
Issued in sheets of four stamps (price £20).

1334 Lemur (Opole) **1335** Post Office Building, Cracow

(Des M. Blażków. Litho)

2005 (30 Sept). Zoological Gardens. T **1334** and similar vert designs. Each black. P 11½ (with one elliptical hole on each vert side).
4198 1z.30 Type **1334**.............................. 2·40 1·50
4199 2z. Siberian Tiger (Panthera tigris altaica)
(Wroclaw) .... 3·75 2·40
4200 2z.20 White Rhinoceros (Ceratotherium
simum) (Poznań).......................... 4·25 2·75
4201 2z.80 Anteater (Warsaw) .... 5·25 3·25
4198/4201 Set of 4................................ 14·00 9·00

(Des M. Blażków. Litho)

2005 (7 Oct). World Post Day. Architecture. P 11½ (with one elliptical hole on each horiz side).
4202 **1335** 1z.30 multicoloured..................... 2·40 1·50

1336 Gingerbread Men **1337** St. Maciej's Church and
St. Stefan's Statue, Budapest

(Des A. Wasik and M. Blażków. Litho)

2005 (14 Oct). 60th Anniv of United Nations. P 11½ (with one elliptical hole on each horiz side).
4203 **1336** 2z.20 multicoloured..................... 4·25 2·75

(Des M. Blażków. Litho)

2005 (24 Oct). European Capitals. T **1337** and similar horiz designs. Multicoloured. P 11½ (with one elliptical hole on each horiz side).
4204 1z.30 Type **1337**.............................. 2·40 1·50
4205 1z.30 Vilnius Cathedral .... 2·40 1·50
4206 2z.20 Arc de Triomphe, Paris................ 4·00 2·50
4207 2z.20 Monument to the Discoverers Belém,
Lisbon................................... 4·00 2·50
4208 2z.80 Government building, Dublin.......... 5·00 3·25
4204/4208 Set of 5................................ 16·00 10·00

1338 "Ploughing in the Ukraine" **1339** Stethoscope in
(L. J. Wyczółkowski) Pocket

(Des A. Pągowski. Photo)

2005 (3 Nov). Art. Polish Impressionists. Sheet 94×130 mm containing T **1338** and similar horiz designs. Multicoloured. P 11½.
MS4209 1z.30×2, Type **1338**; "Still Life" (J. Pankiewicz);
2z.×2, "Flower Sellers" (O. Boznańska); "The Garden"
(W. Podkowiński) .... 12·50 12·00
No. **MS**4209 was issued se-tenant with two stamp-size labels.

(Des M. Dziekańska. Litho)

2005 (24 Nov). Bicentenary of Doctors' Association. P 11½ (with one elliptical hole on each vert side).
4210 **1339** 1z.30 multicoloured..................... 2·40 1·50

1340 Trees and **1341** Athletes
Angel

(Des M. Dziekanska. Photo)

2005 (28 Nov). Christmas. T **1340** and similar vert design. Multicoloured. P 12×11½.
4211 1z.30 Type **1340**.............................. 2·40 1·50
4212 2z.20 Angel facing left........................ 4·25 2·75

(Des J. Brodowski. Photo)

2006 (7 Feb). Winter Olympic Games, Turin. P 12×11½ (with one elliptical hole on each horiz side).
4213 **1341** 2z.40 multicoloured..................... 4·50 2·75
No. 4213 was issued with a stamp sized label.

1342 Heart carved in Apple

1343 Wolfgang Mozart

(Des A. Gosik. Photo)

2006 (10 Feb). St. Valentines Day. P 11½.
4214   **1342**   1z.30 multicoloured...................................... 2·40   1·50
No. 4214 was issued with a *se-tenant* label that could be personalised (*price £4.50 unused, £2.75 used*).

(Des M. Jędrysik. Photo)

2006 (15 Feb). 250th Birth Anniv of Wolfgang Amadeus Mozart (composer and musician). P 12×11½ (with one elliptical hole on each horiz side).
4215   **1343**   2z.40 multicoloured...................................... 4·50   2·75

1344 Students

1345 Zygmunt Gloger (first president)

(Des J. Pietras. Photo)

2006 (17 Feb). 25th Anniv of Independent Students' Union. P 12×11½ (with one elliptical hole on each horiz side).
4216   **1344**   1z.30 black and scarlet vermilion.......... 2·40   1·50

(Des J. Konarzewski. Photo)

2006 (20 Feb). Centenary of Polish Touring Society. P 12×11½ (with one elliptical hole on each horiz side).
4217   **1345**   1z.30 multicoloured...................................... 2·40   1·50

1346 *Pedicularis sudetica*

(Des A. Balcerzak. Litho)

2006 (14 Mar). Endangered Species. Flowers. T **1346** and similar horiz design. Multicoloured. P 12×11½ (with one elliptical hole on each horiz side).
4218   1z.30 Type **1346**...................................... 2·40   1·50
4219   2z.40 *Trapa natans*................................... 4·50   2·75

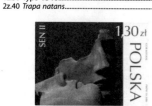

1347 "Dream II"

(Des J. Pietras. Photo)

2006 (27 Mar). Contemporary Sculpture. Igor Mitoraj. T **1347** and similar horiz design. Multicoloured. P 12×11½ (with one elliptical hole on each horiz side).
4220   1z.30 Type **1347**...................................... 2·40   1·80
4221   1z.30 "Lips of Eros"................................... 2·40   1·80
Nos. 4220/1 were issued both in large sheets and together, each×2, in small sheets of four stamps with enlarged margins (*price for sheet £10.50 unused, £10 used*).

1348 Floral Procession, Palm Sunday

1349 Tree, Man and Stars

(Des Agnieszka Sancewicz. Litho)

2006 (3 Apr). Easter. T **1348** and similar horiz design. Multicoloured. P 12×11½ (with one elliptical hole on each horiz side).
4222   1z.30 Type **1348**...................................... 2·40   1·80
4223   2z.40 Smigus-dyngus (dousing with water), Easter Monday................................... 4·50   3·25

(Des Anna Niemierko. Litho)

2006 (5 May). Europa. Integration. P 11½×12 (with one elliptical hole on each vert side).
4224   **1349**   2z.40 multicoloured...................................... 4·50   3·25

1350 "2006 WASHINGTON"

1351 Pope Benedict XVI

(Des Anna Niemierko. Photo)

2006 (19 May). Washington 2006 International Stamp Exhibition. Sheet 115×77 mm. P 12.
MS4225   **1350**   2z.40 blue and vermilion...................... 4·75   4·50
No. **MS**4225 was issued *se-tenant* with a stamp-size label.

(Des J. Wysocki. Litho)

2006 (25 May). Visit of Pope Benedict XVI. P 11½×12 (with one elliptical hole on each vert side).
4226   **1351**   1z.30 multicoloured...................................... 2·40   1·80

1352 Stilo

1353 Spinning Top

(Des Z. Okrassa. Litho)

2006 (29 May). Lighthouses (1st series). T **1352** and similar vert designs. Multicoloured.
4227   2z.40 Type **1352**...................................... 4·50   3·25
        a. Sheetlet. Nos. 4227/30................ 19·00
4228   2z.40 Krynica Morska .... 4·50   3·25
4229   2z.40 Gąski...................................... 4·50   3·25
4230   2z.40 Niechorze.............................. 4·50   3·25
4227/4230 *Set of 4*................................... 16·00   11·50
See also No. **MS**4275.

(Des Agnieszka Sancewicz. Litho)

2006 (1 June). Toys. T **1353** and similar triangular design. Multicoloured. P 11×11½ (with one elliptical hole on each vert side).
4231   1z.30 Type **1353**...................................... 2·40   1·80
4232   1z.30 Windmill................................ 2·40   1·80

1354 Baroque Tankard   **1355** Workers Procession, Poznań

(Des Wang Huming. Photo)

2006 (20 June). Gold and Silver Ware. T **1354** and similar vert design. Multicoloured. P 12×11½.
4233	1z.30 Type **1354**	2·40	1·80
	a. Pair. Nos. 4233/4	5·00	3·75
4234	1z.30 Empire Lasting Forever Gold Cup	2·40	1·80

Stamps of the same design were issued by People's Republic China. Nos. 4233/4 were issued in *se-tenant* pairs within the sheet.

(Des M. Jędrysik. Eng T. Zlotkowski (**MS**4235a) or W. Zajdel (**MS**4235b). Recess and photo)

2006 (25–28 June). 50th Anniv of Workers' Revolt, Poznań (**MS**4235a) and 30th Anniv of Workers' Revolt, Radom (**MS**4235b). Two sheets, each 90×70 mm containing T **1355** and similar horiz design. P 12×11½.
MS4235	(a) 3z.50 grey-blue and slate-black. (28.6) (b)		
	3z.50 deep greenish grey and slate-black	12·00	11·50

Designs: (a) Type **1355**. (b) Workers on lorry, Radom.

1356 Jerzy Giedroyc   **1357** Edward Szczeklik

(Des J. Konarzewski. Eng M. Kopecki. Recess)

2006 (27 July). Birth Centenary of Jerzy Giedroyc (journalist). P 11½×11.
4236	**1356** 1z.30 slate black	2·40	1·80

(Des J. Skakun. Litho)

2006 (8 Sept). Centenary of Internal Medicine Society. T **1357** and similar horiz designs. Multicoloured. P 12×11½ (with one elliptical hole on each horiz side).
4237	1z.30 Type **1357**	2·40	1·80
4238	1z.30 Witold Eugeniusz Orlowskil	2·40	1·80
4239	3z. Antoni Wladyslaw Gluzinski	5·00	3·75
4237/4239 *Set of 3*		8·75	6·50

1358 Lublin Town Hall   **1359** Scream (E)

(Des Joanna Górska. Eng P. Krajewski. Recess and photo)

2006 (20 Sept). 19th Convention of Polish Philatelic Association. Sheet 90×70 mm. P 11½.
MS4240	3z.50 multicoloured	6·00	4·50

No. **MS**4240 also exists imperforate (*price* £15).

(Des J. Pietras (A, f, O, S), M. Jędrysik (B, C, I, J, U), W. Terechowicz (C), M. Osa (D, E, H, L), K. Castellini (G, K, L), E. Libera (M, N, t, Z), A. Niemierko (P, S), J. Wysocki (R, Y) or K. Syta (W). Litho)

2006 (29 Sept). Alphabet. Two sheets, each 130×175 mm containing T **1359** and similar multicoloured designs showing illustrations for letters of the Polish alphabet. P 11½ (with one elliptical hole on each vert side).
MS4241	(a) 10g. Type **1359**; 10g. "I"; 30g. "A" (44×22 *mm*); 30g. "D"; 30g. "K"; 1z. "f"; 1z. "L"; 1z.30 "B"; 1z.30 "C"; 1z.30 "C"; 1z.30 "G"; 1z.30 "H"; 1z.30 "J". (b) 10g. "N"; 10g. "Y"; 30g. "M"; 30g. "Z" (44×22 *mm*); 1z. "P"; 1z. "t"; 1z.30 "L"; 1z.30 "R"; 1z.30 "S"; 1z.30 "S"; 1z.30 "U"; 1z.30 "W"	42·00	40·00

1360 Globe and Flags   **1361** Brandenburg Gate, Berlin

(Des J. Ochendzan. Litho)

2006 (9 Oct). World Post Day. P 11½.
4242	**1360** 2z.40 multicoloured	4·25	3·00

(Des M. Błażków. Litho)

2006 (24 Oct). European Capital Cities. T **1361** and similar horiz designs. Multicoloured. P 11½ (with one elliptical hole on each horiz side).
4243	2z.40 Type **1361**	4·25	3·00
4244	2z.40 Coliseum, Rome	4·25	3·00
4245	2z.40 Royal Theatre, Stockholm	4·25	3·00
4246	2z.40 St. Alexander Nevski Cathedral, Tallin	4·25	3·00
4247	2z.40 St. Paul's Cathedral, Valletta	4·25	3·00
4243/4247 *Set of 5*		19·00	13·50

1362 Ogar Polski (hound)   **1363** The Nativity

(Des J. Brodowski. Litho)

2006 (6 Nov). International Dog Show, Poznań. T **1362** and similar horiz designs. Multicoloured. P 11½ (with one elliptical hole on each horiz side).
4248	1z.30 Type **1362**	2·40	1·80
	a. Horiz strip of 5. Nos. 4248/52	12·50	
4249	1z.30 Gonczy Polski (hound)	2·40	1·80
4250	1z.30 Polski Owczarek (lowland sheepdog)	2·40	1·80
4251	1z.30 Chart Polski (sight hound)	2·40	1·80
4252	1z.30 Polski Owczarek Podralanski (Tatra mountain dog)	2·40	1·80
4248/4252 *Set of 5*		11·00	8·00

Nos. 4248/52 were issued in horizontal *se-tenant* strips of five stamps within the sheet.

(Des Marzanna Dąbrowska. Photo)

2006 (30 Nov). Christmas. T **1363** and similar horiz design. Multicoloured. P 11½.
4253	1z.30 Type **1363**	2·40	1·80
	a. Pair. Nos. 4253/4	7·25	5·25
4254	2z.40 "Christmas"	4·50	3·25

1364 Coal bleeding

(Des J. Konarzewski. Litho)

2006 (16 Dec). 25th Anniv of End of Miners' Strike for Solidarity. P 11½ (with one elliptical hole on each horiz side).
4255	**1364** 1z.30 multicoloured	2·40	1·80

1365 Heart as Planet

(Des Z. Wlodarczyk, P. Salkowski and J. Owsiak. Photo)

2007 (4 Jan). Orchestra of Holy Day Assistance (fund raising charity). P 11½.

4256 **1365** 1z.35 multicoloured .... 2·40 1·80

1366 Ice Dancers

1367 Hearts as Butterflies

(Des J. Górska. Litho)

2007 (22 Jan). European Figure Skating Championships, Warsaw. P 11½ (with one elliptical hole on each horiz side).

4257 **1366** 2z.40 multicoloured .... 4·50 3·25

(Des J. Skakun. Litho)

2007 (8 Feb). St. Valentine's Day. P 11½ (with one elliptical hole on each vert side).

4258 **1367** 1z.35 multicoloured .... 2·40 1·80
No. 4258 was issued with a *se-tenant* label that could be personalised (*price £4.50 unused, £3.25 used*).

1368 Straw Lamb

1369 Flags

(Des Marzanna Dąbrowska. Photo)

2007 (8 Mar). Easter. T **1368** and similar horiz design. Multicoloured. P 11½.

4259 1z.35 Type **1368** .... 2·40 1·80
4260 2z.40 Easter egg chicken .... 4·50 3·25

(Des M. Blażków. Litho)

2007 (20 Mar). 50th Anniv of Treaty of Europe. P 11½ (with one elliptical hole on each vert side).

4261 **1369** 3z.55 multicoloured .... 6·50 4·75

1370 Cake

(Des Joanna Górska. Photo)

2007 (30 Mar). Greetings Stamps. T **1370** and similar horiz designs. Multicoloured. P 11½ (with one elliptical perf on each horiz side).

4262 1z.35 Type **1370** .... 2·40 1·80
4263 1z.35 Grapes, wine and bread .... 2·40 1·80
4264 1z.35 Wedding rings .... 2·40 1·80
4262/4264 Set of 3 .... 6·50 4·75

1371 Recycle Emblem

(Des A. Niemierko. Litho)

2007 (22 Apr). Earth Day. P 11½ (with one elliptical hole on each horiz side).

4265 **1371** 1z.35 multicoloured .... 2·40 1·80

1372 Postal Wagon Type 5G c.1956

(Des J. Skakun. Photo)

2007 (28 Apr). Railways. T **1372** and similar horiz designs. Multicoloured. P 11½ (with one elliptical perf on each horiz side).

4266 1z.35 Type **1372** .... 2·40 1·80
      a. Horiz strip of 4. Nos. 4266/9 .... 14·00
4267 1z.35 Carriage Type Cd21b c.1924 .... 2·40 1·80
4268 2z.40 Carriage Type C3Pr07 c.1909 .... 4·25 3·00
4269 2z.40 Carriage Type Ci29 c.1929 .... 4·25 3·00
4266/4269 Set of 4 .... 12·00 8·75
Nos. 4266/9 were issued in horizontal *se-tenant* strips of four stamps within the sheet.

1373 Scout

(Des A. Pękalski. Litho)

2007 (5 May). Europa. Centenary of Scouting. P 11½ (with one elliptical hole on each horiz side).

4270 **1373** 3z. multicoloured .... 6·50 4·50

1374 "Little Helen with Vase of Flowers"

1375 Karol Szymanowski

2007 (18 May). Death Centenary of Stanislaw Wyspiański (artist and writer). P 12×11½ (with one elliptical hole on each horiz side).

4271 **1374** 1z.35 multicoloured .... 2·40 1·80

(Des A. Pągowski and M. Blażków)

2007 (26 May). 125th Birth and 70th Death Anniv of Karol Szymanowski (composer and writer). P 12×11½.

4272 **1375** 1z.35 multicoloured .... 2·40 1·80

1376 Centre of Cracow, Locating Document and City Arms

(Des K. Sowiński. Recess and photo)

2007 (29 May). 750th Anniv of Cracow. P 12.

4273 **1376** 2z.40 multicoloured .... 4·25 3·25

1377 St. Catherine of Alexandria Church,
St. Petersburg

(Des J. Górska. Eng W. Zajdel. Recess and photo)

2007 (29 May). Saint Petersburg 2007 International Philatelic
Exhibition. Sheet 90×70 mm. P 12.
MS4274 **1377** 3z. multicoloured...................................... 5·75 5·50

1378 Gdańsk

1379 Virgin Mary and
Child

(Des Z. Okrassa. Litho)

2007 (15 June). Lighthouses (2nd series). Sheet 90×125 mm
containing T **1378** and similar vert designs. Multicoloured. P 12.
MS4275 1z.35 Type **1378**; 2z.40 Rozewie; 3z.
Kolobrzeg; 3z.55 Hel.. 19·00 18·00

(Des P. Orzechowska. Litho)

2007 (2 July). 300th Anniv of Leśniów Monastery. P 12 (with one
elliptical perf on each vert side).
4276 **1379** 1z.35 multicoloured...................................... 2·40 1·80

1380 Bay

1381 *Saguinus imperator*
(Emperor Tamarin)

(Des Witold Hyszko. Photo)

2007 (31 Aug). Arab Horses. T **1380** and similar vert designs showing
horses. Multicoloured. P 11½ (with one elliptical perf on each
vert side).
4277 1z.35 Type **1380**.. 2·40 1·80
 a. Horiz strip of 4. Nos. 4277/80................... 22·00
4278 3z. Grey with pink snip .... 5·50 4·25
4279 3z.55 Bright bay with long forelock .... 6·50 4·75
4280 3z.55 Dappled grey.................................. 6·50 4·75
4277/4280 Set of 4.. 19·00 14·00
 Nos. 4277/80 were issued in horizontal *se-tenant* strips of four
stamps within the sheet.

(Des M. Blażków. Photo)

2007 (11 Sept). Polish Zoos. T **1381** and similar vert designs showing
animals. Multicoloured. P 11½ (with one elliptical perf on each
vert side).
4281 1z.35 Type **1381**.. 2·40 1·80
4282 3z. *Ciconia nigra* (Black Stork).................. 4·25 3·25
4283 3z. *Loxodonta africana* (African Elephant) ... 5·50 4·25
4284 3z.55 *Uncia uncia* (Snow Leopard).............. 6·50 4·75
4281/4284 Set of 4.. 17·00 12·50

1382 Visual Interpretation of
Electronic Sound as City Skyline

1383 Performers

(Des M. Dąbrowska. Litho)

2007 (21 Sept). Warsaw Autumn 2007—50th Anniv of Festival of
Contemporary Music. P 12 (with one elliptical perf on each horiz side).
4285 **1382** 3z. multicoloured...................................... 5·50 4·25

(Des M. Dziekańska. Litho)

2007 (5 Oct). Centenary of Theatre of Silesia, Katowice. P 12 (with
one elliptical perf on each horiz side).
4286 **1383** 1z.35 multicoloured.................................. 2·75 2·00

1384 Postmarks

(Des M. Dąbrowska. Litho)

2007 (9 Oct). World Post Day. P 12 (with one elliptical perf on each
horiz side).
4287 **1384** 1z.35 multicoloured.................................. 2·75 2·00

1385 Dragon's Bridge,
Ljubljana, Slovenia

(Des M. Blażków. Litho)

2007 (24 Oct). Capital Cities of European Union States. T **1385** and
similar horiz designs. Multicoloured. P 12 (with one elliptical perf
on each horiz side).
4288 1z.35 Type **1385**................................. 2·75 2·00
4289 1z.35 Roland Monument, Riga, Latvia .... 2·75 2·00
4290 3z. Philharmonic Hall, Luxembourg.............. 5·50 4·25
4291 3z. Plaza de Cibeles, Madrid, Spain............... 5·50 4·25
4292 3z.55 Tower Bridge, London, UK.................. 6·50 4·75
4288/4292 Set of 5 .... 21·00 16·00

1386 Pope John Paul II

1387 *Jubilee Self-Portrait*

(Des D. Belloti. Litho)

2007 (30 Oct). 25th Anniv of Pope John Paul II Foundation. P 12 (with
one elliptical perf on each horiz side).
4293 **1386** 1z.35 multicoloured.................................. 2·75 2·00

(Des J. Pietras)

2007 (5 Nov). Jerzy Duda-Gracz (artist) Commemoration. P 12 (with
one elliptical perf on each horiz side).
4294 **1387** 1z.35 multicoloured .... 2·75 2·00

1388 Teddy and Tree

1389 Script, *Otago* and Joseph Conrad

(Des M. Dąbrowska. Photo)

2007 (27 Nov.). Christmas. T **1388** and similar vert design. Multicoloured. P 12.

4295	1z.35 Type **1388**	2·75	2·00
4296	3z. *Adoration of the Magi* (Mikolaj Haberschrack)	5·50	4·25

(Des Maciej Jędrysik. Eng J. M. Kopecki. Recess)

2007 (3 Dec). 150th Birth Anniv of Józef Teodor Konrad Korzeniowski (Joseph Conrad) (writer and sailor). P 11½.

4297	**1389** 3z. black	5·50	4·25

1390 Envelope and Quill

1391 Heart as Open Door

(Des Janusz Wysocki. Photo)

2008 (15 Jan). PostEurop (Association of European Public Postal Operators) Plenary Assembly, Kraków. Sheet 70×90 mm. P 12 (with one elliptical hole on each vert side).

MS4298	**1390** 3z. multicoloured	5·75	5·50

(Des Marzanna Dąbrowska. Litho)

2008 (7 Feb). St Valentine's Day. P 12 (with one elliptical hole on each horiz side).

4299	**1391** 1z.35 multicoloured	2·75	2·00

1392 Self Portrait—1858

1393 Easter Eggs

(Des J. Konarzewski. Litho)

2008 (29 Feb). History of Polish Photography. 190th Birth Anniv of Karol Beyer. T **1392** and similar vert designs. Multicoloured. P 12 (with one elliptical hole on each vert side).

4300	1z.35 Type **1392**	2·75	2·00
	a. Strip of 4. Nos. 4300/3	11·50	
4301	1z.35 Street scene, Wilanów—1866	2·75	2·00
4302	1z.35 Street scene, Warsaw—1858	2·75	2·00
4303	1z.35 Russian army tents—1861	2·75	2·00
4300/4303	Set of 4	10·00	7·25

Nos. 4300/3 were issued in horizontal *se-tenant* strips of four stamps within the sheet.

(Des Marzanna Dąbrowska. Litho)

2008 (29 Feb). Easter. T **1393** and similar vert design. Multicoloured. P 12.

4304	1z.35 Type **1393**	2·75	2·00
4305	2z.40 Eggs (*different*)	4·50	3·50

Although not *se-tenant*, Nos. 4304/5, together, form a composite design.

1394 Emblem

1395 TS-11 ISKRA

(Des Jerzy Skakun. Litho)

2008 (22 Mar). 80th Anniv of Straż Graniczna (border guard). P 12×11½ (with one elliptical hole on each vert side).

4306	**1394** 2z.10 scarlet and black	4·00	3·00

(Des Jerzy Skakun. Litho)

2008 (31 Mar). Polish Airforce. T **1395** and similar vert design. Multicoloured. P 11½×12 (with one elliptical hole on each vert side).

4307	3z. Type **1395**	5·50	4·25
	a. Pair. Nos. 4307/8	12·50	9·25
4308	3z.55 F-16 JASTRZĄB	6·50	4·75

Nos. 4307/8 were issued in *se-tenant* pairs within sheets of eight stamps.

1396 Sand Storm

(Des Marzanna Dąbrowska. Litho)

2008 (25 Apr). Weather Phenomena. T **1396** and similar horiz designs. Multicoloured. P 12×11½ (with one elliptical hole on each horiz side).

4309	1z.35 Type **1396**	2·75	2·00
	a. Strip of 4. Nos. 4309/12	15·00	
4310	1z.35 Lightning	2·75	2·00
4311	2z.40 Rainbow	4·50	3·50
4312	2z.40 Tornado	4·50	3·50
4309/4312	Set of 4	13·00	10·00

Nos. 4309/12 were issued in *se-tenant* strips of four stamps within the sheet.

1397 Envelope as Plate

(Des Joanna Górska. Litho)

2008 (5 May). Europa. The Letter. P 12×11½ (with one elliptical hole on each horiz side).

4313	**1397** 3z. black and silver	5·50	4·25
MS4313a	90×70 mm. As No. MS4313. Imperf		

1398 Emblem

1399 Magnifier and Emblem

(Des Anna Niemierko. Litho)

2008 (30 May). Euro 2008 European Football Championships, Austria and Switzerland. P 11½.

4314	**1398** 1z.35 multicoloured	2·75	2·00

(Des Anna Niemierko. Litho)

2008 (30 May). EUROSAI Congress, Kraków. P 11½×12 (with one elliptical hole on each vert side).
4315 **1399** 3z.55 multicoloured .... 6·50   4·75

1400 Toy Train   **1401** Child and Rug

(Des Marzanna Dąbrowska. Litho)

2008 (1 June). National Children's Day. Toys. T **1400** and similar triangular design. Multicoloured. P 11×11½ (with one elliptical hole on each vert side).
4316   1z.35 Type **1400**.................................. 2·75   2·00
4317   3z. Xylophone...................................... 5·50   4·25

(Des Maciej Jędrysik. Litho)

2008 (10 June). Child Refugees to Esfahan, Iran during World War II. P 11½ (with one elliptical hole on each vert side).
4318 **1401** 2z.40 multicoloured .... 4·50   3·50

1402 Envelope enclosing Romanian Athenaeum Building   **1403** Madonna and Child

(Des Kuba Sowiński. Eng Przemyslaw Krajewski. Recess and photo)

2008 (20 June). EFIRO 2008 International Stamp Exhibition, Bucharest. Sheet 90×70 mm. P 11½.
MS4319 **1402** 3z. multicoloured...................... 6·00   5·75
No. **MS**4319 also exists imperforate (price £31).

(Des Maciej Jędrysik. Litho)

2008 (21 June). St. Mary's Sanctuaries. St. Mary of the Snow. P 11½.
4320 **1403** 1z.35 multicoloured .... 2·75   2·00

1404 Swimming   **1405** Siekierkowski Bridge, Warsaw

(Des Janusz Wysocki. Litho)

2008 (8 Aug). Olympic Games, Beijing. T **1404** and similar horiz designs. Multicoloured. Phosphorescent paper. P 11½ (with one elliptical hole on each horiz side).
4321   10g. Type **1404**.................................. 50   25
     a. Strip of 4. Nos. 4321/4............. 7·25
4322   10g. Volleyball 50   25
4323   1z.45 Pole vault .... 3·00   2·20
4324   1z.45 Fencing .... 3·00   2·20
4321/4324 Set of 4 .... 6·25   4·50
MS4325 202×116 mm Nos. 4321/4 .... 6·50   6·25
    Nos. 4321/4 were issued in horizontal se-tenant strips of four stamps.

(Des Andrzej Gosik. Litho)

2008 (29 Aug). Bridges. T **1405** and similar horiz designs. Multicoloured. P 11½ (with one elliptical hole on each horiz side).
4326   1z.45 Type **1405**.............................. 3·00   2·20
     a. Strip of 4. Nos. 4326/9............. 18·00
4327   1z.45 Poniatowski Bridge, Warsaw.......... 3·00   2·20
4328   3z. Bridge, Maurzyce .... 5·50   4·25

4329   3z. Ernest Malinowski Bridge, Toruń.............. 5·50   4·25
4326/4329 Set of 4 .... 15·00   11·50
    Nos. 4326/9 were issued in horizontal se-tenant strips of four stamps within the sheet.

1406 Prosper Prowana   **1407** Wladyslaw Raczkiewicz

(Des Maciej Jędrysik. Eng Przemyslaw Krajewski (Prosper Prowana), Maciej Kopecki (Zygmunt August) or Wanda Zajdel (Sebastian Montelupi). Recess and photo)

2008 (15 Sept). 450th Anniv of Polish Postal Service (1st issue). Sheet 120×80 mm containing T **1406** and similar multicoloured designs. P 11½.
MS4330 1z.45×3, Type **1406**; King Zygmunt August (51×31 mm); Sebastian Montelupi .... 8·75   8·50
The stamps and margins of No. **MS**4330 form a composite design. See also No. **MS**4352.

(Des Agnieszka Sobczyńska. Litho)

2008 (24 Sept). Presidents of Government in Exile. Sheet 129×125 mm containing T **1407** and similar horiz designs. Multicoloured. P 11½ (with one elliptical hole on each horiz side).
MS4331 1z.45×6, Type **1407**; Edward Raczyński; August Zaleski; Kazimierz Sabbat; Stanislaw Ostrowski; Ryszard Kaczorowski .... 17·00   16·00
The central stamps of No. **MS**4331 form a composite design.

1408 Sports Men and Women   **1409** Native American, Settler and Map

(Des Marzanna Dąbrowska. Photo)

2008 (30 Sept). Centenary of Lódz Sports Club. P 11½.
4332 **1408** 1z.45 vermilion and silver .... 3·00   2·20

(Des Agnieszka Sobczynska. Litho)

2008 (30 Sept). 400th Anniv of Polish Settlers in America. P 11½ (with one elliptical hole on each horiz side).
4333 **1409** 3z. multicoloured........................... 5·75   4·25

1410 Pigeon Post   **1411** Mieczyslaw Karlowicz

(Des Maciej Jędrysik. Litho)

2008 (9 Oct). World Post Day. P 11½ (with one elliptical hole on each horiz side).
4334 **1410** 2z.10 multicoloured .... 4·25   3·25

(Des Jerzy Skakun. Litho)

2008 (18 Oct). Composers. T **1411** and similar vert designs. Multicoloured. P 11½ (with one elliptical hole on each vert side).
4335   1z.45 Type **1411**.............................. 3·00   2·20
4336   1z.45 Wojciech Kilar .... 3·00   2·20
4337   1z.45 Henryk Mikolaj Górecki .... 3·00   2·20
4338   1z.45 Witold Lutoslawski .... 3·00   2·20
4335/4338 Set of 4 .... 11·00   8·00

1412 Rijksmuseum, Amsterdam

(Des Magdalena Blażków. Litho)

2008 (24 Oct). Capital Cities of European Union States. T **1412** and similar horiz designs. Multicoloured. P 11½ (with one elliptical perf on each horiz side).

4339	1z.45 Type **1412**	3·00	2·20
4340	1z.45 Royal Library, Copenhagen	3·00	2·20
4341	3z. Charles Bridge, Prague	5·75	4·25
4342	3z. Acropolis, Athens	5·75	4·25
4343	3z.65 Parliament, Vienna	7·00	5·25
4339/4343 Set of 5		22·00	16·00

1413 J. Przybora and J. Wasowski

(Des Agnieszka Sobczyńska)

2008 (30 Oct). 50th Anniv of *Kabaret Starszych Panów* (comedy series). P 11½ (with one elliptical hole on each vert side).
4344　**1413**　1z.45 multicoloured　3·00　2·20

1414 Maria Konopnicka　　　**1415** National Arms

(Des Joanna Górska)

2008 (7 Nov). Centenary of *Rota* (the Oath (poem)) by Maria Konopnicka. P 11½ (with one elliptical hole on each vert side).
4345　**1414**　3z.65 multicoloured　7·25　5·50
No. 4345 was printed in sheets of ten stamps and ten inscribed labels.

(Des Jerzy Pietras. Eng Maciej Kopecki. Recess)

2008 (11 Nov). Centenary of Independence Day. P 11½.
4346　**1415**　1z.45 deep carmine　3·00　2·20

1416 Stars　　　**1417** Pope John Paul II

(Des Jerzy Pietras)

2008 (27 Nov). Christmas. T **1416** and similar vert design. Multicoloured. P 11½.
4347　1z.45 Type **1416**　3·00　2·20
4348　3z. Stars (*different*)　5·75　4·25

(Des Marzanna Dąbrowska)

2008 (27 Nov). 30th Anniv of Election of Karol Wojtyla as Pope John Paul II. P 11½.
4349　**1417**　2z.40 multicoloured　4·50　3·50

1418 Zbigniew Herbert　　　**1419** Emblem

(Des Anna Niemierko)

2008 (1 Dec). Tenth Death Anniv of Zbigniew Herbert (writer). P 11½ (with one elliptical hole on each vert side).
4350　**1418**　2z.10 multicoloured　4·00　3·00

(Des Anna Niemierko)

2008 (1 Dec). United Nations Conference on Climate Change, Poznań. P 11½.
4351　**1419**　2z.40 multicoloured　4·50　3·50

1420 Postal Messenger

2008 (14 Dec). 450th Anniv of Polish Postal Service (2nd issue). Sheet 106×75 mm. Self-adhesive. Imperf.
MS4352　**1420**　20z. multicoloured　38·00　36·00
No. **MS**4352 was screen printed on silk.

1421 Louis Braille　　　**1422** Witold Pilecki (historian)

(Des Anna Niemierko. Litho)

2009 (4 Jan). Birth Bicentenary of Louis Braille (inventor of Braille writing for the blind). P 12×11½ (with one elliptical hole on each horiz side).
4353　**1421**　1z.45 multicoloured　3·00　2·30
No. 4353 was printed with a *se-tenant* stamp-size label with embossed Braille letters attached at right.

(Des Magdalena Blażków. Litho)

2009 (6 Feb–3 Apr). Camp Survivors. T **1422** and similar vert designs. Multicoloured. P 11½ (with one elliptical hole on each vert side).

4354	1z.45 Type **1422**	3·00	2·20
	a. Horiz strip of 4. Nos. 4354/7	41·00	
	b. Strip of 4. Nos. 4354, 4355a and 4356/7	18·00	
4355	2z.10 Wladyslaw Wolski	26·00	27·00
	a. Inscr "Jozef Wladyslaw Wolski" (3.4.09)	4·00	3·00
4356	2z.40 Ignacy Ludwik Jeż	4·50	3·50
4357	3z. Stanislawa Maria Sawicka	5·75	4·25
4354/4357 Set of 4		16·00	11·50

No. 4354/7 were printed, *se-tenant*, in horizontal strips of four stamps within sheets of 16.

1423 Heart in Four-leafed Clover   **1424** *Zwiastowanie*

(Des Magdalena Blażków. Litho)

2009 (6 Feb). St Valentine's Day. P 12×11½ (with one elliptical hole on each horiz side).
4358	**1423**	1z.45 multicoloured	3·00	2·20

(Des Malgorzata Osa. Litho)

2009 (6 Mar). Contemporary Polish Sculpture. Tenth Death Anniv of Wladyslaw Hasior. T **1424** and similar vert designs. Multicoloured. P 12 (with one elliptical hole on each vert side).
4359	1z.45 Type **1424**	3·00	2·20
4360	1z.45 *Mucha*	3·00	2·20
4361	2z.10 *Sztandar Zielonej Poetki*	4·00	3·00
4362	2z.40 *Sztandar Rozbieranie do snu*	4·50	3·50
4359/4362	*Set of 4*	13·00	9·75
MS4363	90×125 mm. Nos. 4359/62	14·50	14·00

1425 *Chrystus*   **1426** Fish
Zmartwychwstaly

(Des Magdalena Blażków. Litho)

2009 (1 Apr). Easter. Paintings by Szymon Czechowicz. T **1425** and similar multicoloured design. P 12.
4364	1z.55 Type **1425**	3·00	2·30
4365	3z. *Zlozenie do grobu* (*vert*)	6·00	4·50

(Des Ewa Mońko. Litho)

2009 (16 Apr). China 2009 International Stamp Exhibition, Luoyang. Sheet 90×70 mm. P 11½ (with one elliptical hole on each vert side).
MS4366	**1426**	3z. multicoloured	6·25	6·00

1427 *Berek Joselewicz* (Juliusz Kossak)

(Des Marzanna Dąbrowska. Litho)

2009 (22 Apr). Polish Year in Israel. Sheet 90×70 mm. P 11½ (with one elliptical hole on each horiz side).
MS4367	**1427**	3z. multicoloured	6·25	6·00

1428 Cheetahs

(Des Tomasz Gudzowaty)

2009 (30 Apr). African Animals. Sheet 124×90 mm containing T **1428** and similar horiz designs. Each black. P 11½ (with one elliptical hole on each horiz side).
MS4368	1z.55 Type **1428**; 1z.95 Zebras; 2z.40 Gnu and crocodile; 3z. Elephants	18·00	17·00

1429 Numbers as Starburst   **1430** Grażyna Bacewicz

(Des Agata Tobolczyk)

2009 (5 May). Europa. Astronomy. P 11½ (with one elliptical hole on each horiz side).
4369	**1429**	3z. deep turquoise-blue and new blue	6·00	4·50
		a. *Tête-bêche* (pair)	12·50	9·25

No. 4369 was printed, *tête-bêche*, in horizontal pairs within small sheets, each pair forming a composite design.

(Des Agata Tobolczyk)

2009 (28 May). Birth Centenary of Grażyna Bacewicz (composer and violinist). P 11½ (with one elliptical hole on each vert side).
4370	**1430**	1z.55 multicoloured	3·00	2·30
		a. *Tête-bêche* (pair)	6·25	4·75

1431 Tytus de Zoo   **1432** Lech Wałęsa (leader Trade Union Solidarnosc)

(Des Ewą Mońko)

2009 (29 May). 50th (2007) Anniv of *Tytus, Romek and A'Tomek* (comic created by Henryk Jerzy Chmielewski (Papcio Chmiel)). T **1431** and similar vert designs. Multicoloured. P 11½ (with one elliptical hole on each vert side).
4371	1z.55 Type **1431**	3·00	2·30
	a. Horiz strip of 3. Nos. 4371/4	9·25	
4372	1z.55 Romek	3·00	2·30
4373	1z.55 A'Tomek	3·00	2·30
4371/4373	*Set of 3*	8·00	6·25

Nos. 4371/3 were printed, *se-tenant*, in horizontal strips of three stamps within the sheet.

(Des Agnieszka Sobczyńska)

2009 (30 May). 20th Anniv of Opposition Electoral Success. Sheet 90×70 mm. P 11½ (with one elliptical hole on each vert side).
MS4374	**1432**	3z.75 multicoloured	7·75	7·50

1433 Saint Bruno

(Des Bożydar Grozdew)

2009 (19 June). Death Millennary of Saint Bruno of Querfurt (missionary and martyr). P 11½ (with one elliptical hole on each vert side).
4375 **1433** 3z. multicoloured .... 6·00 4·50

1434 *Dar Młodzieży* (frigate of Naval Academy of Gdynia, built,1982)

(Des Kazimierz Bulik. Eng Tomasz Notkowski. Recess and photo)

2009 (30 June). Tall Ships' Races–Gdynia 2009. Sheet 90×70 mm. P 11½ (with one elliptical hole on each vert side).
MS4376 **1434** 3z.75 multicoloured.................... 7·75 7·25

1435 *Phocoena phocoena* (Porpoise)

1436 Building on Fire

(Des Agata Tobolczyk)

2009 (31 July). Mammals of the Baltic Sea. T **1435** and similar vert designs. Multicoloured. P 11½ (with one elliptical hole on each vert side).
4377 1z.55 Type **1435**.................... 3·00 2·30
 a. Horiz strip of 4. Nos. 4377/80....... 14·50
4378 1z.55 *Halichoerus grypus* (Grey Seal)............... 3·00 2·30
4379 1z.95 *Phoca vitulina* (Harbour seal)............... 4·00 3·00
4380 1z.95 *Phoca hispida* (Ringed Seal)............... 4·00 3·00
4377/4380 *Set of 4* .... 12·50 9·50
Nos. 4377/80 were printed, *se-tenant*, in horizontal strips within the sheet, each strip forming a composite design.

(Des Pawel Myszka. Eng Przemyslaw Krajewski. Recess and photo)

2009 (1 Aug). 65th Anniv of Warsaw Uprising against German Occupation. Sheet 90×70 mm. P 11½ (with one elliptical hole on each vert side).
MS4381 **1436** 3z.75 black and rosine................... 7·75 7·50

1437 *Cerasus avium* (*Prunus avium*) (Cherry)

1438 Jan Czochralski (specialist in metallurgy and inventor of Czochralski process)

(Des Marzanna Dąbrowska)

2009 (10 Aug). Fruit and Flowers. T **1437** and similar horiz design. Multicoloured. P 11½.
4382 1z.95 Type **1437**.................... 4·00 3·00
4383 3z.75 *Calendula officinalis* (Pot Marigold)......... 7·50 5·75

(Des Ewa Szydlowska)

2009 (28 Aug). Poles in Exile. T **1438** and similar vert designs. Multicoloured. P 11½ (with one elliptical hole on each vert side).
4384 1z.55 Type **1438**.................... 3·00 2·30

4385 1z.55 Antoni Norbert Patek (watchmaker)....... 3·00 2·30
4386 1z.95 Ludwik Hirszfeld (microbiologist and serologist)................... 4·00 3·00
4387 1z.95 Marian Rejewski, Henryk Zygalski and Jerzy Różycki (mathematicians and cryptologists who created replica of Enigma, German encrypting machine).. 4·00 3·00
4384/4387 *Set of 4* .... 12·50 9·50

1439 Juliusz Slowacki

1440 Attack on Węgierska Górka (village in zywiec County which held out for three days)

(Des Marzanna Dąbrowska)

2009 (31 Aug). Birth Bicentenary of Juliusz Slowacki (poet, playwright and philosopher). P 11½.
4388 **1439** 1z.55 multicoloured................... 3·00 2·30

(Des Jacek Dąbrowski)

2009 (1 Sept). Defensive War 1939. T **1440** and similar horiz design. Each black and scarlet-vermilion. P 11½.
4389 1z.55 Type **1440**................... 3·00 2·30
4390 2z.40 Wieluń (first town to come under attack)................... 4·75 3·75

1441 Ball and Hoop

1442 Tadeusz Mazowiecki (first premier)

(Des Kazimierz Bulik)

2009 (7 Sept). EuroBasket 2009–European Men's Basketball Championship, Poland. P 11½ (with one elliptical hole on each vert side).
4391 **1441** 3z. multicoloured................... 6·00 4·50

(Des Agnieszka Sobczyńska)

2009 (11 Sept). 20th Anniv of First Non-Communist Government following Elections in June, 1989. P 11½ (with one elliptical hole on each horiz side).
4392 **1442** 1z.55 multicoloured................... 3·00 2·30

1443 Player in Motion

1444 Envelope as Kite

(Des L. Walendziuk)

2009 (25 Sept). Women's European Volleyball Championship–2009, Poland. P 11½ (with one elliptical hole on each horiz side).
4393 **1443** 3z. multicoloured................... 6·00 4·50

(Des Magdalena Błażków. Litho)

2009 (6 Oct). Capital Cities of European Union States. Horiz designs as T **1412**. Multicoloured. P 11½ (with one elliptical perf on each horiz side).
4394 1z.55 Castle, Bratislava................... 3·00 2·30
4395 1z.55 Famagusta Gate, Nicosia................... 3·00 2·30
4396 3z. Town Hall, Brussels................... 6·00 4·50

4397	3z. Courtyard, Warsaw		6·00	4·50
4398	3z.75 National Museum, Helsinki		7·50	5·75
4394/4398 *Set of 5*			23·00	17·00

(Des B. Grozdew. Eng P. Krajewski. Recess and litho)

2009 (9 Oct). World Post Day. P 11½.

4399	**1444**	3z. multicoloured	6·00	4·50

1445 Jerzy Popieluszko   **1446** Volunteer

(Des M. Dąbrowska)

2009 (19 Oct). 25th Death Anniv of Jerzy Popieluszko (priest and solidarity martyr). P 11½ (with one elliptical perf on each horiz side).

4400	**1445**	1z.55 multicoloured	3·00	2·30

(Des E. Szydlowska)

2009 (24 Oct). Centenary of Voluntary Tatra Mountains Rescue Service. P 11½ (with one elliptical perf on each vert side).

4401	**1446**	1z.55 multicoloured	3·00	2·30

1447 Pawel Jasienica   **1448** Jerzy Franciszek Kulczycki

(Des E. Mońko)

2009 (10 Nov). Birth Centenary of Leon Lech Beynar (Pawel Jasienica) (writer and historian). P 11½.

4402	**1447**	1z.55 multicoloured	3·00	2·30

(Des K. Bulik)

2009 (16 Nov). Polish Influence in Europe. Jerzy Franciszek Kulczycki (hero of Battle of Vienna and opened first coffee house in Vienna) Commemoration. P 11½ (with one elliptical perf on each vert side).

4403	**1448**	1z.55 multicoloured	3·25	2·50

No. 4403 was printed in sheets of eight stamps and eight labels, the whole forming a composite design.

1449 Bookplate *Exlibris Willibald Pirkheimer* (Albrecht Dürer)   **1450** Choir

(Des K. Bulik)

2009 (20 Nov). Lost Treasures. Art. T **1449** and similar vert designs. Multicoloured. P 11½.

4404	1z.55 Type **1449**	3·00	2·30
	a. Strip of 3. Nos. 4404/6	9·25	
4405	1z.55 *Christ falls beneath the Cross* (Peter Paul Rubens)	3·00	2·30
4406	1z.55 *Joseph recounts his Dream* (Rembrandt)	3·00	2·30
4404/4406 *Set of 3*		8·00	6·25

Nos. 4404/6 were printed, *se-tenant*, in horizontal strips of three stamps within the sheet.

(Des E. Szydlowska)

2009 (27 Dec). Christmas. T **1450** and similar vert design. Multicoloured. P 11½.

4407	1z.55 Type **1450**	3·00	2·30
4408	2z.40 Holy Family	4·50	3·50

1451 Letter from Kalwaria to Warsaw, franked with 1860 10k. Stamp (As Type **1**)   **1452** Skiers

(Des Maciej Jędrysik)

2010 (15 Jan). 150th Anniv of Polish Stamps. Sheet 90×70 mm. P 11½ (with one elliptical hole on each vert side).

MS4409	**1451**	4z.15 multicoloured	8·00	7·75

(Des Jacek Brodowski)

2010 (27 Jan). Winter Olympic Games, Vancouver. P 11½ (with one elliptical hole on each horiz side).

4410	**1452**	3z. multicoloured	6·00	4·50

1453 British Shorthair   **1454** Frédéric Chopin

(Des Andrzej Gosik)

2010 (17 Feb). Cats. Sheet 122×125 mm containing T **1453** and similar vert designs. Multicoloured. P 11½ (with one elliptical hole on each vert side).

MS4411	1z.55 Type **1453**; 1z.55 Siamese; 1z.95 Somali; 1z.95 Maine Coon; 3z. Persian; 3z. Tortoiseshell and white exotic	26·00	25·00

(Des Marzanna Dąbrowska)

2010 (22 Feb). Birth Bicentenary of Frédéric Chopin (composer). Sheet 90×70 mm. P 11½ (with one elliptical hole on each horiz side).

MS4412	**1454**	4z.15 multicoloured	8·00	7·75
MS4412*a*	4z.15 As Type **1454**. Imperf		36·00	35·00

1455 Lamb   **1456** Warsaw, 1920

(Des Jerzy Pietras)

2010 (5 Mar). Easter. T **1455** and similar vert design. Multicoloured. P 11½.

4413	1z.55 Type **1455**	3·25	2·50
4414	2z.40 Basket of eggs	4·25	3·50

(Des Jacek Konarzewski)

2010 (31 Mar). History of Polish Photography. Jan Bulhak Commemoration. T **1456** and similar vert designs showing photographs. Multicoloured. P 11½ (with one elliptical hole on each vert side).

4415	1z.95 Type **1456**.....................	3·75	3·00
	a. Strip of 4. Nos. 4415/18	16·00	
4416	1z.95 Doorway, Kraków, 1921..................	3·75	3·00
4417	1z.95 Old Town Hall, Warsaw, 1920..................	3·75	3·00
4418	1z.95 Kasimir side altar, Vilnius Cathedral, 1912.................	3·75	3·00
4415/4418 *Set of 4*		13·50	11·00

Nos. 4415/18 were printed, *se-tenant*, in strips of four stamps within the sheet.

1457 Anniversary Emblem

(Des Jerzy Pietras)

2010 (6 Apr). 20th Anniv of Special Services. P 11½ (with one elliptical hole on each vert side).

4419 **1457** 1z.55 scarlet-vermilion, indigo and silver   3·25   2·50

1458 Cross of Polish Badges   **1459** Tower of Belém, Lisbon

(Des Marzanna Dąbrowska)

2010 (7 Apr). 60th Anniv of Katyń Massacre. Sheet 70×90 mm. P 11½ (with one elliptical hole on each horiz side).

MS4420 **1458** 3z. multicoloured .... 6·50   6·25

(Des Jacek Konarzewski)

2010 (30 Apr). Portugal 2010 International Stamp Exhibition, Lisbon. Sheet 90×70 mm. P 11½ (with one elliptical hole on each vert side).

MS4421 **1459** 3z. multicoloured .... 6·50   6·25

1460 Boy reading   **1461** Pope John Paul II and Church of Peter the Apostle, Wadowice

(Des Maciej Jędrysik)

2010 (5 May). Europa. Children's Books. P 11½ (with one elliptical hole on each vert side).

4422 **1460** 3z. multicoloured .... 6·25   5·00

(Des Janusz Wysocki)

2010 (18 May). Pope John Paul II (Karol Józef Wojtyla) Commemoration. P 11½ (with one elliptical hole on each horiz side).

4423 **1461** 1z.95 multicoloured .... 4·25   3·50

No. 4423 was printed, *se-tenant*, with a stamp-size label showing Church of the Presentation of the Virgin, Wadowice (site of baptism of Karol Wojtyla) and Karol Wojtyla as a cardinal.

1462 Bridge over the Vistula   **1463** Jerzy Popieluszko

(Des Andrzej Gosik)

2010 (27 May). 750th Anniv of Tczew. P 11½.

4424 **1462** 1z.55 multicoloured .... 3·25   2·50

(Des Jacek Konarzewski)

2010 (6 June). Beatification of Jerzy Popieluszko (priest and solidarity martyr). P 11½ (with one elliptical perf on each horiz side).

4425 **1463** 1z.95 multicoloured .... 4·00   3·25

1464 Convent and Statue of Christ   **1466** Scouts signalling Semaphore Message, "STO LAT" (100 YEARS)

1465 Battle Scene (Jan Matejko)

(Des Jacek Brodowski)

2010 (24 June). 750th Anniv of Dominican Ursuline Sisters Convent, Sieradtz. P 11½.

4426 **1464** 1z.55 multicoloured .... 3·25   2·50

(Des Marzanna Dąbrowska)

2010 (15 July). 600th Anniv of Battle of Grunvald (First Battle of Tannenberg), during the Polish–Lithuanian–Teutonic War. Sheet 116×82 mm. P 11½.

MS4427 **1465** 8z.30 multicoloured .... 18·00   17·00

(Des Malgorzata Osa)

2010 (17 July). Centenary of Polish Scouts' Association. P 11½.

4428 **1466** 1z.95 multicoloured .... 4·00   3·25

1467 Forget-me-Not   **1468** Lech Walęsa

(Des Marzanna Dąbrowska)

2010 (10 Aug). Flowers. P 11½.

4429 **1467** 4z.15 multicoloured .... 8·50   6·75

(Des Agnieszka Sobczyńska)

2010 (31 Aug). 30th Anniv of NSZZ "Solidarność" (Solidarity). P 11½ (with one elliptical perf on each horiz side).
4430 **1468** 3z.75 black, silver and red .... 7·75 6·25

1469 Sphalerite

1469a Tower of Postmen

(Des Anna Niemierko)

2010 (3 Sept). Minerals. T **1469** and similar horiz designs. Multicoloured. P 11½ (with one elliptical perf on each horiz side).
4431 1z.55 Type **1469**... 3·25 2·50
  a. Strip of 4. Nos. 4431/4............................. 20·00
4432 1z.95 Gypsum... 4·00 3·25
4433 2z.40 Agate.. 5·00 4·00
4434 3z. Chrysoprase... 6·25 5·00
4431/4434 *Set of 4* .... 17·00 13·50
Nos. 4431/4 were printed, *se-tenant*, in strips of four stamps within the sheet.

(Des Maciej Jędrysik)

2010 (9 Oct). World Post Day. P 11½.
4435 **1469a** 2z.95 multicoloured.............................. 4·00 3·25
  a. *Tête-bêche* (pair).............................. 8·25 6·75

1470 Sofia

1471 'A' and Floral Motif

(Des Magdalena Blażków. Litho)

2010 (24 Oct). Capital Cities of European Union States. T **1470** and similar horiz design. Multicoloured. P 11½ (with one elliptical perf on each horiz side).
4436 1z.95 Type **1470**... 4·00 3·25
4437 3z. Bucharest.. 6·25 5·00

2010 (29 Oct). Personal Stamp. P 11½ (with one elliptical hole on each vert side).
4438 **1471** A (1z.55) multicoloured............................. 15·00 14·00
No. 4438 was printed, *se-tenant*, with a stamp-sized label which could be personalised by the addition of a photograph or logo.

1472 Players

1473 Ignacy Paderewski

(Des Janusz Wysocki)

2010 (9 Oct). Centenary of Widzew Lódź Football Club. P 11½.
4439 **1472** 1z.55 multicoloured................................. 3·25 2·50

(Des Marzanna Dąbrowska)

2010 (22 Nov). 150th Birth Anniv of Ignacy Jan Paderewski (composer and Prime Minister (1919)). P 11½ (with one elliptical perf on each vert side).
4440 **1473** 3z. multicoloured.................................... 6·75 5·50

1474 Shooting Star, Trail and Christmas Tree

1475 "Kocham Cię"

2010 (27 Nov). Christmas. T **1474** and similar horiz design. Multicoloured. P 11½.
4441 1z.55 Type **1474**... 3·25 2·50
4442 2z.40 Shooting star, trail and night sky .... 5·00 4·00

(Des Jan Konarzewski)

2010 (30 Dec). Greetings Stamp. P 11½.
4443 **1475** A (1z.55) multicoloured.............................. 3·25 2·50

1476 Jan Heweliusz

(Des Maciej Jędrysik. Litho)

2011 (28 Jan). 400th Birth Anniv of Johannes Hevelius (Jan Heweliusz) (brewer and astronomer). P 11½ (with one elliptical hole on each horiz side).
4444 **1476** 3z. multicoloured.................................... 7·50 6·00
No. 4444 was issued in sheets of six stamps and six *se-tenant* labels.

1477 Players

(Des Jacek Brodowski. Litho)

2011 (4 Feb). Men's World Indoor Hockey Championship, Poznań. P 11½ (with one elliptical hole on each horiz side).
4445 **1477** 2z.40 multicoloured................................. 5·00 4·00

1478 20', EU Stars and Group Colours on Hands

(Des Barnabas Baticz. Litho)

2011 (11 Feb). 20th Anniv of Viségrad Group (cultural, education, science and exchange of information). P 12.
4446 **1478** 3z. multicoloured.................................... 6·75 5·50
Stamps of a similar design were also issued by Czech Republic, Hungary and Slovakia.

1478a Students Demonstrating

(Des Agnieszka Sobczyńska. Litho)

2011 (17 Feb). 30th Anniv of Lódz Independent Students' Association. P 11½ (with one elliptical hole on each horiz side).
4446*a* **1478a** 1z. 95 multicoloured................................. 4·00 3·25

1479 Child's Face and Tree   **1480** Stefan Kisielewski

(Des Jacek Konarzewski. Photo)

2011 (28 Feb). Cystic Fibrosis Awareness Week. P 11½×11.
4447   **1479**   1z.55 multicoloured..................................   3·50   2·75

(Des Ewa Libera. Litho)

2011 (7 Mar). Birth Centenary of Stefan Kisielewski (writer, composer, music critic and co-founder and member of the Union of Real Politics). P 11½ (with one elliptical hole on each horiz side).
4448   **1480**   1z.95 multicoloured....................   4·00   3·25
             a. Tête-bêche (pair)..............................   8·25   6·75
No. 4448 was issued in sheets of 12 stamps.
The elliptical perforation can be on either the left or the right-hand of the horizontal.

1481 Chick and Flowers   **1482** Cardinal Kozlowiecki

(Des Jan Konarzewski. Photo)

2011 (25 Mar). Easter. T **1481** and similar vert design. Multicoloured. P 11½.
4449   1z.55 Type **1481**........................   3·50   2·75
4450   2z.40 Rabbit and flowers........................   5·00   4·00

(Des Maciej Jędrysik)

2011 (31 Mar). Birth Centenary of Cardinal Adam Kozlowiecki. P 11×11½.
4451   **1482**   1z.95 multicoloured....................   4·00   3·25

1483 Boy (Burma)

(Des Marzanna Dąbrowska)

2011 (18 Apr). Smile of the World (photographs by Elżbeita Dzikowska). Sheet 120×127 mm containing T **1483** and similar vert designs. Multicoloured. P 11½ (with one elliptical hole on each vert side).
MS4452 1z.95 Type **1483**; 1z.95 African girl with plaited hair (Ethiopia); 2z.40 Girl with flowers in hair (Burma); 2z.40 Arab man with camel (Palestinian man); 3z. Indian girl (Nepal); 3z. Woman wearing hat (Peru)........   33·00   32·00

1484 Pope John Paul II

(Des Marzanna Dąbrowska. Litho)

2011 (28 Apr). Beatification of Pope John Paul II. Sheet 75×100 mm. P 11½×11 (with one elliptical hole on each horiz side).
MS4453   **1484**   8z.30 multicoloured..................................   19·00   18·00
Stamps of a similar design were issued by Vatican City.

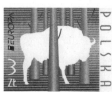

1485 Bison amongst Trees   **1486** Gucio

(Des Anna Niemierko)

2011 (5 May). Europa. Forests. P 12×11½ (with one elliptical hole on each horiz side).
4454   **1485**   3z. multicoloured
                     ....   6·75   5·50

(Des Bohdan Butenko)

2011 (27 May). Cartoon Characters created by Bohdan Butenko. T **1486** and similar vert designs. Multicoloured. P 11½×12 (with one elliptical hole on each vert side).
4455   1z.55 Type **1486**........................   3·50   2·75
             a. Strip of 4. Nos. 4455/8........   18·00
4456   1z.55 Cezar..   3·50   2·75
4457   2z.40 Kwapiszon..............................   5·00   4·00
4458   2z.40 Gapiszon................................   5·00   4·00
4455/4458 Set of 4..................................   15·00   12·00
Nos. 4455/8 were printed, se-tenant, in horizontal strips of four stamps within the sheet.

1487 Arrows as Figures and Flag

(Des Anna Niemierko)

2011 (30 June). Polish Presidency of EU Council. P 12×11½ (with one elliptical hole on each horiz side).
4459   **1487**   3z. multicoloured..................................   7·00   5·75
No. 4459 was printed, se-tenant, with a stamp-size label showing stylised figure and stars.

(Des Marzanna Dąbrowska. Eng Przemyslaw Krajewski. Recess and photo)

2011 (30 June). Birth Centenary of Czeslawa Milosz (poet and writer). Sheet 70×90 mm.
MS4460   **1488**   4z.15 black and bright rose-carmine   9·50   9·00

1489 Maximilian (Maksymilian) Maria Kolbe   **1490** Michal Sędziwój (alchemist, philosopher, and medical doctor)

(Des Maciej Jędrysik)

2011 (12 Aug). 60th Death Anniv of Saint Maximilian (Maksymilian) Maria Kolbe (Franciscan friar, who volunteered to die in place of a stranger in Auschwitz concentration camp). P 11½×12 (with one elliptical hole on each vert side).
4461   **1489**   1z.95 multicoloured....................   4·00   3·25

(Des Janusz Wysocki)

2011 (29 Aug). Personalities. T **1490** and similar horiz designs. Multicoloured. P 12×11½ (with one elliptical hole on each horiz side).

4462	1z.55 Type **1490**.	3·50	2·75
4463	1z.95 Jan Szczepanik (inventor)	3·50	2·75
4464	3z. Jan Józef Baranowski (astronomer)	6·75	5·50
4465	3z. Rudolf Stefan Weigl (biologist and inventor of first vacine against epidemic typhus)	6·75	5·50
4462/4465 *Set of 4*		18·00	15·00

1491 Jan Dzierżon   **1492** Saint Mary's Church, Niegowic (Karol Józef Wojtyla's first parish)

(Des Jacek Konarzewski)

2011 (2 Sept). Birth Bicentenary of Johan (Jan) Dzierżon (pioneering apiarist discoverer of parthenogenesis in bees and designer of first successful movable-frame beehive). P 11½×12 (with one elliptical hole on each vert side).

4466	**1491** 1z.55 multicoloured	3·50	2·75

(Des Janusz Wysocki)

2011 (22 Sept). Pope John Paul II (Karol Józef Wojtyla) Commemoration. P 12×11½ (with one elliptical hole on each horiz side).

4467	**1492** 1z.95 multicoloured	4·50	4·00

No. 4467 was printed, *se-tenant*, with a stamp-size label showing Karol Wojtyla as parish priest with children.

1493 Town Hall and Church, St. Barbar, Polkowice

(Des Malgorzata Osa)

2011 (30 Sept). Polski Związek Felinologiczny (PZF) (cat lovers and breeders association) Congress, Polkowice. Sheet 70×90 mm. P 11½×12 (with one elliptical hole on each vert side).

MS4468	**1493** 4z.15 multicoloured	9·50	9·00

1494 *Double Portrait of Eliza Pareńska* (Stanislaw Wyspiański)

(Des Jacek Konarzewski. Photo)

2011 (21 Oct). Lost Works of Art. T **1494** and similar horiz designs. Multicoloured. P 11½.

4469	1z.95 Type **1494**	4·25	3·50
	a. Strip of 3. Nos. 4469/71	18·00	
4470	2z.40 Scene from the legend of Theophilus of Adana (late 15th century wooden carving) (Wit Stwosz)	5·50	4·50
4471	3z. *Woman standing* (Jean-Antoine Watteau)	6·75	5·50
4469/4471 *Set of 3*		15·00	12·00

Nos. 4469/71 were printed, *se-tenant*, in horizontal strips of three stamps within sheets of six.

1495 Satellite

(Des Jacek Brodowski)

2011 (4 Nov). First Polish Scientific Satellite. Sheet 90×70 mm. P 12×11½ (with one elliptical perf on each horiz side).

MS4472	**1495** 4z.15 multicoloured	9·50	9·25

1496 Nobel Medal

(Des Marzanna Dąbrowska. Eng Piotr Naszarkowski. Recess and litho)

2011 (17 Nov). Centenary of Marie Sklodowska Curie's Nobel Prize for Chemistry. Sheet 84×125 mm containing T **1496** and similar multicoloured design. P 13.

MS4473	3z. Type **1496**; 7z.80 Marie Curie (40×55 mm)	24·00	23·00

A stamp of a similar design was issued by Sweden.

1497 Santa Claus

(Des Marek Kwiatkowski)

2011 (25 Nov). Christmas. T **1497** and similar horiz design. Multicoloured. P 11½.

(a) Ordinary gum. P 11½×12

4474	1z.55 Type **1497**	3·50	2·75

(b) Self-adhesive. Die-cut perf 12

4475	2z.40 Holy Family	5·50	4·50

1498 School Building

(Des Maciej Jędrysik)

2011 (2 Dec). 30th Anniv of Strike at Higher Military Fire Service School in Warsaw. Sheet 70×90 mm. P 11½×12 (with one elliptical perf on each vert side).

MS4476	**1498** 4z.15 multicoloured	9·50	9·25

1499 Cloth as Map of Kazakhstan

(Des Aleksandra Ubukata)

2011 (8 Dec). 20th Anniv of Independence of Kazakhstan. P 11½.

4477	**1499** 2z.40 multicoloured	5·50	4·50

1500 *Rubus idaeus* (Raspberry)

1501 Heart as Globe

(Des Marzanna Dąbrowska)

2011 (16 Dec). Flowers and Fruit. P 11½×12.
4478 **1500** 1z.55 multicoloured .... 3·50 2·75

(Des Jerzy Owsiak, Magdalena Jablońska, Katarzyna Sasin and Krystiana Konieczna)

2012 (8 Jan). 20th Finale of Orchestra of Holy Day Assistance (fund raising charity). Sheet 70×90 mm. P 11½ (with one elliptical perf on each horiz side).
MS4479 **1501** 1z.95 multicoloured .... 4·25 4·00

1502 Arms

1503 Zygmunt Krasiński

(Des Marzanna Dąbrowska)

2012 (14 Feb). 70th Anniv of National Army. P 12×11½.
4480 **1502** 1z.55 multicoloured .... 3·50 2·75

(Des Agata Tobolczyk)

2012 (19 Feb). Birth Bicentenary of Count Napoleon Stanislaw Adam Ludwig Zygmunt Krasiński (writer). Sheet 90×70 mm. P 11½×12 (with one elliptical perf on each vert side).
MS4481 **1503** 4z.15 multicoloured .... 9·50 9·25

1504 Lamb and Flowers

1505 Leopold Kronenberg

(Des Agata Tobolczyk)

2012 (9 Mar). Easter. T **1504** and similar vert designs. Multicoloured. P 12×11½.
4482 1z.55 Type **1504** .... 3·50 2·75
4483 1z.95 Egg and flowers .... 4·25 3·50
4484 3z. Rabbit and flowers .... 6·75 5·50
4482/4484 *Set of 3* .... 13·00 10·50

(Des Bożydar Grozdew)

2012 (20 Mar). Birth Bicentenary of Baron Leopold Julian Kronenberg (banker). P 11½.
4485 **1505** 2z.40 black and gold .... 5·50 4·50

1506 Vienna Station, Warsaw, 1890

(Des Bożydar Grozdew)

2012 (28 Mar). History of Polish Photography. Konrad Brandel Commemoration. T **1506** and similar horiz designs showing photographs. Multicoloured. P 12×11½ (with one elliptical perf on each horiz side).
4486 1z.95 Type **1506** .... 4·25 3·50
    a. Strip of 4. Nos. 4486/9 .... 21·00
4487 1z.95 Krakowskie Przedmieście, 1880 .... 4·25 3·50
4488 2z.40 Three Crosses Square, 1875 .... 5·50 4·50
4489 2z.40 Pancera Viaduct, 1890 .... 5·50 4·50
4486/4489 *Set of 4* .... 18·00 14·50
Nos. 4486/9 were printed, *se-tenant*, in strips of four stamps within the sheet.

1507 Municipal Offices

1508 Ushebti (Funerary figurine), 4th century BC

(Des Bożydar Grozdew)

2012 (30 Mar). 300th Anniv of Suwalki City. P 11½.
4490 **1507** 1z.95 multicoloured .... 4·25 3·50

(Des Marzanna Dąbrowska)

2012 (30 Apr). 150th Anniv of First Polish Discoveries in Egypt. Sheet 95×130 mm containing T **1508** and similar vert designs. Multicoloured. P 11½.
MS4491 1z.55 Type **1508**; 1z.95 Blue Ushebti (Funerary figurine) 6th-7th century BC; 2z.40 Amulet figurine depicting Nefertum; 3z. Michal Tyszkiewicz (Egyptologist) .... 20·00 19·00

1509 *Maskerada* (Tadeusz Makowski)

(Des Piotr Stefankiewicz)

2012 (17 May). 150th Anniv of National Museum, Warsaw. Sheet 110×78 mm. P 11½.
MS4492 **1509** 4z.15 multicoloured .... 9·50 9·25

1510 Signposts showing Attractions

1511 Lips (poster for ARTISAN DE L' AFICHE, Musée des Arts Décoratifs at the Louvre, Paris)

(Des Bożydar Grozdew)

2012 (22 May). Europa. Visit Poland. P 11½ (with one elliptical perf on vert side).
4493 **1510** 3z. multicoloured .... 6·75 5·50

2012 (25 May). Art Work (photography) by Michal Batory. T **1511** and similar multicoloured design. P 11½ (with one elliptical perf on each vert side (4494) or horiz side (4495)).
4494 1z.95 Type **1511** .... 4·25 3·50
4495 3z. Fingers (sepia) (*horiz*) .... 6·75 5·50

1512 *Zajączek Parauszek*

(Des Piotr Stefankiewicz)

2012 (27 May). Cartoon Characters created by Wojciech Próchniewicz, Anthony Bankowski and Luc Toutounghi. Sheet 90×70 mm. P 11½ (with one elliptical perf on each horiz side).
MS4496 **1512** 4z.15 multicoloured...................... 9·50   9·25

1513 Municipal Stadium, Poznań

(Des Bożydar Grozdew)

2012 (8–15 June). Euro 2012, European Football Championships. T **1513** and similar multicoloured designs. P 11½ (4501) or 11½ (others) (with one elliptical perf on each horiz side.
4497	1z.55 Type **1513**.	3·25	2·50
4498	1z.95 National Stadium, Warsaw	4·25	3·50
4499	2z.40 PGE Area, Gdańsk	5·50	4·50
4500	3z. Municipal Stadium, Wroclaw	6·75	5·50
4501	3z. Football (39×39 mm (circular))		
	(15 June)	6·75	5·50
4497/4501	Set of 5	24·00	19·00
MS4502	125×90 mm. Nos. 4497/4500	20·00	19·00

No. 4501 is perforated in a circle around the design, enclosed in an outer perforated square.

1514 Parkland

(Des Marzanna Dąbrowska)

2012 (12 July). World Heritage Site. Muskauer Park. P 11½ (with one elliptical perf on each horiz side).
4503   **1514**   3z. multicoloured...................... 6·75   5·50
A stamp of a similar design was issued by Germany.

1515 Sculls   **1516** Józef Kraszewski

(Des Agata Tobolczyk)

2012 (27 July). Olympic Games, London. Sheet 199×116 mm containing T **1515** and similar horiz designs. Multicoloured. P 12×11½ (with one elliptical perf on each horiz side).
MS4504 1z.55 Type **1515**; 1z.95 Handball; 2z.40 Weightlifting; 3z. Shot put...................... 20·00   19·00

(Des Kazimierz Bulik)

2012 (28 July). Birth Bicentenary of Józef Ignacy Kraszewski (writer, historian and journalist). P 12×11½.
4505   **1516**   4z.15 multicoloured...................... 9·25   7·50
No. 4505 was printed se-tenant with a stamp-size label at right.

1517 *Russula virescens*

(Des Marzanna Dąbrowska)

2012 (3 Aug). Fungi. Sheet 125×152 mm containing T **1517** and similar horiz designs. Multicoloured. P 12×11½ (with one elliptical perf on each horiz side).
MS4506 1z.55 Type **1517**; 1z.95 Morchella esculenta; 3z. Macrolepiota procea; 4z.15 Amillaria ostoyae........ 24·00   23·00
No. **MS**4506 also contains four stamp-size labels showing poisonous fungi.

1518 Exhibition Name   **1519** Piotr Skarga
and National Flags of
Poland and Germany

(Des Bożydar Grozdew)

2012 (6 Sept). Kargowa 2012 Bilateral Polish and German Philatelic Exhibiton. P 11½×12 (with one elliptical perf on each vert side).
4507   **1518**   2z.40 multicoloured...................... 5·25   4·25

(Des Kazimierz Bulik. Photo)

2012 (27 Sept). 400th Death Anniv of Piotr Skarga (Jesuit, preacher, hagiographer, polemicist and leading figure of the Counter-reformation in the Polish-Lithuanian Commonwealth). P 11½.
4508   **1519**   1z.55 multicoloured...................... 3·25   2·50

1520 *Bullfinches and*   **1521** Wawel Cathedral and Karol
Dandelion Seed Heads   Wojtyla

(Des Agata Tobolczyk. Photo)

2012 (10 Oct). Tenth Death Anniv of Piotr Kwit (artist). P 11½.
4509   **1520**   1z.55 multicoloured...................... 3·25   2·50

(Des Janusz Wysocki. Litho)

2012 (13 Oct). Pope John Paul II (Karol Józef Wojtyla) Commemoration. In Cracow. P 12×11½ (with one elliptical perf on each horiz side).
4510   **1521**   1z.95 multicoloured...................... 4·25   3·50
No. 4510 was printed, se-tenant, with a stamp size label showing Karol Wojtyla being created a Cardinal on 26 June 1967 by Pope Paul VI.

1522 Jadwiga Smosarska
(actor)

(Des Marzanna Dąbrowska. Litho)

2012 (31 Oct). Personalities of Theatre and Cinema. T **1522** and similar vert designs. Multicoloured. P 11½×12 (with one elliptical perf on each vert side).

4511	1z.55 Type **1522**	3·25	2·50
4512	1z.95 Aleksander Zabczyński (actor)	4·25	3·50
4513	3z. Eugeniusz Bodo (film director)	6·25	5·00
4511/4513	Set of 3	12·50	10·00

MS4514 121×82 mm. 1z.55 Type **1522**; 1z.95 Aleksander Zabczyński (actor); 3z. Eugeniusz Bodo (film director) ... 14·00 13·50

1523 Turczynek Villa, Milanówek

1524 Angels and Star

(Des Marzanna Dąbrowska. Litho)

2012 (31 Oct). Garden Cities in Poland. Sheet 90×70 mm. P 12×11½ (with one elliptical perf on each horiz side).
MS4515 **1523** 4z.15 multicoloured ... 8·75 8·50

(Des Agnieszka Sobczyńska. Photo)

2012 (30 Nov). Christmas. T **1524** and similar multicoloured design. P 11½.

4516	A (1z.55) Type **1524**	3·25	2·50
4517	2z.40 Angels with Christmas gifts (horiz)	5·25	4·25

1525 Jerzy Turowicz

1526 Emblem

(Des M. Ufnalewski. Litho)

2012 (10 Dec). Birth Centenary of Jerzy Turowicz (Catholic journalist and editor). P 12×11½ (with one elliptical perf on each horiz side).
4518 **1525** 1z.55 black and yellow ... 3·25 2·50

(Des Jerzy Owsiak, Magdalena Jablońska and Katarzyna Sasin. Litho)

2013 (13 Jan). 21st Finale of Orchestra of Holy Day Assistance (fund raising charity). Self-adhesive. Die-cut wavy edge.
4519 **1526** A (1z.60) multicoloured ... 3·50 2·75
No. 4519 was die-cut around in a circle enclosed in an outer square and printed in sheets of six stamps.

1527 'E'

1528 'P'

(Des Marzanna Dąbrowska. Photo)

2013 (8 Mar). Economic and Priority Stamps. Vert designs as **1527** (E stamps) or **1528** (P stamps). Multicoloured (blue). P 12×11½.

4520	a (1z.60) Type **1527**	3·50	2·75
4521	a (2z.35) Type **1528**	5·00	4·00
4522	b (3z.75) As Type **1527**	8·00	6·50
4523	b (5z.10) As Type **1528**	11·00	8·75
4520/4523	Set of 4	25·00	20·00

Nos. 4520/3 are for use on mail up to 350 grams. There are two delivery speeds, economic (E) and priority (P). Those stamps inscribed "a" are for domestic mail and those inscribed "b" are for international mail. Nos. 4520/3 each have a different geometric centre design.

(Des Marzanna Dąbrowska. Photo)

2013 (29 Mar). Economic and Priority Stamps. Vert designs as **1527** (E stamps) or **1528** (P stamps). Multicoloured (green). P 12×11½.
4524 a (3z.70) As Type **1527** ... 7·50 6·00

4525	a (4z.50) As Type **1528**	8·75	7·00
4526	b (4z.75) As Type **1527**	9·00	7·25
4527	b (7z.10) As Type **1528**	14·50	11·50
4524/4527	Set of 4	36·00	29·00

Nos. 4524/7 are for use on mail up to 1000 grams. There are two delivery speeds, economic (E) and priority (P). Those stamps inscribed "a" are for domestic mail and those inscribed "b" are for international mail.
Nos. 4524/7 each have a different geometric centre design.

1529 Alcedo atthis

1530 Wieclaw Chrzanowski

(Des Marzanna Dąbrowska. Litho)

2013 (12 Apr). Polish Birds. Kingfisher. Sheet 90×70 mm. P 11½ (with one elliptical perf on each vert side).
MS4528 **1529** 4z.55 multicoloured ... 9·25 9·00

(Des Marzanna Dąbrowska. Litho)

2013 (16 Apr). 90th Birth Anniv of Wieczlaw Chrzanowski (2012) (politician). P 11½ (with one elliptical perf on each horiz side).
4529 **1530** 3z.80 multicoloured ... 7·75 6·25

1531 Star

1532 Flag

(Des Marzanna Dąbrowska. Photo)

2013 (19 Apr). 70th Anniv of Warsaw Uprising (1st issue). P 11.
4530 **1531** 3z.80 multicoloured ... 7·75 6·25
See also No. **MS**4606.

(Des Jacek Konarzewski. Litho)

2013 (2 May). Flag Day of the Republic of Poland. P 11½ (with one elliptical perf on each vert side).
4531 **1532** 1z.60 multicoloured ... 3·50 2·75

1533 Peugeot Post Van

1534 Goofy, Minnie and Mickey

(Des Jacek Konarzewski. Litho)

2013 (6 May). Europa. Postal Transport. P 11½ (with one elliptical perf on each vert side).
4532 **1533** 4z.60 multicoloured ... 9·25 7·25

(Des Agnieszka Sancewicz)

2013 (1 June). Walt Disney Characters. Sheet 90×70 mm. P 11½ (with one elliptical perf on each horiz side).
MS4533 **1534** 4z.60 multicoloured ... 9·50 9·25
No. **MS**4533 is also known imperforate (price £9.50 unused, £9.25 used).

1535 Darlowo

1536 Boleslaw III
Krzywousty (Boleslaw III
Wrymouth), Prince of
Poland

(Des Jerzy Pietras. Litho)

2013 (14 June). Lighthouses. Sheet 90×125 mm containing T **1535** and similar vert designs. Multicoloured. P 11½×11.
MS4534 1z.60 Type **1535**; 2z.35 Jaroslawiec; 3z.75
Ustka; 3z.80 Czolpino .... 24·00 23·00

(Des Marzanna Dąbrowska. Photo)

2013 (20 June). Economic and Priority Stamps. Vert designs as **1527** (E stamps) or **1528** (P stamps). Multicoloured (red). P 12×11½.
4535   a (6z.30) As Type **1527** .... 13·00 10·50
4536   b (7z.30) As Type **1527** .... 15·00 12·00
4537   a (8z.80) As Type **1528** .... 18·00 14·50
4538   b (10z.90) As Type **1528** .... 22·00 18·00
4535/4538 *Set of 4* .... 60·00 50·00
Nos. 4535/8 are for use on mail up to 2000 grams. There are two delivery speeds, economic (E) and priority (P). Those stamps inscribed "a" are for domestic mail and those inscribed "b" are for international mail.
Nos. 4535/8 each have a different geometric centre design.

(Des U. Cancewicz. Eng M. Kopecki. Recess and photo)

2013 (28 June). 900th Anniv of Chronicles of Gallus Anonymus. Sheet 90×70 mm. P 11½.
MS4539 **1536** 8z.50 black and vermilion .... 18·00 17·00

1537 Kashubian Strawberry

(Des Marek Kwiatkowski. Photo)

2013 (18 July). Polish Regional Products - Kashubian Strawberry. P 11½.
4540   **1537** 4z.60 multicoloured .... 9·25 7·50

1538 Cyclist

1539 BRITE-PL *Heweliusz* Satellite

(Des Janusz Wysocki. Litho)

2013 (30 July). Polish Cycle Race - Tour de Pologne. T **1538** and similar circular design. Multicoloured. P 11½.
4541   1z.60 Type **1538** .... 3·00 2·40
          a. Pair. Nos. 4541/2 .... 13·00 10·50
4542   4z.60 Two cyclists .... 9·25 7·50
Nos. 4541/2 were printed, *se-tenant*, in horizontal pairs within sheets of four stamps. Each stamp was perforated in a circle contained in an outer perforated square. Each square has one elliptical perf on each vert side.

(Des Jan Konarzewski. Litho)

2013 (31 July). Poland's Second Scientific Satellite – BRITE-PL *Heweliusz* (named after Polish astronomer Hevelius). Sheet 90×70 mm. P 11½ (with one elliptical perf on each horiz side).
MS4543 **1539** 4z.55 multicoloured .... 9·50 9·25

1540 Guitar

(Des Jerzy Owsiak, Magdalena Jablońska, Katarzyna Sasin and G. Andrzejewski. Litho)

2013 (1 Aug). Woodstock Free Music Festival, Kostrzyn nad Odrą, Poland (Festiwal Przystanek Woodstock). Self-adhesive. Die-cut perf 11½.
4544   **1540** 2z.35 multicoloured .... 5·00 4·00
No. 4544 was printed on transparent plastic film.

1541 *Fryderyk Chopin* (Polish brig-rigged sailing ship)

(Des Jerzy Pietras. Eng P. Krajewski. Recess and photo)

2013 (3 Aug). Tall Ships' Races, Szczecin 2013. Sheet 90×70 mm. P 11.
MS4545 **1541** 8z.50 new blue and black .... 18·00 17·00

1542 Two General Dynamics (now Lockheed Martin) F-16 Fighting Falcons

(Des Jan Konarzewski. Litho)

2013 (14 Aug). Contemporary Polish Army Weapons. T **1542** and similar horiz designs. Multicoloured. P 11½ (with one elliptical perf on each vert side).
4546   1z.60 Type **1542** .... 3·25 2·50
          a. Vert strip of 3. Nos. 4546/8 .... 10·00
4547   1z.60 KTO Rosomak (Kolowy Transporter
          Opancerzony) wheeled armored vehicle .... 3·25 2·50
4548   1z.60 ORP *Kontradmiral Xawery Czernicki*
          (multitask logistical support ship) .... 3·25 2·50
4546/4548 *Set of 3* .... 8·75 6·75
Nos. 4546/8 were printed, *se-tenant*, in vertical strips of three, within sheets of six stamps.

1543 'E' and
Polymmatus senuargus

1544 'P' and *Gerris
paludum*

(Des Marzanna Dąbrowska. Photo)

2013 (16 Aug). Economic and Priority Stamps. Registered Mail. Insects. Vert designs as **1543** (E stamps) or **1544** (P stamps). Multicoloured (blue). P 12×11½.
4549   a (4z.20) Type **1543** .... 8·00 6·50
4550   b (5z.50) As Type **1543** but with *Rosalia alpina* 12·50 9·75
4551   a (7z.50) Type **1544** .... 14·00 11·00
4552   b (8z.30) As Type **1544** but with *Sympetrum
          faveclum* .... 19·00 15·00
4549/4552 *Set of 4* .... 48·00 38·00

Nos. 4549/52 are for use on mail up to 350 grams. There are two delivery speeds, economic (E) and priority (P). Those stamps inscribed "a" are for domestic mail and those inscribed "b" are for international mail.

Nos. 4549/52 each have a different insect incorporated in the design.

1545 Costumes from Bistriţa-Năsăud, Romania and Kraków, Poland

(Des Marzanna Dąbrowska. Litho)

2013 (11 Sept). 20th Anniv of Poland - Romania Friendship Treaty. Traditional Folk Costumes. Sheet 70×90 mm. P 11½ (with one elliptical perf on each vert side).
MS4553 **1545** 4z.60 multicoloured .... 10·50   10·00
A stamp of a similar design was issued by Romania.

1546 Halite

(Des Marek Kwiatkowski. Litho and varnish)

2013 (20 Sept). Polish Minerals. T **1546** and similar horiz designs. Multicoloured. P 11½ (with one elliptical perf on each vert side).
4554	1z.60 Type **1546**..............................	3·25	2·50
	a. Strip of 4. Nos. 4554/7	18·00	
4555	1z.60 Malachite and azurite	3·25	2·50
4556	2z.35 Marcasite	5·00	4·00
4557	2z.35 Gypsum	5·00	4·00
4554/4557	Set of 4	15·00	11·50

Nos. 4554/7 were printed, se-tenant, in vertical strips of four stamps within sheets of 12.

1547 Lech Wałęsa

1548 St. Mark's Church, Zagreb, Croatia

(Des Jacek Konarzewski. Litho)

2013 (29 Sept). 70th Birth Anniv of Lech Wałęsa. P 11½ (with one elliptical perf on each vert side).
4558   **1547** 3z.80 multicoloured .... 8·00   6·50

(Des Marzanna Dąbrowska. Photo)

2013 (30 Sept). Economic and Priority Stamps. Registered Mail. Insects. Vert designs as **1543** (E stamps) or **1544** (P stamps). Multicoloured (green). P 12×11½.
4559	a (5z.90) As Type **1543** but with Ladybird	12·50	9·75
4560	a (8z.30) As Type **1544** but with Grasshopper	14·00	11·00
4561	b (7z.20) As Type **1543** but with Peacock Butterfly..............................	14·50	11·50
4562	b (11z.) As Type **1544** but with Ant..................	19·00	15·00
4559/4562	Set of 4	55·00	43·00

Nos. 4559/62 are for use on mail up to 1000 grams. There are two delivery speeds, economic (E) and priority (P). Those stamps inscribed "a" are for domestic mail and those inscribed "b" are for international mail.

Nos. 4559/62 each have a different insect incorporated in the design.

(Des Magdalena Blażków. Litho)

2013 (11 Oct). Capital Cities of European Union States. P 11½ (with one elliptical perf on each horiz side).
4563   **1548** 4z.60 multicoloured .... 10·00   8·00

(Des Marzanna Dąbrowska. Photo)

2013 (18 Oct). Economic and Priority Stamps. Registered Mail. Insects. Vert designs as **1543** (E stamps) or **1544** (P stamps). Multicoloured (red). P 12×11½.
4564	a (8z.50) As Type **1543** but with Tiger Moth Butterfly	18·00	14·00
4565	b (9z.50) As Type **1543** but with Stag Beetle	20·00	16·00
4566	a (11z.) As Type **1544** but with Honey Bee	23·00	18·00
4567	b (13z.11) As Type **1544** but with Old World Swallowtail Caterpillar	28·00	22·00
4564/4567	Set of 4	80·00	65·00

Nos. 4564/7 are for use on mail up to 2000 grams. There are two delivery speeds, economic (E) and priority (P). Those stamps inscribed "a" are for domestic mail and those inscribed "b" are for international mail.

Nos. 4564/7 each have a different insect incorporated in the design.

1549 Tree Rings marking Polish Postage from 16th - 21st Century

1550 Ludwik Solski as the Guardian in *Treasure* by Leopold Staff

(Des A. Sancewicz)

2013 (18 Oct). World Post Day. 455th Anniv of Polish Post. P 11½.
4568   **1549** 4z.60 multicoloured .... 10·00   8·00

(Des A. Ubukata. Photo)

2013 (21 Oct). Lost Works of Art. Paintings of Ludwik Solski (actor) by Stanislaw Wyspiański (playwright, artist and poet) in 1904. T **1550** and similar horiz designs. Multicoloured. P 11½.
4569	1z.60 Type **1550**................................	3·25	2·50
	a. Strip of 3. Nos. 4569/71..................	17·00	
4570	2z.35 As Andrew Aguecheek in William Shakespeare's *Twelfth Night*..................	5·00	4·00
4571	3z.80 As Veteran Defender (the old Wiarus) in *Varsovian Anthem* (Warszawianka), by Stanislaw Wyspiański	8·00	6·50
4569/4571	Set of 3	14·50	11·50

Nos. 4569/71 were printed, se-tenant, in horizontal strips of three stamps within sheets of six.

(Des Marzanna Dąbrowska. Litho)

2013 (31 Oct). Personalities of Theatre and Cinema. Vert designs as T **1522**. Multicoloured. P 11½×12 (with one elliptical perf on each vert side).
4572	1z.60 Helena Grossówna (actress and dancer)	3·25	2·50
4573	2z.35 Adolf Dymsza (comedy actor)	5·00	4·00
4574	3z.80 Mieczyslawa Ćwiklińska (actress and singer)........................	8·00	6·50
4572/4574	Set of 3	14·50	11·50

MS4575 121×82 mm. 1z.60 Helena Grossówna (actress and dancer); 2z.55 Adolf Dymsza (comedy actor); 3z.80 Mieczyslawa Ćwiklińska (actress and singer)........................ 17·00   16·00

1551 Krzysztof Penderecki   **1552** *Argiope bruennichi*

(Des Anna Niemierko)

2013 (23 Nov). 80th Birth Anniv of Krzysztof Penderecki (composer and conductor). P 11½.
4576   **1551** 3z.80 multicoloured .... 8·00   6·50

(Des Jacek Konarzewski. Litho and varnish)

2013 (29 Nov). Spiders protected in Poland. T **1552** and similar horiz designs. Multicoloured. P 12×11½ (with one elliptical perf on each horiz side).

4577	1z.60 Type **1552**	3·25	2·50
4578	2z.35 *Atypus muralis*	5·00	4·00
4579	3z.80 *Eresus kollari*	8·00	6·50
4580	4z.55 *Philaeus chrysops*	10·00	8·00
4577/4580 Set of 4		24·00	19·00

1553 Ski Jump

1554 Oskar Kolberg

(Des Agata Tobolczyk)

2014 (7 Feb). Winter Olympic Games, Sochi. Sheet 126×90 mm containing T **1553** and similar horiz design. Multicoloured. P 12×11½ (with one elliptical perf on each horiz side).

MS4581 1z.75 Type **1553**×2; 5z. Nordic skiing×2.......... 30·00 29·00

The stamps and margins of **MS**4581 form a composite background design.

(Des Karol Tabaka)

2014 (22 Feb). Birth Bicentenary of Oskar Kolberg (ethnographer, folklorist and composer). P 11½×11.

4582 **1554** 4z.20 multicoloured .... 9·00 7·25

1555 Athletes

(Des Agata Tobolczyk)

2014 (7 Mar). IAAF World Indoor Championships. P 11½ (with one elliptical perf on each horiz side).

4583 **1555** 5z. multicoloured .... 11·00 8·50

1556 Easter Egg

1557 Towers of Wawel Cathedral

(Des Agnieszka Sancewicz)

2014 (26 Mar). Easter. T **1556** and similar vert design. Multicoloured. P 12×11½.

4584	1z.75 Type **1556**	3·75	3·00
4585	5z. Purple egg	11·00	8·50

(Des Marzanna Dąbrowska. Recess and photo)

2014 (28 Mar). 650th Anniv of Wawel Cathedral. Sheet 77×77 mm containing T **1557** and similar vert design. Each black and carmine-vermilion. P 11.

MS4586 4z.20 Type **1557**; 8z.30 Bell and nave.............. 28·00 27·00

1558 Pope John Paul II

1559 Pope John Paul II

(Des Marzanna and Jacek Dąbrowscy. Recess and litho (**MS**4589) or litho (others))

2014 (2 Apr). Canonization of Pope John Paul II. P 11½ (with one elliptical perf on each vert side).

4587	2z.35 multicoloured	5·00	4·00
MS4588	75×100 mm. Multicoloured (40×50 *mm*)........	10·50	8·50
MS4589	75×100 mm. Gold (40×50 *mm*)........................	18·00	14·50

Design: 2z.35 Type **1558**; 5z. As Type **1558**; 8z.50 As Type **1558**.

(Des Marzanna and Jacek Dąbrowscy)

2014 (2 Apr). Canonization of Pope John Paul II and Pope John XXIII. Sheet 120×75 mm containing T **1559** and similar vert design. P 11½×11 (with one elliptical perf on each vert side).

MS4590 5z.×2, Type **1559**; Pope John XXIII..................... 21·00 17·00

1560 Kamil Stoch   **1561** Jan Karski

(Des Marzanna Dąbrowska)

2014 (11 Apr). Polish Olympic Gold Medalists. Sheet 82×121mm containing T **1560** and similar horiz designs. Multicoloured. P 12×11½ (with one elliptical perf on each horiz side).

MS4591 4z.20×3, Type **1560** (double Olympic champion in the normal hill and large hill); Justyna Kowalczyk (Cross country 10k. classical Olympic champion); Zbigniew Bródka (Olympic 1500m. individual speed skating champion) .... 28·00 27·00

(Des Agata Tobolczyk)

2014 (24 Apr). Birth Centenary of Jana Karskiego (World War II resistance movement fighter and professor at Georgetown University). P 11½.

4592 **1561** 4z.20 multicoloured .... 9·00 7·25

1562 Paper Plane and EU Stars   **1563** Traditional Bagpipes in Shape of Goat

(Des Magdalena Błażków)

2014 (1 May). Tenth Anniv of Accession of Poland to European Union. P 11×11½ (with one elliptical perf on each horiz side).

4593 **1562** 5z.20 multicoloured .... 11·00 8·75

(Des Małgorzata Myszka. Litho)

2014 (5 May). Europa. Musical Instruments. P 11½ (with one elliptical perf on each vert side).

4594 **1563** 5z.20 multicoloured .... 11·00 8·75

1564 Family in the Frame

(Des Karol Tabaka)

2014 (15 May). International Year of the Family. P 11½.
4595   **1564**   2z.35 multicoloured.. 5·00   4·00

1565 Poppy

1566 Crowds and 'Wolności'

(Des Agnieszka Sancewicz)

2014 (18 May). 70th Anniv of Battle of Monte Cassino. P 11½ (with one elliptical perf on each vert side).
4596   **1565**   1z.75 multicoloured.. 3·75   3·00

(Des Agnieszka Sancewicz)

2014 (28 May). Freedom Festival. 25th Anniv of Anti-Communism Revolutions. P 11½×11.
4597   **1566**   2z.35 black, scarlet-vermilion and silver   5·00   4·00

1567 Tinkerbell and the Fairy Pirates

(Des Jacek Konarzewski)

2014 (1 June). Walt Disney Characters. Sheet 90×70 mm. P 11½ (with one elliptical perf on each vert side).
MS4598 **1567** 5z.20 multicoloured.. 11·50   11·00

1568 Kazimierz Górski

(Des Agata Tobolczyk)

2014 (27 June). Polish Football Coaches. Sheet 115×90mm containing T **1568** and similar horiz designs. Multicoloured. P 11½.
MS4599 2z.35×4, Type **1568**; Hubert Wagner; Feliks Stamm; Henryk Lasak.. 21·00   20·00

1569 Zinc Works, Szopienice

1570 Apple

(Des Agata Tobolczyk)

2014 (11 July). History of Polish Photography. Henryk Poddębski Commemoration. T **1569** and similar horiz designs showing photographs. Multicoloured. P 12×11½ (with one elliptical perf on each horiz side).
4600   1z.75 Type **1569**.. 3·75   3·00
   a. Strip of 4. Nos. 4500/3........................ 27·00
4601   2z.35 Machinery, Coal Mine, Kleofas .... 5·00   4·00
4602   3z.75 Royal foundry.. 8·00   6·50
4603   4z.20 Coal Port, Gdynia.................................. 9·00   7·25
4600/4603 Set of 4... 23·00   19·00
   Nos. 4600/3 were printed, se-tenant, in strips of four stamps within the sheet.

(Des Agnieszka Sancewicz)

2014 (18 July). Polish Regional Products - Jablko Ląckle Apple. P 11½.
4604   **1570**   5z. multicoloured.................................. 10·00   8·00

1571 Bee-eater

1572 Soldier

(Des Marzanna Dąbrowska)

2014 (31 July). Polish Birds. Common Bee-eater (*Merops apiaster*). Sheet 90×70 mm. P 11½ (with one elliptical perf on each vert side).
MS4605 **1571** 5z.50 multicoloured.............................. 12·00   11·50

(Des Agnieszka Sancewicz)

2014 (1 Aug). 70th Anniv of Warsaw Uprising (2nd issue). Sheet 90×70 mm. P 11½ (one elliptical perf on each vert side).
MS4606 **1572** 5z.20 multicoloured.............................. 11·50   11·00

1573 Józef Piasudski (statesman and Marshal of Poland)

(Des Karol Tabaka. Eng Przemyslaw Krajewski. Recess and litho)

2014 (6 Aug). Polish Legions. Sheet 90×70 mm. P 11.
MS4607 **1573** 8z.50 multicoloured.............................. 19·00   18·00

1574 Madonna, Drohobycka

(Des Agnieszka Sancewicz)

2014 (14 Aug). Madonnas of the Eastern Borderlands. Madonna Kresowe. T **1574** and similar vert design. Multicoloured. P 11.
4608   1z.95 Type **1574**.. 4·50   3·50
4609   4z.20 Madonna, Kochawińska .... 9·00   7·25

1575 *Cantharellus cibarius*

(Des Marzanna Dąbrowska)

2014 (29 Aug). Fungi. Sheet 125×152 mm containing T **1575** and similar horiz designs. Multicoloured. P 12×11½ (with one elliptical perf on each horiz side).
MS4610 1z.75 Type **1575**; 2z.35 *Agaricus campestris*;
3z.75 *Russula vesca*; 4z.20 *Boletus edulis*..................... 26·00   25·00
No. **MS**4610 also contains four stamp-size labels showing poisonous fungi.

1576 Player

1577 Stethoscope as Smiling Face

(Des Karol Tabaka)

2014 (30 Aug). FIVB Volleyball Men's World Championship, Poland. Sheet 121×125 mm containing T **1576** and similar vert designs. Multicoloured. P 11½ (with one elliptical perf on each vert side).
MS4611 1z.75 Type **1576**; 1z.75 Player 'spiking', blue vest; 2z.35 Player 'blocking', green t-shirt; 5z. Player serving, red t-shirt; 5z.10 Player 'digging', white vest; 5z.50 Player 'spiking', yellow vest.............. 45·00   44·00

(Des Agata Tobolczyk)

2014 (5 Sept). Smiles Heal. Dr. Clown. P 11½.
4612   **1577**   1z.75 multicoloured.................................... 3·75   3·00

1578 Legends of the Giants (Natalia Rak)

1579 Trees, Buildings, Dam and Raptor

(Des Robert Duczkowsk)

2014 (26 Sept). Street Art. Sheet 90×82 mm. P 12×11½ (with one elliptical perf on each horiz side).
MS4613 **1578** 4z.20 multicoloured.. 9·50   9·50

(Des Agata Tobolczyk)

2014 (29 Sept). Alternative Energy Sources. T **1579** and similar vert designs. P 11½.
4614   1z.75 Type **1579**.. 3·75   3·00
        a. Block of 4. Nos. 4614/17...................... 27·00
4615   2z.35 Thermal energy production and pylon.   5·00   4·00
4616   3z.75 Trees, wind turbine and kite.............. 8·00   6·50
4617   4z.20 High-rise buildings and solar array........ 9·00   7·25
4614/4617 *Set of 4*.. 23·00   19·00
    Nos. 4614/17 were printed, *se-tenant*, in a block of four stamps, Nos. 4614 and 4617 laid *tête-bêche* to Nos. 4615/16, within the sheet, the block forming a composite design.

1580 *Aurora Borealis*

(Des Marzanna Dąbrowska)

2014 (30 Sept). Metereological Phenomena. T **1580** and similar horiz designs. Multicoloured. P 11½ (with one elliptical perf on each horiz side).
4618   1z.75 Type **1580**.. 3·75   3·00
        a. Strip of 4. Nos. 4618/21...................... 30·00
4619   2z.35 Solar halo.. 5·00   4·00
4620   4z.20 Smoke.. 9·00   7·25
4621   5z.50 Hoar frost... 11·00   8·75
4618/4621 *Set of 4*.. 26·00   21·00
    Nos. 4618/21 were printed, *se-tenant*, in strips of four stamps within the sheet.

1581 Jan Nowaka-Jezlorańskiego

1582 *Acanthurus sohal*

(Des Karol Tabaka)

2014 (2 Oct). Birth Centenary of Jan Nowaka-Jezlorańskiego. P 11½.
4622   **1581**   4z.20 multicoloured..................................... 9·00   7·25

(Des Jacek Konarzewski)

2014 (10 Oct). Warszawa 2014 National Philatelic Exhibiton. Marine Life. T **1582** and similar vert designs. Multicoloured. P 11½.
4623   35g. Type **1582**... 75   60
        a. Sheet. Nos. 4623/30, plus 4 labels.......... 16·00
4624   45g. *Chaetodon capistratus*....................... 95   75
4625   55g. *Rhinomuraena quaesita*...................... 1·10   90
4626   65g. *Hippocampus sp*................................. 1·40   1·10
4627   1z.10 *Balistoides conspicillum*..................... 2·40   1·90
4628   1z.20 *Pomacanthus xanthometopon*............ 2·50   2·00
4629   1z.30 *Chelmon rostratus*............................ 2·75   2·20
4630   1z.40 *Amphiprion ocellaris*......................... 3·00   2·40
4623/4630 *Set of 8*.. 13·50   10·50
    Nos. 4623/30 were printed in sheets of eight stamps and four stamp-size labels.

1583 Stefan Żeromski

1584 Stéphane Antigi

(Des Maciej Jędrysik)

2014 (14 Oct). 150th Birth Anniv of Stefan Żeromski (writer). P 11½ (with one elliptical perf on each vert side).
4631   **1583**   4z.20 multicoloured..................................... 9·00   7·25

(Des Jacek Konarzewski)

2014 (18 Oct). Poland - Winner of the FIVB Volleyball Men's World Championships. T **1584** and similar horiz designs. Multicoloured. P 11½ (with one elliptical perf on each horiz side).
4632   1z. Type **1584**.. 2·20   1·70
        a. Sheet. Nos. 4632/47 plus 4 labels........... 34·00
4633   1z. Piotr Nowakowski................................
4634   1z. Michal Winiarski.................................... 2·20   1·70
4635   1z. Dawid Konarski...................................... 2·20   1·70
4636   1z. Rafal Buszek.. 2·20   1·70
4637   1z. Pawel Zagumny..................................... 2·20   1·70

4638	1z. Karol Klos	2·20	1·70
4639	1z. Andrzej Wrona	2·20	1·70
4640	1z. Mariusz Wlazly	2·20	1·70
4641	1z. Fabian Drzyzga	2·20	1·70
4642	1z. Michal Kubiak	2·20	1·70
4643	1z. Krzysztof Ignaczak	2·20	1·70
4644	1z. Pawel Zatorski	2·20	1·70
4645	1z. Marcin Możdżonek	2·20	1·70
4646	1z. Mateusz Mika	2·20	1·70
4647	1z. Philippe Blain	2·20	1·70
4632/4647	Set of 16	30·00	23·00

Nos. 4632/47 were printed, *se-tenant*, in sheets of 16 stamps and four stamp-size labels.

(Des Marzanna Dąbrowska)

2014 (31 Oct). Personalities of Theatre and Cinema. Vert designs as T **1522**. Multicoloured. P 11½×12 (with one elliptical perf on each vert side).

4648	1z.75 Tola Mankiewiczówna (singer and actress)	3·75	3·00
4649	2z.35 Antoni Fertner (actor)	5·00	4·00
4650	4z.20 Loda Halama (dancer and actress)	9·00	7·25
4648/4650	Set of 3	16·00	13·00

MS4651 121×82 mm. 1z.75 Tola Mankiewiczówna (singer and actress); 2z.35 Antoni Fertner (actor); 4z.20 Loda Halama (dancer and actress) ..... 18·00 17·00

1585 Holy Family

1586 Ophelia drowning (scene from *Hamlet*)

(Des Agnieszka Sancewicz)

2014 (14 Nov). Christmas. T **1585** and similar vert design. Multicoloured. P 11½.

4652	2z.35 Type **1585**	5·00	4·00
4653	5z.20 Adoration of the Magi	11·50	9·00

(Des Aleksandra Pietrzak)

2014 (21 Nov). 450th Birth Anniv of William Shakespeare. P 11½×12.

4654	**1586**	4z.20 multicoloured	9·00	7·25

1587 Ambassadors to Courts

(Des Maciej Jędrysik)

2014 (28 Nov). 600th Anniv of Poland - Turkey Diplomatic Relations. Sheet 90×70 mm. P 11½ (with one elliptical hole on each horiz side).

MS4655 **1587** 5z. multicoloured ..... 10·50 10·00

1588 Circle of Figures

1589 Emblem

(Des Agnieszka Sancewicz)

2014 (19 Dec). World Youth Day. T **1588** and similar design. P 11½ (with one elliptical perf on each horiz side (1z.75) or each vert side (5z.)).

4656	1z.75 gold and bronze	3·75	3·00
4657	5z. gold and silver (45×23 *mm*)	10·50	8·50

Designs: 1z.75 Type **1588**; 5z. Kraców skyline.

(Des Jerzy Owsiak, Gawel Andrzejewski, Magdalena Jablońska and Katarzyna Sasin)

2015 (7 Jan). 23rd Finale of Orchestra of Holy Day Assistance (fund raising charity). P 11½ (with one elliptical perf on each vert side).

4658	**1589**	2z.35 multicoloured	5·00	4·00

1590 Heart

(Des Marzanna Dąbrowska. Litho, screen printing)

2015 (6 Feb). 'I Love You'. P 11½ (with one elliptical perf on each vert side of outer square).

4659	**1590**	2z.35 multicoloured	5·00	4·00

No. 4659 was perforated around the heart-shape enclosed in an outer perforated square. The screen printing gives a glitter effect.

1591 Kazimierza Przerwy-Tetmajera

1592 Witkacy

(Des Aleksandra Pietrzak)

2015 (12 Feb). 150th Birth Anniv of Kazimierza Przerwy-Tetmajera (writer). P 11½ (with one elliptical perf on each horiz side).

4660	**1591**	1z.75 multicoloured	3·75	3·00

(Des Agnieszka Sancewicz)

2015 (24 Feb). 'Witkacy - Visionary Creator'. 130th Birth Anniv of Stanislaw Ignacy Witkiewicz (Witkacy) (artist, philosopher and writer). Sheet 70×90 mm. P 11½.

MS4661 **1592** 5z.20 multicoloured ..... 11·50 11·00

(Des Agnieszka Sancewicz)

2015 (6 Mar). Easter vert designs as T **1556**. Multicoloured P 12×11½.

4662	2z.35 Purple egg with floral decoration	5·00	4·00
4663	2z.35 Purple egg with floral decoration	11·50	9·00

1594 Figure holding Heart

1595 'IDA'

(Des Maciej Jędrysik)

2015 (20 Mar). Organ Transplantation. P 11½.

4664	**1594**	1z.75 multicoloured	3·75	3·00

(Des Maciej Jędrysik)

2015 (31 Mar). *Ida* (film, directed by Pawel Pawlikowski, 2013). P 11½ (with one elliptical perf on each horiz side).

4665	**1595**	1z.75 multicoloured	3·75	3·00

1596 Tadeusz Kantor

1597 Symbol of Massacre

(Des Alexander Pietrzak)

2015 (3 Apr). Birth Centenary of Tadeusz Kantor (artist, set designer and theatre director). P 11½.

4666	**1596**	1z.75 multicoloured	3·75	3·00

(Des Marzanna Dąbrowska)

2015 (7 Apr). 75th Anniv of Katyń Massacre. P 11½ (with one elliptical perf on each vert side).

4667	**1597**	1z.75 multicoloured	3·75	3·00

1598 Pope John Paul II

1599 Homemade Doll

(Des Agnieszka Sancewicz)

2015 (27 Apr). World Youth Day. T **1598** and similar vert design. Multicoloured. P 11½.

4668	1z.75 Type **1598**	3·75	3·00
4669	5z. 'In You There Is Hope' (30×39 mm)	10·50	8·50

(Des Maciej Jędrysik. Litho)

1915 (5 May). Europa. Old Toys. P 11½ (with one elliptical perf on each horiz side).

4670	**1599**	5z. multicoloured	10·50	8·50

(Des Agnieszka Sancewicz)

2015 (8 May). 70th Anniv of End of World War II. Sheet 90×70 mm. P 11½.

MS4671 2z.35 Flowers growing from soldier's helmet. 5·25 4·25

Type **1600** is vacant.

1601 Apple

(Litho)

2015 (28 May). World EXPO 2015 - Milan, Italy. Sheet 100×100 mm. P 11½.

MS4672 **1601** 5z.20 multicoloured 12·00 9·50

(Des Marzanna Dąbrowska. Litho)

2015 (29 May). Birth Centenary of Jan Twardowski (poet). P 11½ (with one elliptical perf on each vert side).

4673	1z.75 Jan Twardowski	3·75	3·00

Type **1602** is vacant.

1603 Anna (from *Frozen*)

(Des Agnieszka Sancewicz)

2015 (1 June). Walt Disney Characters. Sheet 121×75 mm containing T **1603** and similar vert design. P 11½ (with one elliptical perf on each horiz side).

MS4674 2z.35×2, Type **1603**; Elsa 10·50 8·50

MACHINE LABELS

1996 (Nov). Design showing asterisks surrounding face value. Face values from 40g. to 29z.

No fixed steps available...

1998. Multicoloured designs showing a postal horn emblem. Date shown as day/month/year, re-issued later in the year reversed. Face values from 55g. to 35z.70.

No fixed steps available...

GERMAN OCCUPATION, 1915–18

A German offensive in Galicia on 1 May 1915 broke through the Russian lines and all Poland was in German hands by the end of August. In 1916 Poland was named the "General-Government, Warsaw" and on 5 November 1916, Germany and Austria proclaimed a "Polish Kingdom"; Pilsudski sat on the Council of State of this till he resigned in protest against German control. On 15 October 1917, the Germans set up a Regency Council, which exercised control under German supervision, and took charge of affairs on 12 October 1918 when the Central Powers were on the verge of collapse.

100 Pfennig = 1 Mark

| (1) | (2) |

Contemporary stamps of Germany overprinted.

1915 (12 May). With T **1**.

1	**17**	3pf. brown	1·00	65
2		5pf. green	1·50	65
3		10pf. carmine	1·50	1·00
4		20pf. ultramarine	6·25	1·00
5		40pf. black and carmine	8·75	4·50
1/5	*Set of 5*		17·00	7·00

Nos. 1/5 were for use in the Lódź region.

1916 (1 Aug)–**17**. With T **2**.

6	**24**	2½pf. grey	1·10	2·50
7	**17**	3pf. brown	1·10	3·50
8		5pf. green	1·30	4·50
9	**24**	7½pf. orange	1·50	2·75
10	**17**	10pf. carmine	5·00	2·75
11	**24**	15pf. yellow-brown	4·50	3·75
12		15pf. slate-violet (1917)	1·30	2·75
13	**17**	20pf. deep blue	6·25	3·25
		a. Violet-blue	75·00	£130
		b. Ultramarine	5·00	7·50
14		30pf. black and orange/*buff*	10·00	18·00
15		40pf. black and carmine	3·75	2·75
16		60pf. magenta	3·75	3·50
6/16	*Set of 11*		34·00	45·00

The area north-east of Warsaw was part of the German Eastern Command Area, which also included the Baltic Provinces of Russia. German stamps overprinted "Postgebiet Ob. Ost" were used in this area; these are listed in Part 7 (*Germany*) of this catalogue.

During the period of German occupation several municipal councils organized local postal delivery services. Most used handstamps to indicate payment but the following towns issued stamps, some of which were quickly suppressed by the military authorities: Sosnowiec, Warsaw, Zawiercie, Bialystok (in the Eastern Command Area). Przedbórz and Żarki in the Austrian occupied area also issued stamps.

Polish Military Post

I. POLISH CORPS IN RUSSIA, 1918

In 1917 Poles serving in the Russian Army were transferred into Polish units so that an autonomous Polish Army could be organized. The Polish First Corps was formed on 21 August 1917. By January 1918 the Corps was based at Bobruisk, virtually surrounded by German troops.

An agreement with the Germans in February 1918 established an area of "Polish Occupation" and the forwarding of Polish mail to Warsaw by the German field post. Post offices operated from 1 April to 29 June 1918, after which the Corps was disbanded.

100 Kopeks = 1 Rouble

| (M 1) | (M 2) |

1918 (March). 1912–18 stamps of Russia optd with Type M **1**, by Mr. Podzuinski, Bobruisk. No wmk.

(a) P 14½

M1	**22**	3k. carmine-red	£140	£140
M2	**23**	4k. red	£140	£140
M3	**22**	5k. brown-lilac	33·00	26·00
M4	**23**	10k. deep blue	33·00	26·00
M5	**22**	10k. on 7k. deep blue (170)	£900	£1000
M6	**10**	15k. blue and purple-brown	6·50	10·50
M7	**14**	20k. scarlet and blue	13·00	11·50
M8	**10**	25k. violet and deep green	£160	£130
M9		35k. deep green and brown-purple	6·50	10·50
M10	**14**	50k. green and dull purple	26·00	20·00

(b) Imperf

| M11 | **10** | 70k. vermilion and brown | £500 | £400 |

1918 (March). Stamps of Russia surch as Type M **2**, by the Corps Ptg Wks. No wmk.

(a) P 14×14½

M12A	**22**	10k. on 3k. carmine-red	6·50	6·50
M13A		35k. on 1k. orange	£100	£100
M14A		50k. on 2k. light green	6·50	6·50
		a. Surch inverted	£400	
M15A		1r. on 3k. carmine-red	£130	£120

(b) Imperf

M12B	**22**	10k. on 3k. carmine-red	4·00	4·00
		a. Surch double	£325	
M13B	**22**	35k. on 1k. orange	2·50	2·50
		a. Surch double	£325	
		b. Surch inverted	£400	
M14B		50k. on 2k. light green	4·00	4·00
M15B		1r. on 3k. carmine-red	6·50	6·50
		a. Surch double	£200	
		b. Surch inverted	£400	

II. POLISH ARMY IN RUSSIA, 1942

After the German invasion of Russia in 1941, Polish prisoners of war taken by the Russians in 1939 were released and formed into an army which, after training in the Soviet Union, went to fight in Italy.

M **3** "We Shall Return"

(Eng Polkowski. Typo)

1942 (18 Aug). Issued at Jangi-Jul, near Tashkent. Thick carton paper. Imperf×perf 11½. Edges of sheet also imperf.

M16	M **3**	50k. brown (*shades*)	£300	£8000
		a. *Tête-bêche* (pair)	£750	£1600

Stamps with no full point after "KOP" are forgeries.

Polish Occupation

CENTRAL LITHUANIA

A force of Poles under General Zeligawski seized Vilna and district from the Lithuanians on 9 October 1920.

100 Fenigi = 1 Mark

IMPERF STAMPS. With the exception of Nos. 4/13 all the following exist imperf and perf and the prices are the same.

1

(2 Arms of Poland and Lithuania)

(Des F. Zaniewski. Litho J. Zawadski)

1920 (20 Oct). White or greyish paper. P 11½ or imperf.

1	**1**	25f. dull red	80	90
2		1m. blue	80	90
3		2m. grey-violet	80	90

See also Nos. 20/22.

1920 (23 Nov). Nos. 50, etc., of Lithuania. Surch as T **2**, in black (Bk.) or blue (sideways on Nos. 8/10).

4	**5**	2m. on 15s. mauve	65·00	75·00
5		4m. on 10s. orange-red	65·00	75·00
6		4m. on 20s. Prussian blue (Bk.)	65·00	75·00
7		4m. on 30s. bistre	65·00	75·00
8	**6**	6m. on 50s. yellow-green	65·00	75·00
		a. Error. 4m. on 50s	£325	
		b. Error. 10m. on 50s	£325	
9		6m. on 60s. red and violet	65·00	75·00
		a. Error. 4m. on 60s	£325	
		b. Error. 10m. on 60s	£325	
10		6m. on 75s. red and bistre	65·00	75·00
		a. Error. 4m. on 75s	£325	
		b. Error. 10m. on 75s	£325	
11	**7**	10m. on 1a. red and grey	£130	£200
12		10m. on 3a. red and brown	£2500	£3250
13		10m. on 5a. red and blue-green	£2500	£3250

3 Girl

4 Warrior

5 Ostrabrama Gate, Vilnius

6 St. Stanislaus Cathedral and Tower, Vilnius

7 Rector's Insignia

8 General Zeligowski

(Res F. Ruszczyc. Litho Laskow, Vilna)

1920 (Dec). White or greyish paper. P 11½ or imperf.

14	**3**	25f. grey	45	65
15	**4**	1m. orange	45	65
16	**5**	2m. dull claret	90	1·30
17	**6**	4m. olive and yellow	1·30	1·90
18	**7**	6m. grey and carmine	4·50	5·00
19	**8**	10m. yellow and black-brown	6·25	7·50
14/19 Set of 6			12·50	15·00

1921 (6 Feb). Colours changed. White paper (2m.) also on greyish. P 11½ or imperf.

20	**1**	25f. deep green	80	90
21		1m. sepia	80	90
22		2m. yellow	80	90

D **9** Government Offices

D **10** Castle Hill, Vilnius

(Des F. Ruszczyc. Litho Chominski)

1921 (Feb–July). POSTAGE DUE. Types D **9/10** and similar designs. P 11½ or imperf.

D23		50f. claret	90	1·90
D24		1m. bright green	90	1·90
D25		2m. purple	90	1·90
D26		3m. purple	1·80	2·50
D27		5m. purple	1·80	3·75
D28		20m. vermilion (July)	2·75	5·00
D23/28 Set of 6			8·25	15·00

Designs: Horiz—2m. Castle on Troki Island. Vert—3m. Ostra Brama Gate, Vilnius; 5m. St. Stanislaus Cathedral; 20m. (larger) St. Nicholas Cathedral.

(9) (10)

(11)

1921 (Feb–Apr). Fund for Polish participation in Plebiscite for Upper Silesia. Surch with T **9**, in red or green (G,), by J. Zawadski.

23	**1**	25f.+2m. dull red (G.)	2·75	5·00
24		25f.+2m. deep green	2·75	5·00
25		1m.+2m. blue	2·75	5·00
26		1m.+2m. sepia	2·75	5·00
27		2m.+2m. grey-violet	2·75	5·00
28		2m.+2m. yellow	2·75	5·00
23/28 Set of 6			15·00	27·00

1921 (15 Mar). Red Cross Fund. Surch with T **10** or **11**, in red. P 11½ or imperf.

29	**5**	2m.+1(m.) pale claret	2·20	3·25
30	**6**	4m.+1m. olive and yellow	2·20	3·25

(12)

1921 (21 Apr). White Cross Fund. T **5**, **6** and **8** with white cross added as in T **12**. White or greyish paper. P 11½ or imperf.

31	**5**	2m.+1m. bright claret	1·30	1·90
32	**6**	4m.+1m. olive and buff	1·30	1·90
33	**8**	10m.+2m. yellow and black-brown	1·30	1·90
31/33 Set of 3			3·50	5·00

13 Church of St. Anne in V ilnius

14 St. Stanislaus Cathedral

(Litho State Ptg Wks, Warsaw)

1921 (Apr–July). T **13/4** and similar types. P 13½, 14 or imperf.

34		1m. yellow and slate (July)	1·30	1·90
35		2m. green and carmine (July)	1·30	1·90
36		3m. myrtle-green	1·30	1·90
37		4m. chocolate and brown (July)	1·30	1·90
38		5m. red-brown	1·30	1·90
39		6m. buff and myrtle (July)	1·30	1·90
40		10m. buff and purple (July)	1·80	3·75
41		20m. buff and sepia (July)	1·80	3·75
34/41 Set of 8			10·50	17·00

Design: Vert—3m. Coat of Arms in oval; 5m. Arms in shield. Horiz—4m. Queen Jadwiga and King Wladislaw Jagiello; 6m. Poczbut Observatory, Vilnius University; 10m. Union of Lithuania and Poland, 1569; 20m. Kościuszko and Mickiewicz.

21 Entry into Vilnius

22 Gen. Żeligowski

(Litho Chominski)

1921 (Nov). First Anniv of Entry of Gen. Żeligowski into Vilnius. P 11½ or imperf.

42	**21**	100m. blue and bistre (17.11)	5·00	8·25
43	**22**	150m. olive-green and brown	6·75	10·50

23 Agriculture

24 Arms

25 National Assembly, Vilnius

26 Industry

(Litho Chominski)

1922 (Feb). Opening of National Parliament. P 11½ or imperf.

44	**23**	10m. chestnut	7·25	10·00
45	**24**	25m. carmine and buff	7·25	12·50
46	**25**	50m. deep blue	10·50	19·00
47	**26**	75m. lilac	10·50	35·00
44/47 Set of 4			32·00	70·00

After a plebiscite Central Lithuania was incorporated in Poland on 8 April 1922. The Russians returned it to Lithuania on 10 October 1939 after dividing Poland with the Germans but in August 1940 it was incorporated in the Soviet Union as part of the Lithuanian S.S.R.

Polish Post Offices Abroad

A. CONSTANTINOPLE

100 Fenigów = 1 Marka

The following were used for franking correspondence handed in to the Polish Consulate at Constantinople.

LEVANT
(1)   (2)

1919 (May). Stamps of Poland optd as T **1** (larger on mark values), in carmine. P 11½.

1A	**15**	3f. brown	£130	£170
2A		5f. yellow-green	£130	£170
3A		10f. purple	£130	£170
4A		15f. lake	£130	£170
5A	**16**	20f. blue	£130	£170
6A		25f. olive	£130	£170
7A		50f. green	£130	£170
8A	**17**	1m. violet	£140	£200
9A		1m.50 green	£140	£200
10A		2m. brown	£140	£200
11A	**18**	2m.50 red-brown	£140	£200
12A	**19**	5m. violet	£140	£200
1A/12A Set of 12			£1400	£2000

1919 (Oct). Shiny ink.

1B	**15**	3f. brown	1·00
2B		5f. yellow green	1·00
3B		10f. purple	1·00
4B		15f. lake	1·00
5B	**16**	20f. blue	1·00
6B		25f. olive	1·00
7B		50f. green	1·00
8B	**17**	1m. violet	1·40
9B		1m.50 green	1·40
10B		2m. brown	1·40
11B	**18**	2m.50 red-brown	1·40
12B	**19**	5m. violet	1·70
1B/12B Set of 12			13·00

1921 (25 May). Stamps of Poland surch as T **2** (larger on T **19**), in red-brown.

13	**25**	1m. carmine		2·75
14		2m. green		4·75
15		3m. pale blue		4·00
16		4m. rose		5·50
17	**19**	6m. rose-carmine		6·75
18		10m. vermilion		12·00
19		20m. green		20·00
13/19 Set of 7				50·00

Nos. 13/19 were not issued.

This office was closed down in 1923 under the terms of the Treaty of Lausanne.

B. DANZIG

100 Groszy = 1 Zloty

The Poles operated a postal service in Danzig with a post office by the harbour.

From 1934 Danzig stamps were valid for use throughout Poland.

Stamps of Poland overprinted

PORT GDAŃSK
(R **1**)

PORT GDAŃSK
(R **2**)

PORT GDAŃSK
(R **3**)

1925 (5 Jan). Nos. 218/28 (Arms) optd with Type R **1**.

R1	**40**	1g. yellow-brown	65	3·75
R2		2g. grey-brown	65	8·75
R3		3g. orange	65	2·50
R4		5g. sage-green	19·00	12·50
R5		10g. blue-green	6·25	5·00

R6		15g. scarlet	35·00	12·50
R7		20g. light blue	1·90	2·50
R8		25g. claret	1·90	2·50
R9		30g. bright violet	1·90	2·50
R10		40g. slate	1·90	2·50
R11		50g. magenta	6·25	3·75
R1/11 Set of 11			70·00	55·00

1926 (12 Apr). Nos. 244/5 optd with Type R **1**.

R12	**44**	5g. green (Town Hall, Poznań)	55·00	65·00
R13	**45**	10g. violet (King Sigismund Monument, Warsaw)	15·00	25·00

1926–29. Optd with Type R **2**.

R14	**44**	5g. green (244a)	1·90	3·25
R15	**45**	10g. violet (245a) (1927)	1·90	3·25
R16	**46**	15g. carmine (246a) (Wawel Castle)	25·00	6·25
		a. Optd on No. 246	75·00	90·00
R17	**48**	20g. carmine (Ship) (15.2.28)	3·75	3·25
R18	**51**	25g. yellow-brown (Marshal Pilsudski) (15.2.28)	6·25	7·50
R19	**57**	1z. slate-black/cream (Pres. Mościcki) (30.11.29)	35·00	55·00
R14/19 Set of 6			65·00	70·00

Inverted overprints of Nos. R14/15, R17 and R24 are now believed to be private productions made from the original clichés.

1929 (28 May)–**30**. Optd with Type R **3**.

R21	**61**	5g. violet (Arms)	1·90	3·25
R22		10g. green (1930)	1·90	3·25
R23	**59**	15g. deep blue (Sienkiewicz) (5.1.30)	5·00	9·50
R24	**61**	25g. red-brown	3·75	3·25
R21/24 Set of 4			11·50	17·00

See note below No. R19.

PORT   **GDAŃSK**

PORT GDANSK

(R **4**)   (R **5**)

1933 (1 July). No. 273a (Mościcki) optd with Type R **4**. P 11½.

R25	**57**	1z. slate-black/cream (V.)	95·00	£225

1934 (22 Sept)–**35**. Nos. 284a/285a (Arms) optd with Type R **3**.

R26	**65**	5g. violet	4·50	10·00
R27		10g. green (30.10.35)	44·00	£160
R28		15g. claret	4·50	10·00
R26/28 Set of 3			48·00	£160

1936–37. Nos. 313, 315, 317, 319 and 321 optd as Type R **5** in one or (Nos. R30 and R31) in two lines.

(a) Typo (Aug–Sept 1936)

R29	**79**	5g. violet-blue (Dog's Rock) (15.8.36)	3·75	38·00
R30	–	15g. greenish blue (Pilsudski (liner)) (10.9.36)	3·75	38·00

(b) Recess (Sept 1936-June 1937)

R31	–	5g. violet (Częstochowa) (5.6.37)	1·40	19·00
R32	–	15g. brown-lake (Lwòw University) (5.6.37)	1·40	19·00
R33	–	25g. deep blue-green (Belvedere Palace) (10.9.36)	3·75	12·50

R **6** Port of Danzig

(Des W. Boratyński. Eng M. Dutczyński. Recess Govt Ptg Wks, Warsaw)

1938 (11 Nov). 20th Anniv of Polish Independence. P 12½×13.

R34	R **6**	5g. red-orange	65	31·00
R35		15g. red-brown	65	31·00
R36		25g. purple	65	31·00
R37		55g. bright blue	1·90	50·00
R34/37 Set of 4			3·50	£130

Stamps inscribed "GDANSK" showing a Crown surmounting two Maltese Crosses were issued by a Polish Defence organization but they were not put on sale at the post office.

A set of four stamps showing various views of Danzig with face values of 1+1, 5+5, 10+10 and 20+20z. is bogus.

The Polish Post Office was closed on 1 September 1939 when Danzig was incorporated into Germany.

C. ODESSA

100 Fenigów = 1 Marka

The following stamps were issued at the Polish Consulate during the occupation of Odessa by General Denikin as the normal postal connections with Poland were interrupted.

(Optd typo by E. I. Fesenko, Odessa)

1919 (Nov). Arms (T **15** and **16**) and Agriculture (**17**) issue for Northern Poland optd "ODESA". P 11½.

1	**15**	10f. purple	£500	£500
		a. Opt inverted	£2750	
		b. Red opt	£5000	£5000
2		15f. scarlet	£50000	
3	**16**	20f. blue	£500	£500
		a. Opt inverted	£2500	
4		25f. olive	£3250	£3250
		a. Opt inverted	£6500	
5		50f. green	£500	£500
		a. Opt inverted	£2500	
		b. Red opt	£5000	£5000
6	**17**	1m. violet	£500	£500
		a. Opt inverted	£2500	

The sheets of 100 were overprinted twice in settings of 50. Some smaller blocks were also overprinted.

Only six examples of the 15f. were overprinted, of which four still exist; one is in the Polish Postal Museum and two are in a pair. 50 examples each of the red overprints were made.

This postal agency was closed on 31 January 1920.

Allenstein

100 Pfennig = 1 Mark

On 11 July 1920 a plebiscite was held under the Treaty of Versailles in this district of East Prussia. There was a vote of 98% in favour of remaining in Germany. The district was occupied by Soviet troops in 1945 and has since been administered by Poland under the name of Olsztyn.

PLÉBISCITE

OLSZTYN
ALLENSTEIN

(1)

(2)

1920 (3 Apr–3 Aug). Types of Germany (wmk Lozenges) optd with T **1** at State Printing Office, Berlin. Mark values (a) Engraved, (b) Surface-printed.

1	**17**	5pf. green	65	1·90
2		10pf. carmine	65	1·90
3	**24**	15pf. slate-violet	65	1·90
4		15pf. dull purple-brown (3 Aug)	8·75	19·00
5	**17**	20pf. violet-blue	65	2·50
6		30pf. black and orange/*buff*	65	2·50
7		40pf. black and carmine	65	1·90
8		50pf. black and purple/*buff*	65	1·90
9		75pf. black and dark green-black	65	1·90
10	**18**	1m. red (*a*)	2·50	7·50
		a. Opt double	£450	£1800
11		1m.25 yellow-green (*b*)	2·50	7·50
		a. Opt double		
12		1m.50 brown (*b*)	1·50	6·25
13	**20**	2m.50 lilac-rose (*b*)	50·00	£180
		a. Claret	3·75	18·00
		b. Purple	3·75	25·00
14	**21**	3m. violet-black (*a*)	3·75	7·50
		a. Opt double	£450	£1800
1/14 *Set of 14*			25·00	75·00

1920 (May–June). Stamps as last, but optd with T **2**.

15	**17**	5pf. green	65	1·50
16		10pf. carmine	65	1·50
17	**24**	15pf. slate-violet	65	1·50
18		15pf. dull purple brown (25.6)	31·00	65·00
19	**17**	20pf. violet-blue	1·00	2·50
20		30pf. black and orange/*buff*	65	1·50
21		40pf. black and carmine	65	1·50
22		50pf. black and purple/*buff*	65	1·50
23		75pf. black and dark green-black	1·00	2·50
24	**18**	1m. red (*a*)	2·40	5·75
		a. Opt inverted	£750	£1300
25		1m.25 yellow-green (*b*)	2·40	5·75
26		1m.50 brown (*b*)	1·60	5·75
27	**20**	2m.50 claret (*b*)	4·25	10·50
		a. Purple (*b*)	5·25	20·00
28	**21**	3m. violet-black (*a*)	2·75	5·00
		a. Opt inverted	£600	£1500
		b. Opt double	£325	£950
15/28 *Set of 14*			45·00	£100

The 40pf. carmine, No. 144a, was also overprinted and placed on sale after the plebiscite but was only used on internal parcels and also exists cancelled by favour.

The international use of these stamps was discontinued on 20 August but they could be used internally until the end of October.

Danzig

1920. 100 Pfennig = 1 Mark
1923. 100 Pfennig = 1 Danzig Gulden

FREE CITY

By the Treaty of Versailles, 28 June 1919, Danzig, with surrounding territory, was created a Free City as from 10 January 1920. Unoverprinted stamps of Germany were in use from 10 January to 13 June 1920.

USED PRICES. Used prices for Nos. 1/177 are for cancelled-to order examples.

Stamps of Germany Overprinted

17

18

20

21

22

24

30 L.V.G. Schneider Biplane

Danzig
(1)

10
(2)

(Optd by State Ptg Wks, Berlin)

1920 (14 June–21 Dec). Stamps of Germany, 1905–20, optd with T **1**.

1	**17**	5pf. green	50	75
		a. Pair, one with opt omitted	£130	
2	**30**	10pf. carmine	50	50
3	**24**	15pf. dull purple-brown	50	50
4	**17**	20pf. violet-blue	50	1·60
5		30pf. black and orange/*buff*	50	50
6		40pf. carmine (No. 144a) (13.9)	50	50
7		50pf. black and purple/*buff*	65	50
		a. Pair, one with opt omitted		
8	**18**	1m. carmine (No. 113)	65	90
		a. Pair, one with opt omitted	£130	
9		1m.25 blackish green-blue	65	90
10		1m.50 brown (20.7)	1·30	2·50
11	**20**	2m. blue (No. 94B)	4·50	10·00
		a. Surch double	£550	
12		2m.50 claret	4·50	7·00
		a. Pair, one with opt omitted		
13	**21**	3m. violet-black (No. 95B) (20.7)	12·50	18·00
		a. Pair, one with opt omitted		
14	**17**	4m. carmine and black (21.12)	6·00	8·75
15	**22**	5m. carmine and black (No. 96A)	£3750	

15a		5m. carmine and black (No. 96B)............	3·75	5·75
		ab. Frame inverted..................................	£23000	
		ac. Surch double......................................	£1400	
1/15a (ex. 15) Set of 15			34·00	55·00

Nos. 89 and 140/1 of Germany also exist with this overprint, but were not sold to the public.

(Surch by J. Sauer, Danzig)

1920. (17 Aug–20 Nov) Nos. 4 and 5 with additional surch as T **2**.

16		5 on 30pf. (V.) (1.11)	40	40
17		10 on 20pf. (R.) (17.8)	40	40
		a. Surch double......................................	£160	
18		25 on 30pf. (G.) (10.8)	40	40
		a. Surch inverted....................................	£130	£375
19		60 on 30pf. (Br.) (20.11)	1·00	1·60
		a. Surch double......................................	£130	£450
20		80 on 30pf. (V.) (20.11)	1·00	1·60
16/20 Set of 5			3·00	4·00

(3)    (3a)

(Optd by J. Sauer, Danzig)

1920 (20–30 Aug). Stamps of Germany optd.

*(a) With T **3** or larger (1m.)*

21	**24**	2pf. grey (B.) (30.8)	£150	£300
22		2½pf. grey (B.) (30.8)	£225	£450
23	**17**	3pf. brown (B.) (30.8)	15·00	25·00
		a. Opt double...	£110	
24		5pf. green (B.)	75	1·10
		a. Opt double...	£130	
25	**24**	7½pf. orange (B.) (30.8)	55·00	80·00
26	**17**	10pf. carmine (B.) (30.8)	5·00	10·00
		a. Opt double...	£130	
27	**24**	15pf. slate-violet (B.)	1·00	1·10
		a. Opt double...	£130	
28	**17**	20pf. dark violet blue (B.)	1·00	1·10
29		25pf. black and red/*yellow* (R.).............	1·00	1·10
30		30pf. black and orange/*buff* (B.)...........	75·00	£140
31		40pf. black and carmine (R.) (30.8)	3·25	3·75
		a. Opt double...	£325	
		b. Opt inverted.......................................	£325	
32		50pf. black and purple/*buff* (R.) (30.8)....	£250	£450
32a		60pf. magenta (B.) (30.8)	£1800	£3250
33		75pf. black and blue-green (30.8) (R.).....	1·00	1·10
34		80pf. black and carmine/*rose* (R.) (30.8) .	3·50	6·25
34a	**18**	1m. carmine (R.) (30.8)	£1800	£3250
		ab. Opt double..	£325	

*(b) With T **3a***

34b	**20**	2m. blue (94B) (R.) (30.8)	£6500	
		c. Opt double..	£1800	£3250

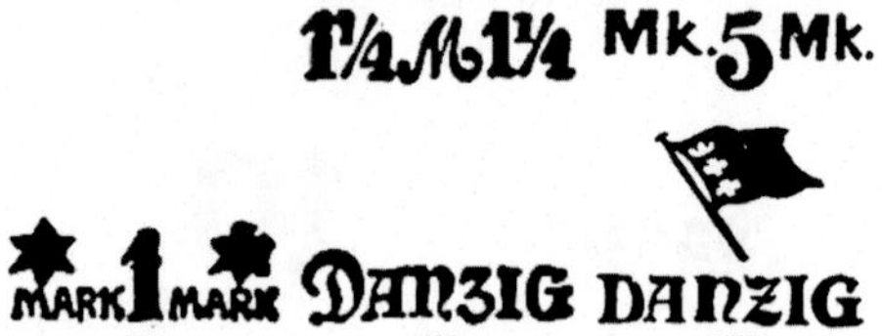

(4)   (5)   (8)

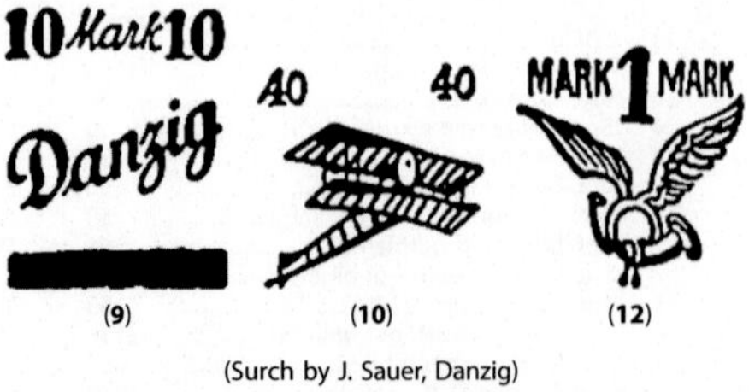

(9)   (10)   (12)

(Surch by J. Sauer, Danzig)

1920. (20 Aug–1 Nov) No. 5 of Danzig and T **17** and **24** of Germany, but with burelé background added, surch as T **4** to **9**.

(a) Background in grey (20 Aug)

A. Burelé background with points upward toward the right

35A	**17**	1m. on 30pf. black and orange/*buff*......	1·30	2·30
36A		1¼m. on 3pf. brown (R.).........................	1·50	2·30
37A	**24**	2m. on 35pf. red-brown (B.)	2·30	2·30
38A		3m. on 7½pf. orange (G.)	1·50	2·30

39A		5m. on 2pf. grey (R.)	1·50	3·25
40A		10m. on 7½pf. orange (R.)	3·75	11·50

B. Burelé background with points downward toward the left

36B	**17**	1¼m. on 3pf. brown (R.)	50·00	65·00
37B	**24**	2m. on 35pf. red-brown (B.)	£650	£500
38B		3m. on 7½pf. orange (G.)	38·00	25·00
39B		5m. on 2pf. grey (R.)	38·00	44·00
40B		10m. on 7½pf. orange (R.)	8·25	19·00

(b) Background in lilac (1 Nov)

A. Burelé background with points upward toward the right

40Aa	**17**	1m. on 30pf.	£130	48·00
40Ab		1¼m. on 3pf. (R.)	7·50	9·50
40Ac	**24**	2m. on 35pf. (B.)	19·00	55·00
40Ad		3m. on 7½pf. (G.)	3·25	3·75
40Ae		5m. on 2pf. (R.)	1·90	3·75
40Af		10m. on 7½pf.	1·90	3·25

B. Burelé background with points downward toward the left

40Ba	**17**	1m. on 30pf.	1·90	3·75
40Bb		1¼m. on 3pf. (R.)	10·00	16·00
40Bc	**24**	2m. on 35pf. (B.)	44·00	75·00
40Bd		3m. on 7½pf. (G.)	65·00	£130
40Be		5m. on 2pf. (R.)	12·50	12·50
40Bf		10m. on 7½pf.	20·00	44·00

The bar in T **9** is of network pattern, not solid as shown in our illustration.

All values exist without burelé background, and all except Nos. 39A and 37B/40B with background double.

1920 (29 Sept). AIR. No. 6 of Danzig surch as T **10** and **12**.

41	**17**	40 on 40pf. carmine (B.)	1·90	4·50
		a. Surch double......................................	£250	£375
42		60 on 40pf. carmine (R.)	1·90	4·50
		a. Surch double......................................	£190	£375
43		1m. on 40pf. carmine (B.)	1·90	4·50
		a. Surch double......................................	£190	£375

On the 60pf. the aeroplane is reversed.

13 Hanse Kogge   **14**   **14a** Large Honeycomb

(Typo J. Sauer, Danzig)

1921 (31 Jan–11 Mar). Constitution of 1920. W **14a**.

(a) Zigzag roulette (31 Jan)

44	**13**	5pf. purple and brown............................	25	25
		a. Centre inverted..................................	£140	
45		10pf. slate-violet and orange	25	25
		a. Centre inverted..................................	£140	
46		25pf. carmine and green........................	75	1·00
		a. Centre inverted..................................	£140	
47		40pf. carmine..	5·75	5·00
48		80pf. ultramarine...................................	65	75
49	**14**	1m. slate and red...................................	2·50	3·25
		a. Centre inverted..................................	£150	
50		2m. deep green and blue........................	7·50	7·50
		a. Centre inverted..................................	£150	
51		3m. emerald and black...........................	3·25	4·50
		a. Centre inverted..................................	£150	
52		5m. red and slate..................................	3·25	4·50
		a. Centre inverted..................................	£150	
53		10m. chestnut and deep green................	3·75	7·00
		a. Centre inverted..................................	£150	

(b) P 14 (11 Mar)

54	**13**	25pf. carmine and green........................	75	1·30
		a. Centre inverted..................................	65·00	
55		40pf. carmine..	75	1·30
56		80pf. ultramarine...................................	8·75	15·00

Nos. 44 and 45 but with centres in red are believed to be proofs. All values exist imperforate (*Price for set of 10:* £550 *un*).

15 Sabaltnig
P111 over
Danzig
    16   **≡60≡**
(17)

(Des M. Buchholz. Typo J. Sauer, Danzig)

1921 (3 May)–**22**. AIR. P 14 (T **15**) or zigzag roulette (T **16**). W **14a**.

57	**15**	40pf. emerald	40	65
		b. Wmk sideways	90·00	£130
58		60pf. dull purple	40	65
		b. Wmk sideways	£130	£200
59		1m. carmine	40	65
60		2m. bistre-brown	40	65
		b. Wmk sideways	£130	£275
61	**16**	5m. blue-violet	1·90	3·25
		b. Wmk sideways	£2250	£3750
		ba. Imperf pair	£3750	£6500
62		10m. olive-green (15.5.22)	3·25	7·00
		b. Wmk sideways	38·00	£200

Nos. 57/62 are also known imperforate (*Price per set of 6* £325)
See also Nos. 112/19.

1921 (6 May). No. 33 surch with T **17**, in blue-black.

63	60 on 75pf. black and blue-green		1·50	1·30
	a. Surch double		£150	£160
	b. Surch double, one inverted		£130	£110

18   **19**

(Des Prof. Petersen. Typo J. Sauer)

1921 (3 June)–**22**. W **14a**. P 14.

64	**18**	5pf. orange	25	25
65		10pf. grey-brown	25	25
66		15pf. green	25	25
67		20pf. slate	25	25
68		25pf. deep green	25	25
69		30pf. red and blue	25	25
		a. Centre inverted	£130	£225
70		40pf. red and green	25	25
		a. Centre inverted	£130	£225
71		50pf. red and deep green	25	25
72		60pf. carmine	65	65
73		75pf. purple (1.2.22)	40	40
74		80pf. red and slate-black	50	65
75		80pf. bright green (1.2.22)	40	40
76		1m. red and orange	75	65
		a. Centre inverted	£130	£225
77		1.20m. blue	1·90	1·90
78		1.25m. red and purple (1.2.22)	40	40
79		1.50m. slate (29.7.22)	25	65
80		2m. red and grey	4·50	8·25
81		2m. carmine (1.2.22)	40	40
82		2.40m. carmine and sepia (1.2.22)	1·90	3·25
83		3m. red and purple (*wmk sideways*)	12·50	15·00
		a. Wmk upright	£130	£250
84		3m. carmine (29.7.22)	25	65
85		4m. indigo (1.2.22)	1·90	3·25
86		5m. deep green (9.11.22)	25	50
		a. Wmk sideways	38·00	90·00
87		6m. carmine (30.10.22)	25	50
88		8m. pale blue (29.7.22)	75	2·50
89		10m. orange (9.11.22)	25	50
90		20m. yellow-brown (30.10.22)	25	50

See also Nos. 106/11.

(Des M. Buchholz. Typo J. Sauer)

1921 (1 Aug)–**22**. W **14a**. Zigzag roulette.

91	**19**	5m. green, black and red	1·90	4·50
		a. Wmk sideways	1·90	4·50
91b		9m. orange and red (1.2.22)	4·50	12·50
		ba. Wmk sideways	4·50	12·50
92		10m. blue, black and red (1922)	1·90	4·50
		a. Wmk sideways	1·90	4·50
93		20m. black and red	1·90	4·50
		a. Wmk sideways	1·90	4·50

Nos. 76 to 93 have a background of faint grey network. Some stamps in this and the following issues are known without network.

D M

(O **20**)

1921 (25 Aug)–**22**. OFFICIAL. Optd with Type O **20**. W **14a**.

O94	**18**	5pf. orange	40	40
		a. Opt double	£160	

O95		10pf. grey-brown	40	40
		a. Opt double	50·00	
		b. Opt inverted	90·00	
O96		15pf. green	40	40
O97		20pf. slate	40	40
		a. Opt inverted	50·00	
O98		25pf. deep green	40	40
		a. Opt double	50·00	
		b. Wmk sideways	£450	£650
O99		30pf. red and blue	90	90
		a. Opt double	50·00	
O100		40pf. red and green	40	40
		a. Opt double	50·00	
O101		50pf. red and deep green	40	40
O102		60pf. carmine	40	40
O103		75pf. purple (15.2.22)	25	65
		a. Opt double	80·00	
O104		80pf. red and slate-black	1·30	1·90
O105		80pf. bright green (15.2.22)	25	4·00
		a. Wmk sideways	12·50	50·00
O106		1m. red and orange	40	40
O107		1.20m. blue	1·90	1·90
O108		1.25m. red and purple (15.2.22)	25	65
O109		1.50m. slate (29.7.22)	50	75
O110		2m. red and grey	25·00	20·00
		a. Opt inverted	£160	
O111		2m. carmine (15.2.22)	25	65
O112		2.40m. carmine and sepia (15.2.22)	1·90	4·00
O113		3m. red and purple (*wmk sideways*)	15·00	18·00
O114		3m. carmine (29.7.22)	50	75
O115		4m. indigo (15.2.22)	1·90	1·50
		a. Opt inverted	£160	
O116		5m. deep green (21.11.22)	50	75
		a. Wmk sideways	12·50	19·00
O117		6m. carmine (30.10.22)	50	75
O118		10m. orange (21.11.22)	50	75
O119		20m. yellow-brown (16.12.22)	50	75

D **20**   **20**

1921 (1 Oct)–**22**. POSTAGE DUE. Typo. W **14a** (sideways). P 14.

(a) Value in "pfennig" (figures only)

D94	D **20**	10pf. purple	50	75
D95		20pf. purple	50	75
		a. Wmk upright	£190	
D96		40pf. purple	50	75
D97		60pf. purple	50	75
D98		75pf. purple (10.6.22)	50	75
		a. Wmk upright	£130	
D99		80pf. purple	50	75
		a. Wmk upright	£130	
D100		120pf. purple	50	75
D101		200pf. purple (10.6.22)	1·30	1·60
D102		240pf. purple	50	1·60
		a. Wmk upright	£190	
D103		300pf. purple (10.6.22)	1·30	1·60
D104		400pf. purple	1·30	1·60
D105		500pf. purple	1·30	1·60
D106		800pf. purple (1.2.22)	1·30	1·60

(b) Value in "marks" (numeral followed by "M")

D107	D **20**	20m. purple (30.10.22)	1·30	1·60

See also Nos. D112/22.

(Des E. Hellingrath. Typo J. Sauer)

1921 (16 Oct). Tuberculosis Week. W **14a**. Zigzag roulette (1.20m.) or P 14 (others).

93b	**20**	30pf. (+30pf.) green and orange	65	1·50
93c		60pf. (+60pf.) carmine and yellow	1·90	2·50
93d		1.20m. (+1.20m.) indigo and orange (25×29 *mm*)	3·25	3·50

21

(Des M. Buchholz. Typo J. Sauer)

1922. W **14a**. Zigzag roulette.

94	21	50m. red and gold	90·00	£180
		a. Wmk sideways	12·50	20·00
		b. Crimson and gold	3·25	10·00
		ba. Wmk sideways	3·25	8·25
95		100m. red and bronze-green	10·00	19·00
		a. Wmk sideways	5·00	8·75

The 50m. has a grey overprinted network. On the 100m. it is brown. The designs of the stamps differ in detail.

D M

(O **22**)

1922. OFFICIAL. Optd with Type O **22**.

O120	19	5m. green, black and red	6·25	16·00
		a. Wmk sideways	5·00	10·00

6 6 8 6

(22)   (23)

1922. (15 May–2 Oct) Surch as T **22/23**. W **14a**.

96	18	6 on 3m. carmine (2 Oct)	50	90
		a. Surch double		
97		8 on 4m. indigo (R.) (15 May)	50	1·30
		a. Surch double	£110	£200
98		20 on 8m. pale blue (R.) (2 Oct)	50	90

1922 (1 Oct). OFFICIAL. No. 96 optd with Type O **20**.

O121	18	6 on 3m. carmine	50	1·30
		a. Opt inverted	44·00	

24 Small Honeycomb

25

25a   **26**

(Des M. Buchholz. Typo J. Sauer)

1922 (Nov)–**23** (Feb). W **24** (sideways). P 14.

99	25	50m. red and pale blue (21.11.22)	25	65
		a. Wmk upright	75	1·30
100	25a	100m. red and deep olive (14.12.22)	25	65
		a. Wmk upright	1·50	1·30
101		150m. red and purple (23.1.23)	25	65
102	26	250m. red and purple (24.1.23)	65	65
103		500m. red and slate (24.1.23)	65	65
104		1000m. pink and black-brown (24.1.23)	65	65
105		5000m. pink and silver (27.2.23)	2·50	9·50

Nos. 99/105 have background of faint grey network.
See also Nos. 136/41.

1922 (Dec)–**23** (Sept). W **24** (sideways on 4, 6m.). P 14.

106	18	4m. indigo (16.12.22)	25	65
107		5m. deep green (1.23)	75	1·30
		a. Wmk sideways	25	65
107b		6m. carmine (9.23)	£3250	
108		10m. orange (1.23)	75	1·30
		a. Wmk sideways	25	65
109		20m. yellow-brown (1.23)	75	1·30
		a. Wmk sideways	25	65
110		40m. pale blue (15.5.23)	40	90
111		80m. scarlet (15.5.23)	40	90

Nos. 106/11 have background of faint grey network.

1922 (Dec)–**23** (Feb). OFFICIAL. Optd as Type O **20**. W **24** (sideways on 4m.).

O122	18	4m. indigo (16.12.22)	40	1·00
O123		5m. deep green (1.23)	1·30	3·75
		a. Wmk sideways	40	1·30
O124		10m. orange (1.23)	1·30	3·75
		a. Wmk sideways	40	1·00
O125		20m. yellow-brown (1.23)		
		a. Wmk sideways	40	1·00
O126	25	50m. red and pale blue (10.1.23)	1·30	3·75
		a. Wmk sideways	40	1·00
O127	25a	100m. red and olive-green (21.2.23)	1·30	3·75
		a. Wmk sideways	40	1·00

See also Nos. O142/7.

1923 (Jan–Apr). POSTAGE DUE. W **24** (sideways on 100 to 400pf.). P 14.

(a) Value in "pfennig" (figures only)

D112	D 20	100pf. purple	1·30	1·30
D113		200pf. purple	4·50	6·25
D114		300pf. purple	1·30	1·30
D115		400pf. purple	1·30	1·30
D116		500pf. purple	1·30	1·60
		a. Wmk sideways	1·30	1·30
D117		800pf. purple	2·10	6·25

(b) Value in "marks"

D118	D 20	10m. purple	1·30	1·60
		a. Wmk sideways	1·30	1·30
D119		20m. purple	£100	
		a. Wmk sideways	1·30	1·30
D120		50m. purple	£100	
		a. Wmk sideways	1·30	1·30
D121		100m. purple	1·30	1·60
D122		500m. purple	1·30	1·60

Nos. D121/2 have background of faint grey network.
Nos. D119l and D120l were prepared for the surcharges.
Remainders of these two stamps with upright watermark were placed on sale, but were not used by the post office.

27

1923 (Jan–Apr). AIR. Typo. W **24** (sideways). Zigzag roulette (5, 10, 20m.) or P 14 (others).

112	15	40pf. emerald (3.1)	90	3·25
113		60pf. dull purple (3.1)	90	3·25
114		1m. carmine (3.1)	90	3·25
115		2m. bistre-brown (3.1)	90	3·25
116	16	5m. blue-violet (3.1)	90	1·50
117		10m. olive-green (3.1)	90	1·50
118		20m. yellow-brown (10.1)	90	1·50
		a. Background omitted	25·00	19·00
119	15	25m. pale blue (5.2)	65	1·10
120	27	50m. orange (27.4)	65	1·10
		a. Background omitted	31·00	25·00
		b. Wmk upright	95·00	
121		100m. scarlet (27.4)	65	1·10
		a. Background omitted	25·00	38·00
		b. Wmk upright	95·00	
122		250m. black-brown (27.4)	1·00	1·10
		a. Background omitted	25·00	38·00
123		500m. carmine (27.4)	1·00	1·10
		a. Background omitted	25·00	38·00
		b. Wmk upright	95·00	

Nos. 118 and 120/3 have background of faint grey network.

28   **29**

(Des Max Buchholz. Typo J. Sauer)

1923 (15 Mar). Poor People's Fund. W **24**. P 14.

123c	28	50 +20m. lake	40	1·00
123d		100 +30m. dull purple	40	1·00

Nos. 123c/d have background of faint grey network.

1923 (Mar–Sept). Typo. W **24** (sideways except 3000m.). P 14.

124	29	250m. scarlet and purple (15.5)	40	90

125		300m. scarlet and emerald (22.3)	40	65
126		500m. scarlet and slate (29.6)...............	40	90
		a. Wmk upright................................	£225	£375
127		1000m. brown (24.7)........................	40	90
128		1000m. scarlet and black-brown (30.7)	25	65
		a. Wmk upright................................	£325	£375
129		3000m. scarlet and violet (13.8).........	40	90
130		5000m. pink (15.8)...........................	25	65
131		20000m. pale blue (25.8)...................	25	65
132		50000m. green (1.9)...........................	25	65
133		100000m. deep blue (6.9)...................	25	65
134		250000m. purple (11.9).....................	25	65
135		500000m. slate (16.9)........................	25	65

Nos. 124/35 have background of faint grey network.

1923 (July–Aug). W **24** (sideways on 200m. to 20000m.). P 14.

136	**25**	50m. pale blue (20.7).....................	40	90
137	**25a**	100m. olive-green (29.7)..................	40	90
138	**25**	200m. orange (20.7)........................	40	90
139	**26**	10000m. scarlet and orange (8.8)...............	1·00	1·00
140		20000m. scarlet and pale blue (13.8)........	1·00	1·60
141		50000m. scarlet and green (20.8).........	1·00	1·60

Nos. 136/41 have background of faint grey network.

1923 (July). OFFICIAL. Optd as Type O **20**. W**24** (sideways on Nos. O144/7).

O142	**25**	50m. pale blue (21.7).....................	40	1·30
		a. Opt inverted...............................	38·00	
O143	**25a**	100m. olive-green (29.7)..................	40	1·30
O144	**25**	200m. orange (21.7)........................	40	1·30
		a. Opt inverted...............................	38·00	
O145	**29**	300m. scarlet and emerald (2.7)........	40	1·00
O146		500m. scarlet and slate (21.7)...........	40	1·30
O147		1000m. scarlet and black-brown (29.7)....	40	1·30

(30) T = Tausend (thousand) (31) (32)

(33) (34) M = Million or Millionen

1923 (Aug–Oct). W **24**.

(a) Surch as T **30**. *Wmk sideways (except No. 145)*

142	**25**	40T. on 200m. orange (1.9)	1·30	3·25
		a. Surch double..............................	£130	
143		100T. on 200m. orange (1.9).....................	1·30	3·25
144		250T. on 200m. orange (1.9).....................	9·50	21·00
145	**25a**	400T. on 100m. olive-green (24.9)	90	1·00
146	**29**	500T. on 50000m. green (8.9)...................	65	1·00

No. 145 has "Tausend" in different type and a fleuron instead of bars. No. 146 has only one bar.

(b) Surch as T **31**. *Wmk sideways*

147	**29**	1M. on 10000m. orange (13.9)..................	5·75	10·00
148		1M. on 10000m. carmine (19.9)...............	40	1·00
149		2M. on 10000m. carmine (19.9)...............	40	1·00
150		3M. on 10000m. carmine (23.9)...............	40	1·00
151		5M. on 10000m. carmine (23.9)...............	50	1·00
		a. Surch double..............................	£130	
152		10M. on 10000m. lavender (15.10)...........	65	1·10
		a. Wmk upright................................	£110	
153		20M. on 10000m. lavender (15.10)...........	65	1·10
		a. Wmk upright................................	£110	
154		25M. on 10000m. lavender (15.10)...........	25	1·10
155		40M. on 10000m. lavender (22.10)...........	25	1·10
		a. Surch double..............................	75·00	
156		50M. on 10000m. lavender (15.10)...........	25	1·10

(c) Surch with T **32** *and* **33**. *Wmk sideways*

157	**26**	100000 on 20000m. scarlet and pale blue (R.) (14.8)...................	1·30	9·50
158		10M. on 1000000m. orange (1.10)..........	65	1·90

No. 158 was not issued without the surcharge and has a background of faint grey network.

(d) Surch as T **34**, *in red. Wmk sideways*

159	**29**	100M. on 10000m. lavender (22.10).........	25	1·10
160		300M. on 10000m. lavender (23.10).........	25	1·10
161		500M. on 10000m. lavender (23.10).........	25	1·10

(D **35**) 35 Etrich/Rumpler Taube (36)

1923 (1 Oct). POSTAGE DUE. Surch as Type D **35**.

D162	D **20**	1000 on 1000m. purple	£190	
D163		5000 on 50m. purple.........................	65	1·30
D164		10000 on 20m. purple.......................	65	1·30
D165		50000 on 500m. purple.....................	65	1·30
D166		100000 on 20m. purple.....................	1·30	2·50

(Des M. Buchholz. Typo J. Sauer)

1923 (18 Oct). AIR. W **24**. P 14.

162	**35**	250000m. scarlet (wmk sideways)...............	50	1·90
		a. Wmk upright................................	75·00	£325
		ab. Imperf......................................	75·00	
163		500000m. scarlet (wmk sideways)...............	50	1·90
		a. Wmk upright................................	75·00	£325
		ab. Imperf......................................	75·00	
164	**35**	2M. on 100000m. Surch as T **36**. scarlet (wmk sideways)...............	50	1·90
		a. Wmk upright................................	£150	£325
		ab. Error. Surch omitted	19·00	80·00
165		5M. on 50000m. scarlet (wmk sideways).....................................	50	1·90
		a. Wmk upright................................	£180	£325
		ab. Error. Surch omitted	65·00	
		ac. Error. Stamp inscribed 10000m......................................	65·00	£250

No. 165ac exists on position 73 in the sheet of 100.

(37) (38) 38a Octagonal Mesh

1923 (31 Oct–5 Nov). Surch as T **37** or **38**. W **38a**.

166	**25**	5pf. on 50m. carmine	75	65
167		10pf. on 50m. carmine	75	65
168	**25a**	20pf. on 100m. carmine	75	65
169	**25**	25pf. on 50m. carmine	5·75	12·50
170		30pf. on 50m. carmine	5·75	3·25
171	**25a**	40pf. on 100m. carmine	3·50	3·25
172		50pf. on 100m. carmine	3·50	4·50
173		75pf. on 100m. carmine	12·50	25·00
174	**26**	1g. on 1000000m. carmine (5.11).....	7·00	9·50
175		2g. on 1000000m. carmine (5.11).....	19·00	25·00
176		3g. on 1000000m. carmine (5.11).....	35·00	95·00
177		5g. on 1000000m. carmine (5.11)......	40·00	£100
166/177 *Set of 12*...			£120	£250

D **39** 39 (O **40**)

1923 (24 Nov)–**27**. POSTAGE DUE. Typo. W **38a**. P 14.

D178	D **39**	5pf. blue and black	1·30	1·30
D179		10pf. blue and black	65	1·30
D180		15pf. blue and black (13.12.27)	1·90	2·50
D181		20pf. blue and black	2·00	3·25
D182		30pf. blue and black	12·50	3·25
D183		40pf. blue and black	3·50	5·00
D184		50pf. blue and black	3·50	3·75
D185		60pf. blue and black	19·00	30·00
D186		100pf. blue and black	28·00	16·00
D187		3g. blue and carmine (13.12.27)	14·00	75·00
D178/187 *Set of 10*..			80·00	£130

See also Nos. D263/7.

(Des M. Buchholz. Typo)

1924 (19 Jan)–**38**. W **24** (sideways). P 14.

177a	**39**	3pf. brown (24.2.27)........................	3·75	3·25
		b. On pale yellow paper (10.35).........	1·90	2·30

178	5pf. orange	25·00	3·25
	a. Interrupted perf (1932)	38·00	15·00
	b. On pale yellow paper (2.35)	4·50	90
	c. Wmk upright	£160	
	d. Pale yellow paper. Interrupted perf (10.35)	18·00	14·00
178e	7pf. yellow-green (27.4.33)	2·50	4·50
178f	8pf. yellow-green (14.8.37)	2·50	9·50
179	10pf. green	19·00	4·00
	a. Interrupted perf (1932)	44·00	19·00
	b. On pale yellow paper (3.35)	8·75	75
	c. Do. Interrupted perf (11.35)	25·00	16·00
179d	10pf. bright blue-green (24.6.37)	7·50	2·50
	e. Interrupted perf (24.8.37)	16·00	23·00
180	15pf. grey	6·25	1·00
180a	15pf. vermilion (20.8.25)	7·50	1·60
	b. On pale yellow paper (2.35)	3·25	1·60
181	20pf. red and carmine-red (26.1.24)	25·00	1·00
182	20pf. slate (20.6.35)	3·75	3·75
183	25pf. red and slate (12.3.24)	38·00	5·75
184	25pf. carmine-red (5.6.35)	25·00	2·50
185	30pf. red and deep green (12.3.24)	23·00	1·30
	a. Red and yellow-green	65·00	4·00
186	30pf. purple (21.8.35)	3·75	6·25
186a	35pf. blue (2110.25)	7·00	2·30
187	40pf. light blue and deep blue (14.2.24)	19·00	1·50
188	40pf. vermilion and brown (15.4.35)	10·00	19·00
189	40pf. deep blue (26.6.35)	3·75	5·75
190	50pf. red and deep blue (12.3.24)	25·00	12·50
	a. On pale yellow paper (3.38)	28·00	50·00
190b	55pf. vermilion and deep claret (4.37)	12·50	23·00
191	60pf. scarlet and bottle green (15.4.35)	10·00	28·00
192	70pf. vermilion and yellow-green (5.9.35)	3·75	11·50
193	75pf. red and purple (12.3.24)	15·00	12·50
	a. On pale yellow paper (1938)	12·50	44·00
194	80pf. vermilion and reddish brown (5.9.35)	3·75	11·50

1924 (1 Mar)–**25**. OFFICIAL. Optd with Type O **40**.

O195	**39**	5pf. orange	3·25	5·00
O196		10pf. green	3·25	5·00
O197		15pf. grey	3·25	5·00
O198		15pf. vermilion (1925)	28·00	15·00
O199		20pf. red and carmine-red	3·25	3·25
O200		25pf. red and slate (12.3.24)	28·00	40·00
O201		30pf. red and yellow-green (12.3.24)	4·50	5·75
O202		35pf. blue (1925)	90·00	75·00
O203		40pf. light blue and deep blue	10·00	12·50
O204		50pf. red and deep blue (12.3.24)	31·00	65·00
O205		75pf. red and purple (12.3.24)	65·00	£180

Double overprints are fakes.

40 Etrich/Rumpler Taube   **41** Airplane   **42** Oliva

(Des M. Buchholz. Typo J. Sauer)

1924 (5 June). AIR. No. 199 has network background. W **24** (upright). P 14.

195	**40**	10pf. vermilion	34·00	5·75
196		20pf. cerise	3·50	2·50
197		40pf. brown	4·75	3·25
198		1g. deep green	4·75	6·25
199	**41**	2½g. plum	28·00	55·00
		a. Without network background	£100	£325

All values exist imperforate.

(Des and eng E. Hellingrath. Recess Berlin State Ptg Works)

1924 (22 Sept–28 Nov). T **42** and similar designs. Wmk Lozenges (T **23** of Germany). P 14.

200	1g. black and yellow-green	31·00	70·00
201	2g. black and purple	70·00	£160
202	3g. black and blue (28.11)	7·50	7·50
203	5g. black and lake (28.11)	7·50	12·50
204	10g. black and brown (28.11)	31·00	£160
200/204 Set of 5		£130	£375

Designs: Horiz—2g. Krantor and River Mottlau; 3g. Zoppot. Vert—5g. St. Mary's Church; 10g. Town Hall and Langeńmarkt.

44 Fountain of Neptune

1920
15. November
1930
(**45**)

1925 (1 Jan)–**32**. As last, colours changed.

205		1g. black and orange	25·00	6·25
		a. Black and bright red-orange (5.32)	25·00	19·00
206		2g. black and carmine	5·75	12·50
See also No. 275.				

(Recess Berlin State Ptg Works)

1929 (7 July). International Philatelic Exhibition. Various frames. P 14.

207	**44**	10pf. (+10pf.) black and green	3·75	6·25
208		15pf. (+15pf.) black and carmine	3·75	6·25
209		25pf. (+25pf.) black and blue	12·50	38·00
		a. Black and ultramarine	75·00	£400
207/209 Set of 3			18·00	45·00

1930 (15 Nov). Tenth Anniv of Constitution of Free City of Danzig. Optd with T **45**.

210	**39**	5pf. orange	3·75	5·75
211		10pf. green (V.)	5·00	7·00
212		15pf. vermilion	8·75	16·00
213		20pf. red and carmine-red	4·50	8·75
214		25pf. red and slate	6·25	16·00
215		30pf. red and yellow-green	12·50	38·00
216		35pf. blue (R.)	50·00	£150
217		40pf. light blue and deep blue (R.)	16·00	55·00
218		50pf. red and deep blue	50·00	£130
219		75pf. vermilion and purple	50·00	£140
220	**42**	1g. black and orange (R.)	50·00	£130
210/220 Set of 11			£225	£650

10 ▬▬ **10**
Luftpost-Ausstellung
1932
(**46**)

(D **47**)

5 **5**
W. H. W.
(**47**)
("Winterhilfswerk")

1932 (23 July). Danzig International Air Post Exhibition ("Luposta"). Nos. 200/4 surch as T **46**.

221	10pf. +10pf. on 1g. (G.)	14·00	35·00
222	15pf. +15pf. on 2g. (P.)	14·00	35·00
223	20pf. +20pf. on 3g. (B.)	14·00	35·00
224	25pf. +25pf. on 5g. (R.)	14·00	35·00
225	30pf. +30pf. on 10g. (Br.)	14·00	35·00
221/225 Set of 5		65·00	£160

On Nos. 222 and 224/5 the surcharge is in four lines; on Nos. 224/5 "1932" is the second line.

1932 (20 Dec). POSTAGE DUE. Surch as Type D **47**. W **38a**. P 14.

D226	D **39**	5 on 40pf. blue and black (R.)	6·25	12·50
D227		10 on 60pf. blue and black (R.)	50·00	15·00
D228		20 on 100pf. blue and black (R.)	4·25	12·50
D226/228 Set of 3			55·00	36·00

1934 (15 Jan). Winter Relief Work Charity stamps. Surch with T **47**.

226	**39**	5pf. +5 orange	14·00	31·00
227		10pf. +5 green	35·00	75·00
228		15pf. +5 vermilion	20·00	55·00
226/228 Set of 3			60·00	£140

≡ **6** ≡   ■ **30** ■

≡   ≡   ■   ■
(**48**)   (**49**)

1934 (28 Dec)–**36**. Nos. 178e and 186a surch.

229	**48**	6 on 7pf. yellow-green (R.)	1·30	2·50
230		8 on 7pf. yellow-green (B.) (5.6.35)	3·25	3·50
		a. Red surch (14.7.36)	1·90	4·00
		b. Green surch (23.12.36)	1·30	3·75

231	**49**	30 on 35pf. bright blue (B.)	15·00	38·00
229/231		*Set* of 3 (*cheapest*)	16·00	40·00

No. 232 is vacant.

50 Junkers F-13   **51**   **52** Stockturm, 1346

(Des M. Buchholz. Typo Post Office Ptg Wks, Danzig)

1935 (25 Oct). AIR. W **24** (upright, except on 1g.). P 14.

233	**50**	10pf. salmon	2·50	1·30
		a. Error. 'DANZIO' instead of 'DANZIG' (pos. 3)	50·00	£180
		b. Error. 'STADL' instead of 'STADT' (pos. 4)	50·00	£180
234		15pf. orange-yellow	2·50	1·90
235		25pf. bottle green	2·50	2·50
236		50pf. blue	12·50	15·00
237	**51**	1g. bright purple	5·00	21·00
233/237		*Set* of 5	23·00	38·00

See also Nos. 263/6.

(Des M. Buchholz. Typo)

1935 (23 Dec). Winter Relief Fund. Designs inscr "Für das Winterhilfswerk", as T **52**. W **24** (sideways on No. 239). P 14.

238		5pf. +5pf. orange	1·00	2·50
239		10pf. +5pf. green	1·80	3·75
240		15pf. +10pf. scarlet	4·25	5·75
238/240		*Set* of 3	6·50	11·00

Designs: Horiz—10pf. The Lege Tor. Vert—15pf. Georgshalle, 1487.

54 Brösen War   **55** Frauentor and
Memorial   Observatory

(Des M. Buchholz. Typo Post Office Ptg Wks, Danzig)

1936 (23 June). 125th Anniv of Brösen. As T **54** (inscr "125 JAHRE OSTEEBAD BROSEN"). W **24** (sideways on horiz stamps). P 14.

241		10pf. deep green	1·50	1·90
242		25pf. carmine	2·00	3·50
243		40pf. light blue	3·50	7·00
241/243		*Set* of 3	6·25	11·00

Designs: Horiz—10pf. Brösen Beach; 25pf. Zoppot end of Brösen Beach.

1936 (25 Nov). Winter Relief Fund. As T **55** (inscr "WINTERHILFE"). W **24** (sideways on horiz stamps). P 14.

244		10pf. +5pf. blue	2·50	7·50
245		15pf. +5pf. blue-green	2·50	10·00
246		25pf. +10pf. maroon	3·75	15·00
247		40pf. +20pf. brown and maroon	5·00	18·00
248		50pf. +20pf. pale blue and deep blue	8·75	25·00
244/248		*Set* of 5	20·00	70·00

Designs: Vert—10pf. Milchkannenturm; 25pf. Krantor. Horiz—40pf. Langgartertor; 50pf. Hohestor.

56 "D(anziger)
L(uftschutz)
B(und)"

1937 (27 Mar). Air Defence League. Typo. W **24** (sideways). P 14.

249	**56**	10pf. deep blue	90	1·90
250		15pf. dull purple	2·50	3·75

57 Marienkirche, Danzig

(Des W. Lüdtcke. Typo)

1937 (6 June). First National Philatelic Exhibition, Danzig ("DAPOSTA"). Sheets 147×104 mm. W **24** (sideways). P 14.

(a) POSTAGE

MS251	**57**	50pf. blue-green/*toned*	6·25	£150

(b) AIR

MS252	50pf. blue/*toned*	6·25	£150

Design: No. **MS252** Marienkirche and Junkers F-13.

57a Danziger
Dorf, Magdeburg

(Des W. Brandt. Typo)

1937 (30 Oct). Foundation of Danzig Community, Magdeburg. T **57a** and similar type, inscr "Danziger Dorf in Magdeburg". W **24** (sideways on 25pf.). P 14.

253		25pf. (+25pf.) carmine	4·50	8·75
		a. Wmk upright	16·00	65·00
254		40pf. (+40pf.) vermilion and blue	4·50	8·75

Design: Horiz—40pf. Village and Arms of Danzig and Magdeburg.

1937 (28 Nov). Danzig Productivity Show. Sheet 146×105 mm.

MS254a	Nos. **253/4** (sold for 1g.50)	75·00	£550

58 Madonna and   **59** Schopenhauer
Child

(Des M. Buchholz. Typo)

1937 (13 Dec). Winter Relief Fund. As T **58** (statues inscr "WINTERHILFSZUSCHLAG" or "WINTERHILFE" (Nos. 258/9)). W **24.** P 14.

255		5pf. +5pf. violet	3·75	12·50
256		10pf. +5pf. brown	3·75	9·50
257		15pf. +5pf. orange and light blue	3·75	14·00
258		25pf. +10pf. green and blue-green	5·00	19·00
259		40pf. +25pf. blue and carmine	8·75	25·00
255/259		*Set* of 5	23·00	70·00

Designs: 10pf. Mercury; 15pf. The "Golden Knight"; 25pf. Fountain of Neptune; 40pf. St. George and the Dragon.

(Des M. Buchholz, after J. Hamel (15pf.), L. S. Ruhl (25pf.) and Daguerre (40pf.). Photo State Ptg Wks, Berlin)

1938 (22 Feb). 150th Birth Anniv of Schopenhauer (philosopher). As T **59** (portraits inscr "Schopenhauer 1788–1860"). P 14.

260		15pf. blue	2·30	3·75
261		25pf. sepia	5·25	12·50
262		40pf. red	2·30	5·00
260/262		*Set* of 3	8·75	19·00

Designs:—Portraits of Schopenhauer as an old man (15pf.) and as a young man (25pf.).

1938 (5 May)–**39**. POSTAGE DUE. W **97** of Germany (Swastikas). P 14.

D263	D **39**	10pf. blue and black (21.5.39)	1·90	£110
D264		30pf. blue and black	3·25	£100
D265		40pf. blue and black (21.5.39)	9·50	£190
D266		60pf. blue and black (21.5.39)	9·50	£190
D267		100pf. blue and black	15·00	£130
D263/267		*Set* of 5	35·00	£650

1938–39. AIR. W **97** of Germany (Swastikas). P 14.

263	**50**	10pf. salmon (7.38)	1·90	6·25
264		15pf. orange-yellow (8.7.38)	3·25	20·00
265		25pf. bottle green (7.38)	2·50	10·50
266		50pf. blue (13.2.39)	6·25	95·00
263/266 *Set of 4*			12·50	£120

1938–39. W **97** of Germany (Swastikas). P 14.

267	**39**	3pf. brown (28.9.38)	1·30	11·50
268		5pf. orange (23.7.38)	1·30	3·25
		a. Interrupted perf (24.8.38)	1·90	11·50
269		8pf. yellow-green (9.38)	6·25	50·00
270		10pf. green (10.38)	1·30	3·25
		a. Interrupted perf (18.7.38)	3·75	15·00
271		15pf. scarlet (28.9.38)	2·50	19·00
272		25pf. carmine (23.7.38)	1·90	10·00
273		40pf. indigo (19.7.38)	3·25	44·00
274		50pf. scarlet and blue (14.7.39)	3·25	£200
275	**42**	1g. black and orange (10.38)	10·00	£180
267/275 *Set of 9*			28·00	£475

60 Yacht *Peter von Danzig*
(1936)

(Des H. Gruber (Nos. 276/9), O. Lienau (No. 280). Photo State Ptg Wks, Berlin)

1938 (28 Nov). Winter Relief Fund. As T **60** (ship types inscr "W H W").
No wmk. P 14.

276	5pf. +5pf. bottle green	2·10	2·75
277	10pf. +5pf. deep orange-brown	2·10	5·00
278	15pf. +10pf. olive-green	2·50	5·00
279	25pf. +10pf. deep blue	3·50	7·50
280	40pf. +15pf. purple-brown	5·00	11·50
276/280 *Set of 5*		13·50	29·00

Designs: 10pf. Dredger *Fu Shing*; 15pf. Liner *Columbus*; 25pf. Liner *Hansestadt Danzig*; 40pf. Sailing vessel *Peter von Danzig* (1472).

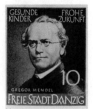

61 Teutonic Knights   **62** Gregor Mendel

(Photo State Ptg Wks, Berlin)

1939 (7 Jan). 125th Anniv of Prussian Annexation. As T **61** (historical designs). No wmk. P 14.

281	5pf. deep green	90	3·25
282	10pf. deep orange-brown	1·30	3·75
283	15pf. indigo	1·90	4·50
284	25pf. chocolate	2·50	6·25
281/284 *Set of 4*		6·00	16·00

Designs:—10pf. Danzig–Swedish treaty of neutrality, 1630; 15pf. Danzig united to Prussia, 2.1.1814; 25pf. Stephen Baton's defeat at Weichselmunde, 1577.

(Photo State Ptg Wks, Berlin)

1939 (29 Apr). Anti-Cancer Campaign. As T **62** (medical-scientists' portraits). No wmk. P 13×14½.

285	10pf. red-brown	1·00	1·30
286	15pf. black	1·00	3·25
287	25pf. olive-green	1·90	4·50
285/287 *Set of 3*		3·50	8·25

Portraits:—15pf. Robert Koch; 25pf. Wilhelm Konrad Röntgen.

On 1 September, 1939, Danzig was reabsorbed into Germany. Since 1945 it has been part of Poland.

For a full range of Stanley Gibbons catalogues, please visit **www.stanleygibbons.com**

STAMP BOOKLETS

The following checklist covers, in simplified form, booklets issued by Danzig. It is intended that it should be used in conjunction with the main listings and details of stamps and panes listed there are not repeated.

Booklets differing in the colour of cover or in the text on the front cover are separately priced. Booklets also occur with other differences, for example in the text on the inside covers; these are not covered by this list, but prices are generally the same for each version.

Prices are for complete booklets

Booklet No.	Date	Contents and Cover Price	Price
SB1	9.25-26	Arms (T **39**)	
		1 pane. No. 178*a*×6; 1 pane, No. 179×6; 1 pane, No. 180*a*×6 (1g.80)	
		(a) Grey cover	£9500
		(b) Pink cover (1.26)	£1100
SB2	4.28-34	Arms (T **39**)	
		1 pane, No. 178×10 1 pane No. 179×10; 1 pane, No. 180*a*×10 (3g.)	
		(a) Front cover inscr "Post- und Telegraphenverwaltung...". Brown cover	£8000
		(b) As a. but pink cover (4.30)	£9500
		(c) As a. but green cover (1.33)	£5000
		(d) Cover inscr "Landespostdirektion...". Pink cover (1.34)	
SB3	1.36	Arms (T **39**)	
		1 pane, No. 178*b*×10; 1 pane, No. 179*b*×10; 1 pane, No. 180*b*×10 (3g.)	£17000
SB4	5.37	Arms (T **39**)	
		1 pane, No. 178*b*×10; 1 pane, No. 179*d*×10; 1 pane, No. 180*b*×10 (3g.)	£10000
SB5	9.38	Arms (T **39**)	
		1 pane, No. 268×10; 1 pane, No. 270×10; 1 pane, No. 271×10 (3g.)	£18000

Marienwerder

100 Pfennig = 1 Mark

By the treaty of Versailles, 1919, a plebiscite was to be held to determine whether this district of West Prussia should belong to Germany or Poland and an Interallied Commission was appointed to supervise this.

2 Mark 2

Commission

Interalliée

Marienwerder

1   **(2)**

(Recess Officine Grafiche Coen, Milan)

1920 (13 Mar–13 Apr). Inscr "COMMISSION INTERALLIÉE" at top. Papermaker's wmk, O.B.M. and two Stars or P. & C.M. in sheet. P 11½.

1	**1**	5pf. green	1·00	3·75
2		10pf. red (13.4)	1·00	3·25
3		15pf. slate	1·00	4·50
4		20pf. orange-brown	1·00	3·25
5		25pf. blue	1·00	4·50
6		30pf. orange (13.4)	1·40	4·50
7		40pf. brown (13.4)	1·00	5·00
8		50pf. violet	1·00	3·75
9		60pf. red-brown (13.4)	6·25	6·25
10		75pf. chocolate (13.4)	1·40	3·75
11		1m. brown and green (13.4)	1·00	3·25
12		2m. purple (13.4)	3·25	7·00
13		3m. vermilion (13.4)	7·50	10·50
14		5m. blue and carmine (13.4)	44·00	31·00
1/14	Set of 14		65·00	85·00

Printings were made on thick bluish and greyish paper and on thin yellowish paper.

All values exist imperforate (*Price: £55 each un*).

1920 (27 Mar–11 May). Stamps of Germany (W **23**), optd as in T **2**.

15	**17**	5pf. green (8.5)	23·00	44·00
		a. Opt inverted	£190	£325
16		20pf. ultramarine (8.5)	11·50	44·00
		a. Opt inverted	95·00	£225
		b. Opt double	£130	
17		50pf. black and purple/*buff* (9.4)	£550	£1300
		a. On cream (90a) (11.5)	£1300	£4500
18		75pf. black and blue-green	7·50	14·00
		a. Opt inverted	95·00	£225
19		80pf. black and carmine/*rose*	£110	£190
20	**18**	1m. carmine-red (No. 93B)	£130	£250
		a. Opt inverted	£650	
15/20	Set of 6		£750	£1700

An official proof sheet was made of the 1m. with the overprint in sans-serif capitals in black. This also exists with the overprint more widely spaced between the lines in seriffed capitals, both in black and in red, whilst the 75pf. and 80pf. exist with the normal overprint in red but they were all private productions None of these were issued although copies have passed through the post.

1920 (21 Apr–11 May). Stamps of Germany (W **23**), surch as T **2**.

21	**24**	1m. on 2pf. grey	35·00	75·00
22		2m. on 2½pf. grey (11.5)	19·00	31·00
23	**17**	3m. on 3pf. brown (10.5)	19·00	31·00
24	**24**	5m. on 7½pf. orange (11.5)	19·00	31·00
21/24	Set of 4		85·00	£150

There are minor varieties of lettering in T **2**, consisting of accented "e" of different type in "Interalliee", "M" of "Mark" or "Marienwerder" with straight or slanting strokes, with or without serifs and two types of figures "2" and "5".

Commission
Interalliée
Marienwerder

(3)   **4**

1920 (9–16 July). Stamps of Germany (offset ptg, W **23**) optd with T **3**.

25	**18**	1m. carmine-red (16.7)	3·75	11·50
26		1m.25 green	5·00	12·50

27		1m.50 brown	6·25	15·00
28	**20**	2m.50 claret (16.7)	3·75	12·50
25/28	Set of 4		17·00	46·00

1920 (11 July–3 Aug). Inscr "PLEBISCITE" at top. P 11½.

29	**4**	5pf. green (3.8)	5·00	3·25
30		10pf. red (3.8)	5·00	3·25
31		15pf. slate (3.8)	18·00	21·00
32		20pf. orange-brown (3.8)	3·25	3·25
33		25pf. blue (3.8)	19·00	28·00
34		30pf. orange (3.8)	3·25	2·50
35		40pf. brown (3.8)	3·25	2·50
36		50pf. violet (3.8)	2·50	3·25
37		60pf. red-brown (3.8)	8·75	8·75
38		75pf. chocolate (3.8)	10·00	8·75
39		1m. brown and green (16.7)	3·25	2·50
40		2m. purple	3·25	2·50
41		3m. vermilion	3·25	3·25
42		5m. blue and carmine	5·75	4·50
29/42	Set of 14		85·00	90·00

The plebiscite was held on 11 July 1920 and resulted in a vote of 92% in favour of remaining in Germany. Marienwerder was restored to Germany on 16 August 1920 and German stamps were used there until 1945, since when it has been administered by Poland under the name of Kwidzyn.

Upper Silesia

100 Pfennig = 1 Mark

By the Treaty of Versailles, 1919, a plebiscite was to be held in Upper Silesia, in Germany, to determine whether the inhabitants of part of the area wished to be included in Poland.

1

(Typo Govt Ptg Wks, Paris)

1920 (20 Feb). P 14×13½.
1	**1**	2½pf. slate	65	1·30
2		3pf. chocolate	65	1·90
3		5pf. green	40	1·30
4		10pf. chestnut	65	2·00
5		15pf. violet	40	1·30
6		20pf. blue	40	1·30
7		50pf. maroon	7·50	12·50
8		1m. pink	7·50	18·00
9		5m. orange	7·50	18·00
1/9 *Set of 9*			23·00	50·00

No. 10 is vacant.

5	**5**	**10**	**10**
Pf	Pf.	Pf.	Pf
(2)	(3)	(4)	(5)

50	**50**	**50**
Pf	Pf	Pf
(6)	(7)	(8)

(Surch by Erdm. Raabe, Oppeln)

1920 (Mar). T **1** Surch.
11	**3**	5pf. on 15pf. violet	£250	£800
12	**2**	5pf. on 20pf. blue	1·80	5·00
13	**3**	5pf. on 20pf. blue	2·50	6·25
14	**4**	10pf. on 20pf. blue (R.)	1·80	5·00
15	**5**	10pf. on 20pf. blue (R.)	3·25	8·75
16	**6**	50pf. on 5m. orange	43·00	£100
17	**7**	50pf. on 5m. orange	50·00	90·00
18	**8**	50pf. on 5m. orange	65·00	£140

No. 11 in violet was printed in error.
Other minor differences exist in the figures of T **2** to **8**, but we only list the most prominent.

9	10 Coal-mine in Silesia

(Typo Govt Ptg Wks, Paris)

1920 (26 Mar). P 13½×14 (T **9**) or 14×13½ (T **10**).
19	**9**	2½pf. slate	50	1·30
20		3pf. dull maroon	90	1·30
21		5pf. green	50	1·30
22		10pf. red	90	1·30
23		15pf. violet	90	1·30
24		20pf. blue	1·30	3·25
25		25pf. grey-brown	1·30	3·75
26		30pf. orange-yellow	1·30	1·30
27		40pf. olive-green	1·30	1·60
28	**10**	50pf. slate	1·60	1·30
29		60pf. blue	90	2·50
30		75pf. green	2·50	3·25
31		80pf. maroon	2·50	1·60
32		1m. magenta	2·50	1·30
33		2m. grey-brown	2·50	1·30
34		3m. violet	2·00	1·30
35		5m. orange	6·25	8·25
19/35 *Set of 17*			27·00	33·00

Plébiscite 20 mars 1921.	Plébiscite 20 mars 1921.	4	M
(11)	(12)	(13)	

1921 (20 Mar). T **9** and **10** optd.
36	**11**	10pf. red	6·25	15·00
37		15pf. violet	6·25	15·00
38		20pf. blue	8·75	21·00
39		25pf. grey-brown (R.)	19·00	50·00
		a. Opt inverted		
40		30pf. orange-yellow	16·00	31·00
41		40pf. olive-green (R.)	16·00	31·00
42	**12**	50pf. slate (R.)	16·00	44·00
43		60pf. blue	19·00	38·00
44		75pf. green	19·00	44·00
		a. Opt inverted	£1300	
45		80pf. maroon	31·00	55·00
46		1m. magenta	38·00	£100
36/46 *Set of 11*			£180	£400

Double and inverted overprints exist, also numerous errors, including "1921" omitted.

1922 (Mar). Surch as T **13**.
47	**10**	4m. on 60pf. olive-green	1·30	3·25
48		10m. on 75pf. red	1·90	4·50
49		20m. on 80pf. orange	10·00	25·00
47/49 *Set of 3*			12·00	29·00

INTER-ALLIED COMMISSION

(O 14)

C. G. H. S.

(O 15)

1920 (14 Feb). Stamps of Germany handstamped with Type O **14**, in blue.

(a) Postage stamps
O1	24	2pf. yellowish grey		£5000
O2		2½pf. grey	£2750	£1100
O3	17	3pf. brown		£1100
O4		5pf. green	£1500	£750
O5	24	7½pf. orange	£2750	£1300
O6	17	10pf. carmine	£1000	£475
O7	24	15pf. slate-violet	£1000	£375
O8	17	20pf. violet-blue	£1000	£475
O9		25pf. black and red/yellow		£4500
O10		30pf. black and orange/rose	£1800	£400
O11	24	35pf. red-brown	£1800	£375
O12	17	40pf. black and carmine	£1100	£375
O13		50pf. black and purple/rose	£1100	£375
O14		60pf. rose-purple	£1800	£375
O15		75pf. black and blue-green	£1000	£375
O16		80pf. black and lake/carmine		£5000
O17	18	1m. carmine-red	£2750	£1100
O18	20	2m. deep blue		£4750

(b) War Charity. Nos. 105/6
O19	17	10 +5pf.carmine	
O20	24	15 +5pf. slate-violet	

(c) National Assembly at Weimar. Nos. 107/10
O21	26	10pf. carmine	£1900	£1500
O22	27	15pf. blue and chocolate		£1500
O23	28	25pf. scarlet and green		£4500
O24		30pf. scarlet and purple	£1900	£2000

Nos. O4, O7, O8, O10/O17 and O22 exist with red overprint. The above were in use between 14 and 19 February pending the arrival of Nos. 1/9.

1920–22. Official stamps of Germany optd with Type O **15**, in black.

*(a) Types O **31**and O **32**, etc. (with figures "21") (April 1920)*
O25		5pf. green	50	3·75
O26		10pf. carmine	50	3·75
O27		15pf. chocolate	50	3·75
O28		20pf. deep blue	50	3·75
O29		30pf. orange/buff	50	3·75
O30		50pf. violet/buff	1·30	5·00
O31		1m. red/buff	10·00	20·00
O25/31 *Set of 7*			12·50	39·00

*(b) Types O **31**, O **32**, etc but without figures (July 1920–22)*
O32		5pf. green	1·30	12·50
O33		10pf. carmine	40	3·75
O34		15pf. brown-purple	40	3·75
O35		20pf. deep blue	40	3·75

O36	30pf. orange/*buff*	40	3·75
O37	40pf. carmine (10.20)	40	3·75
O38	50pf. violet/*buff*	40	3·75
O39	60pf. purple-brown (5.21)	40	3·75
O40	1m. red/*buff*	40	3·75
O41	1m.25 indigo/*yellow* (9.21)	40	3·75
O42	2m. blue (wmk Lozenges) (9.20)	12·50	19·00
O43	2m. blue (wmk Mesh) (2.22)	40	5·00
O44	5m. brown/*yellow*	40	5·00
O32/44	*Set of* 13	16·00	70·00

Many stamps may be found with this overprint inverted, sideways, double, etc., but some of these are from printer's waste.

After the plebiscite of 20 March 1921, Upper Silesia was divided between Germany and Poland.

Stanley Gibbons
Stamp Catalogues

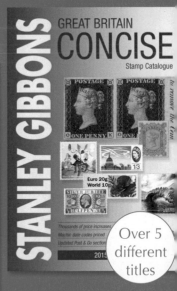

STANLEY GIBBONS
Est 1856

Dear Catalogue User,

As a collector and Stanley Gibbons catalogue user for many years myself, I am only too aware of the need to provide you with the information you seek in an accurate, timely and easily accessible manner. Naturally, I have my own views on where changes could be made, but one thing I learned long ago is that we all have different opinions and requirements.

I would therefore be most grateful if you would complete the form overleaf and return it to me. Please contact Lorraine Holcombe (lholcombe@stanleygibbons.co.uk) if you would like to be emailed the questionnaire.

Very many thanks for your help.

Yours sincerely,

Hugh Jefferies,
Editor.

Hugh Jefferies (Catalogue Editor)
Catalogue Questionnaire Responses
Stanley Gibbons Limited
7 Parkside, Ringwood
Hampshire BH24 3SH
United Kingdom

Questionnaire
2015 Poland Catalogue

1. Level of detail

   Do you feel that the level of detail in this catalogue is:
   a. too specialised   O
   b. about right   O
   c. inadequate   O

2. Frequency of issue

   How often would you purchase a new edition of this catalogue?
   a. Annually   O
   b. Every two years   O
   c. Every three to five years   O
   d. Less frequently   O

3. Design and Quality

   How would you describe the layout and appearance of this catalogue?
   a. Excellent   O
   b. Good   O
   c. Adequate   O
   d. Poor   O

4. How important to you are the prices given in the catalogue:
   a. Important   O
   b. Quite important   O
   c. Of little interest   O
   d. Of no interest   O

5. Would you be interested in an online version of this catalogue?
   a. Yes   O
   b. No   O

6. Do you like the new format?
   a. Yes   O
   b. No   O

7. What changes would you suggest to improve the catalogue? E.g. Which other indices would you like to see included?

   ....
   ....
   ....
   ....

8. Which other Stanley Gibbons Catalogues do you buy?

   ....
   ....
   ....
   ....

9. Would you like us to let you know when the next edition of this catalogue is due to be published?
   a. Yes   O
   b. No   O

   If so please give your contact details below.

   Name: ....
   Address:...
   ....
   ....
   ....
   Email: ....
   Telephone:...

10. Which other Stanley Gibbons Catalogues are you interested in?
    a. ....
    b. ....
    c. ....

Many thanks for your comments.

Please complete and return it to: Hugh Jefferies (Catalogue Editor)
Stanley Gibbons Limited, 7 Parkside, Ringwood, Hampshire BH24 3SH, United Kingdom
or email: lholcombe@stanleygibbons.co.uk to request a soft copy

Poland Order Form

YOUR ORDER

Stanley Gibbons account number ☐☐☐☐☐☐

Condition (mint/UM/ used)	Country	SG No.	Description	Price	Office use only
			POSTAGE & PACK-ING	£3.60	
			TOTAL		

The lowest price charged for individual stamps or sets purchased from Stanley Gibbons Ltd, is £1.

Payment & address details

Name

Address (We cannot deliver to PO Boxes)

Postcode

Tel No.

Email

PLEASE NOTE Overseas customers MUST quote a telephone number or the order cannot be dispatched. Please complete ALL sections of this form to allow us to process the order.

☐ Cheque (made payable to Stanley Gibbons)

☐ I authorise you to charge my

☐ Mastercard ☐ Visa ☐ Diners ☐ Amex ☐ Maestro

Card No. ☐☐☐☐☐☐☐☐☐☐☐☐☐☐☐☐ (Maestro only)

Valid from ☐☐☐☐ Expiry date ☐☐☐☐ Issue No. (Maestro only) ☐☐ CVC No. (4 if Amex) ☐☐☐☐

CVC No. is the last three digits on the back of your card (4 if Amex)

Signature   Date

4 EASY WAYS TO ORDER

Post to
Lesley Mourne,
Stamp Mail Order
Department, Stanley
Gibbons Ltd, 399
Strand, London,
WC2R 0LX, England

Call
020 7836 8444
+44 (0)20 7836 8444

Fax
020 7557 4499
+44 (0)20 7557 4499

Click
lmourne@
stanleygibbons.com/
co.uk?

If YOU Buy at Auction this is How You Can Save £250+ EACH Year

ANDREW PROMOTING PHILATELY ON THE ALAN TITCHMARSH SHOW ITV

POLAND AVAILABLE

... I'll Give You £55 to get you started

(... some Collectors Save thousands of pounds)

By Andrew McGavin, Managing Director, Universal Philatelic Auctions (UPA)

In all my 40+ years in the trade I have never seen an introductory offer to new clients like this .. so you may be wondering the reason why my company UPA can afford to make this offer to you?

In *'plain talk'* most auctions charge 'Buyers Premiums' –YES! You have to pay up to 25% (some charge more) **on top of the *winning price you paid*.** That is Simply an Incredible surcharge. Apparently this significant premium is justified by charging the seller a lower fee in order to entice consignments for sale.

My company UPA does not charge any premiums which is one of the reasons why we hold the UK record of 1,975 different bidders in our last auction – an amazing 89% of whom were successful. Fortunately the average bidder spends an average of £250+ per auction...so that with 4 auctions a year offering 80,000+/- lots from £1 to £100,000 for you to choose from ....

with NO Buyer's Premium You Save up to £250+ <u>EACH YEAR PLUS</u> You take NO RISK with our 28 day unconditional Guarantee

So How can UPA offer You £55 OFF too?

1. **Our Business Model is Different.** Fundamentally I believe that if a stamp/philatelic item is not selling then it is too expensive. Compare that with the stamp business whose stock is the same each time you see or hear from them. At the risk of boring you …

2. **Stamp Industry's BIGGEST problem.** … twenty years ago I started to ponder upon what is the biggest problem faced by the average stamp dealer? The answer came back loud and clear. The biggest problem faced by a stamp dealer is not what sells … **but what does not sell**. This is the reason why most stamp dealers have lots of unsold stock you have seen time and time again – worse still this is what prevents that dealer from buying new stock to offer you.

3. **Surface Sell.** There is an actual name for this – it is called 'surface sell' – good material 'floats' on the surface and sells. Less desirable stock sinks so that unless a dealer pays almost nothing to replace his stock then the profit in the business becomes stagnant and bound in less saleable stock. If only that dealer could move this stock he would have more money to invest in new stock to offer to you.

4. **Cover-up.** Twenty years ago almost the entire stamp industry spent its time disguising what did not sell – in those days so pernicious were 'unsolds' that it was common practice for one auction house to sell batches of 'unsolds' to another auction where the new auction could present them to (hopefully) different collectors as new lots. 'Passing the Philatelic Parcel' was common practice.

5. **E-Bay.** Today the philatelic world is almost unrecognisably different. In large part courtesy of the internet. How things have changed. Few 'pass the parcel'. Really active Dealers - these days they **also** sell on eBay - large lots, small lots, all manner of stamps, covers, down to fakes and forgeries – today's equivalent of the Wild West – there's philatelic 'gold' to be mined in those hills … but Boy – you have to work to find it and sadly 'all that glistens is not gold' – you pays your money and you takes your chance often with little support or recourse. UPA too sells surpluses on eBay backed by support and our guarantee – access eBay links via *www.upastampauctions.co.uk*

Continued overleaf ☞

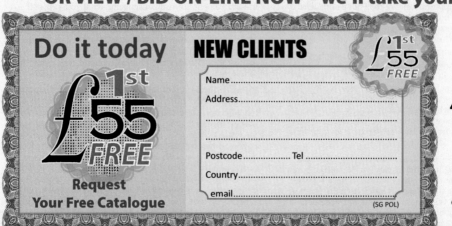